KU-358-363

AIRPORTS:
Design, Construction, and Management

AIRPORTS:
Design, Construction and Management

HORACE K. GLIDDEN, B.S., P.E.

Eastern Editor of *Roads and Streets* Magazine.
Formerly Assistant Superintendent of Airways,
First Region, Civil Aeronautics Administration

HERVEY F. LAW, B.S.

Manager of Washington National Airport.
Formerly Supervisor of Airports,
First Region, Civil Aeronautics Administration

JOHN E. COWLES, C.E., P.E.

Chief, Airport Design Unit,
First Region, Civil Aeronautics Administration

1946

McGraw-Hill Book Company Inc.

NEW YORK AND LONDON

AIRPORTS: DESIGN, CONSTRUCTION, AND MANAGEMENT

PRINTED IN THE UNITED STATES OF AMERICA

CONTENTS

Appendixes

INTRODUCTION

In preparing this text it has been the intention of the authors to acquaint the reader with the important factors which enter into airport problems and to provide procedures and guides for solving the problems which will be encountered in the design, construction, and management of nearly every airport. Since an airport is such a complex facility, a common fault of the airport engineer has been that he does an especially good job on the portion of the work with which he is familiar, but neglects phases which will later assume equal, or possibly greater, importance in the operation of the airport. The authors collectively are fortunate in having been directly connected with all the stages of the development of an airport. They recognize that it is impossible to supply the answer to each problem, particularly in view of the rapid changes which are taking place in the field of airport development. Following the principle that to be forewarned is to be forearmed, they have endeavored to point out the existence of each element so that the reader will be in a position to carry out such investigation as the particular situation with which he is confronted calls for.

At the expense of being repetitious the authors have stressed the need for making provisions for future expansion of the airport and insuring space for operational aids such as radio facilities, clear approaches, adequate buildings, and plane parking.

Regarding the design and construction of the grading, drainage, paving, lighting, and turfing, the text is intended to be sufficiently complete so that the engineer can carry out this work aided only by standard handbooks. The authors have used the guide specifications given in the appendices with a high degree of success. It has been necessary in preparing bid proposals for each airport to make minor revisions to suit local conditions. The drawings used to illustrate each element of runway construction were chosen because experience has shown them to be completely satisfactory when used on construction projects. One of the major difficulties which had to be overcome in actual practice was the development of drawings which clearly indicated the intent of the specifications and the scope of the work to be performed. The illustrations used have been evolved and improved during four years, as deficiencies in the original drawings appeared.

The authors realize that the splendid progress which has been made in airport design and construction practices is the result of the experience of a great many engineers, both civil and military. The only claim they can make to originality in the preparation of this text is their choice of the material presented and the incorporation therein of as much of their experience as possible.

The trend toward improving engineering practices and standards is going forward rapidly under the impetus of the demands of both the aviation industry and the public for airports which will provide satisfactory year-round operation without being a burden on the taxpayers. Economical construction is expected to become increasingly important as the aviation industry is placed more nearly on a pay-as-you-go basis. Accompanying the trend toward economical construction is an increased consciousness of the importance of revenue-producing features which, although not having a direct connection with air transportation, can be located on or near the airport. The airport engineer should be imaginative in this respect and should profit to the fullest possible extent by the practices which have already been proved sound in the operation of other airports.

Advance planning, which is almost impossible without a master plan, is probably as important in airport work as in any other field of endeavor. The results of surveys by fact-finding groups are now available and many more such surveys will be made. Present conditions and the predictions in the reports of such surveys warrant close study at the time plans are being formulated. Some conflict between building project and airport development interests has already arisen. With the boom which can be expected in housing projects and the expansion in private flying coming about simultaneously, careful planning is required or many communities will find themselves without suitable sites for small airports. The desired increase in personal flying cannot be brought about unless adequate facilities for storing, servicing, and operating privately owned aircraft are provided. Urban planning which considers the needs of the private flyer is paramount at this time, particularly in the large metropolitan areas, if communities are to enjoy the benefits private flying can provide in the years to come.

The time has passed when the airport engineer can pose as an authority on the entire subject of airports. Specialized knowledge is becoming increasingly important; hence the best an individual can do is to choose and become a specialist in the phase of the work in which he is most interested. The specialist will need to have a working knowledge of the problem as a whole in order that his particular tree will not obscure the forest. The airport field offers opportunities to men in all branches of engineering and should provide an interesting and lucrative career to those with highway, mechanical, and electrical backgrounds. Agencies employing the services of engineers for the development, maintenance, and operation of airports can avoid costly mistakes by recognizing the specialized nature of the services they are paying for.

The authors sincerely hope that this text, in addition to providing the answers for many problems, points the way to an intelligent study of the subject of airport engineering.

Acknowledgments

This book was undertaken after the authors found from their experience in the design, construction, and management of airports that a great deal of difficulty is involved in the research necessary to acquire a working knowledge of the many factors involved. The amount of time and effort they have spent in acquiring data on tests, procedures, and standards is being used to save the reader as much of this kind of work as possible.

The authors have had the assistance of a great many experts both in their work with airports and in the writing of this text. They desire to acknowledge and give credit to these sources of information and to express their appreciation of the splendid cooperation which they have received.

Throughout the book the authors have used illustrative material taken from the published works of the Civil Aeronautics Administration, Bureau of Public Roads, United States Engineer Department, Bureau of Yards and Docks of the United States Navy, Highway Research Board, Association of State Highway Officials, American Society of Testing Materials, Portland Cement Association, Asphalt Institute, and the Crushed Stone Association. Each of these agencies has contributed its full share to the advancement of airport engineering, and an airport engineer can hardly attain a high degree of proficiency without studying and using the data which the efforts of their experts have made available. They have been generous in extending their permission to reproduce material and in offering the services of their personnel in producing the manuscript. This assistance has been invaluable.

The authors are indebted to the following personnel of the First

Region of the Civil Aeronautics Administration for the assistance they have given in reviewing portions of the manuscript during its preparation: Richard P. Battle, Radio Engineer and Chief of the Signals Branch; Stewart A. Mendell, Airport Service Lighting Engineer; James E. Burgett and Joseph M. Hill of the Airways Engineering Branch Airport Lighting Unit; and William Minuse, B.S., and Harry Schwartz, P.E., of the Airways Engineering Branch Airport Design Unit.

March, 1946

H. K. G.
H. F. L.
J. E. C.

AIRPORTS:

Design, Construction, and Management

CHAPTER I

PRELIMINARY REQUIREMENTS TO AIRPORT PLANNING

GOVERNMENT PARTICIPATION

No text on the subject of airports and related problems would be complete without some discussion of the close association existing between our government and the public agencies having airport problems.

Except in rare instances the United States government will, in one way or another, play some part in the size, location, design, construction, and maintenance of an airport. Its role is usually quite important. The nature of the part played by the government in both air transportation and airports makes it necessary that anyone expecting to take an active part in either of these fields should understand the function, duties, and powers of the Civil Aeronautics Administration (C.A.A.).

The C.A.A., because of its multitudinous responsibilities, is quite a complex organization. Although many of the agency's functions are regulatory, it offers assistance and advice on every airport problem. It has been in the past, and no doubt will continue to be, the agency allocating funds appropriated by Congress for airport-development purposes.

A thorough knowledge of the functions and duties of each division of the C.A.A. will prove advantageous. It is advisable to ascertain the names and addresses of its local and regional representatives. Much information and assistance can be gained through personal contact with C.A.A. officials.

History

In order to assist the reader in becoming familiar with the C.A.A. the following résumé of its history and organization is given.

Recognizing the national as well as the international scope of air commerce, the 69th Congress enacted legislation known as the "Air Commerce Act." This act was approved May 20, 1926. The purpose of the act was to encourage and regulate the use of aircraft in commerce and for other purposes. The Secretary of Commerce was charged with carrying out the provisions of the act.

Among other things, the act made it the duty of the Secretary of Commerce to encourage the establishment of airports, civil airways, and other navigational facilities. The act was amended several times, but its intent remained unchanged.

With the increase of air commerce the number of airports and navigational facilities increased. The problems of regulating the use of aircraft changed and expanded to large proportions. Air commerce assumed such significance by 1938 that the provisions of the Air Commerce Act of 1926 proved to be incapable of fulfilling their original purpose. The 75th Congress passed an act cited as the "Civil Aeronautics Act of 1938." This act was approved June 23, 1938.

The Civil Aeronautics Act of 1938 amended the Air Commerce Act, as well as other pertinent acts, in such a manner that the Civil Aeronautics Authority would be in a position to carry out fully the intent of both acts. The Civil Aeronautics Act was enacted to create a Civil Aeronautics Authority to promote development and safety, and to provide for the regulation of civil aeronautics.

Section 201 of the Civil Aeronautics Act of 1938 reads in part as follows:

> (a) An agency is created and established to be known as the "Civil Aeronautics Authority" which shall be composed of five members who shall be appointed by the President, by and with the advice and consent of the Senate. . . . The President shall designate annually one of the members of the Authority as chairman and one of the members as vice chairman who shall act as chairman in the absence or incapacity of the chairman. . . .
>
> (b) There shall be in the Authority an Administrator who shall be appointed by the President and with the advice and consent of the Senate. . . .

Section 701 of the Act reads in part as follows:

> (a) There is created and established within the Authority an Air Safety Board. Such Board shall consist of three members to be appointed by the President by and with the advice and consent of the Senate. . . . The Board shall annually elect one of its members as chairman of the Board. . . .

The Civil Aeronautics Act defines all aeronautical terms used in the act, makes a declaration of the policy the Authority will follow in the exercise and performance of its powers and duties, and recognizes a public right of freedom of transit through the navigable airspace of the United States. The act outlines the organization of the Authority; sets forth the powers and duties of the various offices; establishes rules and regulations applying to such things as air-carrier operations, nationality and ownership of aircraft, and safety; and provides procedures and penalties.

Section 7 of the Reorganization Plan Number IV, approved April 3, 1940, reads in part as follows:

(a) The Civil Aeronautics Authority and its functions, the Office of the Administrator of Civil Aeronautics and its functions, and the functions of the Air Safety Board are transferred to the Department of Commerce.

(b) The functions of the Air Safety Board are consolidated with the functions of the Civil Aeronautics Authority, which shall hereafter be known as the Civil Aeronautics Board and which shall, in addition to its other functions, discharge the duties heretofore vested in the Air Safety Board so as to provide for the independent investigation of aircraft accidents. The offices of the members of the Air Safety Board are abolished.

(c) The Administrator of Civil Aeronautics, whose functions shall be administered under the direction and supervision of the Secretary of Commerce, and the Civil Aeronautics Board, which shall report to Congress and the President through the Secretary of Commerce, shall constitute the Civil Aeronautics Authority within the Department of Commerce; Provided, That the Civil Aeronautics Board shall exercise its functions of rule-making (including the prescription of rules, regulations, and standards), adjudication, and investigation independently of the Secretary of Commerce; Provided further, That the budgeting, accounting, personnel, procurement, and related routine management functions of the Civil Aeronautics Board shall be performed under the direction and supervision of the Secretary of Commerce through such facilities as he shall designate or establish.

The net result of the President's Reorganization Plan Number IV is that the Administrator of Civil Aeronautics and the Civil Aeronautics Board now constitute the agencies representing the government in air transportation.

Civil Aeronautics Administration

Matters of sufficient importance regarding the airport problems of any given community may warrant the personal attention of the Administrator of Civil Aeronautics or an Assistant Administrator. Ordinarily, however, contacts are made with an official of lesser importance, but one who has more specialized knowledge of the subject under consideration.

C.A.A. Regions

The C.A.A. is a decentralized organization. The offices in Washington act in an administrative capacity, formulating policy, setting up technical procedures, and passing judgment on the activities of the regional offices. In most instances regional office personnel should be contacted as they are more readily accessible and are directly involved with all matters within their own territory. The functions of the Washington office personnel in this connection can be likened to a court of review should there be any reason to question the decision of regional office personnel.

DIRECTORY OF REGIONAL OFFICES OF THE CIVIL AERONAUTICS ADMINISTRATION

Region I	385 Madison Ave., New York City, New York.
For States of:	Maine, New Hampshire, Vermont, Massachusetts, Connecticut, Rhode Island, New York, New Jersey, Pennsylvania, Delaware, West Virginia, Maryland, Virginia, District of Columbia.
Region II	84 Marietta St., N.W., Atlanta 3, Georgia.
For States of:	North Carolina, South Carolina, Tennessee, Georgia, Florida, Alabama, Mississippi.
Region III	22nd Fl., Transportation Bldg., 608 So. Dearborn St., Chicago 5, Illinois.
For States of:	Ohio, Indiana, Michigan, Kentucky, Illinois, Wisconsin, Minnesota, North Dakota.
Region IV	P.O. Box 1689, Forth Worth 1, Texas.
For States of:	New Mexico, Texas, Arkansas, Louisiana, Oklahoma.
Region V	9th Fl., City Hall Bldg., Kansas City 6, Missouri.
For States of:	South Dakota, Nebraska, Kansas, Colorado, Wyoming, Missouri, Iowa.
Region VI	1500 4th St., Santa Monica, California.
For States of:	California, Nevada, Utah, Arizona.
Region VII	Smith Tower Annex Bldg., P.O. Box 3224, Seattle, Washington.
For States of:	Montana, Oregon, Washington, Idaho.
Region VIII	Anchorage, Alaska.
For the territory of Alaska.	
Region IX	Honolulu.
For the territory of Hawaii and Pacific Ocean.	

The regional administrator supervises and coordinates the activities of all regional office personnel. All communications should be addressed to his office where they will be routed to the appropriate branch for action or reply.

Safety Regulations

The Office of Safety Regulation enters the airport picture wherever air-carrier operations are to be provided for. One of the functions of the Air Carrier Division of the Office of Safety Regulations, with respect to scheduled air carriers, is set forth as follows:

> Arranges for inspection of landing and navigation facilities for adequacy for air carrier operation, and recommends limitations as to usage; recommends changes in aids to air navigation for improvement of air carrier operations on specific air routes.

Operation limitations, among other things, govern the minimum ceiling and visibility under which contact or instrument operations are allowed and the type and permissible gross weight of transport-category aircraft which can operate from runways of a given airport. If there is any question as to the effect of either natural or man-made obstructions on air-carrier operations it is advisable to secure the opinion of a representative of this division. This same advice is applicable to questions regarding runway length to accommodate any specific aircraft.

Federal Airways

The Federal Airways Service provides aids to air navigation along civil airways, operates airway radio and other communication facilities, provides traffic control, and carries on technical development projects.

Airports

The great majority of contacts will be with personnel of the airport branch. The trend of all federal legislation makes it safe to assume that there will be no change in the policy which requires this service to approve the plans and specifications for any nonmilitary airport on which federal funds are to be expended. Future federal airport legislation may well change the scope of this division's activities but it is very likely that it can be relied on for engineering, planning, survey, and advisory assistance. Information on standards for every component part of an airport is available from them in the form of bulletins, drawings, and specifications.

TERMINOLOGY

The words employed to designate the component parts of an airport as well as those describing aircraft and their performance have come into such common usage that the various terms have some meaning to almost everyone. In view of the technical aspect of this text, however, the reader is advised to review the glossary of terms given in Appendix 1.

BASIC PRINCIPLES

An aircraft can take off or land in a shorter distance and with less skill required in handling when the take-off or landing is made directly into the wind. The heavier the aircraft, however, the less effect wind direction has on the direction in which it must land or take off. These facts are pointed out at this time as they play a tremendously important part in airport layout.

CLASSIFICATION OF AIRPORTS

In order to simplify and standardize reference to size and degree of development of airports the C.A.A. has established airport size-planning standards for five classes of airports. Table 2–2 is a reproduction of the Airport Size-Planning Standards as they are given in Table 3 of C.A.A.'s publication entitled "Airport Design."

LANDING STRIPS AND APPROACH ZONES

A modern airport is a very complex facility. It is comprised of a varying number of component parts, depending on its degree of development. The landing strip and its approach zones are the basic parts of an airport. All other parts exist for the purpose of increasing the degree of safety or convenience with which each landing strip can be used.

An airport can have any desired number of landing strips and each landing strip can be of such length and width as the limiting factors such as terrain or cost will permit. As is brought out in Table 2–2 the true direction of the percentage of winds having a velocity of 4 mph and over governs the number of landing strips required as well as their direction. The volume of traffic is also a factor entering into the number required. The length of the landing strips will be governed by the distance required to take off or land the aircraft which are normally expected to use the airport.

CIVIL AIR REGULATIONS

The Civil Air Regulations are the regulations issued by the Civil Aeronautics Board governing aircraft certification and the conditions under which they may be operated. Part 04 deals with certification of all aircraft for operation, whereas Part 61 deals only with transport-category aircraft. These two parts affect the runway length of any airport from which transport-category aircraft are operated. Figure 1–3 is a portrayal of the basic requirements of Parts 04 and 61 of the Civil

Air Regulations and is given in order to afford the reader a better understanding of the effective length of a landing area and the effect of obstructions. A study of Figure 1–3 should result in an understanding of the factor of safety the government requires in the operation of transport-category aircraft. It is easily seen that this factor of safety results in landing strips that are considerably longer than normal aircraft performance requires.

LONG-RANGE PLANNING

Before any intelligent approach can be made to the problem of selecting an airport site, several decisions have to be made. These decisions can be correct only if they come as a result of a careful study of the community's transportation requirements and possibilities. The study must be made from a long-range point of view. It must determine the ultimate need for air-transportation facilities and if possible result in the acceptance of an over-all airport plan for the community.

Commission and Consultant

In order that the over-all interests of the community can be best served it is necessary that all interests be represented at the time an airport plan is adopted. A great deal of information must be gathered first. It is recommended that a qualified consultant be employed to secure and compile this information. The best arrangement is for the community to appoint an airport commission to work with the consultant. In the event a consultant is not employed, the city, county, or state engineer, or some other qualified public agency must be designated to secure the information.

The airport commission must be given certain powers, such as the authority to expend funds for a consultant's services, and any other necessary activities. Members of the airport commission should be chosen so that they represent the local business interests, property owners, agriculture, and aviation. Members of the commission should be chosen for their ability to make fair decisions rather than because of any special interest in aviation. The commission should be considered as a review body rather than an agency to secure information.

INFORMATION NEEDED

Before the consultant or local public agencies securing and compiling information can function properly, the commission must establish the boundary of the area which is to be served by the airport plan. A large-scale contour map on which may be shown in addition to the boundaries of the area to be served, the various towns, business districts, permanent residential districts, likely building development sites, slums, and immovable obstructions is best suited for this purpose. This map should be carefully prepared, as it will undoubtedly form a part of the final airport plan. A map having a scale of 1 in. = 1 mile is suggested.

The consultant or local public agency assigned to secure information for the commission will hereafter be referred to as the "engineer."

After the boundary of the area to be surveyed is determined by the commission, the engineer will need to secure information on the following factors which will influence the airport plan.

Population Served

Figures should be secured so that this population can be classified approximately as follows:

a. Percentage engaged in business requiring travel.
b. Percentage likely to perform recreational travel.
c. Percentage which will travel only on special occasions.
d. Percentage which would use airplanes for personal flying.

No doubt the law of supply and demand will operate with respect to the need for airports. The size and relative importance of the community will govern the extent of the demand. As an example, there can be no reasonable doubt that New York City will construct a complete system of airports in its attempt to retain its place of prominence in the air-transportation picture. Conversely, a city relatively close to New York City or any other important air terminal may well be satisfied with one or more airports for private and charter flying, depending on the major terminal to meet its transport requirements.

Differences of opinion as to the importance of various communities in the area are bound to exist. A wide-awake, ambitious, and aggressive community may well assign itself an importance not generally accepted, and by industry and the exercising of good judgment actually achieve this importance by properly developing an airport.

Nature and Volume of Business Activities

This can be shown by figures relating to the volume of manufacturing, postal receipts, and freight and express shipments. Business activities should be divided into the following classifications: manufacturing, agriculture, recreation, and special events. Special events cover such occasions as conferences, sporting events, and the like. Business trends covering a long period should be studied.

Widespread Interest in Airport Development

This information should include as much data as possible on the plans the air lines or airport operators have prepared, contingent on airport facilities being provided.

Assurance that an airport will be used in a manner which will provide a desirable service to the community takes most of the gamble out of the undertaking.

Civil Airways

The location of existing civil airways as well as the likelihood of new civil airways being established has a bearing on airport planning.

A civil airways is defined by Amendment No. 20 to C.A.R. as follows:

> Each civil airways shall include the navigable airspace of the United States above all that area on the surface of the earth lying within five miles of the center line prescribed for each airway, but shall not include any of the airspace of an airspace reservation set apart as provided in Section 4 of the Air Commerce Act of 1926.

Airways are designated by the administrator of the C.A.A. after the necessity for an airway between two points has been established. Federal airways are most essential to air-carrier operations and therefore the existence of a federal airway indicates that the route is used by the air lines for passenger, express, or freight traffic. Being near a federal airway is in effect the same as being located on a main-line railroad. Most cross-country itinerant traffic follows the federal airways. Flights of aircraft along federal airways are subject to restrictions not applicable to other areas but these restrictions and the attendant control should prove to be advantageous.

Since new airways can be designated and existing airways rerouted, the engineer should take federal airways and the navigational facilities which go with them into account in his long-range planning.

Chapter XIII on Radio Aids describes such aids and Figure 13–4 illustrates a desirable location of a radio range in relation to an airport runway. If a radio range is in existence, or if there is any reason to believe that a radio range will be installed, the airport planner must give this aid careful consideration in the selection of the airport site.

In most instances radio ranges can be moved at a cost below $15,000.

Too much, therefore, should not be sacrificed to locate the airport in relationship to an existing facility unless it is known that the range can not be moved. It is possible with the continued development of radio aids that off-airway airports can be tied in with airways by the installation of localizers. Should such development come about, the location of an airport in relation to the airway will be less important.

The Proximity of Competitive Airports

The information on this factor should be as complete as possible, particularly as to the nature and volume of business carried on at such airports and their plans for expansion or development.

The proposed airport's proximity to cities having competitive airports may affect its importance as an air-transportation center either favorably or unfavorably. The speed of the airplane in flight is offset to a considerable extent by the amount of time-consuming maneuvers required for it to make a stop when only short distances are involved. This fact, together with probable airspace congestion, makes it appear unlikely that more than one major air terminal can exist within a radius of at least 100 miles. The development of feeder airline service and intrastate air lines may well increase this radius to a far greater distance. Assuming that major air terminals require the largest airports, and that the airport's size will reduce as the terminal's importance reduces, it follows that this factor influences size.

Other airports already in existence in the community can be considered as competition to the proposed airport and must not be underestimated regardless of their class or condition. The very existence of another airport will convince a certain amount of people that the community's needs are provided for, maybe not perfectly, but well enough. Many people are not and never will be air-minded, especially if this state of mind involves expenditures which will raise taxes. In rare instances, the existence of an inadequate airport can be used to advantage in promoting a new one, but usually this can be done only if some accident or near accident can be associated with the inadequacy of the present airport.

Other airports greatly lessen the chances of making the proposed new airport self-supporting. The natural conclusion is that all of the small planes and charter aircraft will move to the new airport because of better facilities and safer operating conditions, but this is not always the case. Personalities, personal convenience, habit, dislike of more regimented operations, or increases in operating costs at the new airport—

all these things and more may discriminate against the possible revenue the new airport can produce.

Data to be secured on other airports within the area being surveyed should include a history of the development of such airports as well as their present financial and operational status. Full information on the safety features of existing airports as well as the possibilities for their expansion is essential.

Approximate Number of Sites from Which Selection Can Be Made

Ordinarily this information can be secured from a map study, supplemented by a relatively small amount of actual observation. Information should include the approximate size of each possible airport site and the approximate assessed valuation of the property involved. Possible sites should be indicated on the large-scale contour map referred to above or a similar map prepared specifically for this purpose.

A few localities, less in number than would be expected, have several airport sites from which to make a selection. These places seldom have the density of population, however, to allow them to make the most of such a situation.

Public Opinion

The commission must have knowledge of the attitude of the community toward airport development. This can be ascertained from newspaper editorials or public statements, and by discussing the matter with people considered to be in the best position to express public opinion.

Very few airports will ever be constructed which are not directly paid for with funds derived from taxes; therefore the attitude of the majority of the taxpayers has a definite bearing on the size of the airport and the likelihood of its being constructed. This attitude can be swayed by favorable or unfavorable publicity. Unfavorable publicity can be counteracted in many instances by a concise statement of facts outlining the estimated cost of the project, the need which exists for the airport, and the benefits that will accrue to the community from its establishment. If, however, the majority of the taxpayers or the taxpayers' organizations oppose the airport project, it may result in the project being abandoned, or perhaps worse yet, so curtailed that it is impossible to secure a site which meets even the minimum requirements and therefore later becomes an embarrassing problem.

The engineer must keep his finger on the pulse of public opinion regarding the airport, diagnosing the situation carefully, and always prescribing the treatment which is called for. If the survey indicates that a community requires a certain size airport, the airport planner should put forth his best efforts to get the taxpayers to accept that size airport regardless of whether public opinion wants a much more elaborate airport or none at all. At least the skillful airport planner can exert considerable influence in shaping the nature of this factor, often using it to aid him immeasurably.

Applicable Laws

Complete information regarding the laws applicable to the expenditure of public funds for real estate, buildings, and other facilities involved in airport development is essential. This information can be obtained from records of legislation or decisions handed down in regard to such legislation. When the airport construction program first got under way considerable difficulty was experienced because the laws governing the purchase of property were formulated long before it was possible to foresee the need for airports. States, counties, and cities have to a large degree remedied this situation by the passage of rather liberal laws both as to how and where property can be acquired for airport purposes. The right of condemnation and the right to purchase property outside the territorial boundary of the particular political subdivision are nearly always a necessity. Police powers to invoke compliance is quite often necessary, particularly in removing obstructions or evicting recalcitrant tenants.

It often happens that the best airport site available for political subdivision A's airport is located within the legal boundary of political subdivision B. Before a site in political subdivision B is chosen, the airport planner must be sure the laws of A cover the acquisition of property in B, as well as allowing for the proper operation and administration of an airport on such property.

As an illustration, the airport sponsored by Cumberland, Maryland and constructed by the C.A.A. for the city of Cumberland, actually is located across the Potomac River in the state of West Virginia.

The airport planner must know what powers the law grants to the political subdivision for extinguishing easements and rights which may have been granted by previous owners for such things as utility lines, mining or oil rights, rights of way for roads or pipe lines, or leases.

If the local laws limit the area from which an airport site may be selected, limit the indebtedness the public agency may assume to pay for airport property, fail to provide for condemnation, fail to provide required police powers, fail to provide for removal of obstructions without purchase of the property on which obstructions are located, or in any other way make it impossible for the airport planner to select the airport site purely on its own merits, they may adversely affect the size of the airport, or prove to be the reason it cannot be built.

The Need and Desire for Public Developments

The public developments which might be established in conjunction with an airport can be parks, golf courses, etc.

Combining an airport with a public park or other public improvement may well be desirable but may entail the problem of keeping trespassers off the airport. From the point of view of the airport the only advantage will result from possibly decreased construction and maintenance costs or from increased revenue derived from visitors who would otherwise not patronize airport concessions. Such visitors may develop great interest in flying from their contact with the airport while making use of its adjoining recreational facilities. Construction costs may be reduced, in that the portion of the cost of the combined site charged to the airport may be less than it would have been for the airport site alone.

It frequently occurs that acquiring an airport site, because of its shape or location, entails the purchase of a good many more acres than are necessary solely for the airport. If the surplus property can be put to good use it should be a credit to the airport cost as well as a general improvement to the community. The cost of access roadways, or the extension of public necessities can also be prorated between the airport and the accompanying improvement.

It is particularly desirable when an airport and seaplane base can be combined in one site. LaGuardia and Idlewild airports have this combined feature. Such a combination of accommodations for land and seaplanes in one area results in less duplication of buildings, gasoline storage, navigational facilities, and access highways. This situation allows easy transfer of passengers, express, or freight from one type aircraft to the other.

The Direction of the Prevailing Winds

This information must cover both good and bad weather conditions. If no recorded data are available the services of a skilled meteorologist should be secured. It will be found that quite often winter winds hold fairly steady from one direction, with summer winds blowing from another direction. River valleys, mountain ranges, or large bodies of water can have a definite effect on the prevailing winds. Some locations have prevailing winds blowing so consistently from one direction that one runway is all that is needed. Again, in another location, the wind will shift frequently, covering nearly all points of the compass, making four runways necessary. The direction of the instrument runway must whenever possible be the same as the direction of the prevailing wind during periods of low visibility thus allowing the pilot to land straight in under instrument conditions the largest possible percentage of the time.

The runway or runways into the prevailing good-weather winds will be used the largest percentage of the time. It is mandatory that these wind directions be covered. Any provision for multiple runways should give first consideration to good-weather wind direction.

The prevailing wind may require that an airport be located on one side or the other of built-up residential or business areas if objectionable noise is to be kept to a minimum. Aircraft taking off make far more noise than do aircraft which are cruising or approaching for a landing. Whenever possible the engineer should avoid locating the airport so that prevailing winds require any appreciable percentage of take-offs to be made over congested areas. This is true both because of the noise and because aircraft experiencing engine failure on the take-off have very little choice except to land straight ahead regardless of what is there.

Private Assistance

The existence and attitude of persons, institutions, or concerns willing to provide funds or land for airport purposes is important. This factor has a definite promotional aspect. It may well prove to be advisable for the commission, or some particular individual appointed by the commission, to handle the promotion involved rather than entrusting this activity to the engineer.

It often happens that some person, institution, or business concern is willing to provide funds for the purchase of airport property or for airport buildings or improvements. This willingness to provide funds may be entirely philanthropic or may stem from selfish motives. It is very easy to see how any sizable contribution will allow the planner to provide a better airport than would otherwise be possible. Such a contribution has often been the impetus needed to insure the construction of an airport or to allow the selection of the most useful site. A gift with strings attached, however, should be carefully scrutinized.

Engineer's Report

Upon completion of the preliminary survey the engineer will have secured all of the information which will be required by the committee in order for it to take action. The engineer should prepare his report in an easily understandable form and present it to the committee with his recommendation as to the action which should be taken.

TRENDS IN AIR TRANSPORTATION

When sufficient definite knowledge is lacking there can be no starting point in the development of any problem's solution without some things being assumed as correct within reasonable limits. About all we are sure of at present is that airplanes will range in size from craft weighing a few hundred pounds to aerial leviathans, the gross weight of which may well reach 400,000 lb; that the heavier the aircraft the less effect surface winds have on the direction in which it must land and take off; and that there will be constant improvement in aircraft performance. It is therefore believed that the following precepts must be assumed and allowed to govern in the solution of the airport location, design, and layout problems:

1. Airplane performance requirements as set forth in Civil Air Regulations Part 04, and transport-category operating limitations as set forth in Part 6, will remain substantially as they are now.
2. Lengths of runways required can generally be divided into four groups, namely:
   a. Over 7000 ft at sea level to accommodate superairliners used for nonstop, coast-to-coast, or transoceanic traffic, having very high (50 to 75 lb per sq ft) wing loading.
   b. Approximately 5000 ft at sea level to accommodate aircraft in the same class with the Lockheed Constellation, or a commercial version of the C-54.
   c. 4000- to 5000-ft minimum to accommodate aircraft such as the Douglas DC-3, the Lockheed Lodestar, or the Curtis CW-20.
   d. Under 4000 ft to serve smaller aircraft, and found usually on Class 1 and 2 airports, airparks, and flightstops.
3. Transport aircraft will continue to have higher wheel loadings, but take-off and landing run will have to remain within prescribed limits for each class of aircraft.

4. Air transportation must pay its own way to the same extent that other forms of transportation are required to do, which means that for the most part airports must be self-supporting.
5. Low maintenance costs are a more important consideration than low initial construction costs.
6. The maximum number of buildings which will ultimately be required for a given airport cannot be predicted, making it mandatory that the original layout allow for vast expansion.

RECOMMENDED PLAN

Upon completion of its study the commission will find it necessary to secure approval of its recommended action. When approved the report should be in such form that it can be turned over to the engineer charged with the actual selection of the airport site. This report must set forth recommendations with regard to the following:

1. Number of airports needed, as well as the class of each.
2. The most desirable location for each airport, as well as an outline of any zones in which airports are to be prohibited.
3. Amount of money available for each airport.
4. The servicing facilities which will be required in order that the engineer may determine the type and number of buildings to provide for.
5. Any probable improvement which is to be developed in conjunction with the airport.
6. General information, such as the official to whom the engineer should report, the method of handling publicity, and the extent of the authority extended to the engineer.

CHAPTER II

SITE SELECTION

It is difficult to overemphasize the importance of selecting the best possible site for an airport. An improperly located airport will prove to be either limited in usefulness, hazardous to some degree, detrimental to established property values, or unduly expensive. It may very well prove to possess some combination of any or all of these undesirable elements. Proper site selection is also important because experience has shown that it is very difficult to effect the complete abandonment and relocation of an airport, regardless of the seriousness of its shortcomings as disclosed by subsequent operations.

The requirements for an ideal airport site are set forth herein. The factors which influence people in making a site selection will also be enumerated. As is true in the solution of nearly all similar problems, the quality of the final result depends not only on the knowledge possessed by the person making the final decision but also on his experience and good judgment.

SITE REQUIREMENTS

Requirements are much the same for all types of airports. They are in effect the conditions which must be fulfilled in order that aircraft may operate safely and with the greatest possible convenience and economy. Some site requirements however will vary, particularly in scope, depending on the type of aircraft to be accommodated.

Economy of maintenance will be stressed throughout this entire text. There can be no question that money spent to attain site requirements will continue to pay dividends throughout the entire life of the airport in safer operation and lower maintenance costs.

Composite List

The following list of basic airport site requirements is considered complete, with the requirements listed according to the order of their importance:

1. Size.
2. Unobstructed approaches.

3. Best possible weather conditions.
4. Economical development and maintenance.
5. Convenient access.

Size

The size of an airport site should be sufficient to provide space for adequate runway lengths to accommodate the largest type of aircraft normally expected to use the airport, necessary hangars and buildings, airplane parking, car parking, and possible future expansion of all of the above appurtenances.

Assuming an over-all airport plan to have been adopted in accordance with the procedure outlined in Chapter I, the necessity for a certain size airport is firmly established. Regardless of how well a site may meet other requirements, it cannot serve its purpose if it is too small to accommodate the desired type of aircraft. A site of adequate size is, therefore, the prime requirement.

The requirement that it be possible to expand the airport, both as to length and number of runways, will be assigned prime importance by a large number of airport consultants. This text, however, stresses acquiring adequate property to start with and therefore assigns less importance to this requirement. Each community will have to evaluate this requirement for itself on the basis of its estimated future air traffic.

It is entirely possible that many relatively small communities will at some future time have sufficient traffic to require more than one runway in operation at the same time, or possibly more than one airport. Dual runways, or a tangential system of runways appear to be preferable to dual airports.

Present-day traffic control allows approximately sixty landings and/or take-offs per hour under contact conditions from an airport having single runways with a well-designed taxiway system. With winds under 15 mph this number can be increased as traffic then is not confined to one runway. Fifteen landings and twenty-four take-offs per hour under instrument conditions is excellent performance at present. These figures for contact operation apply to scheduled air-carrier operations and can be bettered considerably for light-aircraft operation. Only the largest air terminals, during their peak periods, at present have sufficient traffic to equal the number of landings and take-offs a well-designed single-runway airport allows. It can be seen, therefore, that for very many cities, air-line traffic can expand manyfold before this type of traffic will necessitate multiple runways or two large airports.

Unobstructed Approaches

The value of an airport is greatly affected by its approaches. The area used by an airplane in taking off or approaching an airport is called the approach zone, and this zone should be unobstructed airspace in which an aircraft can operate at a low altitude as it lands or takes off. Figure 2–1 illustrates the location and extent of an approach zone. Figure 1–3 illustrates the adverse effect obstructions in the approach zone have on the effective length of a runway.

If possible, an airport site should be chosen where no obstructions exist. If movable obstructions exist, the property on which they are located may be purchased, or removal rights secured in order to allow their removal. However, if immovable obstructions exist, it may be possible that careful runway alignment may help immeasurably in reducing their hazard.

Zoning ordinances can be passed to prevent erection of obstructions. However, zoning ordinances, of necessity, are passed by civic bodies and therefore such legislation is subject to the efforts of pressure groups. For this reason it is questionable judgment to rely on a zoning ordinance to protect airport approaches where such approaches involve highly valuable industrial or residential property.

All other things being equal, a site should be chosen where approach clearance and protection do not involve entanglements with legal talent representing powerful interests.

Best Possible Weather Conditions

Quite often conflicting claims are made concerning the frequency or duration of periods of low ceiling or restricted visibility between two or more sites. These conditions are largely caused by a discernible set of circumstances such as swamp lands, large bodies of water, river bottoms, or peculiar air currents. After reviewing all available data the engineer will have to pass judgment on the sites involved.

While instrument operation of aircraft is rapidly becoming safe and more dependable, contact operations undoubtedly will always be safer and make for faster handling of traffic. It can be seen, therefore, that this requirement must be met to the fullest possible extent.

Economical Development and Maintenance

Except where unusual circumstances are encountered, an airport will be severely penalized if the cost of its development is excessive. The penalty may be in the form of maximum runway grades, minimum runway lengths, inadequate drainage, or a number of other shortcomings caused by the lack of funds or the stretching of funds too far.

Almost any site of adequate size can be developed into an airport if costs of construction are disregarded. The wisdom of this procedure is always open to question. High development costs will receive increasing scrutiny as aviation and all of its associated enterprises are required to operate on a pay-as-you-go basis.

Economical development, except in instances where the airport is a work-making project, must be considered a prime requirement of an airport site. The possibility of excessive maintenance costs occasioned by inherent site conditions, such as high water table, unstable subsurface conditions, underlying strata of soluble limestone, flooding, etc., has far too often received scant consideration.

Convenient Access

To be completely successful, the airport must be within easy reach of the center or centers of population it serves. A distance of from 3 to 5 miles from congested areas is generally accepted as desirable. This should be the equivalent of 15 or 20 min driving time.

An airport which can be reached easily will come nearer paying interest on the investment than will an inconveniently located airport. Charter service and sight-seeing business will be better. A larger percentage of itinerant aircraft will yield to the temptation to stop. More people will visit the airport while "out riding," making food, drink, and other concessions more valuable.

If the airport can be reached quickly and conveniently, air-line passenger traffic should reach the maximum volume which can be expected. This is true because the saving in traveltime by air, particularly on short trips, will be greater. This desirable condition also reduces the percentage of people who would otherwise take another form of transportation rather than be inconvenienced or pay a high taxi bill to reach the airport. The extension of public utilities such as power, communications, water, gas, and sewage will be cheaper and more feasible, with a corresponding reduction in maintenance costs chargeable to the airport.

An all-weather paved highway designed to handle high-speed traffic from the airport to downtown areas is an important factor in the success of any airport. Large metropolitan areas will, no doubt, require facilities similar to those provided by an express highway.

ECONOMY

Future trends in such matters as feeder air lines, aircraft size, and improvements in aircraft and aircraft engines are too uncertain to warrant anything other than a conservative policy regarding airport size.

FACTORS

The factors entering into the problem of selecting an airport site govern, to a large extent, the degree to which the above requirements are complied with. Factors, as used in this text, include the existence or absence of any conditions, state of mind, physical condition, or any relationship which affects the size, usefulness, construction cost, ability to pay its own way or to show a profit, or the decision as to whether or not the airport will be constructed.

Each factor listed herein will have varying importance depending on the specific situation at hand and the personal interests or experience of the person evaluating it.

Experience in site selection has shown that the effect of certain factors can be anticipated, and further, that familiarity with these factors will enable anyone charged with the responsibility for site selection to properly evaluate them and to be on guard against the confusion and delay some of them can cause.

Topography Limits Size

The topography of the area in which it is desirable to select a site is often the governing factor as the hills, streams, and existing structures may limit the possible size of many otherwise desirable locations. Recent improvements in earth-moving equipment have, however, made the moving of large quantities of earth and rock less of a handicap to the size of an airport than it used to be.

Ordinarily, topography is the first aspect of a site which receives consideration, with the choice of sites limited to those having the most favorable topography. However, the engineer must not let favorable topography influence site selection if this would cause other factors affecting safety and usefulness to be slighted.

Factors Affecting Construction Cost

Types of existing soil determine to a large extent the usefulness of the property for agricultural purposes, while subsurface soil or geological conditions may give the property value for mining or oil production.

If the property has a high value for either purpose it will of course be reflected in property costs. In some instances property values of available sites have been so high as to prohibit their use for airport purposes and in other instances have resulted in the airport being kept to the minimum size.

In many instances under the present airport program it has proved to be false economy to allow the value of the land to be the predominating factor in the location of the airport site or the size of the site acquired.

People charged with the responsibility for the expenditures of public funds are reluctant to remove from the tax rolls property which has previously brought in tax revenue at a relatively high rate per acre. It is advised that very careful consideration be given to all alternate sites before choosing an airport site where the land value and tax revenue are relatively high. Purchasing high-priced land will materially increase the original cost, and the loss of tax revenue must be considered as part of the maintenance cost of the airport.

As is explained in following chapters, soil types dictate paving and drainage design to a very appreciable extent and are directly connected with fertilizing and seeding. Soil condition is a most important factor in determining whether grading, drainage, and paving costs are to be high, normal, or low.

Ground-Water Level and Available Drainage Outlets

Almost everything that has been said concerning the factor of existing soil types can be repeated for ground-water level and available drainage outlets. Drainage requirements must be determined, the measures required to insure satisfactory drainage for each site worked out, and the various sites then considered in the light of this information.

Existence of Hazardous Obstructions

Obstructions which are impossible to remove present the engineer with a serious problem and quite often leave him little, if any, choice as to either the location of the airport or its size. This situation prevails quite often in mountainous country. Chapter IX contains information which is applicable to the effect of obstructions on site selection.

Possible Sites for Radio Aids

Chapter XIII on Radio Aids furnishes detailed information regarding the location of various radio aids with respect to runways.

A study of Chapter XIII will reveal the immensely important part radio aids play in the safety and usefulness of any airport where operations under instrument conditions are to be carried on.

Location of Site

The location of various possible sites with reference to business and thickly settled residential sections has been discussed to some extent in Chapter I. It is very undesirable to have the airport so located that any appreciable percentage of aircraft take-offs have to be over built-up business or residential areas.

It is believed that airports should seldom be closer than 2 miles from well-developed business or residential areas and preferably should be at least 3 miles. Most heavy aircraft take off at about 90 mph and reach 120 mph before they clear the airport boundaries. Thereafter, they ordinarily maintain an air speed of 120 mph and a rate of climb of 500 fpm until cruising altitude is reached. Considering 500 ft to be the minimum allowable operating elevation over congested areas, it can be seen that in one minute's flying after take-off, the equivalent of 2 miles is required to reach this elevation. Allowing for heavily loaded craft without the advantage of much surface wind velocity to aid in securing altitude, 3 miles is considered a much safer figure for a minimum.

Airports too far from town often lose the advantage of the revenue derived from visitors. Such a location also cuts down the time advantage of air travel. Good judgment with respect to all local conditions will be needed by the engineer to determine the desirable minimum distance.

Attitude of Affected Property Owners

The attitude of people owning the land comprising a possible site has a very important bearing on site selection. The engineer's problem is seriously complicated when the owner is hostile toward the idea of selling his property for airport purposes. Such a situation may result in the cost of the property becoming so high it is necessary to choose a less desirable location.

Skill in negotiations for the purchase of property can be acquired only through practice. The engineer who is forewarned of the seriousness of this factor should be in a better position to avoid its adverse effects. Property acquisition, being a specialized field of endeavor, warrants the employment of trained personnel for this phase of the work.

Traffic Pattern

Very serious consideration must be given to the way in which a possible site fits into the local traffic pattern as it can be expected to exist when air transportation for the community reaches its maximum. The chapters on Radio Aids and Control Tower contain detailed advice on the part radio facilities will play. This consideration is far more important than is generally recognized.

General

Several conditions have been found to be generally unsatisfactory for airport sites and should therefore be avoided if possible.

Soluble limestone formations, when the water channels are disturbed by grading operations, often cause far more cave-ins than previously existed. The unpredictable nature of such cave-ins makes airplane operations in such an area extremely hazardous.

Mining operations also often cause unexpected cave-ins. Measures taken to prevent cave-ins from either limestone channels or mining operations are usually very expensive.

Hydraulic filling of marsh or swampland should be done only as a last resort or because such a site offers very great advantages over any other possible site. The drainage and settlement of hydraulic fills are very difficult to control or predict. There are several examples in this country of the difficulties which may be experienced.

RUNWAY LAYOUT

Economy requires that the minimum number of runways needed to fulfill the requirements for wind-direction coverage be constructed. This requirement is that landing strips and runways be sufficient in number to permit take-offs and landings to be made within 22½ deg of the true direction for the percentage shown in Table 2–2 of winds having a velocity of 4 mph and over. The illustrations in this book give a number of satisfactory layouts.

The major considerations in runway layout are allowance for simultaneous operation on two runways at the same time under low wind-velocity conditions and the reduction of taxiing to a minimum, all within the least space. Obstructions, runway grades, construction costs, and topography affect runway layout. The final layout is quite often a compromise between the desirable and the practical.

Equilateral Triangle Layout

Wherever three runways are required, a layout as nearly as possible in the form of an equilateral triangle is recommended. This layout allows a minimum of taxiways to be very effective and is quite adaptable to simultaneous operations.

Multiple Runways

If there is any reason to believe that traffic will eventually become greater than that which a single runway system can handle, the engineer should provide a layout which will allow dual or tangential runways. Table 2–3 applies to this situation.

At this early stage in the development of aviation it is impossible to predict future runway requirements but it certainly can be expected that the number of operations will constantly increase for years to come.

Dual Runways

Dual runways are parallel runways separated by a distance sufficient to allow simultaneous operations. Simultaneous landings, particularly under instrument conditions, are yet to be proved practical. Except for missed approaches on landings there appears to be no doubt that a landing and a take-off at the same time, using parallel runways, can become accepted practice.

The advantage of this layout is that aircraft are always on parallel headings. The disadvantage is that the lateral separation requires a very large airport site and presents taxiing problems.

Tangential Runways

Figure 2–2, The General Plan of New York's Idlewild Airport, illustrates an adaptation of the tangential system. The layout is essentially a number of runways tangential to a circular or elliptical building area.

It will be seen that taxiing can be kept to a minimum by starting the take-off end of the take-off runways at the building area and ending the landing runways at the building area.

The advocates of this layout feel that three landings and three take-offs can be made simultaneously where a twelve-runway ($22\frac{1}{2}$ deg apart) layout is provided. The three landing planes are widely separated as they maneuver to line up with the runways but converge to a point at the building area. The three planes taking off are close together at the start, but follow diverging paths. As an example, with the wind directly out of the North at Idlewild, runways Z, E, and U could be used for take-offs while runways V, B, and Y could be used at the same time for landings.

As long as missed approaches occur in any appreciable percentage of landings, there will be pilots who are opposed to the tangential system of runways because of the intersecting paths. It is quite generally felt that improved aircraft performance, more reliable radio and lighting aids, and more efficient traffic-control methods will reduce the percentage of missed approaches to a negligible quantity. Collision warning devices are expected to further reduce the hazards associated with handling the large volumes of traffic which the tangential system is designed for.

STANDARDS

No site selection or design can be made until the standards upon which the design is based are known. This section gives the standards recommended by the C.A.A. While many airports, even recently, have not been constructed to these requirements, rigid adherence to them is recommended. With the vast expansion anticipated in air traffic and construction of airports, limiting standards will be given more and more importance in order that pilots may be assured of uniform conditions wherever planes are operating, and such standards are expected to be a requirement for certification of the airport for commercial use.

The standards set forth in Tables 2–1, –2, –3, –4, and –5 are recommended by the C.A.A. Any major deviation from the requirements should be approved by the Administration before such changes are incorporated into the design in order to avoid any question in the future as to official approval of the airport. In view also of the changes which may evolve from present experience and a future expanded building program, it is recommended that the designer obtain the latest publications of the C.A.A. covering airport-design standards before work of any magnitude is started.

TABLE 2–1. Recommended Airport Design Standards for Communities, Cities, and Metropolitan Areas (Courtesy C.A.A.)

Type of Community	Planning Classification	Recommended Landing Strip Lengths—Sea Level Conditions—Clear Approaches [a]	Type of Aircraft Which Airport May Safely Accommodate
Small communities not on present or proposed scheduled air carrier system, and auxiliary airports in larger metropolitan areas to serve non-scheduled private flying activities	1	1800′ to 2700′	Small private owner type planes. This includes roughly planes up to a gross weight of 4000 pounds, or having a wing loading (lbs./sq. ft.) times power loading (lbs./HP) not exceeding 190
Larger communities located on present or proposed feeder line airways and which have considerable aeronautical activity. General population range 5000 to 25,000	2	2700′ to 3700′	Larger size private owner planes and some small size transport planes. This represents roughly planes in the gross weight classification between 4000 and 15,000 pounds, or having a wing loading (lbs./sq. ft.) times power loading (lbs./HP of 190 to 230)
Important cities on feeder line airway systems and many intermediate points on the main line airways. General population range 25,000 to several hundred thousand	3	3700′ to 4700′	Present day transport planes. Planes in this classification are represented approximately by those between 10,000 and 50,000 pounds gross weight, or by those having a wing loading (lbs./sq. ft.) times power loading (lbs./HP) of 230 and over
Cities in this group represent the major industrial centers of the nation and important junction points or terminals on the airways system	4 & 5	4700′ to 5700′ 5700′ and over	Largest planes in use and those planned for the immediate future. This approximately represents planes having a gross weight of 74,000 pounds and over or having a wing loading (lbs./sq. ft.) times power loading (lbs./HP) of 230 and over

[a] Approaches shall be clear within a glide path of 20 to 1 from the end of the usable area in the case of class 1 airports and 30 to 1 in the case of classes 2, 3, 4, and 5 airports except for instrument landing runways for which the ratio shall be 40 to 1. These ratios represent the minimum permissible. In all cases it is highly desirable to clear approaches to runways *on as flat a ratio as is possible* in the interest of safety. A 50 to 1 ratio is a desirable minimum.

NOTE: Paved runways shall be 200′ shorter than landing strips.

TABLE 2–2. Airport Size-Planning Standards (Courtesy C.A.A.)

Recommended Minimum Standards	Class I	Class II	Class III	Class IV	Class V
Length of landing strip [a]	1800′ to 2700′	2700′ to 3700′	3700′ to 4700′	4700′ to 5700′	5700′ and over
Width of usable landing strips	300′	500′	500′	500′	500′
Length of runways	None	2500′ to 3500′	3500′ to 4500′	4500′ to 5500′	5500′ and over
Width of runways	None	150′ (night op.) 100′ (day op. only)	200′ (instru.) 150′ (night op.)	200′ (instru.) 150′ (night op.)	200′ (instru.) 150′ (night op.)
Number of landing strips and runways [b] determined by percentage of wind including calms [c] covered by landing strip and runway alignment	70%	75%	80%	90%	90%
Facilities	Drainage Fencing Marking Wind direction indicator Hangar Basic lighting (optional)	Include class I facilities and lighting Hangar and shop Fueling Weather information Office space Parking	Include class II facilities and weather bureau Two-way radio Visual traffic control Instrument approach system (when required) Administration bldg. Taxiways and aprons	Same as class III	Same as class IV

[a] All of the above landing strip and runway lengths are based on sea level conditions; for higher altitudes increases are necessary (see Fig. 3–1). One surfaced runway of dimensions shown above is recommended for each landing strip for airports in classes II, III, IV, and V.

[b] Landing strips and runways should be sufficient in number to permit take-offs and landings to be made within $22\frac{1}{2}°$ of the true direction for the percentage shown above of winds 4 miles per hour and over, based on at least a 10 year weather bureau wind record where possible.

[c] Calms: Negligible wind conditions of 3 miles per hour and under.

TABLE 2–3. Recommended Standards for Airport Distances (Courtesy C.A.A.)

Recommended Standards	Class I	Class II	Class III	Class IV	Class V
Minimum distance between center lines of parallel runways	None	700′	700′	700′	700′
Minimum distance between center line of runway and airport buildings; instrument landing runway		750′	750′	750′	750′
Minimum distance between runway center line and aprons and loading platforms, instrument landing runway		500′	500′	500′	500′
Distance between center line of runway and airport buildings; all other runways	Desirable Minimum	500′ 350′	500′ 350′	500′ 350′	500′ 350′
Minimum distance between center line of runway and aprons and loading platforms and parking areas; all other runways		250′	250′	250′	250′
Maximum landing strip and runway grades; transverse	2%	2%	1½%	1½%	1½%
Maximum landing strip and runway grades; [a] uniform longitudinal	2%	1½%	1½%	1%	1%
Grade breaks longitudinal; [b] maximum algebraic difference	3%	2½%	2%	2%	2%

[a] In the development of initial units the grades should be established to conform with the standards for the ultimate development. In special cases it may be necessary to exceed these maximums for economic reasons.

[b] Longitudinal intersecting grades on a runway or landing strip should be joined by a vertical curve, if the algebraic difference in grades is 0.40% or more. The vertical curve should be at least 300′ in length for each 1% change in grade. It is also recommended that the tangent interval between the point of tangency of one curve and the point of curvature of the succeeding curve be not less than 1000′. If economically practical grade breaks should be so controlled that the sight line will be unobstructed from any point 10′ above the surface of the runway to any other point 10′ above the runway.

TABLE 2–4. Recommended Standards for Taxiway Layouts, etc. (Courtesy C.A.A.)

Recommended Standards	Class II	Class III	Class IV	Class V
Minimum width of taxiways	50′	50′	50′	50′
Minimum distance between runway center line and parallel taxiway center line	275′	275′	275′	275′
Minimum distance from boundary fence, obstructions, etc., to taxiway center line	100′	150′	150′	200′
Maximum longitudinal grade	3%	2½%	2½%	2½%
Maximum transverse grade	1½%	1½%	1½%	1½%
Minimum angle of taxiway intersection with runway ends	60°	60°	60°	60°

Runway grades should not be altered to accommodate taxiway intersections or connections. At large airports where traffic is heavy it may be advisable to construct a warming up apron and by-pass on taxiways connecting to the ends of runways. Taxiways should not connect to the ends of runways at an angle of less than 90° to incoming traffic.

TABLE 2–5. Airport Lighting Standards (Courtesy C A.A.)

Minimum Recommended Facilities	Class I	Class II	Class III	Class IV	Class V
Airport beacon [a]	Include	Include	Include	Include	Include
Boundary lights [b] (including range lights)	Include	Include	Include	Include	Include
Obstruction lights	Include	Include	Include	Include	Include
Illuminated wind cone	Include	Include	Include	Include	Include
Contact lights (including range lights)		Include	Include	Include	Include
Illuminated wind tee or tetrahedron			Include	Include	Include
Landing area floodlighting [c]			Include	Include	Include
Apron floodlighting			Include	Include	Include
Ceiling projector			Include	Include	Include
Taxi lights				Include	Include
Approach lights [d]				Include	Include

NOTE: All lighting facilities provided in any case, should conform to the requirements of the Standard Specifications for Airport Lighting Equipment and Materials, issued by the C.A.A.

[a] The installation of auxiliary beacons, such as identification code beacons, will depend upon individual requirements in each case.

[b] Use boundary lights in lieu of contact lights at all-way type field having no all-night operator to select landing directions.

[c] Landing area floodlights are considered necessary in northern climates where blowing snow conditions are encountered.

[d] Approach lights should be installed for every instrument runway.

CHAPTER III

SURVEY

This chapter will make it apparent that a complete survey is quite expensive and requires a considerable length of time for completion. It is recommended that the procedures outlined herein be followed to the extent that local conditions and the class of airport under consideration require, in order that adequate information be secured. Unusual conditions may require an even more detailed survey. The engineer can select from these procedures the ones that seem to him applicable to the smaller airports or to the survey of tentative sites.

METEOROLOGICAL CONDITIONS

Sources of Information

The meteorological conditions prevailing at an airport site can not be determined by direct survey. Data on such conditions as prevailing winds, rainfall, and duration of periods of low visibility require the keeping of records over a period of several years. Such records are rarely available unless they have been kept by the United States Weather Bureau. This agency is always willing to assist in localities where it has maintained records.

However, in many instances it is necessary to rely on the memories of untrained observers concerning local meteorological conditions. These people cannot give expert testimony, regardless of their intentions, but their statements have some value and must be taken into account.

It is advised that all information secured be correlated and checked by a competent meteorologist.

Barometric Pressure

Barometric pressure, being a measure of the density of the earth's atmosphere, has a direct relationship to runway lengths required.

Figure 3–1 graphically assigns value to the effect of altitude above sea level on runway lengths for each class of airport. An airplane wing acquires lifting power due to the effect of the air flowing over and under it. Both the speed of the plane and density of the air flowing past the wing are positive factors in the amount of lift created. The airplane propeller provides forward thrust by absorbing the horsepower developed by the airplane engine. Most engines which are not equipped with superchargers deliver a decreasing amount of power as the density of the air taken into the carburetor decreases. Since atmospheric density decreases as the elevation above sea level increases, the lift of the wing and the power of the engine decrease, thus reducing the efficiency of the airplane. As a result, longer take-off and landing runs are required.

The barometric pressure prevailing at an airport site is normally a direct function of its altitude above sea level. In some areas this statement is not entirely correct because prolonged barometric pressure variations are caused by the slow movement of areas of high or low pressure. The Weather Bureau should be consulted to determine whether or not there is any tendency for low-pressure areas to remain in the locality of the airport a larger percentage of the time than would normally be expected. If such a condition exists the runway lengths should be increased accordingly.

Another reason for increasing runway lengths over those required for a given altitude is the existence of periods of high temperatures. Atmospheric density is reduced by high temperatures, particularly in a dry climate. The approximate increase can be determined by converting the temperature effect into terms of reduced barometric pressure.

Winds

Since an airplane travels strictly in the medium of the earth's atmosphere, any movement of the atmosphere affects the airplane's operation directly. Winds prevailing at an airport site are therefore of extreme importance.

A type of chart called a wind rose has been developed as a ready means of graphically portraying wind information. Wind roses are based on records of observation of wind velocity and direction. The longer the period covered by the observations the more accurate the results should be. Wind roses are prepared for different conditions of visibility. The normal wind rose covers all conditions, while the low-visibility wind rose is compiled from information recorded during periods when instrument weather conditions prevail. The low-visibility wind rose is useful in determining instrument runway direction. Figure 3–2 illustrates a typical wind rose. A wind rose for the airport site should be prepared if sufficient data are available.

Rainfall

Accurate rainfall data are of particular importance as they are used in both drainage and pavement design. For drainage design, data regarding the maximum intensity which may be expected in any 1-hr period are needed.

Frost

Frost should be studied as to both maximum depth and the number of cycles of freezing and thawing per year. Municipal water departments always have frost-depth data. A study of temperature records will indicate the number of cycles to be expected each year.

Snowfall

Snowfall data are required wherever any appreciable amount of snow can be expected. These data should furnish information, month by month, regarding frequency and depth of individual snowstorms and the accumulated depth of snow which may be expected. Knowledge of the possibility of sudden thaws is also needed.

TOPOGRAPHICAL SURVEY

Purpose

In almost every instance the conversion of the site into a usable airport will require many construction operations such as clearing, grading, drainage, and paving.

Regardless of how it is performed the topographical survey must produce sufficient data to allow the engineer to:

1. Prepare an accurate map showing property lines, roads, streams, buildings, pole lines, cemeteries, and all other pertinent physical features of the airport site.
2. Prepare an accurate contour map having a contour interval which will allow selection of the best runway layout, and an estimate of grading and drainage costs.
3. Establish pay quantities for clearing and grubbing.
4. Establish original elevations for computing excavation quantities.
5. Provide legal description of property to be acquired.
6. Provide information as to the best locations for discharge of the outfall lines of the drainage system and any intercepting ditches

required, even though securing such data often necessitates surveying beyond the limits of the airport property.

Accuracy

One of the first determinations which must be made is the degree of accuracy required to insure satisfactory estimation of construction quantities in preliminary planning and to insure equitable measurement of work actually performed. There is no substitute for experience in making this determination. The writers have found elevations taken on 100-ft centers and on the breaks in grade to be sufficient in the roughest type of terrain. For sites where grades are constant over long distances the distance between shots can be increased considerably, at least for the preliminary study. Elevations to the nearest $\frac{1}{10}$ ft have proved to be satisfactory.

Grid Survey

If there is no question as to whether the site being surveyed is the one on which the airport is to be constructed, the grid survey is recommended. The grid system insures uniform coverage and should be more accurate. It usually takes longer but is little, if any, more expensive in the long run.

It is desirable for design purposes and almost mandatory for determining pay quantities that cross sections be taken normal to the runway center lines. It is seldom possible to arrange the grid layout so that this end is accomplished by the original survey. To obtain accurate cross sections it is necessary in nearly all airport surveys to go over the site at least two times; once to obtain topography and contours, and again after the layout has been determined.

When the distance between shots has been decided on, the airport area is laid out in a rectangular grid with one axis coinciding with a runway direction if possible. Where an airport is to have two runways at right angles a careful grid layout may result in either one or two grid lines coinciding exactly with runway center lines. Stationing the grid lines so that field notes are not confusing requires some study. Figures 3–3 and –4 illustrate a grid survey.

The grid-line intersections can be established by a transit and tape survey or may be a combination of this method and stadia. Elevations may involve a level or a level and stadia. The writers recommend the following method:

1. Establish base lines 500 to 1000 ft apart using a transit and tape for establishing hub points and a level for determining elevations. Check elevations by returning to original bench mark.
2. Use transit for setting balance of points and securing balance of elevations.
3. Set transit up over each base-line point and determine HI by reference to elevations secured by level survey.
4. Establish right angle to base line by turning 90 deg or by sighting on flag on next base line.
5. Measure distance along grid line by tape or stadia.
6. Determine elevation of intermediate points by level rod reading with transit where possible, otherwise use vertical angle and rod reading.
7. Do not use stadia and vertical angles wherever runway location definitely coincides with grid.

Random Lines

Surveys based on random lines using a combination of transit and tape, stadia, and leveling methods may prove desirable, particularly for a strictly preliminary survey. This type of survey allows for a wide variation in the accuracy of the results and may be conducted to conform with the requirements of the problem. It is recommended, however, that a transit and chain be used to set the base-line points and a level used to establish base-line elevations. Stadia traverses should be closed back on a base-line point in all cases.

APPROACH-ZONE SURVEY

Purpose

The approach-zone survey is in effect a topographical survey of the approach zones with special emphasis placed on the elevation of the top of objects in this zone. The use of a United States Geological Survey quadrangle map is no substitute for an actual survey, although prominent points some distance from the airport can be spotted with sufficient accuracy.

Regardless of how it is performed the approach-zone survey must furnish sufficient data to:

1. Establish the location and top and ground elevation of every object which protrudes above the plane of the horizontal sur-

faces, the approach and/or take-off surfaces, and the transitional surfaces described in Chapter X on Lighting.

2. Establish the location and top and ground elevation of any other objects, particularly in the approach zones, which may be considered a hazard.
3. Determine whether the object can be removed and if not, how it can best be marked day and night.
4. Establish the estimated value and ownership of each object to be removed.
5. Determine the best routing for power (overhead line or cable) if the object is to be obstruction lighted.
6. Predict the likelihood of additional objects being constructed.

Method

A random-line survey or a survey where all distances are measured as offsets from center-line stations will prove satisfactory. Where woods or built-up sections are encountered the survey may prove difficult. The engineer must remember that accurate ground and top elevations are essential as it is very embarrassing to erect obstruction light poles or masts only to find them too short or much too long. Accuracy in matters with regard to ownership and location is necessary when purchase, easement, or condemnation proceedings can be expected.

MATERIALS

Purpose

Economical design must be based on information regarding the availability and cost of construction materials. The material survey is an investigation of local material conditions.

The material survey should furnish sufficient data to:

1. Determine the types of construction materials available and the delivery price of each item as well as any local characteristics such as gradations or service records.
2. Estimate the quantity of each item available and the daily production rate.
3. Outline transportation and haulage facilities and difficulties.
4. Furnish names of dealers and producers of construction materials.
5. Furnish applicable freight rates.
6. Outline local preference and experience with materials.

Methods

This survey can be made by personal contacts or by written inquiries. Local contacts produce the best results in most instances as it is otherwise difficult to uncover material sources.

The effect of this survey on the ultimate cost of the airport must not be underestimated. It must be prosecuted with care and zeal.

SOIL SURVEY

Soils engineering is a comparatively new branch of engineering which shows promise of assuming a position of high importance wherever the problem at hand has any connection with the behavior of soils. It must be understood that soils classification is not an end in itself but represents invaluable information to be used in design. The value attached to proper use and treatment of soils is indicated by the increasing number of public agencies which are establishing soils-engineer positions ranking in importance with other specialized aspects of engineering.

Purpose

The purpose of a soils survey is to determine the location and extent of each type of soil to be encountered in the work, or available for importation from outside sources. The survey should also ascertain the characteristics of each type so that it may be classified and its behavior in the finished work predicted. The soils survey can be considered as very similar in purpose to the material survey, as soils must be considered as construction materials. It must also serve the purpose of enabling the engineer to accomplish the most economical grading, drainage, and paving design.

Scope

The field investigations and sampling should cover sufficient area and go to such depths below the ground surface as are required to enable the engineer to consider all factors which can affect any phase of airport design. The survey should be sufficient in scope to:

1. Establish the top and bottom elevation and lateral limits of all natural formations to be encountered in cut areas. Explorations should extend below finished subgrade to a depth of at least 4 ft or the maximum depth of frost penetration, whichever is greater.
2. Establish the top and bottom elevation and lateral limits of all

natural formations within embankment areas with particular emphasis on suitable topsoil material and unsuitable subgrade material. The nature of the material encountered will govern the depth of the explorations but in general they should be at least 2 ft below existing ground surface or 4 ft below finished subgrade elevation whichever is greater.

3. Afford a working knowledge of natural formations existing on balance of airport site. Explorations can be quite limited if there is no indication that desirable construction materials exist in appreciable quantities.
4. Determine location and extent of borrow areas where desirable construction materials exist. Extensive explorations should be made of borrow areas to insure the existence of the quantity of material on which plans are based.
5. Allow an accurate boring log to be drawn. Some engineers may desire a soil profile but the writers have found this to be of little practical value.

Methods

There are several methods of making subsurface explorations, all of which have been standard practice for a number of years. Some of the more common which have been found useful by the writers are described herewith.

Test Pits

Except for the expense the digging of test pits affords the most desirable means of subsurface exploration. Test pits allow soil strata to be observed in an undisturbed condition and unadulterated samples to be taken. The elevation of top and bottom of each stratum can be accurately determined. Test pits are impractical for deep explorations or in soils where moisture content or physical characteristics cause the material to cave easily. This method is recommended wherever practical.

Auger Borings

Auger borings are especially adaptable to preliminary surveys and in many instances prove entirely satisfactory for obtaining final samples. When proper equipment in good condition is used, the cost of this method of sampling is quite low. It is not practical where boulders or loose rock are encountered. When material which has a tendency to cave is encountered a casing must be used. Samples are obtained either from the auger or by bailing, but material from different strata may become mixed unless care is exercised. This method has many good points but its limitations must be recognized where extreme accuracy is essential.

Rod Soundings

Rod soundings are an aid in determining the approximate depth of rock or hardpan. They are not completely reliable because it is impossible to determine what objects caused the rod to refuse to penetrate deeper. Because they are inexpensive and sufficiently accurate for many purposes where conditions immediately above hard strata are known to be quite uniform, rod soundings serve a useful purpose. The procedure consists of driving an iron or steel rod to refusal in much the same manner a pile is driven. If refusal is not accomplished by the time the rod reaches the desired exploration depth it is a safe assumption that a hard stratum does not exist. An experienced operator can tell much about the nature of the strata encountered by the rate of penetration of the rod and the manner in which refusal takes place. An abrupt positive refusal indicates hard rock whereas a gradual increase in the blows required for penetration just before refusal indicates hardpan or shale.

Wash Borings

Wash borings are made by driving a casing into the soil in increments of from 1 to 2 ft and washing up the material collected therein by a water jet. The soil and water mixture is collected and classified by visual inspection. The disadvantage of this method is that a large portion of the fines is washed away in the process so that a true sample of the soil is not obtained. To be of any value the inspection must be made by an experienced operator.

The value of this method is that it allows the driving of a spoon or split shell at definite increments or at apparent changes of strata as determined by the wash boring. These samples are satisfactory when taken below the elevation which has been affected by the jet action. Such samples may be removed from the spoon and placed in glass jars for future reference. The writers have done considerable work of this nature and have found the results satisfactory. The sample of course contains a high percentage of water because of the wash water in the casing and therefore does not represent the true moisture condition of the soil itself. The work can be done with reasonable speed and the cost is not excessive.

Core Borings

Core borings are particularly useful in rock exploration. The method requires a power-operated core drill. The drill usually has a cylindrical cutting edge which is diamond studded or uses shot to cut out a core when rotated.

Undisturbed Sample

Various methods have been devised for removing a soil sample which has not had its physical, chemical, or moisture characteristics changed by the removal procedure. There are also methods for preserving the sample in its undisturbed state during shipment to the laboratory. The writers have found no practical application to airport design for data secured from undisturbed samples.

Sampling Equipment

Equipment for securing the sample will vary with the method of sampling used. Test pits can be dug by pick and shovel, back hoe, steam shovel, dragline, or other excavating equipment. Auger borings can be made by hand or by power-driven equipment similar to that used for digging post or pole holes.

The following equipment is required in order to locate, identify, log, and ship the samples regardless of the sampling method used:

1. Supply of sample bags or other containers.
2. Supply of marking and shipping tags.
3. Transit, tape, and level rod for locating area from which sample was taken, and ground elevation.
4. Rod or tape to measure depth of hole.
5. Notebook for recording data.

Size of Sample

Twenty-five-pound samples are the minimum required to allow a complete analysis including Atterberg's Limits, California Bearing Ratio, and Capillary Rise. It is recommended that at least three 25-lb samples of each soil type encountered be taken and that 10-lb check samples be taken from as many locations as appear necessary to insure all types being included in the 25-lb samples.

Three 25-lb samples of all rock or shale encountered should be taken.

Spacing of Borings

The number of test holes and locations from which samples must be taken will vary with the number of soil types encountered and the topography of the site.

It is suggested that test holes be made on 200-ft centers to start with. If the subsurface conditions are found to be uniform, the spacing can be increased. When the character of the soil changes, sufficient intermediate borings should be made to insure the exploration of the extent of all soil types.

Log of Hole

The written record of the test hole entered in the notebook at the time the exploration is conducted is extremely important. It will serve to permit visual identification of soils, avoid confusion in identification of samples, and record the test hole location.

It is suggested that the log of the test hole follow an outline similar to the following:

1. Names of survey party—indicating chief.
2. Method of sampling.
3. Weather conditions.
4. Stationing of hole.
5. Ground elevation.
6. Elevation of bottom of each stratum encountered.
7. List identifying characteristics of soil in strata.
8. Description of the moisture content of each soil type or any change in moisture content noted.
9. The probable source of free water.
10. The elevation at which ground water stands.
11. Size sample taken and how identified.
12. Disposition made of sample.
13. Remarks on probable behavior of soil such as erosion and stability.

It will prove desirable to have a log of boring form prepared which lists information desired and provides space for each entry.

DRAINAGE SURVEY

A great deal of the data secured for the meteorological, topographical, and soils survey will be used in the drainage design. There are, however, some data required strictly for estimating capacities and the locations of various drainage structures.

Sources of Water

Chapter VI on Drainage advises that all water from sources outside the airport area be intercepted or diverted. The engineer must have accurate knowledge of the source and quantity of the water to be disposed of. The topographical survey of the site can be assumed to furnish this information for the actual airport area.

Formulas are given later in this book for estimating runoff of water from ground surfaces. One of the factors in the equation is drainage area expressed in acres. The extent of the drainage area can be determined either by actually running out the areas or by consulting maps and aerial photographs. United States Coast and Geodetic Survey Quadrangle Maps or other contour maps are extremely useful for estimating drainage areas, particularly in view of the fact that the slope of the area is also a factor in most runoff formulas. It can be appreciated that the slope, expressed in ft per 1000 ft, will have to be an approximate average in rough terrain.

The runoff coefficient is an important factor in all runoff formulas. Its value depends on the permeability of the soil together with surface conditions such as turf, brush, woods, or pavement which will tend to accelerate or retard the rate of flow of water. The notes pertaining to drainage areas should clearly indicate the nature of the area's surface conditions and the extent of the area of each particular condition.

It often occurs that a stream must be diverted or confined to a culvert under a runway. Such a situation requires that the survey clearly indicate the maximum flow of water which may be expected. While this flow can be calculated by a runoff formula it is certainly desirable to check the calculations against the manner in which nearby culverts or bridges have handled the stream under flood conditions. Data regarding channel cross section, highest recorded floodwater elevation, and the size and service record of nearby drainage structures on the same watercourse should be secured.

Outlets

The importance of drainage outlets is mentioned several times in this text. This importance makes it imperative that the survey notes contain information regarding every possible outlet.

The location of an outlet relative to the airport layout and the possible flow-line elevation with reference to the airport runway elevations comprise the most essential data. Next in importance is a description of the outlet which will allow the engineer to determine its suitability, capacity, and whether its use for disposing of airport water can possibly involve damage to lands of adjacent property owners.

The survey chief can quite often anticipate the path which the pipe line or ditch will take in connecting the airport drainage system to the outfall. In all such instances a center-line profile should be run to furnish data as to depth of ditch needed or cover which can be secured over pipe. In the event the path can not be anticipated, data for a contour map covering all possible pipe or ditch locations should be secured.

Ground-Water Level

Wherever there is any reason to believe that at any season of the year the ground-water level will be sufficiently high to affect the stability of the airport subgrade or to interfere with construction operations, complete data are required. Ground-water data will normally be secured at the same time test holes are dug for soil samples. It must be borne in mind that ground-water elevation varies from time to time and that the data must reflect the highest elevation which may be normally expected. Accurate data therefore often require observations over a long period of time or during the wettest seasons.

FLOODWATERS

Wherever an airport site is situated so that any part of it may be subjected to overflow during periods of high water it is necessary that the engineer know the maximum elevation the floodwaters may reach. It is also necessary for him to know whether current, tide, or wave action of any appreciable magnitude will accompany the high water.

GENERAL INFORMATION REQUIRED

Much which is of use in airport design can be learned from the experience of other agencies concerning highway and city paving, drainage, and seeding.

The soil survey should include a report on the performance of various types of local pavements, their subgrade treatment, and provisions for drainage. The report should cover pavement subgrades which have given good performance as well as those which have failed.

Properly designed airport grades and seeding will take into account the erosional characteristics of the soil types encountered. Although the grade at which a soil will start to erode badly can be predicted from its classification, there is no substitute for a record of local experiences.

It is also true that a soil analysis will reveal turf possibilities, but again local experience is preferable. The securing of a turf suitable for airport requirements is a sufficiently controversial subject so that a knowledge of how well various grasses grow on local soils is essential.

AERIAL PHOTOGRAPHY

The C.A.A. has sponsored a research project carried on by Purdue University to determine the feasibility of classifying soil strata from aerial photographs. The method shows much promise and quite likely may find wide application. It is recommended that engineers study the research developments as reported in *Highway Research Board Proceedings Twenty-third Annual Meeting.*

PLATE-BEARING TEST

Purpose

The plate-bearing test is included under the heading of survey because one of its most important functions is the furnishing of data for design purposes. It is essential to the United States Navy's method of determining pavement thickness by load application to test sections. The value of the modulus of subgrade reaction K as used in Westergaard's formula for the design of rigid pavements may be obtained by this test. This test is also valuable for assigning safe load-bearing values to existing pavements.

Principle

The plate-bearing test is basically the application of a known load to a pavement or subgrade through plates of predetermined size, and the recording of deflection or deformation resulting therefrom.

Equipment

The equipment takes different forms, depending upon the manner in which it was developed, but that used by the First Region of the C.A.A. in New York is typical of all such apparatus. The equipment consists of:

1. A 24-in. I beam 18 ft long with a socket joint welded on the bottom flange to receive a jack, and cross members bolted to each end so that the cross member can bear on the underside of

truck frames. The trucks when loaded offer the reaction to the thrust of the jack.

2. A hydraulic jack of at least 50-ton capacity, and pump with a pressure gauge calibrated to indicate the load applied in pounds.
3. Plates 12, 18.3, 27.5 and 32 in. in diameter respectively, which may be used separately or nested to avoid excessive deflection in the large size plates. On the basis of 60-lb tire pressure and 1.1 rigidity factor, the 18.3-, 27.5-, and 32-in.-diameter plates represent contact area of tires for 17,500-, 37,000-, and 53,200-lb wheel loads respectively. The plates are circular resulting in the elliptical pattern of the actual tire contact being disregarded.
4. A 5-in. beam 16 ft long to support the recording device with suitable blocks at each end to give solid support and fittings suitable for mounting surface gauges welded to the center.
5. Two Ames surface gauges and mounts for recording deflection.

Procedure

The location of the test should be carefully selected so as to insure the test results being representative of a particular site condition. The nearer the subgrade condition can approach that which will prevail at the time the pavement is constructed, the more useful the results will be.

Because of the weight of the equipment and the high pressures applied to the plate, tests on saturated subgrades are impractical.

The ground surface must be leveled and precautions taken to insure against false recordings due to imperfect or unequal seating of the plate. A layer of fine dry sand or plaster of Paris can be used in seating the plate. On completion of all preliminary preparations and after all equipment is in place, a load of approximately 5 psi is placed on the plate to take up slack and seat the plate. This loading may have to be increased where previous consolidation or compaction has not been carried out.

Eight feet is generally accepted as the minimum distance allowable between the test plate and any other piece of equipment involved. This minimum distance is set up to guard against the effect of ground surface distortion affecting the dial readings. Figures 3–7a, –7b, and –7c are photographs of actual tests which show the manner in which the equipment is assembled.

The jack must be of the hydraulic type to allow easy variation of the load in the desired increments. The jack must have a ball-and-socket-joint connection to the reaction beam to avoid eccentricity in loading.

After the seating load is applied, both dials are set at zero, or read. The load is then applied in the desired increments. After each increment is applied the dials are allowed to come completely to rest indicating full deformation, before their readings are recorded.

The manner in which the load is applied depends on the test procedure being followed. The load may be increased in increments until the desired maximum is obtained or until the yield point is passed. This load is normally one and one-half times the static tire pressure of the heaviest aircraft for which the airport is being designed. Again the test procedure may call for applying and then releasing each loading several times before the load is increased to the next level.

Tests must be made in sufficient number so that the average results give a true indication of the subgrade reaction.

Plotting of Results

The test results are plotted in the form of a load deformation curve. If the load is carried to the yield point, a point on the curve conforming to maximum allowable deformation can be chosen as the safe load-bearing capacity. The bearing power can then be figured in pounds per square inch. Laboratory tests such as the California bearing test will then have to be run on comparable samples in order to set up probable values for the bearing value when stability has been reduced by increased moisture content due to subgrade saturation.

Application

Plate-bearing test results are assuming increasing importance for supplying design data, correlating other data, and checking actual pavement bearing value against the design value. Engineers are advised to follow the developments of the uses found for this test as they are reported from time to time in technical publications.

This test is presently applied for the most part in determining the modulus of soil reaction K of the subgrade.

DRAWINGS REQUIRED

The writers have found it difficult to secure a complete survey unless the field parties understood the use which would be made of the survey information. As an aid in outlining the work required, a list of the necessary drawings is given.

Master Plan

This drawing, or set of drawings, should show the original contours, ultimate runway, taxiway and parking apron layout, proposed administration building, hangars and other miscellaneous buildings, access roads, ramp facilities, utilities, auto parking areas, and other facilities.

Topographic Plan

Show all topography such as existing buildings, utilities, trees, woods, roads, etc., all property lines, proposed runway, taxiway and apron layout to be constructed under present contract, proposed airport property line and limit of clearing, and location of borings if any.

Grading Plan

Show original and final contours, proposed runway, taxiway apron, and building layout to be constructed under present contract. Show ultimate development in broken lines if it will aid in clarity. Berms, ditches, and typical section should be shown.

Grading Profiles

Show profiles of center line and 250 ft right and left, with both original and final surfaces, control elevations, per cent of grades, vertical curve data, etc.

Drainage Plan

Show runway, taxiway, apron, and building layout to be constructed under present contract. Use conventional symbols to show all pipe lines indicating type, drainage structures, direction of flow, size of pipe, and invert elevations.

Drainage Profiles

Show original and final ground surface elevations along drainage lines, size of pipe, per cent of grade, structures, and invert elevations.

Table of Pipe

Give size, type, station-to-station location, structures involved, length.

Table of Structures

Give location of each structure by station and offset, designating type.

Drainage Details

Show details of structures, berms, ditches, special connections, headwalls, etc.

Paving Plan

Show runway, taxiway and apron layout as well as auto parking area, access roads.

Paving Section and Details

Furnish typical sections, thickness, width, joints, etc., and jointing arrangements.

Paving Intersection Contours

Give 0.1- or 0.2-ft contour interval for intersections where section is not normal.

Paving Transitions

Show transitions for gutter and edge of all intersections.

Lighting Plan

Show runway, taxiway and apron layout, duct layout, location of lights, cables, transformer vault utilities connection, and controls.

Fertilizing and Seeding Plan

Show runway, taxiway, apron, and building layout. Indicate limits of seeding and type of treatment.

Obstruction Plan

Prepare as described in Chapter IX.

Other plans or details may be necessary or may be added by the engineer to clarify or amplify the design. The arrangement of the work will depend upon the practice of the design office involved. Typical drawings as listed above will be given as their preparation is covered in the text.

CHAPTER IV

SOILS—TESTS AND CLASSIFICATION

DESIGN TESTS REQUIRED

Composite List

The following tests are considered necessary before a reliable soils classification can be made.

1. Mechanical analysis of soils, A.S.T.M. Designation D-422–39 or A.A.S.H.O. Designation T-88–42.
2. Hydrometer test, A.S.T.M. Designation D-422.
3. Liquid limit, A.A.S.H.O. Designation T-89–42.
4. Plastic limit, A.A.S.H.O. Designation T-90–42.
5. Plasticity index, A.A.S.H.O. Designation T-91–42.
6. Shrinkage limit, A.A.S.H.O. Designation T-92–42.
7. Field moisture equivalent, A.A.S.H.O. Designation T-93–42.
8. Volumetric change at field moisture equivalent, A.A.S.H.O. Designation T-116-42. (See Appendix 3.)
9. Specific gravity, A.A.S.H.O. Designation T-100–38.
10. Modified compaction test (moisture-density) A.A.S.H.O. Designation T-99–38, as modified by C.A.A. Spec. P-102. (See Appendix 3.)
11. Capillary rise in soil passing the No. 10 sieve. Test is described later in this chapter.
12. California bearing ratio. Test is described later in chapter.

The two publications referred to above as authorities on test procedures are: *A.S.T.M. Standards*, Part II, published by the American Society for Testing Materials, 260 South Broad Street, Philadelphia; and *Standard Specifications for Highway Materials and Methods of Sampling and Testing* published by the American Association of State Highway Officials, 1220 National Press Building, Washington, D.C.

Since the complete details of each test are given in these publications only a short discussion of the purpose of each test is given herein. The capillary rise and California bearing-ratio tests are covered in detail, however, as they are not described in the reference publications.

Mechanical Analysis

Mechanical analysis is the determination of grain size of the soil by the use of standard screens. This test is important in determining soil texture.

Hydrometer Test

The hydrometer test is an adjunct to the mechanical analysis test in which the grain size of material passing the 200 mesh sieve is determined. This test assists in textural classification with regard to silt, clay, and colloids.

Liquid Limit

This test is an indication of a soil's cohesion. At the liquid limit the soil's cohesion is practically zero and its shear resistance is very low. It is the moisture content at which a soil changes from a liquid to a plastic state.

Plastic Limit

This test is an indication of the moisture content at which cohesive soils pass from a semisolid to a plastic state.

Plasticity Index

The plasticity of a soil is defined as the difference between the liquid limit and the plastic limit and represents the range of moisture content through which the soil is in a plastic state. Since sands and noncohesive soils are not plastic their plasticity index can not be determined.

Shrinkage Limit

The shrinkage limit is the moisture content below which there is no volume change. It marks the division between the semisolid and solid state.

Field Moisture Equivalent

This test furnishes an indication of a soil's ability to absorb moisture when not compacted.

Volumetric Change at Field Moisture Equivalent

This test indicates the volume change which may occur due to changes in the moisture content of the soil in its natural state.

Modified Compaction Test

This test is important to determine the relationship between moisture content and maximum density obtainable. It has been definitely established that for every soil there is only one water content at which maximum compaction can be secured. This amount is referred to as the optimum moisture.

Specific Gravity

This test is needed in connection with other tests and in general is not an indicator of any quality of field performance. A low value may indicate the presence of mica or organic matter.

Capillary Rise

This test is for the purpose of determining capillary rise in soils where saturation of the subgrade and consequent danger from loss of stability or frost action are anticipated.

While this test gives only an indication under laboratory conditions of the upward movement of water through soils and cannot possibly take into account the effect of varying periods of time, it is felt to be valuable. It is useful mostly for comparing the characteristics of various soils encountered.

The test is run upon material passing a No. 10 sieve. The apparatus consists of the following and is assembled as shown in Figure 4–4.

1. Glass filter tube.
2. Cork disk fitted to the shoulders of the filter tube.
3. Glass tube of same diameter as filter tube and 39 in. long.
4. Rubber hose connector.
5. Glass tube 5 cm in diameter and 122 cm long.
6. Cork.
7. Glass petcock.
8. Number 200 sieve disk to fit filter tube.
9. Ring stand.
10. Three clamps.
11. Rule.

Finely divided soil is first placed on the sieve in the filter tube to a depth of 4 cm. If, however, the soil is sufficiently fine to pass the No. 200 sieve, a filter paper should be inserted between the sieve and soil sample. The large tube or jacket is then filled with water until the water level is somewhat above the top of the soil and allowed to stand for 5 min. After this interval the water is lowered to the bottom of the cork disc and the excess water allowed to drain from the sample. The water level is then lowered in 2-in. increments with 5 min. allowed between each successive drop to allow additional drainage. When the water column in the filter tube breaks, a reading is taken of the distance from the top of the soil sample to the break. This distance is the capillary rise. The writers have found that the addition of red or green dye, available at photo-supply houses, aids in observing the water column.

California Bearing Test

This test is the basis of the United States Engineer Department's design of flexible pavements and is essential to C.A.A.'s soils classification.

The relative stability of a soil compared to the stability for crushed stone as determined by this test is known as the California bearing ratio. It is a penetration test on a soil sample compacted and saturated to approximate subgrade conditions. The test is based on the assumption that all subbase and subgrade soils under impervious pavements will eventually become saturated. This assumption is based on experience and field observation.

This test is used to obtain the bearing characteristics of foundation soils and material proposed for subgrades or bases. The test is performed on the material as proposed for use in the work, except that any particles of the material retained on the $\frac{3}{4}$-in. sieve are removed from the sample and replaced by an equal percentage of material passing the $\frac{3}{4}$-in. sieve and retained on the No. 4 sieve. In the event that it is used to test blended samples of material for subgrade or base construction, the mineral aggregate and the binder material should be combined in the proportions as proposed for use in the work before test determinations are made.

A sample of sufficient size to provide a specimen about 5 in. high and 6 in. in diameter when compacted is first brought to optimum moisture and then consolidated in a cylindrical mold six inches (6″) in diameter, under a load of 2000 psi. A duplicate specimen prepared in the same manner is soaked in water for 4 days before testing.

A piston with a bearing area of 3 sq in. is then caused to penetrate each specimen at the rate of 0.05 in. per min after seating the piston with an initial load of 10 lb. The loads required to obtain penetration in increments of 0.1 in. to a total penetration of 0.5 in. are recorded. The loads for each increment of penetration of both the soaked and unsoaked specimens are expressed in percentages of the standard loads (called bearing ratio) listed in the following table:

Penetration	Loads psi
0.1 in.	1,000
0.2 in.	1,500
0.3 in.	1,900
0.4 in.	2,300
0.5 in.	2,600

When a minimum bearing ratio is specified, the bearing ratio shall not be less than that specified for all units of penetration both soaked and unsoaked, unless definite penetrations are stipulated.

An expansion test is made during the soaking period. The sample after being compacted is confined within the mold by a porous disc and a 10-lb weight which represents the surcharge effect upon the subgrade of a 4- to 5-in. thickness of pavement. After the specimen has soaked for 4 days, the swell is recorded. The expansion of the specimen during the test is figured and reported in per cent of the volume of the compacted sample before soaking.

The writers feel that this is one of the most important tests which can be made on a soil sample and recommend its use. The chief exponent of this test for airport pavement design is the Office of the Chief, United States Corps of Engineers and the test is described in detail in Chapter XX of the *Engineering Manual* issued by the U.S.E.D. The reader is advised to study a paper, "The Preparation of Subgrades" by O. J. Porter, *Proceedings*, Highway Research Board, Part II, December, 1938.

REPORTING TEST DATA

The laboratory report shown in Figure 4–5 gives the results of the tests described above and represents the information necessary to proceed with the soils classification.

Before making the soils classification it is well to consolidate the material received from the survey and laboratory into a more convenient and usable form. Figures 4–5, –6, and –7 give forms used or developed by the writers for tabulating the information and have been used with success.

CLASSIFICATION OF SOILS

Classification of soils even from adequate field information and complete laboratory tests is not a simple matter and should be undertaken by a soils engineer well versed in the importance of the factors involved. Theory alone is not sufficient and the necessity for experience over a wide range of soil types and field conditions can not be underestimated.

Purpose

Soils are classified in order that their behavior may be predicted. Any prediction made is based on observation and experience with soils in other localities having approximately the same set of characteristics. It is to be emphasized that soil classification in airport design is not an end in itself, but only an aid in designing subgrades, subbases, and pavements.

Methods

There are three generally accepted criteria for soil classification: Public Roads Administration (P.R.A.), Casegrande, and C.A.A. These three methods are supplemented by a textural classification described in Appendix 6 and by the determination of the California bearing ratio. Figure 4–8 graphically illustrates the interrelationship and overlapping of various soil-classification methods.

Public Roads Administration Classification

The P.R.A. has divided soils into eight groups according to their physical characteristics as determined by laboratory tests. This method of classification has been in use in connection with highway construction for a considerable period of time. It is the oldest of the methods to be discussed and is probably the most widely known.

Table 4–2 is a summary of soil characteristics and classification as prepared by P.R.A.

It is to be noted that overlapping of soil groups occurs to an extent and that although the selection can be narrowed to a small field, the final choice is a matter requiring experience and good judgment. (Refer to Fig. 4–9.) It is also to be noted that the California bearing ratio, capillary rise test, and conditions of frost and drainage are not given direct consideration.

Casegrande Soil Classification for Airfields

This soil classification, as given in the *Engineering Manual*, Chapter XX, is reproduced in Figure 4–10.

C.A.A. Method

The C.A.A. publication *Design Manual for Airport Pavements* sets forth the C.A.A. Soil and Material Classification. Table 4–1 is a reproduction of C.A.A.'s Chart 1.

It will be noted that soils are divided into classification groups ranging from E-1 to E-10 and that a number of subgrade and subbase classifications are given. Overlapping of groups occurs as shown in Fig. 4–11.

Soil classification is determined by mechanical analysis, Atterburg limits, capillary rise, and California bearing ratio.

The writers in their use of this classification since it was adopted in March, 1944, have found it entirely satisfactory and adequate. The overlapping of the classifications is not excessive, making interpolation quite easy without having to attach too much importance to any one test.

Having determined the soil classification the material is then given a subgrade or subbase classification by taking into account the local conditions of frost and drainage. This latter classification is determined for use in connection with both flexible and rigid pavements. In Table 4–2, *F* indicated flexible and *R* indicated rigid pavement.

It will be noted that the letters *F* and *R* are supplemented by letters and figures to indicate a specific designation for a soil type in combination with local conditions. As an example an E-5 soil on a site where severe frost and good drainage conditions prevail has a subgrade classification of F3, R2b. The weight this system gives to local conditions is indicated by the fact that an E-3 soil on a site where severe frost and poor drainage exist has the same subgrade classification of F3, R2b.

The application of the *F* and *R* classifications in pavement design is discussed in Chapter VII on Pavement.

Organic Content

The purpose of making tests to determine the organic content of a soil is to determine its chemical composition as it affects plant growth. The engineer is normally concerned with a soil's alkalinity and the available amount of nitrogen, phosphorus, and potassium. He should also be concerned with the soil's color and texture as these may be just as important indications as those resulting from the chemical analysis.

The advice given in Chapter III regarding the importance of full and complete notes describing soil samples pertains especially to samples taken to determine organic content. The tests performed on these samples can be conducted much more intelligently when a description of the texture, color, and apparent fertility is available.

Soil-testing kits for quick determinations in the field are available. Most such kits require the treatment of the soil with chemicals and then allowing the solids to settle out. The color of the liquid above the solids is compared with standard color charts in order to obtain an indication of the available amounts of nitrogen and phosphorus. Other types of tests are made for alkalinity.

Field tests supplemented by a survey of local turf conditions usually furnish adequate information to insure whatever soil treatment is necessary in starting a turf. Wherever there is any doubt, however, analysis and recommendation by a competent laboratory is recommended.

The United States Department of Agriculture Miscellaneous Publication No. 259 *Comparison of Various Chemical Quick Tests on Different Soils* describes a number of tests for factors that play a part in plant nutrition. This publication is obtainable from the Superintendent of Documents, Washington, D.C. at a cost of 5¢.

USE OF CLASSIFICATIONS

It is desired to again emphasize the fact that soil classification for airport purposes is not an end in itself but is performed solely for the purpose of assisting in the design of some component of the airport.

It must be remembered that, at best, soil sampling leaves a great deal to be desired in the way of actual representation of the characteristics and state of the natural formations. Test results must be considered as indications and the figures on a test report must not be allowed to assume a more factual significance than is warranted. Test reports, taken together with careful observation of the soil's in-place behavior as indicated by other local projects, are invaluable.

Where test results are relied on to make important decisions, the engineer must make certain that an adequate number of samples were tested and that the tests were carefully performed. Check tests by more than one laboratory are often advisable.

FIELD CONTROL TESTS

Purpose

The selection of well-considered field control tests, together with the exercising of good judgment regarding any remedial action required by the results obtained, is most important. Otherwise, there is no way to insure the excellence of the completed work equaling that anticipated by the design engineer.

Tests

The specifications ordinarily are written with the intention of securing the desired stability of embankment, subgrade or subbase, by a combination of selective grading and compaction to design standards.

Three sets of tests can be performed on the job by a semiskilled technician. Because it is impossible to fully anticipate job conditions these tests should be run continually throughout the work.

Satisfactory results can be obtained only if samples for use in tests whose results must be correlated are taken as nearly as possible from exactly the same place.

Identification Test

Identification of materials usually requires the performance of sieve analysis and liquid limit tests and the determination of the plasticity index. In many instances textural classification is desirable. Identification of materials is necessary in order that in-place or imported materials may be compared with those called for in the specification.

Modified Standard Density Tests

Knowledge of the degree of compaction obtained in earth fills, foundations courses, and subbases is of the utmost importance to the engineer. Most specifications provide for the contractor attaining a specified percentage of a standard density.

The purpose of this test is to determine the standard maximum density obtainable with a given soil under specified conditions. The maximum dry weight per cu ft attainable by the following test procedure is hereafter referred to as "modified standard density" and the moisture content at which this density is attained as "optimum moisture."

Apparatus. The following apparatus and equipment are required for the field test:

1. Standard Proctor mold with base and extension.
2. Modified Proctor rammer, weight 10 lb, drop 18 in.
3. Twelve-inch steel straightedge.
4. Twenty-kilogram solution balance with weights.
5. Six-hundred-and-ten-gram balance with 500-g and 1000-g weights.
6. Number 4 U.S. Standard sieve.
7. Small spatula (blade about $\frac{1}{2}$ in. $\times$ 4 in.).
8. Glass graduate, 25-ml capacity.
9. Screw driver, about 12 in. over all, strongly made.
10. Two-burner gasoline or kerosene stove.
11. Sugar scoop.
12. Two large galvanized pails (12- or 14-qt, size).
13. Large roasting pan (about 18 in. $\times$ 18 in. $\times$ 3 in.).

14. Small pie tin (about 6 in. in diameter).
15. Two 2-in. paint brushes.
16. Large mason's trowel, with point cut off square about 2 in. from tip.
17. Piece of heavy tin or light sheet metal about 6 in. square (large enough to cover one burner of stove).

Sampling. A representative sample of the soil to be tested should be selected, rejecting any large stones which are not coated with fines. It cannot be overemphasized that the selection of a representative sample is fully as important to the results of any test as is the accuracy of the laboratory procedure. The sample may be taken from the cut area or from the fill as it is delivered. A 12- or 14-qt pailful will be required.

The station and offset or grid coordinates and the elevation of the point where the sample was taken should be recorded for the test report, and the technician should note for his own information where the material is being used in the fill if sampling is being done from a cut area.

Moisture Determination. On arrival in the field laboratory, the sample should be passed through a No. 4 U.S. Standard sieve, care being taken to detach any fines clinging to stones present in the material. Lumps may be broken up by grinding with moderate force under a block of wood. Only a small quantity at a time should be placed in the sieve. The portion remaining on the sieve after reasonably thorough manipulation should be rejected and wasted. If the sample is too wet to sieve properly, it should be spread in a thin layer on a piece of canvas or other smooth, clean surface and allowed to air-dry to proper consistency for sieving. The use of artificial heat for drying the sample is not advisable because it tends to change the characteristics of the material. If artificial heat must be used, a very low temperature should be maintained and the soil should be constantly stirred to prevent overheating and burning.

The material which has passed the No. 4 sieve should be thoroughly mixed and a moisture test taken as follows: The small pie tin should be carefully weighed on the 610-g balance to the nearest 0.1 g. It will be found very convenient if the pie tin can be adjusted by trimming its edges or weighting it symmetrically with pieces of wire fastened through holes in the edge so that its weight will be exactly 100.0 g. The moisture sample should consist of exactly 200.0 g of the material. The tared pie tin containing 200.0 g of soil should be placed on the metal plate over one of the stove burners so that the direct heat of the burner flame is prevented from striking the bottom of the tin. The 200.0-g soil sample should then be dried to constant weight, care being taken to avoid burning the soil. Drying may be hastened by stirring the sample and by crushing the lumps with the end of a stick about $\frac{3}{4}$ in. square. Great care should be taken not to lose any of the sample in this process. The weight of the dried soil should be checked from time to time on the 610-g balance until there is no further loss in weight, at which point the dry weight of soil and pan should be recorded. The percentage of moisture may then be calculated from the following formula:

Per cent moisture =

$$\frac{\text{wet weight of soil and pan} - \text{dry weight of soil and pan}}{\text{dry weight of soil and pan} - \text{weight of pan}} \times 100$$

For example:

weight of pan = 78.2 g
wet weight of soil and pan = 278.2 g
dry weight of soil and pan = 268.0 g

Then:

$$\text{Per cent moisture} = \frac{278.2 - 268.0}{268.0 - 78.2} \times 100$$

$$= \frac{10.2}{189.8} \times 100 = 5.4 \text{ per cent.}$$

Density of Dry Soil. The test should be started with the soil at about 3 per cent below the estimated optimum moisture. Considerable experience is necessary in order to be able to make a good estimate of what the optimum moisture of a given soil will be. In general a sandy soil will have a relatively low optimum, usually between 9 and 14 per cent. Silty soils may run from 12 to 30 per cent while clays usually range from 15 to as high as 28 per cent. When starting a test on an unfamiliar soil it is far better to begin with the sample too dry than too wet. Some points on the lower part of the curve may be wasted but the eventual result will be assured.

Let it be assumed that a sandy soil is to be tested and that the moisture present in the sample is 5.4 per cent. By inspection of the material an optimum of 12 per cent appears likely and it is decided to start the test at a moisture of 9.0 per cent. Since 5.4 per cent of moisture is already present, 3.6 per cent must be added. Three thousand five hundred grams, dry weight, of the material should be used for the test sample. The quantity of soil needed to produce 3500 g dry weight is calculated by the following formula:

Weight of material at N per cent moisture to produce 3500 g dry weight $= 3500 \times \left[1.000 + \frac{N}{100}\right]$. In the example being cited, this would be: $3500 \times 1.054 = 3689$ g

The sample for test will thus consist of 3689 g of soil at 5.4 per cent moisture. To this must be added enough water to raise the moisture content to 9.0 per cent or an additional 3.6 per cent. The water to be added is found as follows:

Water to be added =

$$\frac{3500\,(\text{per cent moisture desired} - \text{per cent moisture present})}{100}$$

or $3500\frac{(9.0 - 5.4)}{100} = 3500 \times .036 = 126$ g

With the above quantities known the sample may be made up. The weight of the large roasting pan should be found and marked on the side of the pan. Let it be assumed that the pan weighs 1053 g. This is to be added to 3689 g, a total of 4742 g, and the 20-kg scale is set to weigh out this total. The roasting pan is placed on the scale, and sufficient soil which has passed the No. 4 sieve is added to bring the scale to balance. The pan should then be removed from the scale and 126 cu cm of water measured out with the 25-ml glass graduate and thoroughly mixed with the soil by means of the square-ended trowel. The sample is now ready for test.

The base of the Proctor mold should rest on a firm, solid foundation. A good field arrangement is to fasten the base to an approximately 12-in. high section of an 18-in. log by means of nails driven into the wood and clinched over the edges of the base plate. The whole assembly in turn should rest on the ground or a solid floor. Care should be taken to see that the base plate is level so that the mold will be truly vertical. The tare weight of the Proctor mold alone, without base plate and extension, should be carefully determined and recorded.

The Proctor mold, mounted as above, is assembled with the extension in place and the whole tightly screwed down to the base plate. This is important because the stresses developed by the rammer are so great that any looseness will result in broken screws. Enough soil to produce a compacted layer about 1 in. thick is measured from the roasting pan into the mold by means of the sugar scoop. The amount of loose soil required to produce a 1-in. compacted layer will vary with the soil under test but will generally be about 6 heaping scoopfuls.

The surface of the soil in the mold is lightly tamped and smoothed with the end of the Proctor rammer in order to produce a level surface. The sleeve of the rammer is then held in the left hand, the hammer is raised to its full height by the right hand, the end of the sleeve kept in contact with the surface of the soil in the mold, and the sleeve carefully maintained in a vertical position at all times during the process. When the hammer is at the top of the sleeve it is allowed to fall absolutely freely for the full 18-in. length of its stroke. After each blow the rammer is advanced around the inside of the mold about 1½ in. and the sleeve is held in contact with the side of the mold at all times. In this way the blows of the hammer are evenly distributed over the surface of the soil in the mold. A total of 25 blows of the hammer is struck each layer.

After the first layer has been compacted, a similar increment of soil is added and the process is repeated. The object is to fill the mold to a point not over ½ in. above the joint between the mold and the extension with 5 equal layers of soil, each compacted as described above.

When the mold has been filled with 5 equal compacted layers the extension is carefully loosened and removed. In turning the extension to unlock it from the pins on the mold, the top layer of soil may very easily be broken loose from the layer beneath it. This may spoil the sample and can be avoided by passing the blade of the small spatula around the inside of the extension between the soil and the metal so as to break the bond. The extension may then easily be turned and removed. After this, the soil extending above the top of the mold is carefully trimmed level with the top of the mold by means of the 12-in. steel straightedge. The excess soil should be returned to the large roasting pan. Next the wing nuts holding the mold to the base plate are loosened and the mold and the sample carefully lifted from the base plate. The mold and sample are then placed on the 20-kg scale and their weight determined and recorded to the nearest gram.

The remaining soil in the large roasting pan is pushed to one side and the mold and sample placed on the bottom of the pan. By means of the screw driver about ½ in. of the compacted soil from one end of the mold is removed and returned to the large roasting pan. About 70 g of the soil beneath this layer is then removed and placed in the small pie tin. A similar quantity of soil is likewise obtained from the other end of the mold, and a third portion taken from the soil in the center of the specimen. These portions are rapidly mixed in the small pie tin and weighed out on the 610-g scale to produce a 200.0-g moisture sample as described in the test for the initial moisture content of the original bulk sample of material passing the No. 4 sieve. The sample is then dried and the percentage of moisture determined by exactly the same process and the results recorded.

There are now sufficient data available to determine the dry weight per cubic foot of the compacted material. The method can best be shown by the following example.

Given:

Moist weight of mold and compacted soil = 4151 g
Tare weight of mold = 2202 g
Moisture in compacted soil = 9.2 per cent

then:

1. Moist weight of compacted soil = moist weight of mold and compacted soil − tare weight of mold = 4151 − 2202 = 1949 g
2. Dry weight of compacted soil $= \frac{\text{moist weight of compacted soil}}{\text{per cent of moisture} + 100.0} \times 100 = \frac{1949}{9.2 + 100.0} \times 100 = 1785\text{ g}$
3. Dry density (pounds per cubic foot) = 0.066 × dry weight of compacted soil $\doteq$ 0.066 × 1785 = 117.8 lb per cu ft

The constant 0.066 is arrived at by dividing 30 by 454. The mold holds $\frac{1}{30}$ cu ft and there are 454 g per lb.

Recording of data and computing results are greatly simplified by the use of a form shown in Fig. 4–15. It is recommended that a slide rule be used in making computations as with care a perfectly satisfactory degree of accuracy can be attained. It is, of course, necessary only to record the data as the test progresses. Computations may be completed after the manual operations of the test have been finished.

While the moisture sample from the first test is drying, the remaining soil in the mold is removed with the screw driver, the mold is wiped entirely clean and the mold and extension are reassembled on the base plate. The hard soil from the mold is broken up and mixed with the other soil in the large roasting pan by means of the square-ended trowel. The 25-ml glass graduate is filled to its top with water (the graduate holds about 35 cu cm of water when completely filled) and this water is thoroughly mixed with the entire sample of soil in the pan. By the end of this mixing, the soil should be sufficiently well pulverized to be capable of passing a No. 4 sieve. The amount of water added as above should raise the moisture content of the soil about 1.0 per cent. In very warm weather a slightly larger quantity of water may be needed to bring about a 1.0 per cent rise in moisture due to evaporation during the mixing process. All operations should be performed in the shade.

After the increment of moisture is added, the soil is again compacted by the method previously described and the same data obtained and recorded. The process should be repeated in the same manner until the optimum moisture is clearly exceeded. A good curve can often be obtained with 5 moldings of the material, but more may be necessary. As the successive increments of moisture are added, the moist weight of the compacted specimens will become greater until a point slightly beyond optimum (as computed on a dry-weight basis) is reached. Beyond this point the moist weight of the compacted specimens will decrease. If 3 molds can be obtained, the moist weights of which show a gradual increase, followed by 2 molds of decreasing weight, a satisfactory test is indicated.

This test should be run continuously and as rapidly as possible until all necessary molds have been made. Any considerable interruption may break the continuity of the curve. The test should be started with the material below optimum moisture and each mold should be made with the moisture content higher than that in the mold preceding it. After molding has been begun, any attempt to dry the soil being molded in order to reduce its moisture content is likely to produce a "wild point" and also to affect any succeeding points on the curve.

The appearance of the material should be noted while the test is in progress. The soil will generally look quite dry at the start of the test, slightly moist to considerably moist near optimum, and considerably moist to wet in the final mold. These observations will help in judging the moisture content of the material as seen in the field. Soils tend to change color as the moisture content changes.

It is often helpful to preserve a portion of the unsieved sample in a closed glass jar marked with the test number for later comparison with field density test cores. This is particularly true where several different soil types are present on a project and will frequently make it possible to relate a field density test to its proper modified standard density.

Moisture Density Curve. After the necessary molds have been made and the per cent of moisture and the dry weight per cubic foot of each have been computed, the results should be plotted on standard 10 in. × 10 in. graph paper. The dry weights per cubic foot are plotted as ordinates (vertically) to a scale of 1 in. = 2 lb and the percentages of moisture are plotted as abscissas (horizontally) to a scale of 1 in. = 1.0 per cent.

After all points have been plotted, a smooth curve as shown in Fig. 4–16 should be drawn to connect them. This will be generally parabolic in form, ascending from left to right to a high point and then descending. The peak of the curve represents the modified standard density for the given material, and the percentage of moisture at this point represents the optimum moisture which is the percentage required in the material to obtain this compaction. These values are scaled from the curve and reported as the modified standard density and optimum moisture of the material under test.

As may happen with all experimental data, it is possible that now and then a point will be plotted which will not match the other points on the curve. If there are a sufficient number of other points to define the curve clearly and unmistakably, such a "wild point" may be neglected. Otherwise it will be necessary to rerun the test on a fresh sample of the same material.

A complete set of specimen computations and the resulting curve are given in Figs. 4–15 and –16. Examples cited therein are a part of these computations.

Field Density Test

Purpose. The purpose of this test is to determine the in-place dry weight per cubic foot, hereafter referred to as "field density," of the portion of a given soil passing a No. 4 U.S. Standard sieve. In conjunction with the modified standard density test, this test will give the percentage of a standard density actually obtained by the contractor.

Apparatus. The following equipment has been found to be essenial to the proper and efficient performance of the test.

1. Field density cone (pycnometer top) as shown in Fig. 4–17.
2. Two 2-qt mason jars with screw covers and rubber rings.
3. Number 4 U.S. Standard sieve.
4. Twenty-kilogram solution balance with weights.
5. Six-hundred-and-ten-gram balance with 500 g and 1000 g weights.
6. Two-burner gasoline or kerosene stove.
7. Four 2-qt pails with covers.
8. Screw driver, about 12 in. over all, strong enough to hammer on.
9. Carpenter's hammer.
10. Sugar scoop.
11. Large tablespoon.
12. Long-handled (iced-tea) spoon.

13. Two 2-in. paint brushes.
14. Folding rule.
15. Large mason's trowel with point cut off square about 2 in. from tip.
16. Two small roasting pans, about 8 in. × 14 in. × 3 in.
17. Two round pans about 15 in. × 3 in.
18. Two small pie tins (about 6 in. in diameter) for moisture tests.
19. Supply of standard sand (Ottawa Flint Shot recommended).
20. Medium-sized metal garbage pail with cover for storing standard sand.
21. Tin cup for handling sand.
22. Sieve just large enough to pass standard sand.
23. Carrier for jars and small tools.

Density of Standard Sand. The field density cone and one of the 2-qt mason jars must be calibrated and the density of the standard sand determined. The density cone is screwed tightly on one of the jars with the rubber ring in place, and the weight of this assembly determined using the 20-kg scale. The apparatus is placed with the cone upward and the valve of the cone opened. Water is poured through this cone until the jar is full and the water level is above the valve. Care should be taken to see that all air has been driven from the jar and lower part of the cone. The valve is then closed, the excess water above it poured off, and the entire outside of the apparatus thoroughly dried. The weight of the apparatus filled with water is then determined. After weighing, the apparatus is taken apart and thoroughly dried inside and out.

The dried apparatus is then reassembled with the rubber jar ring again in place, set with the cone upward and the valve open as before, and standard sand poured through the cone and into the jar. The cone should be kept as full as possible while the sand is running through the valve which should be wide open and present a smooth surface within the orifice. During the operation of filling the apparatus with sand, the greatest care should be taken to see that there is no jarring. When the jar is full the valve is closed, the excess sand poured from the cone, and the weight of the apparatus filled with sand is determined.

The density of the standard sand is computed by means of the following formula:

$$\text{Density of standard sand (pounds per cubic foot)} = \frac{\text{Weight of sand to fill apparatus}}{\text{Weight of water to fill apparatus}} \times 62.4$$

The following numerical example will illustrate the use of the above formula:

Weight of apparatus filled with water	= 3064 g
Weight of dry apparatus	= 1204 g
Weight of water to fill apparatus	= 1860 g
Weight of apparatus filled with sand	= 4074 g
Weight of dry apparatus	= 1204 g
Weight of sand to fill apparatus	= 2870 g

$$\text{Density of standard sand} = \frac{2870}{1860} \times 62.4 = 96.3 \text{ lb per cu ft}$$

Several trials should be made to check the weight of sand to fill the apparatus, and in general the results should not differ by more than 10 g. An average should be used for computing the density of the standard sand, and this value used in Fig. 4–19 as Item 10, "Density standard sand, lb per cu ft."

Calibrating Cone. It is also necessary to determine the weight of sand required to fill the cone between the valve and the rim. The apparatus, after being filled with sand and weighed, is placed with the opening of the cone down on a plane surface such as the bottom of a pan. The valve is fully opened and the sand is allowed to run until the cone is full and the sand stops running. No jarring can be permitted. The valve is closed, the apparatus lifted so that the sand filling the cone remains in the pan, and the weight of the apparatus and remaining sand in the jar determined and recorded. This procedure is repeated until the sand remaining in the jar is no longer sufficient to fill the cone. In general, four such trials can be made from a jar of sand. The amount of sand used each time to fill the cone is found by subtraction of the weights before and after filling.

The figures below show a typical example of the results of this part of the calibration:

Trial No.	1	2	3	4
Weight of apparatus and sand before filling cone (grams)	4074	3447	2824	2202
Weight of apparatus and sand after filling cone (grams)	3447	2824	2202	1582
Weight of sand to fill cone (grams)	627	623	622	620

$$\text{Weight of sand to fill cone} = \frac{627 + 623 + 622 + 620}{4} = 623 \text{ g}$$

The extremes of the weights of sand to fill the cone should not generally vary by more than 10 g. An average should be used for the final value, as shown, and this value used in Fig. 4–19 as Item 4, "Sand left in cone."

Storing Standard Sand. This completes the calibration of the apparatus and the determination of the density of the standard sand. The sand should be stored in a covered metal container such as a garbage pail so that the moisture content will change as little as possible. It is advisable to check the density of the standard sand from time to time and also whenever there is any possibility of a change in its moisture content. If any considerable difference in density is found, the weight of sand to fill the cone should be redetermined. The same jar should be used throughout for calibration.

Field Procedure. When preparing the apparatus for use in the field, it is not necessary to fill the jar through the cone. Two tests can be conveniently made on each visit to the field and two jars are therefore used. The jars are filled with the standard sand to within about ½ in. of the top. The weight of each jar and the sand contained in it is found and these weights are recorded in Fig. 4–19 as Item 1, "Sand in container." The weight of the jar need not be deducted because after use in the field the remaining sand will again be weighed in the same jar and the weight of the jar will cancel. The jars should be marked No. 1 and No. 2. After the weights of the two sand-filled jars have been determined and recorded, the field density cone is screwed on jar No. 1 and a standard mason jar cover is placed on jar No. 2. The rubber jar rings are not used on either of the jars except during calibration because they tend to allow the sand to get into the threads and cause binding.

The equipment can be most conveniently and safely transported to the field in an oblong wooden box with a sling. A compartment can be made at each end of the box just large enough to hold the jars, and the space between used to carry small tools.

The area of soil selected for the test must have a level and plane surface. If a flat-wheel roller has been used for compaction the resulting surface is usually ideal. If the area is rough it should be leveled and smoothed by means of the trowel. Loose material normally left by a sheepsfoot roller should be removed since it is assumed that this will be compacted with the following layer. The apparatus is placed over the selected area with the cone in contact with the soil and pressed down or turned slightly so that the cone leaves a circular mark to serve as a guide in digging the core hole. The area should be brushed clean of loose particles for some distance beyond the guide mark. If the surface is very dry or sandy, it may be sprinkled with water to bind the particles together.

The manner in which the core hole is dug will depend upon the character, hardness, and stone content of the soil. The sugar scoop and the large spoon may be used, or it may be necessary first to loosen the soil with the screw driver and a hammer. It is best to begin in the center of the area and to work slowly and carefully toward the guide marks. In this way the hole may be shifted while being dug if a large stone is encountered. Cutting should be done toward the center of the hole in order to avoid disturbing the soil around the edges. All material taken from the hole must be carefully preserved and placed in a 2-qt pail. Every effort should be made not to lose any of this material. If stones are encountered, they should be removed and preserved with the rest of the core. Those extending only slightly within the hole may sometimes be left in place or cut off with the screw driver.

Digging should be continued until the core hole is 6 in. deep, unless the layer being tested is less than 6 in. thick, and of such a diameter that the cone will just completely cover the opening. The sides should be nearly vertical and any depressions left by the removal of stones should be rounded out and opened so that the sand will completely fill all parts of the hole. The sides should be brushed down to collect any loose particles adhering to them. All loose material should be completely removed with the iced-tea spoon and the sides and bottom of the core hole finished smooth and clean. If it is impossible to remove all the fine particles in the bottom of the hole they may be lightly tamped with the handle of the screw driver to embed them. If water runs into the core hole and stands in the bottom the test will not be reliable and should be abandoned for the time being.

The pail containing the material from the core hole should be covered and set aside. This pail should be numbered to correspond with the number on the sand jar used to measure the volume of the hole.

The No.-1 jar with the field density cone in place is now inverted over the core hole so that the cone completely covers the opening. If the soil is soft, care should be taken to see that the rim of the cone does not sink into it as this would reduce the apparent volume of the space within the cone. The valve is fully opened and the sand is allowed to run freely into the hole and cone until both are filled and the sand ceases to run. The valve is then fully closed and the apparatus lifted vertically from the hole. With the cone held upward, the valve is opened for a moment and then closed again in order to allow any sand caught in the space within the valve to drop back into the jar. The field density cone is then unscrewed from the No.-1 jar. It is necessary to hold the apparatus over a pail or pan while this is being done so that any sand which may be spilled can be recovered and returned to the jar. The mason-jar cover is removed from the No.-2 jar and used to close the No.-1 jar and the field density cone screwed onto the No.-2 jar. This makes the No.-2 jar ready for the second test.

The standard sand left in and over the core hole may be partially recovered with the sugar scoop and spoons and placed in another pail or a cloth bag. Any sand that has become heavily contaminated with fine soil or that has become moist should be abandoned.

It is often desirable to take a sample of soil for a moisture test from a point close to where the core hole was dug. A representative sample of from 500 to 1000 g, not containing any of the standard sand, should be selected from below the surface and placed in a tightly closed container such as a covered 2-qt pail. The container should be labeled "No. 1 Moisture," and should be kept in the shade to prevent evaporation. However, the moisture sample will have no significance if the moisture content of the soil has changed since the area was compacted. The information sought is the moisture content of the soil during compaction for comparison with the optimum moisture of that soil type. It is always better to take moisture samples from the fill material as it is delivered and compacted so that any serious variation from the optimum moisture may be detected and corrective measures taken at once.

The station and offset or grid coordinates and the elevation or distance below finished grade of the point where the field density and/or moisture samples were taken should be recorded for the test report. The soil type, type and weight of compaction equipment, number of passes of same, moisture corrections (if any) made on the material as compacted, thickness of layers, and the type of fill (subgrade for pavement, gravel base, or unpaved area) should also be noted and reported.

The second field density test is performed in a similar manner, except that the No.-2 sand jar is used and all samples should be correspondingly labeled No. 2. The field density cone is left in place on the No.-2 jar while the samples and equipment are transported back to the field laboratory.

The two small roasting pans and the two round pans should have their tare weights determined in advance. The roasting pans should be marked No. 1 and No. 2, the round pans No. 3 and No. 4, and the weight of each pan should be marked on it. These weights should be verified from time to time during use. The sizes given for the roasting pans are only approximate, and the largest pans which will fit side by side on the top of the stove should be selected.

Laboratory Procedure. On arrival in the field laboratory the pail containing the No.-1 core-hole sample should be emptied into the No.-1 roasting pan, and the No.-2 core placed in the No.-2 roasting pan. All particles adhering to the pails should be brushed into the proper pans. The pans should be placed on the stove and the soil in them dried to constant weight, care being taken to avoid any appreciable loss of weight from burning the material. The drying process can be hastened by spreading the material in a thin layer on the bottom of the pan, frequently stirring it and breaking up lumps. This will also help prepare the material for sieving. The weights of the pans and contents should be checked from time to time on the 20-kg scale until there is no further loss of weight. The pans should then be removed from the stove, set aside, and allowed to cool until the material can be handled.

During this drying process the mason-jar cover should be removed from the No.-1 jar and the field density cone from the No.-2 jar. Any sand which escapes during this process should be caught in a pan and returned to the proper jar, and any sand caught in the density cone valve should be allowed to fall into the No.-2 jar as previously described. The weight of each jar and the remaining sand in it should be determined and recorded in Fig. 4–19 as Item 2 "Sand left in container." The jars should then be recharged with standard sand for the next set of tests, after which the recovered sand may be screened into the storage container. A sieve of such a size that it will just pass the standard sand should be used, generally a No. 16 U.S. Standard sieve is satisfactory. The recovered sand should be mixed thoroughly with that already in the storage container.

Also during this time the moisture samples may be passed through a No. 4 U.S. Standard sieve and 200.0-g portions of the material finer than the No. 4 sieve be weighed out in tared small pie tins, using the 610-g scale. These samples may be dried after the other pans are removed from the stove, and the percentages of moisture computed as described under the method of test for modified standard density.

When the field density core samples have cooled sufficiently to permit safe handling, the No.-1 roasting pan and core should be weighed and the weight recorded. The dried material should then be screened through a No. 4 U.S. Standard sieve into the No.-3 round pan. The portion passing the No. 4 sieve will hereafter be called minus No. 4 material, and that retained on the No. 4 sieve will be described as plus No. 4 material. After thorough sieving, the plus No. 4 material should be placed in the No. 4 round pan. When the sample has been completely separated into plus No. 4 and minus No. 4 material, the pans containing these two portions should be weighed and the weights recorded.

Some soils are easily separated on the No. 4 sieve while others are very difficult to handle. Soils containing clay generally form hard lumps when dried and these lumps are very difficult to distinguish from small stones. Also fine soil particles tend to cling to stones and must be separated from them. A block of wood about 1 in. thick and just small enough to fit within the No. 4 sieve may be placed in the bottom of the pan and the sieve rested upon it so that the mesh of the sieve is in contact with the top of the block. A small portion of the sample may then be placed in the sieve and ground under a second block of wood about 2 in. square so that the lumps are broken up and the soil on the stones loosened. This will not wear the mesh of the sieve unduly. Also, after partial separation the remaining plus No. 4 material may be poured into the round pan which is supplied with all regular U.S. Standard sieve series, the cover placed on the pan, and the pan and contents vigorously shaken. This will often accomplish the desired result and the sieving may then be completed. If some lumps still remain it may be necessary to pick over the material and crush the lumps individually. A very thorough, though slow method is: After the total weight of the minus No. 4 and plus No. 4 material has been carefully determined, wash all the material over a No. 4 sieve. In this way all the soil particles will be dissolved and nothing but stone will remain on the sieve. This must be dried and resieved. That portion retained on the No. 4 sieve will be true plus No. 4 material.

An ordinary dry separation would give the following results:

Weight of dry core and pan No. 1	= 2491 g
Weight of pan No. 1	= 826 g
Weight of dry core (Enter in Fig. 4–19 as Item 6)	= 1665 g
Weight of plus No. 4 material and pan No. 4	= 704 g
Weight of pan No. 4	= 306 g
Weight of plus No. 4 material (Enter in Fig. 4–19 as Item 7)	= 398 g

Weight of minus No. 4 material and pan No. 3	= 1579 g
Weight of pan No. 3	= 314 g
Weight of minus No. 4 material	= 1265 g

It will be noted that the total for the minus No. 4 and plus No. 4 materials as weighed separately is 398 + 1265 or 1663 g as compared to a net weight of 1665 g for the same materials before separation. This will generally be the case since some dust is lost during sieving. The difference is added to the weight of the minus No. 4 material, and the corrected value of 1267 g is entered in Fig. 4–19 as Item 8, "Dry wt soil (minus No. 4)."

When plus No. 4 material is present, Item (11) "Specific gravity of rock in mixture" in Fig. 4–19 must be determined. This may be done on representative samples of each type of stone encountered by the method described under A.A.S.H.O. Designation T-85, "Specific Gravity and Absorption of Coarse Aggregate." The specific gravity to be used is "Bulk Specific Gravity" as computed by the formula in paragraph 5 of A.A.S.H.O. Designation T-85.

Referring to Fig. 4–19, it will be noted that the operation under Item (12) changes the computations from grams to a unit volume and density basis in pounds per cubic foot. If the computation is performed by longhand multiplication and division, it will be more accurate to multiply Item (8) by Item (10) and then to divide this product by Item (5) for arithmetical reasons. If Item (9) is 0, Item (12) shall be carried to Item (17).

The computations involved in items 13 to 16 inclusive serve the purpose of eliminating the effect of the plus No. 4 material in the sample. The product of Item (11) which is the Bulk Specific Gravity of the stone, and the constant 62.4 represents the weight of a cubic foot of the stone on an absolute volume basis; and this product will in turn remain a constant for this particular type of stone.

Item (15) "Volume of soil per cu ft of mixture" is the difference between Item (14) and unity, since a unit volume of the mixture of minus No. 4 and plus No. 4 material is under consideration.

It is evident that since the weight and volume of a quantity of the minus No. 4 material are both known, the unit weight of the minus No. 4 material can readily be computed as shown under Item (17). This is the field density of the material under consideration, and the determination of this value is the purpose of the test.

Item (18) "Modified standard density" previously mentioned is a constant since the test, like the field density test, is performed on minus

No. 4 material and is independent of the amount of plus No. 4 material present in the natural soil. Field density is therefore directly comparable with modified standard density if the material upon which both tests have been performed is of the same soil type. The value as determined by that test should be entered as Item (18). In the specimen computations this value is taken as 126.4 lb per cu ft.

Item (19) "Per cent modified standard density obtained" is found by dividing Item (17) by Item (18) and multiplying the quotient by 100. This percentage represents the combination of the results of the field density test and of the modified standard density test. It should be computed to the nearest whole per cent. The field density is of greatest significance when expressed as a percentage of the modified standard density of the same material. The percentage required is indicated in the specifications for the work being done, and the performance of the contractor can be checked by comparison with the percentage obtained. If the percentage obtained falls below that specified, the contractor should be notified and directed to recompact the area making such corrections to the moisture in the material as may be necessary to obtain the specified compaction.

A given project may involve only one soil but is much more likely to have several different soils present at various locations. The modified standard density and optimum moisture of each must be determined, and the appropriate set of values selected to correspond with the soil upon which each field density test is run. Under the explanation of the test for modified standard density it was suggested that a portion of the unsieved sample used for this test be preserved in a closed glass jar. If this has been done the material taken from the field density test core hole may be compared, before drying, with these samples of the original soils upon which the modified standard density tests were performed. It will then usually be possible to relate the field density test sample to the proper modified standard density test by color, texture, and general physical characteristics of corresponding samples.

In the event of a persistent series of field density test failures in a given area, it is advisable to select a sample in that area and to run a check test for the modified standard density of the material. In this way any error in classification may be found, or the classification may be confirmed.

Percentages obtained, based on modified standard density, seldom exceed 100 per cent. However, it is entirely possible to exceed 100 per cent, and this need not signify that either of the tests is incorrect. Modified standard density is not an ultimate density but is simply a degree of compaction obtained under specific conditions. Under very favorable field conditions it may sometimes be exceeded.

The section of Fig. 4–19 directly below Item (19) and headed "Moisture determination" is for the purpose of recording and computing the moisture tests taken in conjunction with the field density tests. A sample computation is shown on the specimen form, but the procedure is fully explained in the description of the modified standard density test and will not be repeated here. The optimum moisture corresponding to the modified standard density being used should be noted in the space next to the section heading. The per cent of moisture found may then be compared with the optimum moisture for the material. In general, if the moisture in the material being compacted is more than 2 or 3 per cent above or below optimum moisture, the contractor will find it difficult to secure the specified degree of compaction.

TABLE 4–1. (Courtesy C.A.A.)

Soil	Material Passing # 10 Sieve			Material Passing # 40 Sieve			Capillary Rise of Minus 10 Material	Calif. Bearing Ratio (Soaked)	Subgrade & Subbase Classification			
	Sand %	Silt %	Clay %	Liquid Limit	Plasticity Index	Volume Change at FME			No Frost Good Drainage	Severe Frost Good Drainage	No Frost Poor Drainage	Severe Frost Poor Drainage
E–1	85+	0–10	0–5	25–	0–6	0–6	0–12	20+	F_a R_{1a}	F_a R_{2a}	F_a R_{1a}	F_a R_{2a}
E–2	75+	0–15	0–10	25–	0–6	0–6	0–36	20+	F_a R_{1a}	F_a R_{2a}	F_1 R_{1a}	F_2 R_{2a}
E–3	55+	10–40	0–20	35–	0–10	0–10	36+	18+	F_a R_{1a}	F_1 R_{2a}	F_2 R_{1a}	F_3 R_{2a}
E–4	55+	10–30	5–25	45–	5–15	5–15	36+	13–40	F_1 R_{1a}	F_2 R_{2b}	F_3 R_{1a}	F_4 R_{2b}
E–5	65–	20–75	0–20	45–	0–10	0–15	36+	9–20	F_2 R_{1a}	F_3 R_{2b}	F_4 R_{2a}	F_6 R_{2b}
E–6	55–	5–70	10–40	50–	10–30	10–30	36+	6–12	F_3 R_{1b}	F_4 R_{2b}	F_6 R_{2b}	F_7 R_{2c}
E–7	55–	5–70	15–50	60–	15–40	20–40	36+	4–8	F_4 R_{1b}	F_6 R_{2b}	F_7 R_{2c}	F_8 R_{2c}
E–8	55–	5–50	30+	70–	20–50	30–50	36+	3–5	F_5 R_{2b}	F_7 R_{2c}	F_8 R_{2c}	F_9 R_{2d}
E–9	55–	5–50	30+	80–	30–60	40–60	36+	2–4	F_6 R_{2b}	F_8 R_{2c}	F_9 R_{2d}	F_{10} R_{2d}
E–10	55–	30–80	30–	60+	0–25	——	36+	1–3	F_8 R_{2c}	F_9 R_{2d}	F_{10} R_{2d}	F_{10} R_{2d}

5-20529

Chart I
Soil and Material Classification

TABLE 4–2. Summary of Soil Characteristics and Classification (Courtesy P.R.A.)

Group	A–1	A–2		A–3
		Friable	Plastic	
General stability properties.	Highly stable at all times.	Stable when dry; may ravel.	Good stable material.	Ideal support when confined.
Physical constants:				
Internal friction	High	High	High	High
Cohesion	do.	Low	do.	None
Shrinkage	Not detrimental.	Not significant.	Detrimental when poorly graded.	Not significant.
Expansion	None	None	Some	Slight
Capillarity	do.	do.	do.	do.
Elasticity	do.	do.	do.	None
Textural classification:				
General grading	Uniformly graded; coarse-fine excellent binder.	Poor grading; poor binder.	Poor grading; inferior binder.	Coarse material only; no binder.
Approximate limits:				
Sand .... percent	70–85	55–80	55–80	75–100
Silt .... do	10–20	0–45	0–45	[a]
Clay .... do	5–10	0–45	0–45	[a]
Physical characteristics:				
Liquid limit	14–35 [b]	35 (maximum)	35 (maximum)	NP [c]
Plasticity index	4–9 [b]	NP–3[c]	3–15	NP [c]
Field moisture equivalent.	Not essential	Not essential	Not essential	Not essential
Centrifuge moisture equivalent.	15 (maximum)	12–25	25 (maximum)	12 (maximum)
Shrinkage limit	14–20	15–25	25 (maximum)	Not essential
Shrinkage ratio	1.7–1.9	1.7–1.9	1.7–1.9	do.
Volume change	0–10	0–6	0–16	None
Lineal shrinkage	0–3	0–2	0–4	do.
Compaction characteristics:				
Maximum dry weight, pounds per cubic foot.	130 (minimum)	120–130	120–130	120–130
Optimum moisture, percentage of dry weight (approximate).	9	9–12	9–12	9–12
Maximum field compaction required, percentage of maximum dry weight, pounds per cubic foot.	90	90	90	90
Rating for fills 50 feet or less in height.	Excellent	Good	Good	Good
Rating for fills more than 50 feet in height.	Good	Good to fair.	Good to fair.	Good to fair.
Required total thickness for subbase, base and surfacing, inches. [d]	0–6	0–6	2–8	0–6

[a] Percentage passing No. 200 sieve, 0 to 10.

[b] When used as a base course for thin flexible surfaces the plasticity index and liquid limit should not exceed 6 and 25, respectively.

A–4	A–5	A–6	A–7	A–8
Satisfactory when dry; loss of stability when wet or by frost action.	Difficult to compact; stability doubtful.	Good stability when properly compacted.	Good stability when properly compacted.	Incapable of support.
Variable	Variable	Low	Low	Low.
....do	Low	High	High	Do.
....do	Variable	Detrimental	Detrimental	Detrimental.
....do	High	High	....do	Do.
Detrimental	....do	....do	High	Do.
Variable	Detrimental	None	....do	Do.
Fine sand cohesionless silt and friable clay.	Micaceous and diatomaceous.	Deflocculated cohesive clays.	Drainable flocculated clays.	Peat and muck.
55 (maximum)	55 (maximum)	55 (maximum)	55 (maximum)	55 (maximum).
High	Medium	Medium	Medium	Not significant.
Low	Low	30 (minimum)	30 (minimum)	Do.
20–40	35 (minimum)	35 (minimum)	35 (minimum)	35–400.
0–15	0–60	18 (minimum)	12 (minimum)	0–60.
30 (maximum)	30–120	50 (maximum)	30–100	30–400.
Not essential	Not essential	Not essential	Not essential	Not essential.
20–30	30–120	6–14	10–30	30–120.
1.5–1.7	0.7–1.5	1.7–2.0	1.7–2.0	0.3–1.4.
0–16	0–16	17 (minimum)	17 (minimum)	4–200.
0–4	0–4	5 (minimum)	5 (minimum)	1–30.
110–120	80–100	80–110	80–110	90 (maximum).
12–17	22–30	17–28	17–28	
95	100	100	100	Waste.
Good to poor	Poor to very poor.	Fair to poor	Fair to poor	Unsatisfactory.
Fair to poor	Very poor	Very poor	Very poor	Do.
9–18	9–24	12–24	12–24	

[c] NP—nonplastic.
[d] Authors' note: For 10,000-lb wheel load only.

CHAPTER V

GRADING DESIGN

GENERAL CONSIDERATIONS

Grading is the one permanent physical feature of the airport around which all further design as well as all future development must evolve. It is frequently the most costly single item of the proposed work and the one that is most difficult to revise in a satisfactory manner once it is completed. Therefore extreme care must be exercised in making decisions, and all factors affecting the drainage and pavement designs must be given due consideration.

The grading design consists of establishing suitable grades, typical sections, transitions, etc., and the computation of the earthwork quantities involved. A study of the chapters on drainage and pavement designs is necessary before a complete picture of the grading requirements can be obtained. Of equal importance with the mechanics of establishment of lines, grades, and quantities is the consideration of the soil types to be encountered, the slopes to be used, and the determination of selective grading necessary to obtain proper materials in the subgrade.

Slopes

Slopes having a horizontal component of 2 ft for each 1 ft of vertical component (2 on 1 slope) have proved satisfactory for most cut-and-fill side slopes. Local highway practice should be determined and used as a guide. Five on 1 or flatter slopes are desirable at the ends of runways.

Slopes in cut sections should always be sufficiently flat so that an airplane taxiing near the toe of slope will not dig a wing into the bank. In such instances a slope of 7 on 1 is recommended by the C.A.A.

When fills exceed about 20 ft in height, the pressure on the toe and the shearing strength of soils must be taken into consideration. It may be necessary to flatten the slopes, bench the original ground under the fill, or possibly remove the existing ground to a point where a stable foundation exists.

Maps

The initial step in the preparation of the grading design is the preparation of topographic and contour maps. No description of such preparation is required as the work is done in accordance with the standard practice.

A scale of 1 in. = 200 ft is common and entirely satisfactory. It is important, however, to keep in mind that such plans prepared to cover only the area of the field itself are rarely sufficient and that the limits, at least for the preliminary investigation, should cover sufficient adjacent areas to show watersheds, locations of natural runoff, and obstructions. A quadrangle sheet of the United States Geological Survey will be helpful in orienting the site with the surrounding terrain. The topographic map should show all property lines and owners for use in land acquisition. Contours should be drawn to as small an interval as practicable—1-ft intervals for very flat country to 10-ft intervals in very rugged country. It is good policy for the initial topographic and contour plans to be worked up on tracing paper so that prints may be immediately available for the purpose of trial layouts.

MASTER PLAN

The master plan serves a most useful purpose in the coordination of various phases of planning and construction. Its importance will be continually stressed.

The master plan can best be prepared in conjunction with grading design as economy of grading will usually influence runway layout. A master plan should furnish at least the following information:

1. Original contours.
2. Present or presently proposed developments.
3. All existing facilities.
4. Ultimate airport development.
5. Extent of various stages of construction.
6. Plans for radio aids and traffic control.

A master plan may actually consist of several drawings forming a set.

With the contour map completed, trial layouts may be made. It is helpful to use strips of transparent material cut so that their width and length correspond to those of the landing areas proposed. By shifting the location of the strips on the contour map, while at the same time observing the contours, the advantages of various runway locations can be readily observed.

In general the direction of one runway is fixed either by wind direction or other conditions discussed in previous chapters. It is advisable to commence with this runway, basing the location of the other runways on the most desirable location of the first runway. Where a satisfactory runway layout is obtained the layout is drawn on the map, the taxiways added, and the building area outlined. Center-line profiles and in some instances edge-of-runway profiles are drawn from the contour map. From the profiles tentative grades can be established and grading quantities estimated.

Before proceeding further, the following questions should be answered.

1. Does the layout of the runways satisfy all requirements?
2. Can the runways, if built under this plan, be extended without excessive cost?
3. What is the glide angle in the approaches and what are the obstructions?
4. Can the extension of the runways or the approach zones be improved by change in alignment?
5. Are the taxiways sufficient and in the best location?
6. Is the building area expandable and readily accessible?
7. Are utilities available?
8. Is the watershed known and what will be the effect of surface water? How will grading affect natural runoff?
9. What effect will ground water have?
10. Is there outfall for drainage? Where? Is it satisfactory? Will any damage be caused to adjacent property?
11. Is the grading economical?
12. What template or typical section shall be used?

Questions 1 to 7 cover alignment and grades which, within limits, may be varied when necessary or desirable depending upon conditions and the effect on grading quantities. Attention is called to question 3 and to the previous discussion of the subject of approaches. It may be necessary at this point to make an approach-zone survey or acquire additional information. The importance of approaches, however, warrants a complete investigation.

GRADE DESIGN

When the above questions have been answered to the satisfaction of the engineer, the templates and cross sections may be plotted and the earthwork computed in order to determine the answers to 11.

Cross Section

Table 2–3 should be allowed to govern the template and cross section used, giving consideration to economy, runoff time, and erosion.

There is no way to advise the engineer as to the best template to use as this will be governed by the conditions encountered. A typical section such as Fig. 5–3 is considered standard, while Fig. 5–4 may be used to advantage in sidehill cuts to decrease the amount of excavation. The desirable pavement template also depends upon various factors which will be discussed under the chapters on drainage and pavement design. The use of various sections along one runway, however, is not good practice; nor is it wise to design longitudinal transitions into the pavement areas more often than necessary. Thus, where a runway crosses two others so that a full bank in the same direction occurs at each intersection, the runway should remain at a full bank for the entire distance between the intersections. However, should one leg extend for a considerable distance beyond an intersection, it would be good design to transition to a normal crowned section. In general, taxiways are kept on a full bank sloping toward the interior areas in order to throw the runoff to a positive drainage system and keep water from flowing toward slopes or building areas.

Longitudinal Grades

The limits C.A.A. recommends for longitudinal grades are given in Table 2–3. The nearer these grades approach 0.0 the more useful they are for aircraft operation. However, a minimum longitudinal grade of 0.20 per cent has the advantage of corresponding to minimum practical flow-line grades for pipes. This allows drainage to be installed without causing excessive depth of cut in trenches as the flow line falls away from a flatter field surface.

Transitions

Before the grade sheets are made up and the sections plotted transitions must be computed. The writers feel that this step is unnecessary for the initial trial of earthwork quantities as a balance is rarely obtained at the first attempt; however, this step should be done before the templates are plotted. Transitions are necessary because a pavement or landing area, when approaching and crossing another runway, cannot be maintained at its theoretical cross section but must vary uniformly from its normal section to meet the established center line of the crossing runway. Also taxiways when crossing other taxiways and meeting runways must vary in cross sections to conform to the other paved areas. Figures 5–5b and c show typical transition curves. It is absolutely necessary, because of high-speed operation, that no sudden grade breaks occur at runway intersections. The tentative grade shown by the engineer together with the vertical curve corrections and the elevations scaled from the transitions is entered on the grade sheets (see Fig. 5–6) and these sheets are used in plotting the typical cross sections.

Computations

Before the earthwork is computed from the sections, a word as to scale and accuracy should be added. Because of the area involved the majority of sections will be long. For this reason a scale of 1 in. = 100 ft longitudinally and 1 in. = 5 ft vertically is frequently used. Such a scale, however, although it makes the sections a reasonable length, gives great distortion and makes accuracy difficult when setting limits in a horizontal direction; also the use of a planimeter gives areas of doubtful accuracy. The writers feel that a scale of at least 1 in. = 50 ft horizontally should be used, and that 1 in. = 5 ft vertically is satisfactory. The use of a planimeter for computing areas is satisfactory for preliminary work.

Calculating machines can be used to secure very accurate results for the areas of cross sections. The manufacturers of various types of this equipment have included in their instruction manuals descriptions of the method most applicable to any given machine. Most methods are adaptations of the double-meridian-distance principle of determining areas. The authors have found the use of a calculating machine much to be preferred over other common practices of computing areas. Less accurate methods may be desirable for estimating purposes.

Shrinkage Factor

In computing earthwork for airports it must be borne in mind that the attack varies somewhat from standard highway practice. The width of the sections, and especially the large interior triangles involved in three-runway layout, cause tremendous differences of quantities for slight changes in grades. Shallow cuts and fills over large areas and the waste from stripping will give factors considerably larger than found in highway practice. A factor of 1.20 is generally the lowest advisable; a factor of 1.35 in most cases gives satisfactory results. Consideration of bulking of fills made from heavy rock cuts is essential and is more or less a question of judgment.

In many areas suitable locations for airports are in shale or hard-rock country. In computing earthwork the additional amount of material needed to cover the completed rock fills must be taken into consideration either by stock-piling suitable material available on the site, or by acquiring topsoil from the nearest available source. Another factor to consider is the necessity for removing rock on landing areas at least 12 in. below finished grade strips to obtain satisfactory cushion under proposed pavements. These items can easily account for as much as 50 per cent of the total excavation and cause a large overrun of excavation quantities if neglected.

Balancing

Once the cuts and fills have been determined and a factor applied, the balance will indicate the additional revision that must be done. In sidehill work, the shifting of a runway into or away from an adjacent hill will change the factor rapidly, whereas a change in runway grade for only part of its length may be sufficient to obtain the balance desired. Two, and occasionally three trials may be necessary before the desired result is obtained. This phase of the work is not difficult as it incorporates only the basic principles of grading design, but at the same time it requires much good judgment and careful operation so that a well-balanced layout will result. Once the proposed lines and grades are established the other phases of the design may be begun.

As soon as a satisfactory balance is obtained and the sections completed, a final contour map of the area may be drawn. The 250-ft right and left profiles should first be drawn so that a smooth profile may be obtained. Special consideration should be given to the portion which crosses proposed taxiways, runways, and other areas of fixed elevation. However it will frequently be found that slight revisions in the sections will be required. Berms, ditches, toe of slope, and property limits should be shown so that all factors which are involved can be studied. Contour maps, areas of doubtful drainage, and pavement intersections should be drawn with a contour interval of 0.20 ft.

SELECTIVE GRADING

Many airports have required extensive repairs because of the unstable nature of the material of which the embankments have been composed. Generally there is no excuse for failures such as excessive erosion, extensive slides, undue settlement, or soft spots. It is therefore the function of the engineer to determine, from visual observation and from the results of the laboratory analysis of the field samples, the action of the soils encountered in the grading operations and the manner in which they are to be placed in the embankments. The soil classification, described in Chapter IV, and the boring log will give the engineer the necessary information as to the types of material available and the location at which such material will be encountered. The specifications may then be prepared so that suitable material will be used to the best advantage and unsuitable material placed in areas where no future damage will result. It may be necessary to use borrow in the embankments and in many cases this may be more economical than extensive grading of the airport site merely to obtain material for fills. The engineer must make his decision keeping in mind both good engineering and economy.

CLASSIFICATION OF EXCAVATION

It seems that a perfect method of providing for measurement and payment for excavated material containing any appreciable percentage of rock or material having characteristics similar to rock will never be devised. This is demonstrated by the variety of contractual procedures used by various public agencies and the number of claims revolving about classification which are passed on every year.

A contract is theoretically an equitable agreement between two parties based on an understanding of the conditions one party will encounter in performing certain work for the other party.

Classified

When material is classified rock is defined and certain tests prescribed to determine whether the material encountered comes within the definition of rock. Methods for measuring rock are outlined. One would gain the impression that it is a very simple problem from reading the specifications. It is simple if the rock occurs in a form which leaves no doubt in anyone's mind as to its nature, and is located so as to be easily measured. Claims arise when the material is on the borderline or when actual rock occurs in such irregular formations that it is difficult to expose for measurement. Strangely enough, such a simple question as "How big does a piece of rock material have to be before it is classified as rock?" has been the bone of contention in many court-of-claim cases.

The writers do not favor classification except in locations where rock occurs in easily distinguishable form, stratified or deposited with relatively uniform sides, top, and bottom.

TABLE 5–1. Refer to Sample Wind Rose, Fig. 3–2.

SAMPLE COMPUTATION FOR RUNWAY COVERAGE OF WINDS

Wind Direction	% of Winds - in M.P.H.			Reducing to 8 Points			4 Runway Directions	Runway Coverage 22.5° Each Side		
	4-15	15 Up	Total	4-15	15 Up	Total		4-15	15 Up	Total
N	5.0	4.0	9.0	6.2	5.3	11.5	N-S	12.95	8.55	21.5
NNE	1.1	0.9	2.0							
NE	5.8	2.2	8.0	6.75	2.75	9.5	NE-SW	16.15	4.35	20.5
ENE	0.8	0.2	1.0							
E	4.2	0.8	5.0	5.35	1.15	6.5	E-W	14.85	3.15	18.0
ESE	1.5	0.5	2.0							
SE	9.5	3.5	13.0	10.8	4.2	15.0	NW-SE	23.05	12.95	36.0
SSE	1.1	0.9	2.0							
S	5.5	2.5	8.0	6.75	3.25	10.0				
SSW	1.4	0.6	2.0							
SW	7.9	1.1	9.0	9.4	1.6	11.0				
WSW	1.6	0.4	2.0							
W	8.4	1.6	10.0	9.5	2.0	11.5				
WNW	0.6	0.4	1.0							
NW	11.3	7.7	19.0	12.25	8.75	21.0				
NNW	1.3	1.7	3.0							
CALMS	-	-	4.0	-	-	4.0		-	-	4.0
TOTALS	67.0	29.0	100.0	67.0	29.0	100.0		67.0	29.0	100.0

1 Runway NW-SE 40.0% Coverage

2 Runways NW-SE NF-SW 60.5% Coverage

3 Runways NW-SE NE-SW N-S 82.0% Coverage

CHART No. 8

Airports Service Mar. 18, 1944 Dwg. No. 566

CHAPTER VI

DRAINAGE

PURPOSE

Although the purpose of drainage is generally understood by engineers, airport drainage serves purposes sufficiently different to require elaboration. The necessity for the airport drainage system being designed and constructed so that it will accomplish all of the purposes listed cannot be overemphasized. Adequate drainage is a prime requirement for safe operation and low-maintenance costs at all airports, regardless of size.

Surface-Water Removal

A study of a number of airports, including the largest terminals, reveals that a very high percentage of any airport area is unpaved.

Since forced landings, take-off accidents, and other unpredictable happenings usually result in aircraft having to use unpaved areas, these areas must be maintained in as safe a condition as is possible. One of the main purposes of airport drainage is, therefore, to increase the safety of off-pavement operations. It also serves the purpose of lowering maintenance costs and enhancing the appearance of the turfed areas.

Stabilize Pavement Subgrades

The stabilizing of runway subgrades has features which involve safety of aircraft operations. This is possible, however, only if operations are allowed to continue after the pavement shows signs of failure. Since this condition exists in numerous instances and because pavement failures are nearly always associated with inadequate drainage one of the purposes of airport drainage certainly is to insure safe operation from paved runways.

Interception of Water from Adjoining Areas

The large areas involved, even in small airports, make the problem of handling surface water resulting from rainfall sufficiently difficult so that the engineer will desire to keep water from adjoining areas from reaching the site if possible.

Floodwaters from adjoining areas can in many instances be of sufficient magnitude to cause serious flooding of buildings or erosion of field surfaces.

In order to reduce the volume of water to be handled and to prevent flooding or erosion damage, one of the purposes of the airport drainage system will be to intercept and divert water away from the airport area. The water so intercepted may quite often be subsurface but will more likely be surface water.

DATA REQUIRED

In general, airport drainage design differs but little from the practices followed in removal of storm water from cities, or the subsurface drainage of highway subgrades or farming areas. The same basic data are required in each instance, with the adequacy of the design depending largely on the reliability and extent of the data at hand.

Checking Notes

Most of the data required will be supplied by the survey notes. If these notes are taken as outlined in Chapter III on Survey they should prove adequate particularly regarding rainfall, snowfall, and drainage areas. It is advised that the data furnished by the notes be checked against such standard curves, tables, and agricultural soil surveys as are available. The writers' experience has been that it is difficult to impress the members of survey parties with the extreme importance of such data and this makes checking mandatory.

Topographical Maps and Profile Drawings

The topographical map, drawn to a scale of at least 1 in. = 200 ft, must show the pavement and building layout presently proposed, future pavement and building layout, finished contours of all areas to be graded, and existing contours for all other pertinent areas. The contour interval should be no greater than 1 ft. For ready reference there should be listed on this map in condensed form all drainage data and assumed coefficients. The actual flow-line elevation of all outfall points should be given.

The topographical map should be supplemented by pavement-edge profile drawings. It is advised that these drawings have the same horizontal scale as the topographical map and a vertical scale of 1 in. = 5 ft. Profile drawings should indicate existing subsurface soil conditions to a depth of at least 4 ft, particularly if any unusual conditions such as rock or ground water are to be encountered.

The topographical map and the profile drawings will supply all required information regarding surface grades.

Aerial Photographs

A good-sized aerial photograph of the airport area will prove invaluable for many purposes but is especially helpful in checking drainage data. The photograph should be prepared so that the property lines, paving, and building layouts are accurately located. Since almost all of the United States has been carefully mapped from the air, good photographs are usually available. If suitable photographs are not available it is advisable that they be taken.

The development of optical equipment for the study of aerial photographs has advanced to a point where such a photograph can produce much data regarding topography and soil classification. Without any special equipment, however, the engineer can check outfall locations, drainage areas, and the general layout of existing contours.

The engineer is again advised to become familiar with the research work carried on by C.A.A. in conjunction with Purdue University to determine the usefulness of aerial photographs in soils classification. This is done for the reason that the drainage characteristics of various soils are closely identified with their soil classification.

Erosional Grades

For every type of soil there is a per cent of grade above which serious water erosion can be expected to occur until the surface is protected by a suitable turf. Many soils have such bad erosional characteristics that this factor must be considered in planning surface water disposal. These data are readily available by observation of conditions existing at or adjacent to the airport site. They are most essential for the types of soil which will be used for top soiling or topping out embankments, and are pertinent to flow-line grades of open ditches.

Ground-Water Level

Since the elevation of ground water usually varies with seasonal rainfall intensity, data in this regard must be gathered carefully. Local records are useful when available. Data which reflect the highest elevation ground water may be expected to reach are essential and may prove to be difficult to obtain.

Frost Penetration

Since it will be undesirable to place certain drainage structures at elevations where they may be affected by frost heave or freezing, data regarding the depth of frost should be obtained.

Disposal Locations

The fact that inlet elevations, flow-line grades, and pipe sizes are entirely dependent on the location and elevation of points where collected water may be disposed of makes it mandatory that the engineer's data in this regard be accurate and complete. As previously suggested it can be shown to advantage on the topographical map.

Local Practices

In almost every instance information is available regarding local practices which have proved to be either satisfactory or unsatisfactory. Such information may be in regard to coefficients or constants used in standard formulas, measures to control erosion, the permeability of the soil, or grades at which silting occurs. It is often possible in this way to profit by other people's experiences.

DRAINAGE STRUCTURES AND MATERIALS

Drainage structures and materials as used in the construction of airports differ in some respects from those found in standard practice but require no extensive description. Since all airport drainage systems employ the same or similar structures, these structures will be described before the selection of systems is discussed. Following are listed the structures and materials most commonly used, together with references to the necessary detailed drawings and notes.

Pipe

The various types of pipe available for use, their flow characteristics, strengths, and construction limitations must be familiar to the engineer if satisfactory and economical results are to be obtained.

The following classifications give the types of pipe generally available:

1. Single-strength vitrified tile.
2. Extra-strength vitrified tile.
3. Plain concrete.
4. Reinforced concrete culvert.

5. Extra-strength reinforced concrete culvert.
6. Cradle invert pipe (tile).
7. Porous concrete pipe.
8. Transite sewer pipe.
9. Transite pressure pipe.
10. Asphalt impregnated fiber.
11. Corrugated metal.

It is not the purpose of this book to discuss the merits and shortcomings of various types of pipe. Many books have been written on the subject and manufacturers' literature and tests are available. See Appendix 4—Specification 1–213 which covers the requirement of the Airways Engineering Branch of the First Region of C.A.A. for all types of pipe listed above.

The standards of the American Society for Testing Materials or the American Association of State Highway Officials give dimensions, strength requirements, and other necessary information for all standard types of pipes. These publications should be available to every engineer.

Figures 6–1, –2, –3, –4, and –5 gives curves and data on pipes which the writers believe will be helpful.

Manholes, Catch Basins, Inlets

A manhole is usually provided at every point along a line of pipe where it can be used in cleaning out the pipe in case of stoppage. On long pipe runs, a manhole should be provided every 300 to 400 ft. A manhole, catch basin, or inlet should be installed at all points where pipes change direction, size, flow-line elevation, or where several pipes come together.

All such structures must be large enough not to allow turbulence to restrict the capacity of the system, and to permit working room for men and equipment. They must be designed to carry the heaviest possible wheel load.

These structures can be designed to act as settling basins to collect sand or silt carried by the water. This is done by allowing considerable depth below the pipe flow line.

Grates and Covers

Refer to Specification 1–213, Appendix 4, for structural requirements of grates and covers. Grates should be set 4 in. to 6 in. below finished grade (refer to Fig. 6–6) in all turfed areas to allow for ground settlement and to allow for grading the surface in the form of a dish section surrounding the structure. Such grading is necessary to bring runoff to the basin and overcome by-passing with consequent overloading of inlets farther along the line. In pavement areas, the grates should be set approximately $\frac{3}{4}$ in. low for the same purpose.

It is essential that the openings in all grates be carefully designed to give the maximum area without weakening the structure. Small openings can cause a great deal of trouble, particularly during the first year or two, because twigs, trash, grass cuttings, etc., clog them easily. It is good practice to double the theoretical inlet area required in order to provide for partial plugging.

The writers advocate the assumption that a minimum head of 0.4 ft of water will be available at each pavement inlet. The maximum allowable head can be quite accurately determined in areas where ponding is allowed.

Headwalls and Stilling Basins

Headwalls should always be provided at the outfall end of pipes to control erosion. In fill sections they should be at the toe of the slope or preferably some distance out from the toe. If possible, they should be located so that they are constructed in original ground.

As a precaution against erosion occurring due to water collecting behind the structure, a slot should be provided in the center to allow water from the slope to escape without running along the back.

Stilling basins or similar velocity-retarding devices must be provided in conjunction with the headwall at the outfall end of pipes having steep grades.

Berms

Wherever the transverse grades of a landing strip cause water to be discharged along the edge, berms are required to prevent erosion of fills. Berms should be placed along the edge of all fills over 3 ft in height. An earth berm 2 ft high, 2 ft wide at the top, and 5 ft wide at the bottom is recommended with spillways every 300 ft to dispose of the water collected.

In most instances it is necessary to make some provision to prevent the water running along the edge of the berm from scouring out a ditch or cutting out the berm. Sod has been found to be superior to anything else for this purpose. The inner face of the berm and 3 ft or more of the gutter should be sodded. If sod is not practical riprap, concrete, or lumber may be used. It has been found that most rigid construction cracks, due to settling or frost action, allow the water to start damaging channels.

Spillways

Spillways in the form of wooden flumes, riprap, and sod gutters have been used extensively to remove water collected by berms, and failures have resulted quite frequently. Wooden flumes have proved to be completely unsatisfactory in every instance with which the writers are familiar. Riprap often cracks or is undercut. Sod has proved satisfactory for handling small volumes of water. Well-designed concrete boxes or troughs have been satisfactory but are quite expensive and are subject to undercutting.

To overcome these objectionable features the writers have used a pipe spillway which collects water from behind the berm section and carries it to the bottom of the fill-in pipe. This spillway is illustrated in Fig. 6–8 which shows the catch basins, pipe, and headwall involved. It is to be noted that the headwall forms a stilling basin to break up the velocity of the water and has a cutoff wall to prevent undercutting.

Riprap

Stone riprap (see Appendix 4—Specification 1–213) is useful at various locations to prevent erosion. It has, however, several serious drawbacks.

Riprap is not suitable for constructing gutters to take any large amount of water in plastic soils where frost action is serious or where overflow of the channel is expected at any time. Settling and frost heave will form cracks through which the water can penetrate and cause disruptive action. Any undercutting will cause disintegration of the riprap. Many cases are on record where one severe storm has washed out riprap gutters completely.

Its chief use should be in lining ditches adjacent to headwalls, extending headwall aprons, and facing slopes.

Sod Gutters

The writers have found sod superior to riprap for gutters where large volumes of water are not encountered. Its light weight makes it less likely to settle when the soil becomes saturated, and frost will not cause disruptive action. Sod is especially useful in facing berms and in forming shallow gutters in landing areas. (See Appendix 4—Specification 1–213.)

Ditches

While the use of ditches is restricted in airport design, they form one of the most useful and important adjuncts to the drainage system. Ditches can not be used in landing areas nor should they be introduced at any location where planes might possibly land or inadvertently travel due to undershooting, overshooting, or ground-looping. Ditches should never be placed across the ends of runways, even beyond the grading limits proper.

The engineer must keep in mind that ditches normally require considerable maintenance. Ditches should be of sufficient size and of such cross section and flow-line grade that maintenance costs are kept at a minimum. The proper flow-line grade can be determined from a study of the grade natural watercourses seek in similar local soils. Sharp turns and breaks in grade must be avoided or protected by riprap.

Intercepting Structures

It often proves desirable to intercept water, particularly in building areas, without any ponding whatsoever. Concrete boxes with suitable grate cover, precast horseshoe-shaped pipe, or web type of cradle invert clay pipe can be used.

Blind Drains

Blind drains constructed by filling a trench with porous material of rather open gradation can be used to advantage. Blind drains laid out in a herringbone pattern under pavements are useful to assist in the drainage of plastic soils.

DRAINAGE SYSTEMS

Airport conditions may require a system designed to handle surface water only, subsurface water only, or a combination of both. Because of this possibility, airport pipe drainage can be divided into two distinct classifications which are sealed joint and open joint.

Sealed Joint

A sealed-joint system is one where water can enter or leave the pipe only at inlets or outlets provided purposely. It is identical in operation to the standard storm sewer in every way. The pipe used is not porous or perforated and all joints are watertight.

This type of system is used for the purpose of disposing of surface water which has been collected by gutters, ponding basins, and intercepting ditches, or in disposing of subsurface water which has been collected and brought to some type of basin.

Particular care should be exercised in sealing joints under or adjacent to paved areas, otherwise water forced into the subgrade under a head may saturate the subgrade sufficiently to cause loss of bearing power.

Open Joint

An open-joint system is one designed to collect water by allowing it to enter the pipe through unsealed joints, porous walls, or perforations. Water will enter or leave the pipe freely, depending on the difference in pressure inside and outside of the pipe. Figures 6–9 and –10 show typical sections of open-joint pipe.

This type of system is used to best advantage for collecting and disposing of subsurface water. The trench around and above the pipe is usually backfilled with porous material to facilitate the collection of ground water. The porous backfill can also act as a cutoff wall to prevent shoulder area ground water from reaching pavement subgrades.

Open-joint pipe, where the trench is backfilled with porous material to ground level, can be used to remove surface water.

Any type of pipe which will allow water to enter freely through its walls or its unsealed joint can be used in an open-joint system. Cradle invert, porous, and perforated pipes are designed purposely for open-joint systems and therefore have advantages over standard pipe. Unsealed joints should always be covered in such a manner that they will not retard the entrance of water into the pipe, but at the same time, that backfill material can not enter the pipe or clog the opening. Tar paper or burlap can be used to cover the joints of all types of pipe except cradle invert.

Combined System

In almost all instances, except in very dry climates, subsurface drainage is of some value. Quite often the type of soil or the ground-water level is such that an open-joint system strictly for subsurface drainage is not warranted, although removal of surface water is essential. In such places as well as those where surface and subsurface drainage are both essential the engineer may desire to give consideration to a single system which will perform both functions.

A combined system ordinarily is simply a sealed-joint system where open-joint pipe has been substituted for sealed-joint pipe and the trench backfilled with porous material to within approximately 1 ft of the surface. Gutters and inlets are used to collect surface water as in the closed system with subsurface water entering in the same way it does in the open-joint system.

The advantage of this system is its economy. Pipe sizes may have to be increased somewhat over the sizes required by the sealed-joint system to allow the pipe to handle both surface and subsurface water, but the cost of one line of pipe is saved. This system also saves some of the problems associated with establishing grades where the pipes of the two systems would otherwise cross.

While the C.A.A. does not favor the combined system, there are several airports where they have permitted its use with entirely satisfactory results. The principal objection to the system is that during periods of heavy surface runoff, water may be forced out of the pipe into the subgrade by pressure of the head above the flow line.

Advocates of the system point out its economy and contend that surface runoff time is of such short duration that little subgrade saturation can result. They also contend that the use of proper pipe sizes will seldom allow the pipe to run completely full, therefore but little water normally comes in contact with the subgrade. Where the combined system has been properly installed no instances of failure have been seen. However, trouble can be expected where improper aggregate gradation or poor construction methods are allowed.

Independent Systems

In locations where both surface and subsurface water must be handled, the installation of a sealed- and an open-joint system, each independent of the other, overcomes all objections to the combined system. Under favorable conditions where convenient outfalls are available along the edges of the landing strips an independent system can be as cheap or cheaper than the combined system.

The independent system under favorable conditions is illustrated in Fig. 6–12. It will be noted that pipe for subsurface drainage only is required adjacent to the pavement as surface water is removed directly from the pavement basins to an outfall, ditch, or drainage system. Ordinarily, hilly sites or landing strips largely in fill are favorable to the independent system. Flat land is not favorable owing to the lack of a large number of convenient natural outfall locations.

The advocates of the independent system point out its economy under favorable conditions, its positive action without endangering subgrade, and its advantageous construction features.

DESIGN METHODS

The first step in the actual design of the drainage system will usually be a study of the airport layout drawing on which final contours have been plotted. This study will show the direction of flow of surface water for all of the areas involved. Preliminary plans can be made for disposal of surface water, both the portion which will be carried in pipes and the portion which will run on the surface.

It is considered advisable to divide the over-all layout into as many independent systems as possible in order to decrease pipe sizes and to avoid having to handle large volumes of water due to concentration. It is usually false economy to use an insufficient number of drainage structures or to attempt to space inlets too far apart.

It often develops that the most economical drainage layout will require considerable cutting and trying. This process can not be avoided in most instances, but the number of tries can be reduced by an intelligent study of the contour map.

Rainfall

Rainfall is the most important factor in determining the amount of water to be handled by the drainage system. In order to compute such quantities it is necessary to establish a time element having a practical relationship to removing water before it can pond to excessive depths. It is generally accepted that the provisions made to remove the maximum rainfall which can be expected in 1 hr, within a given period of time, will also prove ample for any other rainfall condition which may be expected.

It has proved to be practical to design the drainage system so that the water which falls on shoulder or graded areas in 1 hr is removed in 2 hrs, and that the water which falls on paved areas is removed by the time the rain ceases. It has been found that, except in rare instances, the heaviest rains fall for periods of less than 1 hr.

The longer the period of time which the rainfall records cover, the higher the maximum rainfall rate recorded is likely to be. Figures 6–13a and –13b show the rainfall curves for the United States for 2- and 5-yr periods. The maximum rainfall to be expected once in 2 yr is generally used, although the figure for a 5-yr or longer period is more conservative. Many cities keep rainfall records and these ordinarily will be more valuable than the rainfall curves. It is often economically unsound to design for the maximum rainfall which has ever been experienced, but information in this regard will allow the engineer to design surface grades so that damage is kept at an allowable minimum.

Snowfall

Snow, unlike rain, does not become dissipated in a relatively short time and therefore does not present the problem of providing a method of quick removal in order to prevent flooding. Snow usually accumulates and presents a maintenance problem requiring plowing or some other method of removal from the runways and taxiways. Where snow is plowed the piles so formed often act as dams which keep surface runoff from taking its expected course and so cause serious ponding during periods of thaw. For this reason, drainage adjacent and parallel to runways (preferably a gutter type pavement section) is recommended in all localities where any appreciable amount of snowfall is expected.

Runoff

Studies of runoff from airport areas have not been conducted for a long enough period of time to indicate the need for any more reliable methods than those used for designing storm sewers. The rational method and the Burkli-Ziegler formula are generally used.

The formula for the rational method is:

$$Q = AIR$$

in which, Q = rate of runoff, in cubic feet per second
A = area to be drained, in acres
I = runoff coefficient
R = maximum average rate of rainfall selected, in inches per hour.

It will be noted that this formula does not take into account the time allowed for removal of water after the rain ceases. The formula is therefore often changed, when the time factor is employed, as follows:

$$Q = \frac{AIR}{T + t}$$

in which, T = duration of rainfall, in hours
t = time allowed for removal of water after rain ceases.

The map giving finished contours will supply the value of A for areas within the airport. Runoff from adjacent areas can be determined by consulting United States Geological Survey quadrangle maps or other contour maps. In some instances a drainage-area survey will have to be made, and may well be done at the same time the preliminary survey is performed. A planimeter furnishes sufficiently accurate results for determining watershed areas.

I, the runoff coefficient, is used to measure the permeability of the various surfaces drained. Table 6–1 furnishes values of *I* for various surfaces.

R, 1 hr maximum rainfall, is the factor about which there is often insufficient information. It can be readily appreciated that the value of *R* affects pipe sizes to a great extent and must therefore be determined with utmost care. In arriving at a value for *R*, the engineer must evaluate possible flood damage and the damaging effects of excessive ponding against the cost of providing sufficient capacity to handle flash storm water. Local experience with storm-sewer systems can furnish a valuable guide.

T, duration of rainfall, is another factor which can vary greatly. The writers have found 1 hr to be satisfactory for use in the northeastern states.

t, time allowed for removal after the rain ends, is generally taken as 2 hr, if ponding is allowable. A shorter period may be necessary if the ponding areas are shallow. *t* becomes zero when immediate runoff is required, which is usually the case with pavement gutters.

The Burki-Ziegler formula is:

$$Q = AIR \sqrt[4]{\frac{S}{A}}$$

The symbols have the same meaning as given for the rational method, with *S* equaling the slope of the ground in ft per 1000 ft.

The results obtained by using the Burki-Ziegler formula are considered by many experts to be more accurate than the rational method because the degree of slope of the area to be drained is taken into consideration. Although the difference is not large in airport work, flat slopes give smaller quantities than are obtained by the rational method and steep slopes give larger quantities. Either method is considered suitable.

Area of Openings

In order to remove rainfall through pipes it is necessary to provide inlets and catch basins with grate covers.

The spacing of inlets may be arbitrarily established. The volume of water reaching each basin is calculated by use of one of the above formulas, and then a structure is provided which has ample effective grate-opening area to remove the water reaching the grate before it ponds sufficiently to exceed some depth which has been determined as the desirable maximum. Pavement inlets are usually placed a uniform distance apart except where unusual cross sections are used or where intersections break up the spacing.

Since it is advantageous to standardize on grate sizes the more common practice is to place an inlet at each location where sufficient water collects. Rather than design over- or undersized grates, a standard grate will be used even though it is much larger than necessary, or two or more inlets will be placed adjacent to each other instead of using one large grate. The cost of inlets and catch basins is small enough compared to possible flood damage so that it is wise economy to be generous with such structures.

The volume of water which will flow through an inlet grating under a given head can be computed by the following formula:

$$A = \frac{2Q}{c\sqrt{2gh}}$$

in which, $A =$ total grate opening in square feet
$Q =$ quantity of water to be handled in cubic feet per second
$c =$ coefficient of discharge $= 0.7$ in most instances
$g =$ acceleration due to gravity $= 32.2$
$h =$ head of water allowable over grating

In order to provide for partial reduction in grate capacity due to plugging of the openings a factor of safety of two has been included in the formula. Most grates can be set at an elevation so that h equals at least 0.4 ft.

There are a good many standard grates available, both square and round. Any grate used must be designed to easily support the wheel load of any aircraft which may run over it.

Flow in Pipes

The quantity of water which will flow in a pipe depends on several factors which have been incorporated in Manning's formula. This formula is widely used and has largely replaced the Chezy and Kutter formulas from which it is derived.

The Manning formula is:

$$Q = A\frac{1.486}{n}R^{2/3}S^{1/2}$$

in which Q = discharge in cubic feet per second
A = cross-sectional area of flow in square feet
R = hydraulic radius in feet = area of section divided by the wetted perimeter
S = slope, or grade in ft per 100 ft
n = coefficient of roughness

It can be seen that n is the only factor about which there can be any uncertainty. The value assigned to n requires judgment and of course depends on the type of pipe, the smoothness of the joints, and the number of bends in the pipe runs. The established values of n for various materials and conditions are based on many experiments and actual experience. They range from about 0.013 for very smooth pipes to 0.021 for corrugated metal pipe.

The P.R.A. as well as other authorities agree that a value of 0.015 is satisfactory for concrete and vitrified clay pipes. The writers have found this practice to be entirely satisfactory.

Charts portraying the pipe sizes indicated by Manning's formula for various values of n have been prepared for convenient use of the formula. Figures 6–15a, –15b, and –15c give the diameter of pipes in inches as computed by Manning's formula where $n = 0.013$, 0.015, and 0.017.

The above information is considered sufficient to allow an engineer to design pipe sizes for airport drainage. It is advised, however, that all engineers not familiar with the theory of the flow of water in pipes study the subject.

Regarding the value of S, it is the writers' practice in airport drainage to keep the flow-line grades the same as the corresponding surface grades wherever the surface grade equals or exceeds 0.2 ft per 100 ft. While this is not always practical the writers have found that in most cases a satisfactory layout allowing practically uniform cover over the pipe can be obtained. Figure 6–16 illustrates drainage profiles as prepared for a C.A.A. airport project.

Ditches

The Burkli-Ziegler formula or the rational method may be used to calculate the quantity of water which will enter an intercepting ditch. The quantity which will be discharged into a ditch from pipes can be calculated as described herein using Manning's curves. The cross section of the ditch to handle a specific quantity of water can be found by the Chezy formula:

$$A = \frac{Q}{c\sqrt{RS}}$$

in which, A = cross-sectional area of open ditch in square feet
Q = quantity of water to be handled expressed in cubic feet per second
c = a coefficient of roughness for which a value of 50 is satisfactory for open ditches with unpaved sides
R = hydraulic radius in feet = area of section divided by the wetted perimeter
S = slope or grade expressed in ft per 100 ft

Ditches should always have a flat bottom with the bottom width a minimum of 2 ft. A balance between depth and width, so that neither is disproportionate, is desirable. The practical slope for the sides of the ditch can best be determined by observation of streams and ditches in the vicinity.

Earth Backfill

The provisions of the specifications covering earth backfill must be very exacting yet practical of accomplishment. Settling of pipe trenches causes hazardous operating conditions and costly maintenance, particularly in paved areas.

It has been found that the more nearly the moisture content of the backfill material approaches optimum, the easier it is to secure satisfactory compaction. It is recommended that the specification requirements be similar to those given in Appendix 3.

A construction procedure which the writers have adopted is that of having all pipes in fill sections placed only after the fill has been brought to a height of 3 ft above the top of the pipe. This procedure requires that a trench be excavated for the pipe. Such construction has allowed better compaction of the fills adjacent to pipes and has proved entirely satisfactory. It has also eliminated damage to pipe because of compaction of fills with heavy equipment on insufficient cover.

Porous Backfill

The general acceptance of the fallacy of using a coarse material for backfilling subsurface drain lines has occurred only recently. Previous to the experiments started in 1941 by the United States Corps of Engineers at Vicksburg Waterways Experiment Station it was the practice of each engineer to use a gradation of gravel or crushed stone which seemed most logical to him or which was most economical.

It has been found through extensive tests conducted by the War Department that the following criteria should be met:

$$\frac{\text{15 per cent size of filter material}}{\text{85 per cent size of natural soil}} = \text{not more than 5}$$

$$\frac{\text{15 per cent size of filter material}}{\text{15 per cent size of natural soil}} = \text{more than 5}$$

$$\frac{\text{85 per cent size of filter material}}{\text{size of perforation or slot opening}} = \text{more than 2}$$

The 15- and 85-per cent sizes are the "per cent finer sizes" determined from the mechanical analysis curve. The 15-per cent size of the filter material need not be less than 0.1 mm if the natural soil is cohesive.

The gradation limit of the filter material is determined in the following manner: The average fine limit of the natural subgrade soil is plotted as shown in Figure 6–17. The allowable course and fine limits of the 15-per cent size of filter material are then determined as shown by points X and Y. The minimum allowable fine limit of the 85-per cent size of filter material adjacent to the drainpipe is determined as shown by point Z. Gradation of the filter material should be within these limits.

Since the experiments, the recommendations given in Section 21–76, Chapter XXI of the *Engineering Manual* of the War Department, Office of the Chief of Engineers, have been very widely considered to be the most reliable information on the subject.

Erosion

In soils having bad erosional characteristics it is essential that grades be kept flat and water be removed before large volumes accumulate and cause serious washes. Numerous low points and catch basins or continuous box drains may be required to achieve the desired results. Berms are required to prevent washing of slopes and are recommended wherever fills higher than 3 ft are made. To the engineer unfamiliar with erosional problems found at almost every airport the extensive steps taken to prevent erosion may seem unnecessary. However, the writers have found that erosion always occurs in newly graded areas and is difficult to stop. The planting of grass, sprigging, mulching, and the final establishment of turf are the best method of controlling erosion, but in general material damage requiring maintenance has begun before such growth becomes effective. The extent of such damage can be reduced by properly locating drainage facilities.

Bedding and Calking

The construction methods employed in bedding, laying, calking, and backfilling pipe must be the best possible. Appendix 4—Specification 1–213 presents the requirements of the C.A.A. which do not vary appreciably from standard practice. Recent developments in sealing joints merit the attention of the engineer. Prepoured asphaltic joints and manufactured rubber type of seals appear to be an improvement over the older method of calking and sealing with mortar.

Pipe Cover

Since the loads imposed on airport drainage are greatly in excess of those found in highway practice it would be expected that stronger pipes or greater covers should be used. However, experience indicates that the loads imposed by the compacting equipment, especially on subdrains under pavement areas, are more severe than those imposed by planes after the grading is completed.

The least cover possible will give the most economy by decreasing the quantities of trench excavation, backfill, and porous material involved.

The writers have made an extensive study of reports from several reliable sources regarding the cover required to support given loads. Unfortunately, many tests and computations have not given similar results so that the writers feel that no real solution has been reached. Based on investigation and the fact that no pipe failures have been reported at airports with which the writers were connected, it is considered that 3 ft of cover, which they have used as a standard minimum, is sufficient for plain concrete or standard-strength tile pipe in sizes 8 in. and over. Smaller size pipe, reinforced concrete pipe, and corrugated metal pipe require less cover.

For the designer who wishes to check pipe cover, the formulas developed by Dean Anson of Iowa State College are considered standard and are contained in practically all drainage handbooks.

Removal of Surface Water

A number of the first airports constructed used an open-joint system, backfilled with porous material to ground surface, both adjacent to the edge of pavement to remove pavement runoff and in shoulder areas in order to intercept the flow of surface water. Catch basins were used at low points where water could be ponded. Figure 6–9 shows a typical cross section of open-joint pipe used at the edge of a pavement. It will be noted that a layer of material having a more open gradation, bound with bituminous material or cement, is used at ground level. This layer is to prevent displacement of the backfill material and is intended to prevent easy clogging of the voids near the surface. There are two principle objections to using an open-joint system for removal of surface water.

One is that in order to remove the surface water rapidly enough to effect the desired results, the size of the porous backfill material usually has to be larger than that which would be called for by the design formula given in this chapter. The rapid flow of water quite often results in the carrying away of the finer materials forming the walls of the trench. The displaced material causes the bank to cave in forming sinkholes along the drainage line. The displaced material may also clog the pipe.

The other reason is that silt and other fine material carried by the water into the porous backfill closes all the voids making the backfill material impervious, or is washed into the system and clogs the pipe.

Failures have occurred in a number of instances whereas entirely satisfactory results have been obtained in others. Whenever this system is to be used for handling surface water, very careful design and excellent construction methods are required. It is not recommended for use in connection with new pavements, as gutter type of drainage is preferable. It may prove advantageous for improving drainage along existing pavements. Transit-mix trucks equipped with long discharge spouts were used with excellent results for placing porous backfill material at the Washington National Airport.

Designs depending entirely on surface runoff do not allow removal of pavement drainage before the water from the pavement has crossed the shoulder area. Erosion frequently occurs before turf becomes established. In other instances turf and swelling of the ground surface adjacent to the pavement, through frost action and the development of grass roots, create a dam which when broken through by a sufficient volume of water results in extensive erosion. Also, the dams caused by snowplowing pond water on the pavement areas cause damage to pavement and operational difficulties.

In order to avoid the retention of any surface water on the pavement, various types of gutters and inlets along the pavement edge are now being used extensively. The design used by C.A.A. for gutter-type pavement has proved highly satisfactory both by keeping pavement water from newly graded shoulder areas and by giving positive removal to water collected behind snow dams during periods of thaw. There is sufficient objection to the flow of pavement water across shoulder areas, even after turf has become established, so that the writers feel that gutter-type pavement with inlets should be used wherever possible. It is believed to be the best system for handling pavement runoff devised to date, and the benefits derived therefrom more than offset its additional cost.

Water from turfed areas which can not be removed by surface runoff should be ponded where it will interfere with operations as little as possible. The ponded water is removed through inlets and sealed-joint pipe. Infield areas and areas between runways and taxiways usually require such treatment.

Subsurface Drainage Adjacent to Pavements

It is necessary to excavate a trough for all types of pavement. With increasing wheel loads, the depth of the trough has increased, being over 2 ft in numerous instances. These troughs serve to collect water before as well as after the pavement is placed. Because of the slope of the pavement, this water runs to one side or the other or both. Unless the subbase is thickened at the edge as shown in Figure 6–4, a gutter type of pavement will pond water to the greatest depth along the gutter center line.

The water collected is very undesirable both during construction and throughout the life of the pavement. The subgrade softening effect is less pronounced in free-draining soils, but is serious unless a sand or gravel subgrade allows almost perfect vertical drainage. In rock cuts or impervious soils it is possible for the water to saturate the base course. When such saturation occurs, longitudinal flow may take place with the water appearing as a spring at the low point in the paving. Even with concrete pavement it is impossible to keep water from collecting in the trough as it can come from percolation through cracks and joints in the pavement, condensation, capillary action, or ice lenses. Very few pavements provide a leakproof roof over the subgrade, and even then water can infiltrate along the pavement edges.

Since water is almost surely bound to collect under pavements and if left alone soften the subgrade to a point where pavement failure may occur, a good drainage design arranges to remove such water. The first step is to insure the flow of the water to the pavement edge by the use of a pervious base, or subbase course, under the pavement. The second and most important step is the installation of a properly designed open-joint system using porous backfill as is shown in Figure 6–9.

Before an engineer dismisses pavement-edge drainage as unnecessary, it will be well for him to consider it as pavement insurance. The cost of pavement-edge drainage is usually a very small percentage of the cost of the pavement it protects. Wet seasons occur periodically in even the driest climates. Pavement-edge drainage serves three purposes. It removes water from under the pavement, it removes subsurface water, and it acts as a cutoff wall to prevent lateral movement of subsurface water into the pavement subgrade. Its use is considered mandatory in connection with all subgrades not having good vertical drainage.

Capacity of Subdrains

The amount of subsurface water to be removed from the soil is usually directly connected with the percentage of rainfall which permeates the soil. One inch of water in 24 hr is generally considered the maximum rate with $\frac{3}{8}$ to $\frac{1}{2}$ in. the rate for the average permeable soil.

Table 6–3, "Recommended Depth and Spacing of Subdrains," and Table 6–4, "Discharge of a Drain in Cubic Feet per Second to Remove Various Depths of Water in 24 Hr," can be used to determine subdrain pipe sizes.

Selection of System

Since inadequate drainage has proved to be the cause of a high percentage of all pavement failures, shoulder softening, and erosion, the selection of the proper drainage system is considered second in importance only to proper airport site selection.

It is recommended that gutter type of pavement be used for collecting pavement runoff. Pavement-edge and subsurface drainage is recommended wherever there is any doubt as to the ability of the vertical drainage of the soil to keep the ground water at least 4 ft below ground-surface elevation.

It is necessary for the engineer to keep in mind the erosion-resisting qualities and the plastic nature of the soil when the type and layout of the drainage system are being considered. It is much more economical to design so as to protect against potential failures than it is to make costly repairs later. Pavement failures, shoulder areas cut up by erosion ditches, or areas so soft as to be unusable are expensive to the community and certainly no credit to the engineer.

CONCLUSION

Airport drainage must be adequate, and of good design, quality, and workmanship if pavement failures are to be avoided. There has long been a lack of appreciation of the fact that a pavement is no better than the subgrade on which it is placed. It should always be the main purpose of drainage to keep the subgrade in the most stable condition possible.

Surface drainage should serve the purpose of removing rainfall before any large percentage of it can percolate into the subsurface soil. Surface drainage also serves the purpose of limiting or eliminating ponding.

Subsurface drainage should reduce the moisture content of subsurface soils to the minimum which their free-draining characteristics will allow. It is recommended that subsurface drainage lines be placed along all pavements where the moisture content of the soil can possibly rise to a point at which it can affect the stability of the soil.

TABLE 6–1. Runoff Coefficients

Type of Area	Factor
Pavement	0.85 to 0.90
Clay soil	0.40 to 0.70
Granular soil	0.20 to 0.40
Turfed areas	0.15 to 0.25
Wooded areas	0.01 to 0.20

TABLE 6–2. Commonly Used Minimum Cover Over Drain Pipe in Feet

Type of Pipe	15,000 Lb Wheel Load						37,000 Lb Wheel Load					
Concrete and clay	6″	12″	24″	36″	48″	60″	6″	12″	24″	36″	48″	60″
Clay sewer pipe C13–40	1.5	3.0	3.0	3.5	—	—	2.5	4.5	5.0	5.0	—	—
Clay culvert (A.A.S.H.O. M-65-38)	—	1.5	2.0	2.0	—	—	—	2.5	3.0	3.0	—	—
Concrete sewer C14–40	1.5	2.5	3.0	—	—	—	2.5	4.0	5.0	—	—	—
Reinforced concrete sewer C75–41	—	2.0	3.0	3.5	—	—	—	3.0	4.0	5.0	—	—
Reinforced concrete culvert C76–41	—	1.5	2.0	2.0	2.0	2.0	—	2.5	3.0	3.0	3.0	3.0
Extra strength reinforced concrete	—	—	1.0	1.0	1.0	1.0	—	—	2.0	2.0	2.0	2.0
Corrugated metal:												
Gauge 18	1.0	—	—	—	—	—	1.0	—	—	—	—	—
16	—	1.0	1.5	—	—	—	—	1.5	3.0	—	—	—
14	—	—	1.0	2.0	—	—	—	1.0	1.5	3.5	—	—
12	—	—	—	1.0	2.0	—	—	—	1.0	2.0	3.0	—
10	—	—	—	—	1.0	1.5	—	—	—	1.0	1.5	2.0
8	—	—	—	—	—	1.0	—	—	—	—	1.0	1.5

TABLE 6–3. Recommended Depth and Spacing of Subdrains (Courtesy Armco Drainage and Metal Products, Inc.)

Soil Classes	Percentage of Soil Separates			Depth of Bottom of Drain in Feet	Distance Between Subdrains in Feet
	Sand	Silt	Clay		
Sand	80–100	0–20	0–20	3–4	150–300
				2–3	100–150
Sandy Loam	50–80	0–50	0–20	3–4	100–150
				2–3	85–100
Loam	30–50	30–50	0–20	3–4	85–100
				2–3	75–85
Silt Loam	0–50	50–100	0–20	3–4	75–85
				2–3	65–75
Sandy Clay Loam	50–80	0–30	20–30	3–4	65–75
				2–3	55–65
Clay Loam	20–50	20–50	20–30	3–4	55–65
				2–3	45–55
Silty Clay Loam	0–30	50–80	20–30	3–4	45–55
				2–3	40–45
Sandy Clay	50–70	0–20	30–50	3–4	40–45
				2–3	35–40
Silty Clay	0–20	50–70	30–50	3–4	35–40
				2–3	30–35
Clay	0–50	0–50	30–100	3–4	30–35
				2–3	25–30

Above data to be considered rough approximations only.

TABLE 6-4. Discharge of a Drain in Cubic Feet per Second to Remove Various Depths of Water in 24 Hr (Courtesy P.R.A.)

Depth		Discharge	
Fraction Inches	Decimal Inches	Per Acre Cubic Feet per Second	Per Square Mile Cubic Feet per Second
1	1.000	0.0420	26.88
$\frac{15}{16}$	.938	.0394	25.20
$\frac{7}{8}$	.875	.0367	23.52
$\frac{13}{16}$	.812	.0341	21.84
$\frac{3}{4}$	.750	.0315	20.16
$\frac{11}{16}$	.688	.0289	18.48
$\frac{5}{8}$	.625	.0262	16.80
$\frac{9}{16}$	.562	.0236	15.12
$\frac{1}{2}$	.500	.0210	13.44
$\frac{7}{16}$	.438	.0184	11.76
$\frac{3}{8}$	.375	.0157	10.08
$\frac{5}{16}$	.312	.0131	8.40
$\frac{1}{4}$	.250	.0105	6.72
$\frac{3}{16}$	.188	.0079	5.04
$\frac{1}{8}$	.125	.0052	3.36
$\frac{1}{16}$	.062	.0026	1.68

CHAPTER VII

PAVEMENTS

It has been found true in most instances that airport pavement is one of the most expensive items of airport construction. The pavement may also prove to be an unduly expensive maintenance item. It therefore behooves the engineer to base his pavement type and design on an exhaustive and detailed study of every factor affecting its construction, maintenance, and use. The selection of a pavement type is all too frequently based on the lower initial cost of one type against another. A large number of examples can be cited where expensive maintenance, frequent interference to operations for repairs, and poor service have demonstrated within a few years that the lower initial cost type can prove to be not only unsatisfactory, but most costly.

The pavement thickness and section should in every case be based on predetermined maximum design loads and frequency of operations. Safe designs can be arrived at by the use of any one of the accepted design formulas in popular use. It often happens that pavement design is the result of the engineer's personal preference and is based entirely on his engineering judgment and experience. This procedure is not recommended although the value of experience and good judgment in the use of any design method is clearly recognized.

Regardless of how good the engineer's judgment is in selecting pavement type and design, failures will occur unless proper consideration has been given to drainage and subgrade. Most of the trouble experienced with airport pavements has been found to be due in a very large measure to inadequate drainage and low bearing value of the subgrade. Pavement surfaces must never be considered a cure-all for poor drainage or unstable subgrades. They should be considered as a roof over the subgrade, placed there to protect the load-bearing value built into the subgrade during construction, to distribute the wheel load over the maximum possible area, as well as to lessen the destructive effects of plane operation. Last but not least in importance is to furnish a smooth-riding, safe, nonskid, weather-resistant surface, a surface which will require the minimum of maintenance and repair.

The authors have found that satisfactory runway pavements can be constructed by the use of several combinations of aggregates meeting standard specifications and tests, provided the design is adequate for the load and proper construction control is secured. The importance of construction control to carry out all design requirements and to recognize and propose necessary changes or revisions which may develop during the progress of the work is to be stressed.

It is desired to point out the fallacy of a penny-wise and pound-foolish aspect of a situation where a community will spend a large sum of the taxpayers' money for a pavement, yet seriously jeopardizes the quality of the pavement by failure to require the services of a well-qualified and adequately equipped resident supervisory staff to insure securing the quality of construction being paid for. The authors have been responsible for the design and construction control of a rather large number of airports. The fact that there have been no indications of pavement failure on any of these projects is attributed largely to the high quality and competency of the supervisory and inspection services engaged thereon.

Most manufacturers of materials or equipment used in connection with airport pavements will welcome the opportunity of assisting in solving any pavement problem which may confront the engineer. This is usually done by making available to him the services of their technical staff or those of the experts of any trade organization of which they may be a member. The authors have found these services to be gratuitous, competent, reliable, and often highly specialized. These services will prove invaluable in securing or checking design information as well as in solving unusual construction problems.

Various manufacturers and trade organizations publish technical data, guide specifications, and descriptive literature covering a wide range of subjects. This information is generally issued to promote the use of a particular product and to assist the engineer in obtaining the best possible results from its use. It is recommended that all airport engineers take advantage of this service, as publications covering every phase of airport design and construction are readily available.

FACTORS AFFECTING DESIGN

Pavement designs and types will vary with different locations, soils, available materials, and climatic conditions. They will also vary in accordance with the judgment and experience of different engineers. It is understandable that different engineers will treat the same design data and governing factors differently, yet each may secure satisfactory results. It seldom happens, however, that engineers will attain or produce the desired results or economical costs unless they thoroughly analyze and study all factors and conditions which may, or do, affect the design and subsequent pavement usage.

Subgrade

As will be noted later in this chapter, pavement thickness, as determined by design formulas, is largely dependent on the stability and bearing value of the subgrade. The engineer should, therefore, have all possible information as to the soil's character and load-bearing value of the subgrade upon which the pavement is to be constructed. If the stability and bearing value are low, a heavier and more costly pavement is required. On the other hand, the higher the subgrade-bearing value the less costly the pavement. On this basis the highest possible bearing value consistent with reasonable cost should be built into the subgrade.

The tests described in Chapter IV should be used to classify the subgrade materials as well as other materials which may be economically imported for use in the subgrade. Proper use of these tests can result in large savings in pavement costs.

Wherever possible pavement design and selective grading should be closely coordinated. Selective grading should serve the purpose of securing a uniform pavement subgrade consisting of the best excavated material available on the site or within the limits of economical haul. If A-3, E-3, or better soils are available at excavation cost it will usually prove economical to remove all unsuitable subgrade material to a depth of at least 2 ft, or deeper if frost conditions warrant, and replace it with the better material.

Any section of subgrade which weaves under the load imposed by hauling or compacting equipment should be removed and replaced. Any poor section of subgrade which can not be improved by removal and replacement must be given extraordinary drainage treatment. Blind drains with proper outlets on a herringbone, gridiron, or parallel pattern often reduce the moisture content sufficiently to allow satisfactory stability.

Wherever possible, samples taken directly from the finished subgrade should be used for the tests required to classify the soil. The engineer should make certain that samples of the least desirable subgrade materials are secured as the pavement must be designed against the worst subgrade conditions. The prime requirement of pavement design is: Know all there is to know about the subgrade—be sure it is properly compacted.

Drainage

The efficiency of the drainage system which controls the moisture content of the subgrade can have as much effect on the bearing power and life of the pavement as any other factor, including the subgrade material. It is considered secondary in importance to subgrade only because drainage often can be installed or extended after the pavement is in place.

Drainage conditions, as used here, are intended to cover ground-water level, permeability, surface runoff, and any other condition which affects the moisture content of the subgrade. The engineer should be able to predict with reasonable accuracy whether the subgrade, in its worst condition, will be well drained, fairly high in moisture content, or saturated.

While some excellent pavement-design formulas are based on the bearing power of the saturated subgrade, there can be no doubt that a well-drained subgrade possesses the maximum stability and bearing power possible of attainment with the particular soil being dealt with. The writers favor the allowance the C.A.A.-design method gives to good drainage. They feel, however, that without provisions for adequate surface and subsurface drainage the subgrade moisture will reach the saturation point during at least one season of the year, except in arid sections of the country. It also appears logical to expect adequate drainage to cut the periods of subgrade saturation to such short duration that the effect will not, for the most part, be serious. The writers have designed and supervised the installation of drainage systems in connection with existing pavements where failure appeared imminent. In each instance, the improved drainage resulted in the disappearance of all previous indication of serious pavement failure. Subgrades which can not be or are not adequately drained require a high factor of safety in pavement design.

Frost

Frost action in subgrades can heave a pavement, displacing it so that its horizontal alignment may be disturbed. It may also seriously weaken subgrade bearing power or make it nonuniform. In certain types of soil, frost may cause ice lenses to form in the subgrade. When these ice lenses melt, the subgrade may be practically liquefied if the soil is of a type which is sufficiently unstable when saturated. Highway experience has shown plainly that frost is damaging to pavements.

Wherever the depth of frost is in excess of the thickness of the granular base or subbase, some provision must be made to protect the pavement against the action of the frost on the subgrade. Frost will not ordinarily affect granular materials. Frost can have the effect of slaking semihard materials such as soft rock and shale, reducing them to a very unstable state. A particularly bad situation can exist when the upper portion of a deep frost has thawed leaving an impervious layer of frozen ground to prevent vertical drainage.

Aggregates Available

Coarse and fine aggregates are essential to the construction of most types of pavements. Some types of stabilization and sand-mix surface courses require only fine aggregate. The kinds of aggregates available, their delivered cost, and their durable properties have a great deal to do with the economics of pavement types.

Coarse aggregates may consist of any hard durable substance which can be crushed or broken into required sizes. In most localities uncrushed gravel, crushed gravel, crushed stone, or slag constitutes the main type of aggregate.

Fine aggregate may consist of natural sand, crushed sandstone, finely crushed stone particles, or finely crushed slag.

The survey procedure, as recommended in Chapter III calls for securing information regarding available aggregates. This information is often of a general nature and is mainly useful for elimination of unsuitable pavement types. As the work of pavement design progresses, a point is reached where most of the uncertainties have been disposed of, making it possible to actually compare the probable cost and performance of one type of pavement against another. It is usually necessary at this time to secure more factual information regarding different aggregates. It is suggested that answers be obtained to each of the following questions:

1. Does the aggregate meet the requirements of the paving specifications? See Appendix for guide specifications.
2. What volume is available and at what rate per day can it be delivered?
3. What is the cost per ton or per cubic yard delivered to the site?
4. Is the service record of the material such as to warrant its use in airport pavement?

Local Customs and Equipment

This factor will assume little importance where the engineer is dealing with a problem in a locality with which he is entirely familiar. It is advised, however, that it be given consideration by the engineer who prepares or checks design specifications for airports scattered over an appreciable area, such as a state.

Construction materials and procedures vary from one locality to another. Aggregate gradations, their durability requirements, and other tolerances are far from uniform. Local contractors have become familiar with processing materials in ways which are different in some aspects from those in vogue at other locations. Permanent equipment is often installed for producing aggregates, preparing asphaltic mixes, or producing ready-mixed concrete. These permanent installations usually provide some special features necessary in developing the product to conform to local requirements, or are adapted to use local materials.

While it can not be said that all local customs are up to date or conform to the required standards, it is usually true that people do not continue to use materials or follow practices over long periods of time unless satisfactory results are achieved.

It is advisable for the engineer to study local aggregates, local construction practices, and permanently installed construction equipment. This will allow him to use such aggregates, customs, or equipment to his advantage, if they are of suitable quality, and will also save the extra cost and embarrassment which can come from his failure to do so. The writers have found that competition between paving types is usually beneficial and therefore they do not advocate restricting design to conform strictly to local practices if it appears that other desirable methods are economically feasible.

Wheel Loading

The writers feel that there must be a great deal of research carried out and a great deal of data on existing pavements compiled and correlated before the effect of aircraft wheel loading on airport pavements can be predicted with any high degree of accuracy. It is interesting to note the general lack of failures where airport pavements have been called on to handle numerous landings of aircraft having a wheel load considerably in excess of the design loading. Most failures which have come to the writers' attention have resulted from insufficient subgrade consolidation, inadequate drainage, or poor pavement-construction methods.

There can be no doubt that the higher the wheel loading the thicker the pavement section must be. The increase, however, after the design is sufficient to support a wheel load of approximately 37,000 lb seems to depend on the trend which aircraft landing-gear design takes. The contact area of the aircraft's wheels will be influenced by the allowable tire pressure and the number of wheels used. At present the best the engineer can do is to take the information given him as to the type of aircraft which will use the airport, and use his judgment as to which of the current design methods he will use to arrive at a pavement suitable for such aircraft.

Landing impact, vibration stresses, repetition of loading, and the effect of braking action are relatively unknown quantities.

Present practice is to discount landing impact completely due to the fact that an airplane's wings have lift at all times when the airplane has any appreciable amount of forward speed. The lift of the wings together with the long travel of the landing-gear shock absorbers makes this theory generally acceptable. According to this premise, an airplane at rest exerts a larger vertical component on the pavement than does an airplane in making any landing except a crash landing.

Vibration stresses set up while taxiing an airplane or revving up the motors are generally considered to increase the vertical component by 15 to 25 per cent. These stresses can be expected in all aprons and taxiways, and the ends of runways.

Many authorities feel that it is so seldom that aircraft land or take off along identical paths that fatigue from repetition of loading is greatly reduced as compared with experience under highway traffic conditions. A proper consideration of this factor affects the economy of design.

Airplane brakes are often applied suddenly and with sufficient pressure to lock the wheels. The horizontal component of the airplane's weight during such action must be considered as must be the locked wheel turns. Severe braking action can roll up or corduroy a flexible pavement surface which is too soft or too thin.

Research projects dealing with wheel loadings are presently being conducted and no doubt will continue to be for some considerable length of time. Engineers concerned with airport pavements should make an effort to keep posted on the findings in this field.

Granular Subbase Materials

Almost all present pavement design methods require that as large a portion of the bearing value of a pavement be accomplished by improving subgrade and subbase conditions as is economically feasible. This development has resulted in sources of suitable subbase material becoming an important factor in pavement design. Specification C.A.A. 689, given in Appendix 7, adequately describes acceptable subbase materials, and the construction methods which should be used in their production and placement.

The four questions listed above regarding aggregates are also applicable to subbase materials.

Subgrade Stabilization

Since subbases are in effect foundations placed on the subgrade to assist it in supporting the loads transmitted to it by the pavement, any good foundation material will suffice whether it is granular or not.

As outlined later in this chapter, the study of the subgrade which is required for pavement thickness determination will indicate whether the subgrade material is suitable for stabilization by the incorporation of some binding agent. If stabilization appears feasible, tests should be conducted to determine whether this procedure is more desirable or more economical than importing granular subbase materials. It is suggested that the California bearing ratio of the stabilized subgrade be determined and used as a guide.

If stabilization is proved to be desirable and economical it can be accomplished by use of one of the stabilization construction methods discussed later in this chapter.

Subgrade stabilization often has other than economical advantages over the use of granular subbase material. Under the proper circumstances a stabilized subgrade will suffice as a pavement for a time. This works out well if further paving operations must be delayed on account of lack of funds or for any other reason. The moisture control afforded by bituminous stabilization under concrete pavements is claimed by some experts to reduce warping to a negligible amount. A bituminous subbase under a bituminous pavement actually results in a much thicker bituminous section.

GENERAL DESIGN FEATURES

Airport pavements have a great many aspects in common with highway pavements. However, the operational characteristics of the airplane and the scope of the pavement do pose problems, the solutions for which are not found in highway practice.

Surface Texture

Surface texture need not vary appreciably from highway practice. The main consideration is the insurance of sufficient friction to insure effective braking action with the minimum wear on tires.

It is to be remembered that airplane tires are subjected to a tremendous scuffing action at the time the wheels first contact the runway in a landing. The airplane will be travelling at a high rate of speed yet the wheels are not rotating so must be accelerated at a high rate on contact with the pavement. A surface which is rough enough to be very efficient for braking purposes may be so rough as to damage tires excessively on landings. A rather coarse sandpaper finish is recommended.

Color

There has been a great deal of discussion regarding the most desirable color for airport pavements. The wide divergence of opinions indicates that it may be a matter entirely governed by the pilot's personal preference.

The writers' observations have been that any color which is in contrast with the color of the shoulder area tends to make the pavement outline stand out. Light colors accomplish the contrast most readily. It was found at the Washington National Airport that an eggshell white cover aggregate darkened quite rapidly in the area of heavy traffic, but remained white along the outer edges of the pavement. The effect of a white border on dark runways received favorable pilot comment.

Since night lighting is not predicated on the runway lights illuminating the pavement, pavement color is not a factor in this regard.

Data presently available indicate that the expenditure of any appreciable amount of money to secure a certain color of pavement is not warranted.

Width

Present standards of pavement width are shown in Tables 2–2 and –4. The writers feel that these widths will remain adequate for the airplanes which will normally use airports other than large major terminals. There can be no doubt, however, that when planes weighing in excess of approximately 120,000 lb are built, the landing-gear spread will increase to a point where a 150-ft-wide runway and 50-ft taxiway will prove to be too narrow.

From the pilot's point of view it will be difficult to provide a runway which is too wide so the engineer has nothing to fear from an operational standpoint if he chooses to exceed C.A.A. standard widths.

It is very difficult to provide for any appreciable widening of airport runways. This can be done, however, by very careful planning of grades, transitions, intersections, and drainage. Original construction on such a basis is usually so much more expensive than normal design that it is seldom used.

PAVEMENT-THICKNESS DETERMINATION

Because of the multitude of factors which enter into all instances of pavement failures and because identical subgrade conditions almost never exist the subject of pavement thickness will always be controversial. Competition between types and between pavement materials keeps the controversy at a high pitch continually.

A great many observations of pavement behavior have been correlated and much research work has been and is being performed. It is advised that engineers concerned with airport pavements keep themselves posted, as improvements in design methods, particularly with regard to heavy wheel loadings, may be expected for some time to come. There are four design methods in general use at present. They are discussed herewith with the idea that the engineer should study each method and then choose for himself the method he feels will prove most useful to him. The discussion herein will necessarily be limited by the space available in a volume of a general nature. Each method is given special treatment in one or more publications which the engineer should secure. The authors have found the C.A.A. method of pavement design to be entirely satisfactory, and recommend its use. It is believed that it is described herein in sufficient detail to allow a completed pavement design to be prepared.

C.A.A. METHOD

The C.A.A. method is described in a pamphlet entitled "Design Manual for Airport Pavements" dated March 1, 1944. This publication is available from the Superintendent of Documents, Washington, D.C. at a cost of 5¢. This method is based on C.A.A.'s long experience with all phases of airport-pavement design, construction, and maintenance. It represents the consensus of thoughts and ideas of a large number of engineers. While this method allows the engineer latitude when required by unusual conditions, it very definitely takes pavement-thickness determination and design out of the personal-opinion category.

Basic Principles

The basic principles of the C.A.A. method are as follows:

1. The use of a standard thickness of pavement for any given wheel load regardless of subgrade, drainage, or frost conditions prevailing, except in very unusual circumstances.
2. The improvement and thickening of the subbase to bring it up to the standards required for the design wheel loading.
3. Increased thickness where vibration stresses or locked wheel turns may occur.
4. Competition between different types of pavement wherever there is any question as to the most economical type Alternates are limited to two types in most instances. Each type is, of course, based on the same soil classification and design wheel loading.

Design Methods

Table 4–1, which gives the details of the C.A.A. method of classifying soils, supplies *F* and *R* designations required to be used in the thickness charts given in Fig. 7–1 for concrete pavement, Fig. 7–2 for flexible pavement and nonbituminous base, Fig. 7–3 for flexible pavement with bituminous concrete base, and Fig. 7–4 for flexible pavement with emulsified asphalt aggregate base.

As an example, the following are the steps which the engineer goes through in arriving at the thickness of the various types of pavements, assuming a gross loading of 74,000 lb is expected.

1. Determine *E* classification of the soil from laboratory tests performed on samples.
2. From survey notes describing texture of soil, local frost conditions, drainage conditions, and performance of similar material as used in highway subgrades determine the *F* and *R* classification of the sample.

The following quotation from C.A.A.'s "Design Manual" will assist in this classification:

On the basis of the information obtained in the soil and material surveys and laboratory analysis, all available materials should be classified in accordance with Chart 1 [Table 4–1] SOIL AND MATERIAL CLASSIFICATION. It is realized that most materials will not fall exactly in one class on basis of all characteristics. Interpolation will be necessary to arrive at the proper "F" and "R" classification for use in design of flexible and rigid pavements respectively. Judgment should be used in such interpolation but the placing of undue importance on any one characteristic should be avoided.

It should be noted that the same "F" and "R" classifications are obtained by various soils with different climatic and drainage conditions. Under most favorable conditions of frost and drainage, an E-3 soil becomes an F_a material and an E-5 soil is an R_a material; while under the most severe conditions of frost and drainage, only the E-1 soil is classed as F_a material and an E-4 soil falls outside the R_a category.

Severe frost is defined as a condition where frost is likely to penetrate to the subgrade. Poor drainage is defined as a condition in which the subgrade is expected to become saturated because of poor vertical drainage, condensation, capillary moisture or any other cause that may result in a saturated subgrade.

There is some difference of opinion as to the conditions under which subgrade saturation may occur. The following quotation from paragraph 20–17 of the U.S.E.D. *Engineering Manual* plainly sets forth their opinion in the matter: "Experience and field observation have shown that subgrade and base course soils (except clean sand) under impervious pavements will eventually become saturated by capillarity and condensation of moisture, regardless of ground water elevation."

3. Using *R* or *F* value arrived at, enter the appropriate pavement chart and determine therefrom the required subbase thickness as indicated in the lower portion of the chart.

The thickness of the concrete or the flexible base and surface course is indicated in the upper portion of the chart. It is to be noted that for any given gross loading these thicknesses remain constant regardless of soil classification.

General

The C.A.A. method is contingent on the engineer using specifications which in general follow the intent and the requirements of approved C.A.A. specifications. A list of these approved specifications, most of which are given in the appendix, is as follows:

Approved Specifications

CONCRETE

Specification No. P-501
Chart No. 2—(Fig. 7–1)

Bituminous Surface

Specification No. P-401
P-406
P-407
P-408

These surface courses only to be used on base types shown on Charts Nos. 3, 4, and 5 (Figs. 7–2, 3, and 4)

Special Surface at Runway and Taxiway Ends

Specification No. P-409
P-408-A

Flexible Pavement—Nonbituminous Base

Specification No. P-205
P-206
P-209
P-210
P-211
P-212
P-301
P-302

Chart No. 3 (Fig. 7–2)

Flexible Pavement—Bituminous Base

Specification No. P-204
P-201

Chart No. 4 (Fig. 7–3)

Flexible Pavement—Emulsified Asphalt Aggregate Base

Specification No. P-204
P-215

Chart No. 5 (Fig. 7–4)

Soil Survey Instructions

Specification No. P-601

The following conditions as set forth in C.A.A.'s "Design Manual" are pertinent:

Regarding rigid pavements on all aprons, taxiways, runways used extensively as taxiways, and for a length of 500′ on each end of all runways, the concrete pavement thickness will be increased by one inch to provide for the more severe condition of static loading and engine vibration. No change will be made in the subbase design.

Regarding flexible pavements on all taxiways, runways used extensively for taxiways, aprons and for a length of 500′ on the ends of all runways, the total pavement thickness shall be increased by 20% where a subbase material is used. This increased thickness shall be provided by additional subbase material. Where no subbase is required the base course shall be increased on these portions of the pavement by an amount equal to 20% of the total pavement thickness.

For a length of 200′ on the ends of all runways and the adjacent 200′ of taxiways serving the runway ends and on all aprons the bituminous surface course will be constructed using a bituminous mixture produced in accordance with the approved specifications for those specially paved areas. Where the normal surface course thickness is two inches, the surfacing in these areas shall be increased to two and one-half inches and placed in two courses. (Refer to Fig. 7–5a; and 5b.)

U.S. ENGINEER DEPARTMENT METHOD

The Office of the Chief of Engineers has published instructions for guidance in the design and construction of runways, parking aprons, turnarounds, and taxiways for airfields for the Army Air Forces. These instructions are set forth in their *Engineering Manual,* Chapter XX. This manual is kept current by revisions and the issuance of additional sections which are published from time to time as investigations and studies progress.

It is advised that every engineer concerned with airport pavements study Chapter XX as it represents the results of a vast amount of research work, the coordination and evaluation of numerous tests, and the consensus of opinion of several of the country's outstanding soils and pavement engineers.

Although the instructions are for Army Air Force fields, and therefore necessarily allow for rapid investigation and decision, they are considered entirely applicable to commercial airport construction.

Design Considerations

The *Engineering Manual* gives consideration to a number of factors in arriving at pavement thickness and design.

Frequency of operation, drainage, frost action, soil classification, California Bearing Ratio of soils and base course material, subgrade compaction and subgrade reaction are among these factors. Soils are classified according to the Casagrande Soil Classification for airfields, shown in Fig. 4–10.

Flexible Pavements

The design of flexible pavements is based on the California method. This empirical method of design of base courses for flexible pavements as developed and used by the California State Highway Department is described in the paper, "The Preparation of Subgrades" by O. J. Porter, *Proceedings*, Highway Research Board, Part II, December 1938. The *Engineering Manual* makes special provisions for conditions where the required thickness of base course materials as determined by the California method is not sufficient to preclude frost penetration in the subgrade or lower zones of the base course.

Tentative design curves have been developed by the Corps of Engineers. The *Engineering Manual* states that additional laboratory and field traffic tests are being conducted and the service behavior of actual fields is being studied to determine whether further modification of the design curves are necessary.

Rigid Pavements

Westergaard's formulas are the basis of the determination of pavement thickness as set forth in the *Engineering Manual*.

PUBLIC ROADS ADMINISTRATION METHOD

The method of pavement thickness determination and design used by the P.R.A. is set forth in their publication entitled "Principles of Highway Construction as Applied to Airports, Flight Strips and Other Landing Areas For Aircraft." This volume is available by purchase from the Superintendent of Documents, U.S. Government Printing Office, Washington, D.C., at a cost of $1.00. It is recommended for study in this regard as well as for information pertaining to other features of airport design and construction.

Flexible Type

Based in part on the observed behavior of soils in highway construction and in part on such results of research as are available, P.R.A. has arrived at a minimum and maximum total thickness of subbase, base course, and surface course for each wheel load and each class of soil. These are set forth in Table 7–2. For each given load and class of soil, the total thickness may be varied within the range given, depending on variations in the soil characteristics, degree of compaction, natural soil moisture, and climate.

Rigid Pavements

Westergaard's formulas using an expected maximum static load and temperature warping stress of approximately 500 psi are the basis for P.R.A.'s estimated minimum thicknesses as shown in Table 7–3.

U.S. NAVY DEPARTMENT METHOD

The Bureau of Yards and Docks handles airfield design for the Navy Department. This office has issued three manuals dealing with soils and pavements which are of interest to any engineer connected with making airport paving determinations.

Soil Classification

Manual No. 3 entitled "Soil Classification for Airfield Projects" discusses the Navy soil classification requirements. The Casagrande soil classification chart as given in Fig. 4–10 is used. The California bearing ratio test is not used to any extent except as a means of differentiating between soil types and estimating the relative stability of different soils and soil mixtures. This manual discusses the relative stability of the different soil groups.

Flexible Types of Pavements

Manual No. 1 entitled "Procedure for Determination of Thickness of Flexible Type Pavements" defines pavement thickness and gives the basis for design of pavement thickness. The manual makes reference to the limiting value of 0.2 in. for deflection when the applied load is equal to the maximum anticipated wheel load as agreed upon by the Committee on Flexible Pavements Design of the Highway Research Board on November 14, 1942.

The Bureau of Yards and Docks relies on the method of loading trial pavement sections for determining the thickness of flexible types of pavements. The manual states that a trial section for loading should have minimum dimensions of 20 ft by 20 ft. The diameter of the plate for loading tests for usual conditions is such as to equal the tire contact area taking into account a rigidity factor of 1.1.

In order to reduce the number of sections required to determine a pavement thickness the manual makes use of a curve which allows an estimation of thickness after the first trial section. The second trial section allows a closer estimation by use of the curve. The final estimation, however, requires checking by actual load test.

The Bureau considers the Standard Specification for Stabilized Base Course, Specification M-56-38, adopted by the A.A.S.H.O. as the most useful information available regarding the grading and physical properties of base course materials.

Manual No. 2 contains a very instructive description of the Navy method of conducting loading tests.

Rigid Types of Pavements

Manual No. 2 entitled "Procedure for Determination of Thickness of Rigid Pavements" states that the Westergaard analysis is the basis of the design of their concrete pavements. The manual gives the publication "Stresses in Concrete Runways of Airports," *Proceedings*, Highway Research Board, Volume 19, 1939, pp. 199–205 as sufficient for computing concrete pavement thicknesses for wheel loads in excess of 15,000 pounds.

The manual discusses the design of subbase thickness under concrete pavements taking note of the relationship between cost of construction of various thicknesses of subbase compared with the required thickness of the concrete slab. The effect of frost heave and loss of bearing power in soils affected by frost action is taken into consideration.

Recognizing the importance of securing the proper value of *K*, the modulus of soil reaction for use in Westergaard's formulas, the manual gives explicit instructions for carrying out both the field and laboratory tests.

The manual calls for the thickening of airport paving slabs to at least 1.5 times the interior slab thickness at all longitudinal outside edges and longitudinal free joints. The necessity for adequate subgrade compaction and proper drainage of the subgrade under thickened edges is recognized.

The manual gives very illustrative examples of computations of concrete pavement thickness.

HIGHWAY RESEARCH BOARD PROCEEDINGS

Two articles appearing in *Proceedings* Twenty-Third Annual Meeting—1943 of the Highway Research Board contain valuable information regarding airport pavement design.

BINDING AGENT

All pavements depend on some agent to bind the particles of aggregate together so that the interlocked stability of the aggregate is maintained. Binding agents all have cohesive properties, reduce voids to a minimum, and in many instances waterproof the mixture.

MISCELLANEOUS BINDERS

Clays, limestone screenings, and several other finely divided materials can be used to bind or stabilize stone or sand bases.

PORTLAND CEMENT

Portland and natural cements bind aggregates into rigid pavements. Cement is universally available at standard prices.

During recent years, and particularly during the war period, vast strides have been made in developing Portland cement concrete which is highly resistant to the deleterious effects of freezing and thawing which often accompany the use of deicing agents. This result is achieved principally by entrainment of air in the concrete through use of air-entraining Portland cement or by addition of suitable air-entraining agent to concrete mix (on the job) where normal Portland cement is used.

In addition to the development of greatly increased durability the use of air-entraining concrete is accompanied by improved workability and freedom from water-gain, and it generally reduces labor in placement and finishing.

BITUMENS

Bitumens are available in a very wide variety of compounds with the price of each being governed by several factors such as cost of production, freight rate, and competition. Considerable study will be required on the part of the engineer before he can feel himself to be on home ground when such bitumen compounds as MCO, RC-3, RT2, etc., are discussed. The letters used to designate a material usually refer to length of curing time, penetration, viscosity, or some other physical characteristic.

ASPHALT

The following material, through and including Tables 7–4 to –8, is presented through the courtesy of the Asphalt Institute.

Liquid asphaltic materials are made in two ways. Cut-back asphalts, both of the medium curing and rapid curing group, and emulsified asphalts are prepared by taking asphalt cement and making it into a liquid state either by solution with a petroleum distillate or by emulsification with water.

Slow curing products, such as road oils, however, are asphaltic materials which have never been refined to a hard asphalt cement, and their fluidity is dependent upon the contained softer petroleum constituents. These constituents are usually of high boiling point character and are therefore very resistant to change under conditions of use.

In the selection of any one of the liquid asphaltic materials, therefore, it is important in making a selection of a particular grade to accomplish any particular kind of work, to appraise the conditions which are to be met with respect to manipulation. Rapid curing products set up very quickly, as their name designates, and therefore are generally suitable for employment with clean-graded aggregates. Medium curing cut backs set up more slowly and therefore may be employed with fine-graded aggregates with longer period for manipulation. Emulsified asphalts are made in several grades to meet both rapid curing and slow curing conditions.

Slow curing materials include the formerly designated road oils, and, as their name designates, are to be employed where a longer manipulative period is required, such as in the case of surfaces that are to be mixed in place or to be bladed for a considerable period. In general, medium curing cut-back asphalts and slow curing asphaltic materials may be used for substantially the same types of work.

From the total of twelve grades of cut-back asphalts covered by the new RC and MC specifications, the engineer will be able to select a type and grade suitable for practically any airport or highway use for which a cut-back is required. His selection will be governed largely by his past experience, purpose to be served, character of available mineral aggregate to be used, method of manipulation and weather conditions. As the various grades of RC products primarily differ *only* in the quantity of volatile solvent present it is possible by varying manipulation to make a number of grades serve the same purpose. The same is true of the MC products and in fact it is often possible to obtain equally good results in a given type of work by using proper grades of either RC or MC products.

Table 7–4 showing the principal uses of these materials is therefore offered merely as a guide to selection when some doubt may exist on the part of the engineer.

Temperature limits governing the use of these materials so as to insure a sufficiently liquid condition at time of application are as follows:

Material	Temperature °F.
RC–0 and MC–0	50–120
RC–1 and MC–1	80–125
RC–2	100–175
MC–2 and RC–2	150–200
MC–3, MC–4, RC–4 and RC–5	175–250
MC–5	200–275

NEW SPECIFICATIONS (RC AND MC)

The new specifications for type RC and type MC materials shown in Tables 7–5 and 7–6 have been approved by the Public Roads Administration and adopted by the Asphalt Institute. They are recommended for general adoption to supersede all earlier specifications for types RC and MC materials.

The . . . new specifications [in Table 7–7] have been adopted by the Asphalt Institute to supersede all earlier specifications for type SC (slow curing) materials.

As compared with the old specifications, the new SC specifications contain a requirement for percent of asphalt residue, and ductility of such residue. The float test on residue from distillation has also been defined by both minimum and maximum limits and the presence of water has been eliminated from all but the two lightest grades.

SCOPE AND USES OF EMULSIFIED ASPHALT

Principal uses of the emulsified asphalts specified in [Table 7–8] are as follows:

RS-1—These specifications cover emulsified asphalt for penetration and surface treatment.

MS-1—These specifications cover a low consistency emulsified asphalt for road-mixes with coarse aggregate, substantially all of which is retained on a ⅛" sieve and with practically no material passing a No. 200 sieve.

MS-2—These specifications cover a medium consistency emulsified asphalt for plant mixes with coarse aggregate, substantially all of which is retained on a ½" sieve and with practically no material passing a No. 200 sieve.

MS-3—These specifications cover a high consistency heavy pre-mix grade of emulsified asphalt, for plant mixing or patching with coarse aggregate, substantially all of which is retained on a ⅛" sieve and with practically no material passing a No. 200 sieve.

SS-1—These specifications cover emulsified asphalt for fine aggregate mixes in which a substantial quantity of aggregate passes a ⅛" sieve and a portion may pass a No. 200 sieve.

SS-2—These specifications cover emulsified asphalt (of low penetration) for fine aggregate mixes and for admixture with soil aggregates in which a portion passes a No. 200 sieve.

TAR

Road tars are produced by the destructive distillation of organic material such as coal and petroleum. Their designations are generally based on the type of material or the process by which they are derived. For instance, coal tars are produced by the destructive distillation of bituminous coal; coke-oven tars are produced in the manufacture of coke from bituminous coal; and water-gas tars are produced by cracking oil vapors at high temperatures in the manufacture of carburetted water-gas. Tables 7–9 and –10 relating to specifications and uses of tars are taken from Federal Specification R-T-143, August 3, 1940.

FLEXIBLE PAVEMENT CONSTRUCTION DETAILS

The details of construction of flexible types of pavements can be varied to allow for the use of a wide variety of aggregates, binding agents, and construction procedures. Much of the variance is due to the economics of aggregate and binding-agent production with the less expensive materials being utilized wherever they prove satisfactory. Some of the variance is attributable to the school of thought to which the top engineers in the organization adhere. Flexible pavements are sufficiently versatile so that reasonably good design judgment coupled with good construction methods usually gives satisfactory results.

The flexibility of this type of pavement allows for a small amount of settlement and deformation without causing pavement failure.

Flexible pavements require surface treatment periodically to maintain the seal coat in good condition. Many engineers advocate the use of the softer bituminous products in airport pavements for the reason that the kneading action of traffic required to keep bitumens alive is missing in many pavement areas.

The most common flexible pavement section and its components are discussed herein.

Typical Section

Except for the thickness of the various courses, and relatively slight differences in aggregate gradation and binding-agent characteristics there is very little variance between this section and one which would be arrived at by any of the other common design methods.

It is felt that every pavement section must be designed to overcome any deficiencies in bearing power or natural drainage characteristics of the subgrade. The fact that paving sections designed for soils subject to frost action require special consideration is clearly recognized by the generally accepted design methods.

Subbase

Subbase materials are usually composed of the cheapest material available whose characteristics regarding stability, drainage, and resistance to frost action are satisfactory for the protection of actual pavement courses.

The C.A.A. method allows subbase materials to be chosen according to Specification C.A.A. 689 which is reproduced in Appendix 7. Other methods, particularly the California method, rely on the California bearing ratio to determine the suitability of subbase materials.

Subbase materials must be compacted to at least 95 per cent of the theoretical density at optimum moisture.

By careful selection of excavated materials it is often possible to place the subbase material under the excavation item in a satisfactory manner both in regard to cost and construction procedures.

The surface of the subbase should be smoothed to a reasonable tolerance as this assists in obtaining a uniform thickness of base course layers.

Base Courses

Macadam base courses have been used in pavement construction for a great many years and are well adapted to use in airport construction. Highway practices which have been proved satisfactory can be applied to airport pavements except that binding by traffic is not feasible. The aggregates may be of any desirable gradation and may be dry or water bound. A macadam base course is nearly always considered a part of the actual pavement. Macadam specifications can be patterned after one of those given in Appendices 10, 11, and 12. The engineer may desire to incorporate the California bearing ratio of the materials into base course design.

In many localities aggregates ordinarily required for macadam base courses are not available locally or are more expensive than other local materials. Caliche, shell, or some manufacturing by-product may be available. Where this condition prevails the specifications given in Appendices 13, 14, and 15 can be used as a guide.

A high degree of compaction and surface smoothness is required in all cases.

Bituminous Base Courses

Many engineers prefer a base course bound with a bituminous material to one bound with screenings, stone dust, or similar material. Bituminous concrete, sand asphalt, or penetrated macadam are the more common forms of such base courses. C.A.A. specifications P-201, P-202, and P-215 reproduced in Appendices 16, 17, and 24 are excellent guides for bituminous design.

Asphalt Emulsion Sand Mix and Soil Stabilization

In many localities there is an abundance of sand, nearly all of which passes a No. 10 sieve and usually about 15 per cent to 25 per cent will pass a No. 80 sieve. If from 5 per cent to 10 per cent passes the No. 200 sieve a stable material will result from the addition of the proper amount of emulsified asphalt which can be determined by the following formula:

$P =$ .75 (0.05A plus 0.10B plus 0.5C) in which
A = The per cent of sand retained on the No. 10 sieve
$B =$ The per cent of sand passing a No. 10 sieve and retained on a No. 200 sieve
C = The per cent of sand passing a No. 200 sieve, by wet sieve analysis
$P =$ The per cent of emulsified asphalt based on the weight of sand

A fine aggregate mixing grade of emulsified asphalt must be used such as A.S.T.M. Designation D-631.

Several methods of testing the bearing value of the asphalted sand have been developed. We will not attempt to outline these methods as it will no doubt be advisable to adopt the C.A.A. or an A.S.T.M. method or one that is known by the laboratory in the location where the work is being done. If after testing the asphalted sand the bearing value is found to be too low or if the *P* value as determined by the preceding formula is too high, admixtures may be incorporated with the existing sand to improve the stability and economy of the mix.

Mixing may be done by "travel plant," or by "blade and harrow" if the sand is in place, or by "central plant" if not in place. Compaction of the mix to as near maximum density as possible is necessary. This can be done by means of pneumatic-tired rollers working in conjunction with blade graders which spread and compact the mix in thin layers as taken from windrows, or by depositing the mix from a central plant in thin layers and blading and compacting until the full thickness of the foundation course is built up. A heavy smooth-faced steel-wheeled roller is usually used for final rolling. Mixing can be done in moderate rain since water is necessary to facilitate mixing. The mix can be compacted either while it contains the optimum amount of moisture for compaction or it can be compacted as an ordinary "cold-lay" asphaltic mix after it has dried out. The latter method only applies at atmospheric temperatures above 75F while the wet method of compaction is applicable at any temperature above 45F. After compaction, the foundation course should be permitted to dry until the moisture content does not exceed 5 per cent after which the seal coat or wearing surface may be constructed. C.A.A. has developed a specification No. P-204, April, 1942, for travel-plant method of mixing which is reproduced in Appendix 20.

Penetration macadam type of paving is one of the oldest forms of paving in use today. It, however, has been greatly abused and is considered only a temporary method by many paving engineers. Emulsified asphalt full-penetration pavements are becoming more popular as engineers discover that by their use many of the defects previously experienced are automatically eliminated. Smaller stone, which is more easily raked or placed with a "black top" paving machine, can be used; thus the good riding quality of this type equals that of the plant-mix types. This type of paving is usually somewhat less expensive than plant-mix types and is often selected even if there is a mixing plant in the area.

A specification which has proved to be satisfactory for full-penetration macadam is given in Appendix 21.

Prime Coat

In order to assure cohesion between the base course and the binder or surface course a prime coat of bituminous material is applied to the surface of the base course. The material should be of a grade which will penetrate the base course as much as possible and is normally applied in an amount between 0.25 and 0.50 gal per sq yd. An excess amount should be avoided as it tends to flux or fatten the surface course and may cause the finished pavement to bleed. (Refer to Appendix 22.)

Binder Courses

A binder or leveling course is generally used to remove irregularities in the base course. It may be asphaltic concrete or full-penetration macadam. A binder course is not ordinarily used on new pavements where the surface-course thickness is not too thick to allow spreading and compacting in one layer. The bitumen content of binder courses should be somewhat less than that used in the surface course for economy and increased stability.

Many times it becomes necessary to correct the contour of paved runways or construct a new pavement at slightly higher elevations than the existing pavement. It is not good practice to place nonasphalted aggregate over an impervious pavement for a leveling or foundation course and it is very expensive to build up with regular wearing surface material. The C.C.A. has developed a specification No. P-215, September, 1943, in which A.S.T.M. designation D-631 emulsified asphalt is used for mixing with bank gravel or other low cost aggregate. This is a dense graded mix which is suitable for leveling course or foundation course placed over old pavements. This type of mix has also been used extensively for foundation courses on new construction.

Mixing can be done in an ordinary concrete mixer or pugmill type of mixer and no drying or heating equipment is required. The mix is placed and compacted by blading and rolling.

Tack Coat

Wherever a binder course or any two-course bituminous wearing surface is used, a tack coat is recommended to insure a bond between the courses. The minimum amount of bituminous material, usually between 0.10 and 0.25 gal per sq yd, should be applied with a pressure distributor. (Refer to Appendix 23.)

Surface Course

While the surface course provides some bearing power its main function is to provide a waterproof roof over the base courses and to provide a tough, durable wearing surface. It is essential that the surface course be laid so that it possesses good riding qualities.

The surface course may consist of bituminous concrete—hot or cold laid, sand asphalt, sheet asphalt, full-penetration macadam, rock asphalt, or a surface treatment. Any surface course material should be as dense as possible and compacted to the highest practical degree. The material must be stable in order to resist deformation from locked wheel turns and the full application of brakes.

C.A.A. specifications P-401, P-402, P-406, P-407, and P-408 reproduced in Appendices 16, 17, 25, 26, and 27 respectively are considered excellent guides.

Seal Coat

A seal coat is designed to provide waterproofing and may be used to affect changes in the pavement color or texture.

An application of bituminous material, usually rapid-curing cutback asphalt or quick-breaking emulsified asphalt, is applied to the finished surface course at a rate between 0.15 to 0.25 gal per sq yd. Stone chips, sand, or other acceptable aggregate is spread over the bituminous material at the rate of from 7 to 15 lb per sq yd and then rolled and broomed until it is firmly embedded. Surplus aggregate should be broomed off of the pavement as it will damage propellers and airplane surfaces. (Refer to Appendix 28.)

RIGID PAVEMENT CONSTRUCTION DETAILS

Since concrete is the only rigid type of pavement considered in this text all discussion will be limited to this material.

Concrete pavement is considered entirely practical for all airport uses. It is recommended wherever gasoline or oil from aircraft may deteriorate bituminous surfaces. Concrete pavement is considered superior for use wherever locked wheel turns may be anticipated.

C.A.A. Specification P-501 given in Appendix 29 sets forth acceptable standards of materials and workmanship.

Subbase

Subbase under concrete is used to minimize the effect of frost heaving, prevent pumping action, and in some cases to increase the subgrade bearing power.

Granular subbase materials described in specification C.A.A.-689, Appendix 7, have proved satisfactory.

Research studies of concrete pavements in several states have shown that under normal subsurface drainage conditions, unstable subgrades develop with soils having combined silt and clay fractions in excess of 45 per cent of the total material. Under conditions of very poor subsurface drainage where the ground water causes complete saturation, sandy silt soils having fine and poorly graded sand fractions have been found to pump. Pumping has not occurred on soils having combined sand and gravel fractions in excess of 55 per cent of the total material.

Unstable conditions have been prevented by the use of subbases of selected sandy soils or granular materials of 4 to 6 in. compacted thickness. Densely graded materials have been constructed without provision for subsurface drainage and have performed satisfactorily. Open-textured subbases require drainage, and may, depending upon their water-holding capacities, need to be constructed to slightly greater depths than do the densely graded subbases.

Mulch treatments consisting of sand cut into the existing soils have proved satisfactory when good mixes having more than 55 per cent sand have been obtained.

Soil-Cement Subbase

Standard soil-cement remains hard under conditions of wetting and drying and freezing and thawing, and therefore can be used as an improved subgrade and also to prevent pumping on soils normally conducive to pumping. Its use will be more economical than the granular types in some areas. Minimum design thicknesses have not been established for various conditions of traffic on different types of soil but 4 to 6 in. of compacted depth should prove satisfactory.

Test procedures for standard soil-cement construction are given under A.S.T.M. Standards D558–44, D559–44, and D560–44 and in the equivalent A.A.S.H.O. Standards T-134–45, T-135–45, and T-136–45. The cement requirements for soil-cement for the above purposes should be identical with the requirements for standard soil-cement paving. Specifications for construction are the same as for soil-cement.

Emulsified Asphalt-Sand or Soil-Mixtures Subbase

Discussion of emulsified types would be incomplete without mention of this new use of emulsified asphalt mixtures in the paving field. Deterioration of concrete pavement slabs, like other types of surfacing, soon follows increase in moisture content and resultant decrease of support value of its base or foundation. Such moisture accumulates by capillarity from the ground as well as from leakage through poorly sealed joints and unavoidable cracks in the pavement. Excess moisture at the bottom of the slabs tends to expand the lower part of the concrete at the same time that evaporation is contracting the exposed surface, with the result that slabs warp upward at the ends. In the areas adjacent to joints, the base may be so weakened under heavy traffic that water is forced to the pavement surface through expansion openings and contraction cracks, a condition which results in breaks at corners and ends of slabs.

Emulsion-treated sand or soil material is highly resistant to water absorption. A substantial base of treated material beneath concrete pavement arrests upward movement of capillary water from the ground and preserves uniform bearing value. Decided benefit in retarding deterioration of concrete pavement is plainly indicated on sections built on this type of base.

This usage is the subject of a paper contributed by Mr. C. L. McKesson to the 1945 Highway Research Board *Proceedings*, study of which is recommended to all designers of concrete pavement.

Design of Cement Concrete Mix

The design of cement concrete mixes has been the subject of much discussion and study.

For a thorough presentation of the basic principles of producing concrete we recommend a study of this subject as developed by the Portland Cement Association in their publication, "The Design and Control of Concrete Mixtures." Also for a quick approach to a mix design for meeting given conditions of materials the writers consider the treatment of this subject given by Mr. A. T. Goldbeck, Engineering Director and J. E. Gray, Testing Engineer for the National Crushed Stone Association in the January, 1945, issue of the publication, "Stone Briefs," to be very useful. With the permission of the National Crushed Stone Association the article, "How to Proportion Concrete for Pavements," is reproduced in Appendix 31.

Air-Entraining Agents

The use of air-entraining agents either as admixtures or interground with the cement has been proved to increase the durable properties of concrete, particularly its resistance to freezing and thawing and action of deicing salts. Engineers concerned with concretes are advised to keep abreast of developments in this field. It is recommended that the Tentative Specification for Air-Entraining Portland Cement for Concrete Pavements, A.S.T.M. Designation C175-44T be followed.

The writers recommend the use of air-entraining agents particularly in locations where snow and ice removal presents a problem.

Thickened Edges

From a theoretical point of view there is much to be said for thickening the edges of the slabs comprising airport pavements. From a construction point of view this practice has two drawbacks. The shaping of the subgrade for the thickened edge does not lend itself readily to thorough compaction. At the same time the excavation for the thickened edges being the low point in the subgrade may pond any water which reaches the subgrade and unless properly disposed of may result in unstable areas in these locations.

The writers favor a uniform thickness of paving slab in which the depth is comparable in structural strength to the design of cross section for the thickened-edge slab. It is realized that this is a compromise between the theoretical and the practical. The writers, in two instances, found contractors willing to construct a 7-in. uniform pavement at the same price for which they had contracted to construct 8–6–6–8 pavement. In both instances the uniform 7-in. slab required more concrete than the thickened-edge design.

Reinforcement

The writers feel that reinforcement in airport pavement slabs may have application under special conditions. The use of dummy groove contraction joints to control cracking lessens the need for reinforcement.

Dummy Groove Joints

Dummy groove joints are cut into pavement slabs at specified intervals to constitute planes of weakness for control of cracking. The joints are spaced at such intervals that cracks will occur at these locations without intermediate cracking. Forcing the pavement to crack at dummy joints allows easier maintenance of the crack and reduces spalling which might occur at uncontrolled cracks. Dummy groove joints are usually cut a depth equal to one-quarter of the pavement thickness.

Longitudinal Construction Joints

Slab widths are limited by design considerations and also by the width of the concrete spreading and finishing equipment. Twenty-five feet is about the maximum practical width. Widths of 10, 12.5, and 15 ft are quite common.

Longitudinal construction joints are of keyed or plain butt type depending on over-all design.

Transverse Expansion Joints

Transverse expansion joints in concrete pavements are used to allow movement of the slab due to expansion and contraction. These joints should be of such width and spacing as will prevent excessive compressive stresses occurring at times of maximum expansion. Joints ranging in width from 1 in. to $\frac{3}{4}$ in. have proved adequate. Spacing of joints on approximately 100- to 125-ft centers is common practice. Somewhat longer spacings have also proved satisfactory.

Spacing and Design of Joints

Figure 7–6 presents recommendations of the Portland Cement Association as given in their publication entitled "Design Data and Recommended Details for Concrete Airport Pavements," 1942. Figures 7–7a and –7b from the same publication give typical jointing arrangement at intersections.

Load-Transfer Devices

The problem of strengthening slab ends by transfer from one slab to the other has brought forth a number of load-transfer devices. Most commercial types are satisfactory. The care with which they are placed is often more important than the form of the device itself. A simple, yet adequate, dowel is shown on sheet 5 of Appendix 9.

JOINTS

The following are quotations from P.C.A.'s "Concrete Pavement Manual."

It is of paramount importance in joint construction that the joint be installed truly perpendicular to the surface of the pavement. If it is not, the pressure of expansion will cause one slab to slide on the sloping end of the other, making a "high joint." Joints should run straight across the pavement, if they are to look well, and it is important that the filler be continuous from one edge of the slab to the other, for if even a small wedge of concrete spans the joint, spalling or cracking will follow.

Installation

When premolded filler is used, it is held upright by a bulkhead or a metal cap staked in the proper position on the subgrade. Metal bulkheads are better than plank because they are thin and leave only a small cavity along the filler as they are removed, making it easier to get a perpendicular joint. A much used type of metal bulkhead is one which is folded over to form an envelope for the top of the filler, holding it down in spite of the tendency of the concrete to float it. If the bottom half of this bulkhead is notched like a saw, the concrete will come in contact with the filler through these notches and hold it in place when the bulkhead is lifted.

Plank Bulkhead

When a plank bulkhead is removed, a large space is left on one side of the joint filler. The pressure of the concrete on the other side of the filler will force it out of line toward this unsupported side unless the bulkhead is removed slowly, from one end, and the cavity filled as the bulkhead is lifted.

Finishing at Joints

When filler is held in place by a metal cap the filler is of such width that the top of the cap is $\frac{1}{4}$ to $\frac{1}{2}$ in. below the pavement surface. Then the slab is finished right over the joint, as though it were not there, and when all finishing operations have been completed, the concrete over the joint is removed and the edges are rounded. Under no circumstances should concrete be left over the filler, for the pressure of the expanding slab will break out this thin layer and cause spalling.

Continuous from Edge to Edge

To insure continuous expansion space from edge to edge, the filler is one piece of the proper length or shorter pieces fastened securely end to end with clips.

Permanent Seal Joints

Asphaltic joint fillers have never been entirely satisfactory because they are not compressible without extrusion. Instead, they squeeze from the joint, making a bump on the pavement when the joint closes. And they do not expand to fill the joint as the joint opens, thus leaving a space through which water can flow to the subgrade or where dirt can enter and eventually plug the joint. Premolded fillers that do not extrude and that expand considerably after being compressed are on the market.

Concrete in Ends of Joints

Wherever the end of an expansion joint is exposed to view it is inspected and if any concrete bridges the joint it is cleaned away with a chisel.

Expansion Around Structures

A $\frac{1}{2}$-in. expansion joint is provided around all fixed manhole covers, water cut-off boxes or other structures which protrude through the pavement. Some movement of the slab is certain to take place, and, unless allowance is made for it at these rigid structures, the pavement will be cracked. A piece of premolded joint filler, held in place with a strand of wire, is the best.

Joint Fillers

Expansion joints are intended to provide space in which the pavement can expand. To permit such expansion, preformed joint fillers are used.

The function of the filler is to relieve compressive stresses due to expansion. It is therefore highly important that fillers readily compress under expansion and recover under contraction of the pavement. It is equally important that the joint space be completely filled and watertight at all times. An efficient and effective filler for slab movement and a watertight joint is one which will compress 50 per cent of its thickness without extrusion and recover at least 90 per cent of its original thickness.

Joint fillers which do not successfully resist and survive weathering and which do not maintain their full elastic properties permit infiltration of water. This in turn adversely affects the load-bearing value and stability of the subgrade, causes settlement and pumping of the slab ends, and rusting of the load-transfer dowels.

Observation and service records indicate that such types of joint fillers as "preformed cork strips" and "redwood board," meeting Standard Specifications and Tests, more successfully meet all of the requirements for desirable elastic properties and watertight joints than any of the other types.

Equally important is the final sealing of joint openings.

When poorly designed or carelessly constructed, joints in pavements do not function as intended. Poor design and construction, and the use of an improper joint filler permitting infiltration of water, all too frequently result in objectionable joints.

CURING

Proper curing of concrete pavements is essential to the development of maximum strength, the prevention of hair checking, and the increase of watertightness. There are a number of satisfactory curing methods. Several of these are specified in C.A.A. Specification P-501 given in Appendix 29.

STABILIZATION

The stabilization of natural or imported soils by the use of admixtures or binding agents offers unlimited opportunity for constructing satisfactory low-cost subbases, base courses, and completed pavements. This type of construction may prove to be very adaptable to airports where light wheel loadings are expected, and to portions of major terminals receiving only occasional use.

The writers' experience with soil-cement and bituminous stabilization indicates that all instances of unsatisfactory service of stabilized areas have resulted from the use of poor judgment in attempting to stabilize unsuitable soils, from improper design, or poor construction methods rather than any inherent weakness connected with stabilization.

Wherever suitable subgrade and drainage conditions exist, together with a soil which lends itself readily to stabilization, there appears to be ample reason to believe that wheel loads considerably in excess of 15,000 lb can be provided for.

Stabilization can be used as a temporary pavement very satisfactorily and with a minimum amount of money expended for temporary expedients in instances where a shortage of funds or some other reason delays the final pavement construction. In such instances the stabilized soil can be given a light surface treatment or a wearing surface suitable for temporary operations. When final pavement operations are commenced the stabilization can remain in place as excellent subbase material.

In order to have any assurance of the successful use of soil stabilization, the engineer must understand the principles pertaining to the method being considered.

Generally speaking, stabilization of soil is accomplished in one of two ways. The first is to bind together materials such as gravels and sand which have good load-bearing characteristics so that the compacted mass will retain its shape, density, and watertightness. The second method is to lower the plasticity of clays while at the same time waterproofing the material so that changing moisture can not lower its stability.

Binders vary with the material to be stabilized and may consist of bitumen, cement, road oil, chemicals, or clay. Although water is used in conjunction with several of the above binding agents, it may under proper conditions serve as a binding agent by itself.

Thorough mixing with the proper percentage of binder incorporated is mandatory with any method of stabilization. It must be remembered that most materials which are to be stabilized are almost entirely lacking in stability unless the binding agent is present. Inadequate mixing allows pockets of the unstable material to exist in the layer and almost always results in a failure. Pulverization is essential to thorough mixing in nearly all soils. Future stabilization projects will benefit immensely from the thorough job which can be expected from equipment now being manufactured to pulverize and mix the material to the proper depth in one operation.

Soil-Cement

Soil-cement stabilization results in a rigid slab in which no attempt is made to control cracking. Soil-cement consists of properly pulverized native or borrowed soil which, after being thoroughly mixed with the required percentage of Portland cement, is rolled to a high degree of compaction while its moisture content is at or near optimum. Compaction should take place prior to the initial set.

While soil-cement has the appearance, as well as a number of the characteristics of lean-mixed concrete, its internal structure is different except possibly where very granular material is stabilized. The process and results are distinctly different from those achieved with concrete.

Soil-cement is most adversely affected by freezing and thawing. For this reason the freeze-thaw soil-cement test, identified as A.S.T.M. Designation D560–40T, is used to show:

1. Whether there is sufficient cement in the specimen to overcome the expansive force of the water freezing in the voids.
2. Whether there is sufficient cement in the specimen to overcome the formation of ice layers.

The freeze-thaw test is used in conjunction with the wet-dry soil-cement test identified as A.S.T.M. Designation D559–40T.

The above two tests supplemented by moisture-density tests allow an accurate prediction of the suitability of any soil for use in a soil-cement mixture.

The Portland Cement Association has issued two related publications on the subject of soil-cement, both of which are available free upon request in the United States and Canada. These publications, "Soil-Cement Mixtures—Laboratory Handbook" and "Soil-Cement Roads—Construction Handbook" are recommended for study by all engineers concerned with soil stabilization.

The service records of a number of soil-cement projects indicate that this type of construction has a great deal to offer in economical airport development.

Bituminous Stabilization

Bituminous stabilization results in layers of flexible material whose stability relies on the cohesive action of the bitumen to hold interlocked soil particles in place, and the coating of the soil to result in a watertight mixture. The writers do not favor the bituminous stabilization of soils which can not be shown by laboratory test to achieve a high stability and bearing power by the addition of the proper amount of bituminous material. Admixtures of granular material may improve a soil's characteristics to the point where bituminous stabilization is feasible.

The discussion of asphalt emulsion sand mix under "Bituminous Base Courses" is applicable to bituminous stabilization.

Figures 7–9a to c illustrate steps in the process described above.

Chemical Admixtures

Vinsol resin, calcium chloride, and sodium chloride have been used in soil stabilization. These chemicals depend on moisture control or waterproofing to aid in stabilization.

FIELD CONTROL TESTS

Regardless of the type of pavement or stabilization method being employed, the writers have found it to be excellent practice to conduct as many field control tests as possible on the site of the work.

The contractor is generally required to furnish a building suitable for use as a laboratory and to furnish running water, electricity, and heat.

An employed technician and a small amount of laboratory equipment have proved sufficient for most jobs. Bituminous pavements have usually required a contact with a commercial laboratory to perform a number of exacting tests.

The laboratory equipment and the tests to be conducted are governed by the contract specifications. The writers feel that the engineer should be prepared to conduct all of the tests prescribed by the specifications and to be able to do so as often and as readily as may be necessary.

TABLE 7–1. Design Data for Paved Runways (in pounds) (Courtesy C.A.A.)

Recommended Standards	Class I	Class II	Class III	Class IV and above
Static design loads for runway, taxiway, and apron paving based on present day aircraft. Load considered distributed equally between two main wheels or sets of wheels	No paving recommended	30,000	74,000	120,000
Probable future (10 years) maximum static gross loads to be considered in the design of runway, taxiway, and apron paving and drainage structures	20,000	60,000	150,000	300,000
Probable range of static airplane tire pressures	10 to 25 per sq. in.	15 to 50 per sq. in.	30 to 75 per sq. in.	50 to 85 per sq. in.

NOTE: Practical experience indicates any designs adequately supporting maximum static load will be sufficient.

TABLE 7–2. Total Combined Thickness of Subbase, Base Course, and Surface Course for Flexible Pavements (Courtesy P.R.A.)

Class of Soil	Wheel Load			
	10,000 pounds	25,000 pounds	40,000 pounds	80,000 pounds
	Inches	Inches	Inches	Inches
A–1	0– 6	3– 6	3– 9	4–12
A–2 friable	0– 6	3– 6	3– 9	4–12
A–2 plastic	2– 8	4–10	6–12	8–15
A–3	4– 6	5– 8	6– 9	8–12
A–4	9–18	15–25	18–30	24–36
A–5	9–24	15–30	18–36	24–48
A–6	12–24	18–30	24–36	30–54
A–7	12–24	18–30	24–36	30–54

TABLE 7–3. Estimated Minimum Thicknesses for Concrete Runway Pavements (Courtesy P.R.A.)

Static Wheel Load	Minimum Slab Thickness	
	Excellent subgrade support	Inferior subgrade support
Pounds	Inches	Inches
10,000	6	7
25,000	8	9
40,000	10	11
80,000	12	14

TABLE 7–4. Cut-Back Asphalts

Principal Uses of Materials Meeting New Specifications (Courtesy Asphalt Institute)

SPECIFICATION	RC RAPID CURING						MC MEDIUM CURING					
GRADES	0	1	2	3	4	5	0	1	2	3	4	5
Priming												
Tightly bonded surfaces							x					
Loosely bonded fine grained surfaces								x				
Loosely bonded coarse grained surfaces									x			
Seal and Carpet Coats												
With or without light sand cover	x											
Coarse sand cover		x							x	x		
Clean $\frac{1}{4}''$ aggregate cover			x									
Clean $\frac{1}{2}''$ aggregate cover				x								
Clean $\frac{5}{8}''$ aggregate cover					x							
Clean $\frac{3}{4}''$ aggregate cover						x					x	x
Graded gravel aggregate cover									x	x		
Gravel mulch									x			
Road Mix												
Open graded aggregate												
Sand		x	x							x		
Max. dia. 1″, high % pass. 10 mesh										x	x	
Macadam aggregate			x	x								
Dense graded aggregate												
High % pass. 200 mesh									x			
Max. dia. 1″, med. pass. 200 mesh									x	x		
Cold Patch												
Open graded aggregate			x							x		
Dense graded aggregate									x			
Cold Laid Plant Mix												
Open graded aggregate												
Sand			x	x								
Max. dia. 1″, high % pass. 10 mesh				x								
Macadam aggregate					x	x						
Dense graded aggregate												
High % pass. 200 mesh										x	x	
Max. dia. 1″, med. % pass. 200 mesh											x	x
Primer to be followed with soft A.C.							x					
Penetration Macadam (cold weather)						x						

TABLE 7–5. New Specifications for Type RC Materials (adopted December 13, 1939). (Courtesy Asphalt Institute)

Specification Designation	RC–0	RC–1	RC–2	RC–3	RC–4	RC–5
General Requirement	The material shall be free from water and shall meet the following requirements when tested in accordance with the methods hereinafter enumerated.					
Flash point (open tag.) ° F.	—	—	80+	80+	80+	80+
Furol viscosity at 77° F.	75–150	—	—	—	—	—
" " " 122° F.	—	75–150	—	—	—	—
" " " 140° F.	—	—	100–200	250–500	—	—
" " " 180° F.	—	—	—	—	125–250	300–600
Distillation						
Distillate (per cent of total distillate to 680° F.)						
To 374° F.	15+	10+	—	—	—	—
" 437° F.	55+	50+	40+	25+	8+	—
" 500° F.	75+	70+	65+	55+	40+	25+
" 600° F.	90+	88+	87+	83+	80+	70+
Residue from distillation to 680° F.						
Volume per cent by difference	50+	60+	67+	73+	78+	82+
Tests on residue from distillation						
Penetration 77° F., 100 g., 5 sec.	80–120	80–120	80–120	80–120	180–120	80–120
Ductility 77° F.	100+	100+	100+	100+	100+	100+
Per cent soluble in carbon tetrachloride	99.5+	99.5+	99.5+	99.5+	99.5+	99.5+

TABLE 7–6. New Specifications for Type MC Materials (adopted December 13, 1939). (Courtesy Asphalt Institute)

Specification Designation	MC–0	MC–1	MC–2	MC–3	MC–4	MC–5
General Requirement	The material shall be free from water and shall meet the following requirements when tested in accordance with the methods hereinafter enumerated.					
Flash point (open tag.) ° F.	100+	100+	150+	150+	150+	150+
Furol viscosity at 77° F.	75–150	—	—	—	—	—
" " " 122° F.	—	75–150	—	—	—	—
" " " 140° F.	—	—	100–200	250–500	—	—
" " " 180° F.	—	—	—	—	125–250	300–600
Distillation						
Distillate (per cent of total distillate to 680° F.)						
To 437° F.	25 –	20 –	10 –	5 –	0	0
" 500° F.	40–70	25–65	15–55	5–40	30 –	20 –
" 600° F.	75–93	70–90	60–87	55–85	40–80	20–75
Residue from distillation to 680° F.						
Volume per cent, by difference	50+	60+	67+	73+	78+	82+
Tests on residue from distillation						
Penetration 77° F., 100 g., 5 sec.	120–300	120–300	120–300	120–300	120–300	120–300
Ductility 77° F.[a]	100+	100+	100+	100+	100+	100+
Per cent soluble in carbon tetrachloride	99.5+	99.5+	99.5+	99.5+	99.5+	99.5+.

[a] NOTE: If penetration of residue is more than 200 and its ductility at 77° F. is less than 100, the material will be acceptable if its ductility at 60° F. is 100+.

TABLE 7–7. New Specifications for Type SC Materials (adopted May 14, 1940). (Courtesy Asphalt Institute)

Specification Designation	SC–0	SC–1	SC–2	SC–3	SC–4	SC–5
General Requirement	The material shall meet the following requirements when tested in accordance with the methods hereinafter enumerated.					
Furol viscosity at 77° F.	75–150	—	—	—	—	—
" " " 122° F.	—	75–150	—	—	—	—
" " " 140° F.	—	—	100–200	250–500	—	—
" " " 180° F.	—	—	—	—	125–250	300–600
Water, per cent	0.5 –	0.5 –	Material shall be free from water.			
Flash, Cleveland open cup, ° F.	150+	150+	175+	200+	225+	250+
Distillation						
Total distillate to 680° F.	15–40	10–30	5–25	2–15	10 –	5 –
Float test on residue at 122° F., sec.	15–100	20–100	25–100	50–125	60–150	75–200
Asphalt residue of 100 penetration %	40+	50+	60+	70+	75+	80+
Ductility asphalt residue at 77° F.	100+	100+	100+	100+	100+	100+
Per cent soluble in carbon tetrachloride [a]	99.5+	99.5+	99.5+	99.5+	99.5+	99.5+

[a] NOTE: If the material fails to meet the requirement for solubility it will be acceptable if its solubility in carbon disulphide is 99%+, and proportion of bitumen soluble in carbon tetrachloride is 99.65%+.

TABLE 7–8. Specifications for Emulsified Asphalts (adopted September 11, 1940). (Courtesy Asphalt Institute)

	Rapid Setting	Medium Setting			Slow Setting	
Specification Designation	RS–1	MS–1	MS–2	MS–3	SS–1	SS–2
Tests on emulsion						
Viscosity, furol @ 77° F., sec.	20–100	20–100	100+	—	20–100	20–100
Residue by distillation	55+	55+	60+	65+	55+	55+
Settlement, 5 days	−3	−5	−5	—	−3	−3
Demulsibility						
(a) 35 c.c. N/50 $CaCl_2$	60+	—	—	—	—	—
(b) 50 c.c. N/10 $CaCl_2$	—	−30	−30	—	1.0−	1.0−
Sieve test—ret. on 20 mesh	−0.10	−0.10	−0.10	−0.10	−0.10	−0.10
Miscibility, 2 hrs.	—	Pass	Pass	Pass	Pass	Pass
Stone coating (3 min.)	—	Pass	Pass	Pass	—	—
Cement mixing, % max.	—	—	—	—	2.0−	2.0−
Tests on residue						
Penetration @ 77° F., 100 g., 5 sec.	100–200	100–200	100–200	100–200	100–200	40–90
Soluble in CS_2 (pet. asphalt) %	97.5+	97.5+	95.7+	97.5+	97.5+	97.5+
Soluble in CS_2 (nat. asphalt) %	95.0+	95.0+	95.0+	95.0+	95.0+	95.0+
Ash	−2.0	−2.0	−2.0	−2.0	−2.0	−2.0
Ductility @ 77° F., cm.	40+	40+	40+	40+	40+	40+

TABLE 7–9.

Grade	Engler Specific Viscosity		Float Test		Specific Gravity at 25° C./25° C. not less than—	Total Bitumen, per cent by Weight not less than—	Water, per cent by Volume, not more than—	Distillation Per Cent by Weight					Softening Point of Distillation Residue, ° C.
	at 40° C.	at 50° C.	at 32° C.	at 50° C.				To 170° C.	To 200° C. not less than—	To 235° C.	To 270° C. not more than—	To 300° C. not more than—	
RT–1	5–8	......	......	......	1.08	88	2.0	0.0–7.0	......	......	35.0	45.0	35–60
RT–2	8–13	......	......	......	1.08	88	2.0	0.0–7.0	......	......	35.0	45.0	35–60
RT–3	13–22	......	......	......	1.09	88	2.0	0.0–7.0	......	......	30.0	40.0	35–60
RT–4	22–35	......	......	......	1.09	88	2.0	0.0–5.0	......	......	30.0	40.0	35–60
RT–5	......	17–26	......	......	1.10	83	1.5	0.0–5.0	......	......	25.0	35.0	35–65
RT–6	......	26–40	......	......	1.10	83	1.5	0.0–5.0	......	......	25.0	35.0	35–65
RT–7	......	......	50–80	......	1.12	78	1.0	0.0–3.0	......	......	20.0	30.0	35–65
RT–8	......	......	80–120	......	1.14	78	0	0.0–1.0	......	......	15.0	25.0	35–65
RT–9	......	......	120–200	......	1.14	78	0	0.0–1.0	......	......	15.0	25.0	35–65
RT–10	......	......	......	75–100	1.15	75	0	0.0–1.0	......	......	10.0	20.0	40–70
RT–11	......	......	......	100–150	1.16	75	0	0.0–1.0	......	......	10.0	20.0	40–70
RT–12	......	......	......	150–220	1.16	75	0	0.0–1.0	......	......	10.0	20.0	40–70
RTCB–5	......	17–26	......	......	1.09	80	1.0	2.0–8.0	5.0	8.0–18.0	......	35.0	40–70
RTCB–6	......	26–40	......	......	1.09	80	1.0	2.0–8.0	5.0	8.0–18.0	......	35.0	40–70

TABLE 7–10

Grade	Typical Uses	Suggested Temperature for Application
RT–1........	Prime coat..	60°–125° F.
RT–2........	....do..	60°–125° F.
RT–3........	Prime coat and surface treatment................	80°–150° F.
RT–4........	....do..	80°–150° F.
RT–5........	Surface treatment and road mix..................	80°–150° F.
RT–6........	....do..	80°–150° F.
RT–7........	Surface treatment road mix, premix and seal coat...	150°–225° F.
RT–8........	....do..	150°–225° F.
RT–9........	....do..	150°–225° F.
RT–10.......	Surface treatment premix, seal coat, penetration and crack filler.	175°–250° F.
RT–11.......	....do..	175°–250° F.
RT–12.......	....do..	175°–250° F.
RTCB–5......	Surface treatment road mix and premix when low temperature application and quick setting are desired.	60°–120° F.
RTCB–6......	....do..	60°–120° F.

CHAPTER VIII

TURF

PURPOSE

Beautification

It has been stated that buildings govern the impression an airport makes on its visitors. Turf areas and landscaping also affect the visitors' impression to a large extent. People react in the same manner to unsightly weeds, bare spots, and brush at an airport as they do when the same conditions exist around homes or public buildings. The beautification afforded by a well developed turf together with proper landscaping usually pays dividends by making the airport one of the local show places.

Many municipalities have, in connection with airport development, planned recreational areas with the intent of making the airport a center of outdoor community interest. In such cases landscaping is of first importance.

Landing Surface

Turf is an excellent surface for airports devoted to light-plane operation. Even on airports having paved runways it is common practice for light planes to use turfed areas in preference to the pavement. Turf will stand up well under the operation of relatively large planes when the subgrade is firm and the turf well established.

Erosion

The control of erosion in all unpaved areas is extremely important, and references to the serious conditions caused by erosion have been made in previous chapters. A well-established turf will practically stop erosion and reduce graded-areas maintenance costs to a minimum.

Dust Control

Blowing dust and sand constitutes a serious hazard to aircraft operation. Dust can hide runways and landing areas from approaching aircraft and can reduce visibility to zero for pilots of aircraft taxiing on the airport. Dust also causes building maintenance to become a major problem. A good turf reduces dust to a minimum.

Blowing dust and sand is most undesirable as far as human comfort is concerned. Dust in the air causes inflammation of the nose and eyes, contaminates food, and makes it difficult for people to keep a fresh, clean appearance. A spectator or employee caught in a propeller blast suffers enough without being subjected to a miniature dust storm at the same time.

Airplane propellers and surfaces are easily damaged by sand and stones picked up in the propeller blast. Drawing dust into the motor through the air intake or getting it into exposed bearings accelerates wear. The smooth finish of plane surfaces is dulled by the abrasive action of dust and sand, thereby decreasing speed.

TYPES OF TURF

Temporary Grasses

Temporary grasses or grain crops are often used because of their quick growth. Lespedeza, oats, rye, or wheat can be used. These crops provide quick cover thereby retarding erosion until permanent grasses can take hold. Crops adaptable to local conditions give the best results. The seasonal characteristics of temporary grasses must be given consideration or otherwise the area may be bare during a critical period.

As most temporary grasses grow to a greater height than is desirable, they must be cut prior to maturity. Care must be taken to see that temporary grasses do not shade or smother permanent grasses and cause them to die out.

Permanent Grasses

Permanent grasses are those which grow from a root system, retaining life throughout the entire year. They have a long life. Blue grass, Bermuda grass, bents, and fesques are permanent grasses.

The root system of permanent grasses has the qualities desired for supporting wheel loads and preventing erosion.

Permanent grasses are usually difficult to grow and require considerable study in order that the proper grasses for the locality may be chosen.

It may prove desirable to use one type of grass in the building area, another type in shoulder areas, and still another type for slopes. On slopes there is no objection to grasses which grow to considerable height, while in building areas where a lawn effect is desired, low-growing grasses are required.

There are so many factors to be taken into account when planning turf that the engineer will do well to obtain the services of an agronomist. It should be borne in mind, however, that shoulder areas and slopes do not need the type of turf found on golf-course fairways or lawns. A growth similar to good pasture land is satisfactory. Good turfs can not be acquired in a short time without the expenditure of large sums of money for materials, watering, and maintenance. If erosion and dust can be controlled in the meantime, there is usually no objection to waiting 2 or 3 yr for turf to reach a high state of development.

It is to be remembered that, in general, very little maintenance is performed on airport turf because of the expense attendant upon mowing, watering, refertilizing, and reseeding. The result is that the establishment of vegetation common to the vicinity is essential because it will be more likely to survive. A great deal of money has been spent in seeding some airports only to find after a relatively short time that none of the grasses planted are growing, but that the existing vegetation in such cases is entirely volunteer growth which would have been obtained with no seeding whatsoever.

FACTORS AFFECTING TURF

Rainfall

Rainfall must be taken into account when the grasses are chosen. It is useless to plant a type of grass which requires more moisture than can reasonably be expected in the locality under consideration, whereas other grasses may suffer from too much moisture.

Rainfall is the one indispensable factor in securing turf. With ample moisture grasses can be grown in the most barren soil, but without moisture a turf is impossible. Rainfall at the proper time after grasses are planted is very essential because without moisture the seed will not germinate or thrive after germination.

Soil Characteristics

The density of a stand of grass depends on the amount of plant nourishment available in the soil. Acidity also affects the growth of many types of grasses. Most of them grow best in a neutral or slightly alkaline soil.

The physical characteristics of the soil, such as its permeability, density, grain size, rock content, and resistance to erosion affect grass growth. The more nearly a soil approaches a sandy loam, the better are its turfing possibilities.

Farmers very often build up a poor soil by crop rotation, terracing, mulching, and fertilizing over a period of years. This building-up process can not be carried out on an airport as shoulder areas are extremely hazardous when soft from plowing, disking, or such farming operations. The engineer must take all the necessary steps to improve the airport's soil characteristics before turfing operations are started. Various methods of improving soil characteristics are discussed later in this chapter.

Crop Value

Developing a turf is an expensive operation under the best of circumstances, so all possibilities of realizing any revenue from the turf should be exploited. There are many possibilities, depending on local conditions, and the engineer should carefully look into each one to determine which will prove most profitable. The advice of the county farm agent as well as that of successful farmers should always be solicited.

Grasses which reach a height in excess of about 12 in. are hazardous to small-plane operation. However the C.A.A. in its operation of intermediate landing fields has found that many types of turf furnish valuable hay crops without reaching such a hazardous height. Some grasses, such as blue grass, if free from an appreciable percentage of other vegetation are valuable for a seed crop.

Crop Damage

Certain grasses, such as Bermuda grass, have highly desirable characteristics for airport use but come in the weed classification as far as farming is concerned. Such grasses spread rapidly and are very difficult for a farmer to exterminate. It is advised that the county farm agent be consulted before any such grasses are imported into a locality where they might become a problem to near-by farms.

Bettering Soil Conditions

Various clovers and other vegetation introduce nitrogen into the soil with the result that the soil fertility is improved. White clover has been found particularly adaptable for starting turf as it catches quite easily in an alkaline soil and has good turf characteristics.

Planting soil-improving vegetation along with other grasses is wise because the desirable permanent grasses usually crowd out such vegetation as soon as the soil reaches a sufficiently high state of fertility. Most of this type of vegetation requires reseeding frequently, owing to its annual characteristics.

SOIL IMPROVEMENT

Tests

The soil tests described in Chapter IV will reveal the elements which are lacking in the soil, as well as its acidity. The engineer must then decide upon the extent of soil improvement necessary to secure an acceptable turf within a reasonable period of time. Where improvement is indicated it can be accomplished in several ways.

Topsoiling

Topsoiling can be accomplished with material which has been stripped and stock-piled prior to grading operations, or with material imported from outside sources. Stock-piling site material is usually the least expensive, but should be done only if site material has good grass-growing qualities, as determined by soils tests. If there is very little difference between the topsoil and the parent material, it will probably be more satisfactory to build up the parent material by selective grading, fertilizing, and liming.

Topsoiling is nearly always desirable, if suitable material is economically available, because poor turf can be expected where grasses are planted in clays, sands, or disintegrated rock obtained from excavation.

A minimum depth of 6 in. of topsoil is desirable, but this depth may be so expensive that a lesser amount must be used. Two inches is the minimum practical depth which can be spread. Because of the large acreage involved in airports the cubic yardage of topsoil becomes very high even for a small depth.

Fertilizing

Fertilizers consist of manures, chemical compounds, animal refuse, activated sludge, and other agents containing nitrogen, phosphates, and potash. Each type has its advantages and disadvantages, depending on the cost and the soil in which it is to be used. It is wise to investigate local farming practice before choosing the fertilizer and deciding on the amount to be used.

Many types of fertilizer are almost entirely dissipated at the end of one season. These should be considered as starters and not as cure-alls for a poor soil condition. In very pervious soils, fertilizer often leaches into the subgrade quite rapidly and is entirely wasted. Excessive use of some types of commercial fertilizer tends to burn out the grasses. However, the use of sufficient fertilizer to insure the grasses a good start is advocated. If the engineer will remember that securing a turf is essentially a farming operation, hampered only by the restrictions safe aircraft operations impose, his judgment in the use of fertilizer should be good.

The highest per cent of organic nitrogen obtainable in fertilizers should be used. Manures, sludges, and forms of fertilizer designed to prolong the benefits of the ingredients over the longest possible period of time should be favored.

Liming

Lime is available in two forms: ground limestone and hydrated lime.

Ground limestone has some effect immediately and is absorbed into the soil gradually. It is effective over a long period of time. Its use is recommended wherever it is economically available.

Hydrated lime can be applied in a lesser amount per acre because it is effective immediately. Because of its chemical composition and its fine grain size, hydrated lime is incorporated into the soil rapidly, neutralizing the acid until either the acid or the lime is completely expended. Any hydrated lime, over and above that necessary to neutralize the acid, rapidly leaches out of the soil.

Mulching

Any material used for mulch is usually in a half-rotten or overripe state. Manure, leaves, straw, hay, grass cuttings, stalks, and like materials that will decay and be readily assimilated into the soil with beneficial results, either as to fertility or workability, make desirable mulch. Mulching is excellent to improve the characteristics of heavy pervious soils, particularly of parent material.

Mulching is advisable even after grasses have sprouted. It is recommended for use in maintenance during the second and succeeding years of the grasses' life. In general, mulching is necessary on slopes where the use of equipment to drill or cover the seed is impossible and where seed is frequently lost by washing down the slopes during rainstorms.

PLANTING

Season

In most localities planting should be done in the early spring or early fall. Early spring seeding has the disadvantage of usually being performed when the ground surface is soft, and therefore easily rutted by planting equipment. When spring seeding is delayed until ground surface conditions are suitable, it is often too late to take full advantage of the growing season. Sowing grass seed on top of a late snow, allowing the seed to settle to the ground as the snow melts, has produced excellent results. Where seeding on snow is done, the ground surface must have been placed in proper condition prior to the snowfall. Leveling and smoothing operations can not be performed after the seeding is accomplished. One disadvantage of spring seeding is that weeds will develop more readily, retarding the growth of the desired grasses.

Fall seeding is advisable even if it must be done later than is generally accepted as safe practice. Seed which is planted early enough in the fall to germinate and get a fair growth before heavy frosts occur is ready to assume growth with the first warm spring weather. Grasses having such a start are usually mature enough to easily weather the hot, dry, summer season.

Sometimes grading, paving, or drainage construction is in full swing right up until the time winter halts operations. The completion of these items in many instances amounts to a race against the time when winter sets in. Careful planning, however, of the time of contract award, notice to proceed, time of performance, and scheduling of activities will often make fall seeding possible. Should severe weather occur prior to germination the seed may lie dormant over the winter and sprout in the spring. If definite killing conditions occur, the damage can be overcome by snow seeding or broadcast seeding in the spring without disturbing the surface other than by possibly a light harrowing. Fewer weeds will develop in fall seeding as most weeds die during the winter.

Rate of Application

The proper rate of application of grass seed to produce a satisfactory airport turf is the subject of considerable controversy. Forty pounds per acre for seeds of average fineness should be the minimum. One hundred and twenty-five pounds is usually the maximum. Since the actual cost of the seed itself is a small portion of the total cost of securing a turf, the writers favor a generous rate of application.

The usual practice is first to determine the seed formula; that is, the various seeds which are to be sown and the percentage of each to be used in the mixture. Some seeds are extremely small while others are quite bulky. If the formula contains mostly fine seed, the required number of plants can be secured by a lower rate of application than is possible if a considerable amount of bulky seed is used.

Seed Formula

Choosing the seed formula is seldom given sufficient thought or study. The grasses included should each have a definite purpose. One or more grasses should be a quick-growing variety to provide cover while the slower-growing grasses are taking hold. These grasses may well be temporary, but should not be planted thick enough to smother the more desirable grasses.

Some of the grasses may be seasonal as far as their desirable characteristics are concerned. If this is the case, enough varieties should be included so that proper cover is maintained throughout the year. One type of grass, such as timothy, may grow in bunches. If possible, other grasses should be grown which will fill in between the bunches.

At major terminals the operation of planes on the shoulder areas will be prohibited. Grasses which will prevent water or wind erosion will therefore be sufficient in such places.

At airports where small planes are to operate without paved runways, the expenditure of a considerable sum for turfing is warranted. The seed formula should be designed to secure a turf with a thick, wear-resistant root system.

The engineer should study the characteristics of the various grasses carefully before including them in a seed formula. The seed formula should represent long-range planning so that the ultimate turf has the highest possible percentage of desirable characteristics.

CONSTRUCTION METHODS

Topsoiling

Good topsoil must be a friable, natural loam possessing ingredients conducive to the growth of the type of turf desired. It must be free from objects which make it difficult to till or which could cause damage to airplane tires.

Topsoil should be placed only after all other grading has been completed and the ground surface smoothed to meet acceptable standards. The surface of the ground on which topsoil is placed should be loosened by disking or scarifying in order that the two soils may bond together readily. Very satisfactory results have been obtained by tilling the soil, immediately after topsoil is placed, to such a depth that the two soils are thoroughly mixed in about equal proportions. Topsoiling operations always precede the preparation of the seedbed.

Topsoil can be paid for in several different ways. One method is to measure and pay for topsoil on the basis of the truck measurement of material removed, placed, and spread. Another method is to measure the material by cross-sectioning the cut from which it was removed and computing the volume by the average-end-area method. In many instances it proves most practical to measure the work by the number of acres over which topsoil has been spread a designated thickness in accordance with the specification.

Seedbed

A seedbed should never be prepared until the area is cleared of all brush, trash, or heavy growths of vegetation which can interfere with pulverizing the soil or interfere with planting operations. Seedbeds should be prepared when the soil does not contain either an excess or deficiency of moisture, as otherwise it will be impossible to properly pulverize the soil.

The depth of the seedbed will vary with the seeding or planting operations which are to follow. Since soft shoulders are extremely hazardous to aircraft, the seedbed depth must be kept at a minimum. Four inches is the maximum depth recommended.

Any type of equipment that will loosen and pulverize the soil to the desired depth will prove satisfactory. The operations must be conducted so as not to leave dead furrows, ruts, or bumps in the area. All undesirable objects encountered, such as oversized stones, roots, and trash, should be picked up and removed during the preparation of the seedbed.

Preparation of the seedbed is generally paid for on the basis of the number of acres satisfactorily prepared.

Fertilizing and/or Liming

Any method by which fertilizer or lime can be spread at a uniform predetermined rate over the prescribed area is acceptable, provided the method does not disturb the ground surface excessively. Grain drills, or special spreading equipment are ordinarily used. Fertilizer and lime can be spread simultaneously or as independent operations.

In order to prevent the fertilizer from being blown or washed away, and to distribute it throughout the seedbed, the area over which it is spread should be immediately disked or harrowed to a moderate depth.

Fertilizer and lime are almost always measured and paid for on the basis of the number of tons delivered and spread.

Mulching

Mulch may be incorporated into the soil during the preparation of the seedbed or may be spread after the seedbed is prepared. Mulch is usually a light material and therefore must be anchored to prevent its being blown about by wind or washed away by rain. Local practice should be used as a guide in mulching operations. A manure spreader or any equipment with which the mulch can be uniformly spread will prove acceptable.

Mulch can be paid for by the ton, truck measurement, or by the number of acres covered.

Seeding

Specifications must require seed to be sown on an acceptable seedbed at the proper time of the year, with suitable equipment and under atmospheric conditions that will insure even distribution. By the use of proper equipment, lime, fertilizer, and seed may be spread simultaneously.

The results of a good job of seed distribution can be partially spoiled by wind blowing the seed away or birds eating the seed. It is necessary therefore to cover the seed. A light harrowing followed by rolling with a cultipacker, roller, or similar equipment covers the seed, reduces the voids to a minimum, and tends to reduce wind and water erosion. The tracks or indentations left by the compacting equipment should always be at right angles to the direction of slope of the ground surface. Compacting the surface must be avoided in some types of clay soils as they tend to bake to a concrete-like density.

Seeding can be paid for in a number of ways. If the extent or number of operations is expected to vary, it is advisable to measure and pay for each operation separately. If there is no doubt as to the process to be used or the quantity of lime, fertilizer, or seed required, a price per acre or a job price may prove advantageous. In any event the method of measurement and payment must be specific.

Sprigging

Sprigging consists of removing living plants, such as beach grass or Bermuda grass, from their original location, separating them into sprigs, and planting them on a prepared seedbed.

Sprigs should be obtained from a source where the plant grows and thrives naturally. Sprigs should be plants which have attained full growth, represent a healthy variety of the plant, and have a complete root system attached. There should be a minimum amount of soil adhering to the root system. The sprigs should be free from deleterious weeds.

Sprigs may be removed from their place of natural growth by any means which does not damage the plant or its root system. If the plants have excessive height, the area should be mowed and raked prior to the removal of the plants.

During the period which intervenes between the plant's removal and its being replanted, extreme care must be taken to keep it in a healthy and viable condition. The length of time which can transpire between removal and replanting will vary according to the plant being handled. Almost all plants require moisture and protection from excessive heat during this period.

Good results can be expected from sprigging only when this operation is performed during the right season and under conditions favorable to the growth of the plant.

Sprigs may be broadcast or planted. Where sprigs are broadcast, by hand or by a spreader, they must be covered. This can be done by hand tools or by disking.

When sprigs are planted they may be placed by hand or planting machines. Furrows are often opened a specified distance apart and the sprigs placed in the furrow. After the sprigs are placed in the furrow, the furrows are filled in so as to properly cover the plant and maintain a smooth surface. Furrows should never remain open long enough to allow the soil to dry out.

A cultipacker or similar rolling equipment should be used to compact the soil immediately after the sprigging is completed.

Sprigging can best be measured and paid for on the basis of the number of acres sprigged.

Sodding

Sodding is the operation of removing a satisfactory turf from one location and transplanting it carpet-fashion in the desired location. The thickness of the sod is governed by the amount of the plant's root system which must be transplanted to insure continued growth. It is usually desirable to mow the turf prior to its being removed. Sod is usually removed by a machine which loosens and rolls up a strip of uniform width and thickness. Sod must always be placed on a prepared seedbed.

Successful sodding depends on the maintenance of the sod in a moist condition, protected from air and sun, during the period intervening between cutting and placing, and the placing of the sod on a seedbed which simulates as nearly as possible the bed on which the sod grew naturally. Watering during the early stages is essential to sod growth unless rains occur at proper intervals to keep the sod moist. It is also essential that the sod roots be protected from exposure to the air by filling all cracks with finely pulverized earth and by thoroughly tamping and rolling the sod so that it is joined to the seedbed. It may be necessary to use wooden pegs to hold sod in place on slopes.

Sod can best be paid for by the square foot or square yard of sod properly placed and maintained until growth is assured.

Watering

It can be realized that the preparation of a seedbed, spreading lime and fertilizer, and the actual sowing of seed or planting of turf are quite expensive. This expense may produce no turf if moisture is not available to germinate the seed or nurture the plant.

Watering large areas is also expensive but is often necessary. Watering can be done by gravity or pressure distributors. Care must be taken to secure a uniform application of water without erosion caused by excessive quantities, or excessive rutting of the surface by the distributor wheels.

Water can best be measured and paid for on the basis of 1000-gal units of water applied in a satisfactory manner.

Appendix 30 is a practical airport turfing specification which has been used by the writers with success on several airport contracts. Section 3.9 of appendix 4 contains specifications for placing sod.

CHAPTER IX

OBSTRUCTIONS

OBSTRUCTION DEFINED

An obstruction is any structure, growth, or other object existing in the vicinity of an airport which is of such elevation that it presents a potential hazard to aircraft operations. Common obstructions are buildings, trees, pole lines, smokestacks, tanks, hills, radio towers, and bridges. They may occur singly or in groups. Not all obstructions which may constitute a potential hazard will prove an actual hazard after a study is made of the aeronautical problems involved. Obstructions should be removed whenever possible.

POINTS OF VIEW

An existing obstruction or construction which may create a hazard can be considered from three points of view.

The most common point of view is that which determines the relation the obstruction has to the usefulness of a landing strip for contact flight operations.

A second point of view is that which determines whether obstruction lighting for night operations is required. As might be expected, standards for determining actual hazard are more rigid for night operations. These standards are discussed in Chapter X on Lighting.

The third point of view applies only to new construction and has no bearing on existing obstructions. In an effort to control to some extent the erection of structures and the like which constitute an actual hazard, Section 1101 of the Civil Aeronautics Act of 1938, as amended, granted the Administrator certain authority. The applicable regulations are discussed later in this chapter.

APPROACH ZONES

It has been stated in Chapter I that the basic element of an airport is the landing strip and its two approaches. The strip and its approaches are inseparable, with the quality of the approach directly affecting the usefulness and safety of the landing strip.

Approaches are judged solely on the extent of their freedom from obstructions. An obstruction affects the usefulness of a runway, first, by its location laterally with reference to the center line of the strip, secondly, by its height above the landing strip, and thirdly, by the distance existing between the obstruction and the end of the strip.

Experience has provided a basis for determining the zone through which an aircraft may reasonably be expected to pass in a take-off or landing operation. Under contact conditions this zone is generally accepted to be a trapezoid 500 ft wide at the end of the landing strip and widening to 2500 ft at a distance of 2 miles. Instrument-runway approach zones should be taken as 1000 ft wide at the end of the landing strip, widening to 4000 ft at a distance of 2 miles.

OBSTRUCTION RATIO

Experience and airplane operating characteristics must be relied on to determine the height at which an obstruction any given distance from the end of the landing strip becomes hazardous. It is most convenient to express this as an obstruction ratio. It is also spoken of as the glide angle. An obstruction ratio, or glide angle, is the ratio of the difference in elevation between the top of the obstruction and the elevation of the nearest point on the landing strip, to the distance from the obstruction to that same point on the landing strip. As an example, an obstruction 40 ft higher than the nearest point on the landing strip, located 1200 ft distant from the landing strip, has an obstruction ratio of 40 on 1200 or 1 on 30. It would also be correct to express this as a 30 to 1 glide angle. It must be remembered that the difference in elevation is used rather than the height of the obstruction above the ground where it is located.

TURNING ZONES

The zones between the approach zones are termed turning zones over which approach or take-off of aircraft are clearly impractical operations. Obstructions in these zones are not of as great concern as those in the approach zones.

APPROACH STANDARDS

The C.A.A. has set up tentative approach standards for each class of airport. These approach standards are primarily to indicate obstructions which should be removed, or to establish limits for heights of structures proposed. These tentative standards must not be confused with airport lighting standards, or the standards governing public notice which are required by the Civil Aeronautics Act of 1938, as amended, with respect to construction or alteration of structures along or near civil airways. Table 9–1 sets forth these standards.

CIVIL AERONAUTICS ACT OF 1938

Pursuant to the intent of Section 1101 of the Civil Aeronautics Act of 1938, as amended, the Administrator effected Part 525 of the Civil Air Regulations, with respect to the construction or alteration of structures along or near civil airways. Any person who fails to comply with the requirements of this regulation is liable to a penalty of $500 imposed by Section 902 (a) of the Civil Aeronautics Act of 1938, as amended.

The Administrator caused to be published an "Obstruction Marking Manual," dated August 1, 1943. This manual is recommended for study as it sets forth in detail the regulations and standards pertaining to Part 525 of C.A.R. Page 3 of this manual is quoted herewith:

> The intent of Regulations of the Administrator of Civil Aeronautics, Part 525, is to require any person, before engaging in the construction or alteration of a structure covered by the regulation, to give adequate notice of intention to do so in order that pilots of aircraft can be informed of such work and thereby further insure safety in air commerce. Although the regulation has been prepared in a simple and understandable form, it is appropriate to explain in detail some conditions which might be open to question. To this end, the following explanatory information is provided.
>
> The scope of this regulation extends 20 miles beyond the limits of a civil airway. As the width of a civil airway is 10 miles, it follows that the prescribed area may also be described as extending for 25 miles on either side of the center line of such an airway. It will be found that in many sections of the country the civil airways are so located that the only large areas excluded from this regulation are remote regions in the western states.
>
> The term "navigable water" as used in Section 525.1 of the regulation includes all water suitable for the take-off or landing of water aircraft. Other geographical features which combine hydrographic and topographic characteristics, such as marshes, swamps and bogs, come within the meaning of the term "land" as used in the regulation.
>
> The distance between the nearest boundary of a landing area and the site of the construction or alteration may be measured by the use of maps, or on the surface of the earth by an automobile mileage meter, or other convenient but reasonably accurate means. Generally, if a landing area is day marked or boundary lighted, the limits of that part of the landing area maintained for the use of land aircraft in taking off or landing are indicated by such day markers or boundary lights, or both.

In the case of an existing structure on which a proper notice has already been submitted, some latitude for repairs is permitted by an explanation of the term "alteration." Notice may be omitted if the alteration or alterations will not increase or decrease the height of the top or any part of the structure from that previously reported by more than 1 foot for each 500 feet, or fraction thereof, of the distance that the structure is situated from the nearest boundary of the landing area involved. Notice must be given, however, of any alteration or alterations increasing or decreasing the height of the top or any part of a structure by more than 10 feet from that previously reported.

The information required on proposed construction is clearly explained in the forms prepared for that purpose and is essentially that material needed to warn airmen of a potential hazard to air navigation. It is, therefore, necessary that all questions therein be answered without exception. Copies of these forms, together with a list of landing areas coming within the scope of the regulation, may be obtained from any Regional Office or the Washington Office of the Civil Aeronautics Administration.

A study of obstructions and their markings as called for in the "Obstruction Marking Manual" will help the engineer in forming his own opinion of the best standards and markings to adopt.

REMOVAL OR LOWERING

The only completely satisfactory manner of handling an obstruction is to remove it. Any other course of action can only decrease the hazard it constitutes.

Obstructions which can not be removed must be given very careful consideration at the time the airport site is selected. Landing strips should always be laid out so that such obstructions fall in the turning zones if possible.

Most man-made obstructions can be removed or relocated, provided sufficient funds are available. It has too often been the case that the removal of a flight hazard has been postponed, because its removal was costly or inconvenient, until after it has caused a bad accident. The removal of every possible obstruction should be given priority over projects which result in improving the convenience or appearance of the landing strip.

Permission to cut trees is often hard to secure because of their sentimental value or their value as shade. Sentiment is difficult to overcome and such instances usually require condemnation proceedings. Shade trees can sometimes be replaced by trees which do not attain great height. Low-growing shade trees in place of hazardous trees will usually provide satisfactory shade for cattle.

Power and telephone lines, with the exception of high-voltage transmission lines, can usually be placed underground. It is possible in many instances to reroute a pole line without great expense. Rerouting of high-voltage transmission lines, particularly where the line is supported on steel towers, is usually almost impossible to accomplish, but has been done.

Structures can very often be moved a short distance with small cost and the hazard eliminated or reduced materially.

Since height is usually the only variable factor connected with an obstruction, the next best action is to decrease its height. The standards such as 1/30 obstruction ratio for Class II, III, or IV noninstrument run way approaches are at best a compromise between a desirable 1/100 ratio and that which is practically obtainable. From this it will be seen that reducing an obstruction's height is always desirable.

Many types of trees can be topped without danger to their growth. Topping of trees should be performed at the season of the year recommended by local tree experts.

Pole lines can very often be materially reduced in height at small cost. Local regulations governing permissible height and separation of lines may have to be waived and some special safety measures taken. Power lines should be lowered whenever possible due to the extreme likelihood of fire resulting when an airplane collides with them.

Careful planning will often allow a hazardous hill close to the airport to be reduced in height by taking borrow excavation from it to make the airport fills.

The following standards for day marking of various types of hazards to air navigation are taken from pages 11 and 12 of C.A.A.'s "Obstruction Marking Manual." Where obstructions can not be removed or lowered in order to eliminate their hazardous aspect, it is advised that the following standards be complied with.

STANDARD FOR THE MARKING OF HAZARDS TO AIR NAVIGATION

In the preceding paragraphs [referring to "Air Marking Manual"] a general guide has been provided to determine when a structure presents a hazard to air navigation, and when adequate day and night marking should be provided to insure safety in air commerce. The amount and type of marking required for the protection of air navigation are determined by a study of the height of the structure and adjacent buildings, topography, atmospheric visibility, flow of air traffic, and location of the structure with respect to landing areas and other navigation facilities, and civil airways.

In view of these many influencing elements, it is appropriate to mention that specific marking recommendations for each particular problem will be made by specially trained personnel of this Administration.

DAY MARKING (PAINTING)

The purpose of day marking a structure which presents a hazard to air commerce is to warn airmen during the hours of daylight of the presence of such a structure. To accomplish this objective it may be necessary to paint such a structure so as to be visible from aircraft at any angle of approach.

No standards for day marking, however, can be given more than general application as a structure may already be conspicuous by contrast of color or construction, or it may be so located in reference to other structures or to the contour of the ground that the hereinafter described standards should be applied to the upper part of the structure only.

TOWERS, POLES, SMOKESTACKS AND SIMILAR STRUCTURES

Towers, poles, smokestacks and similar structures which present a hazard to air commerce should be painted throughout their height with alternate bands of international orange and white, terminating with orange bands at both top and bottom.

Painting need not be applied on the lower one-third of a structure that is situated more than three miles from a landing area, provided the unpainted portion will not exceed a height of 100 feet above ground.

All structures should be cleaned or repainted as often as necessary to maintain good visibility.

Where the over-all height of such structures exceed 250 feet, the width of the white bands should be approximately one-seventh of the height, or the width of the orange bands should be approximately one-seventh of the height and the width of each white band should be approximately one-half that of the orange band.

Where the over-all height of such structures exceed 250 feet, the width of the orange bands and the width of the white bands should be approximately 40 feet, or the width of the orange bands should be approximately 40 feet and the width of each white band should be approximately one-half that of the orange band.

WATER TANKS, GRAIN ELEVATORS, GAS HOLDERS AND SIMILAR STRUCTURES

Water tanks, grain elevators, gas holders and similar structures which present a hazard to air commerce should be painted so that they will be readily visible from the air. The top and upper portion of the vertical surface of such a structure should be painted a checkerboard pattern of alternate squares of international orange and white. The sides of the squares should not measure less than 10 feet nor more than 30 feet. At least three rows of squares should be provided on the vertical surface.

In the event such structures, because of their shape or type of construction do not permit application of the method of marking described in the preceding paragraph, then such structures should be painted as specified for towers, poles, smokestacks and similar structures. Where this method of marking is employed, the top orange band should be continued from the vertical surface so as to cover the entire top of the structure.

STRUCTURAL HAZARD AREAS

Where towers, poles and other structures of extraordinary height are so grouped as to present a common hazard to air commerce, or where the hazard of a particular structure is increased by guy wires or other appurtenances, the outer limits of the area in which the structural hazards are situated should be day marked by four or more symbols consisting of the letters "H A Z," located so that at least one symbol will be visible from aircraft at any angle of approach.

The letters of such symbols should be legible and present the appearance of being on a horizontal plane at an altitude of 3,000 feet and a distance of two miles. Moreover, the symbols should consist of uniform block letters having a height of at least 30 feet and a width equal to two-thirds of the height. The width of each stroke should be approximately one-seventh of the height of the letters. In addition, the letters should be painted an international orange. If the strokes of the letters are constructed of wood or metal panels, such construction should be designed to prevent an accumulation of snow.

The foregoing marking is intended to provide additional protection for air commerce and does not lessen the need for day marking the particular structure or structures.

RADIO OBSTRUCTION MARKERS

Where a serious hazard to air commerce is presented by a structure which is located on or near a civil airway and approaches or exceeds an over-all height of 500 feet above ground, or water if so situated, the installation and operation of an effective radio marker of a type approved by the Administrator may be necessary for the proper protection of air commerce.

Specifications for an acceptable type of radio marker beacon will be made available on request directed to any Regional Office or to the Washington Office of the Civil Aeronautics Administration.

NIGHT MARKING

Night marking is discussed in the chapter on airport lighting as it almost always is a part of the airport lighting system.

LEGAL ASPECTS

Several federal statutes apply to marking obstructions and to the erection of any structure which will constitute a hazard. These are summarized in Appendix A of C.A.A.'s "Obstruction Marking Manual" which is reproduced herewith.

FEDERAL STATUTES

Air Commerce Act of 1926, as Amended

Section 11 (e). Any person (1) who, with intent to interfere with air navigation in the navigable airspace or waters of the United States, exhibits within the United States any false light or signal at such place or in such manner that it is likely to be mistaken for a true light or signal required by regulation under this Act, or for a true light or signal in connection with an airport or other air navigation facility, or (2) who, after due warning from the Administrator in the Civil Aeronautics Authority continues to maintain any false light or signal, or (3) who knowingly removes, extinguishes, or interferes with the operation of any such true light or signal, or (4) *who without lawful authority knowingly exhibits any such true light or signal,* shall be guilty of an offense punishable by a fine not exceeding $5000 or by imprisonment not exceeding five years, or by both such fine and imprisonment. [Italics supplied.]

Civil Aeronautics Act of 1938, as Amended

Definitions

Section 1 (7). "Air navigation facility" means any facility used in, available for use in, or designed for use in, aid of air navigation, including landing areas, lights, any apparatus or equipment for disseminating weather information, for signaling, for radio-directional finding, or for radio or other electrical communication, and any other structure or mechanism having a similar purpose for guiding or controlling flight in the air or the landing and take-off of aircraft.

Air Navigation Facility Rating

Section 606. The Authority is empowered to inspect, classify, and rate any air navigation facility available for the use of civil aircraft of the United States, as to its suitability for such use. The Authority is empowered to issue a certificate for any such navigation facility.

Amendment, Suspension, and Revocation of Certificates

Section 609. The Authority may, from time to time; reinspect any . . . air navigation facility . . . and, after investigation, and upon notice and hearing, may alter, amend, modify, or suspend, in whole or in part, any . . . air navigation facility certificate . . . if the interest of the public so requires, or may revoke, in whole or in part, any such certificate for any cause which at the time of revocation, would justify the Authority in refusing to issue to the holder of such certificate a like certificate. In cases of emergency, any such certificate may be suspended, in whole or in part, for a period not in excess of thirty days, without regard to any requirement as to notice and hearing. . . .

Interference With Air Navigation

Section 902 (c). A person shall be subject to a fine of not exceeding $5000 or to imprisonment not exceeding five years, or to both such fine and imprisonment, who—

(1) with intent to interfere with air navigation within the United States, exhibits within the United States any light or signal at such place or in such manner that it is likely to be mistaken for a true light or signal established pursuant to this Act, or for a true light or signal in connection with an airport or other air navigation facility; or

(2) after due warning by the Administrator, continues to maintain any misleading light or signal; or

(3) *knowingly removes, extinguishes, or interferes with the operation of any such true light or signal.* [Italics supplied.]

Hazards to Air Commerce

Section 1101. The Administrator shall, by rules and regulations, or by order where necessary, require all persons to give adequate public notice, in the form and manner prescribed by the Administrator, of the construction or alteration, of any structure along or near the civil airways where notice will promote safety in air commerce.

Federal Communications Act of 1934, as Amended

Radio Towers

The Federal Communications Commission, pursuant to Section 303 (q) of the Communications Act of 1934, as amended, requires marking of radio towers where such may constitute a menace to air navigation. This section reads:

. . . the Commission from time to time, as public convenience, interests, or necessity requires, shall—

Have authority to require the painting and/or illumination of radio towers if and when in its judgment such towers constitute, or there is a reasonable possibility that they may constitute, a menace to air navigation.

War Department Construction Permits

War Department construction permits authorizing the construction of any structures in or over navigable waters contain the following provisions:

That if the display of lights and signals on any work thereby authorized is not otherwise provided for by law, such lights and signals as may be prescribed by the U.S. Coast Guard, Department of Treasury, shall be installed and maintained at the expense of the owner.

That the permittee shall promptly comply with any future regulations or instructions affecting the work hereby authorized, if and when, issued in accordance with law, by any department of the Federal Government, for the aid or protection of aerial navigation.

LOCAL LAWS

Local laws covering acquisition of property, condemnation, and police powers must be studied in connection with each airport. The condemnation of obstructions is a relatively new procedure. It is advised that the experience of other cities be studied if undue difficulties are encountered. Several large cities, including Philadelphia, have had to go very thoroughly into the matter of acquiring rights of removal, lowering, and marking obstructions. The results of their study are no doubt available on request.

APPROACH-ZONE DRAWINGS

The preparation of approach-zone plans and profiles is a necessary and important step in the preparation of the airport design. This work has frequently been one of the last tasks accomplished, or considered merely an incidental step in the work. However, these plans and profiles should be worked up as soon as a general layout has been decided upon so that the laborious work in connection with plotting sections and computing earthwork will not require revision if, in the end, it is found that adequate approaches have not been obtained.

The obstruction plan is a topographic plan showing all buildings, trees, power lines, etc., within the approch-zone limits as described in Chapters III and X. It is sufficient to show only the objects above a 1 on 30 glide angle on noninstrument runways; 1 on 40 glide angle for instrument-approach runways. The C.A.A. takes all topography for the distance of 1000 ft from the end of the runway, whether obstructions exist or not, to provide information in the possible installation of air navigation aids. Property lines should be shown for reference when clearing easements must be obtained.

It is sometimes the practice to indicate the elevation of the ground and top of the obstruction on the approach-zone plan. However, the writers feel that the elevations may be shown much better on the profile. A plan drawn to a scale of $\frac{1}{2}$ in. = 100 ft is good, although a somewhat smaller scale will prove satisfactory.

The obstruction profile should be placed above the plan so that a projection of the obstructions will show in their relative location on the profile. In general, the tops of all obstructions should be shown, with only a center-line ground profile included. Where, however, the ground along the edges of the approach zone enter into or approach closely to the glide angle, the edge profiles should also be shown. Hills, knobs, etc., within the approach zone must be shown where such natural obstructions project into the glide angle. A horizontal scale equal to the plan scale should be used and a vertical scale of between 1 in. = 5 or 10 ft is desirable. It is necessary, however, for vertical scales to be such that the profile may be kept within the drawing limits and in rugged country scales as great as 1 in. = 30 ft may be necessary. A typical approach drawing is given in Fig. 3–5 of Chapter III.

TABLE 9–1. Obstruction Ratio

Zone	Class I	Class II	Class III	Class IV
Turning zones	$\frac{1}{20}$	See Note		
Noninstrument approach zones	$\frac{1}{20}$	$\frac{1}{30}$	$\frac{1}{30}$	$\frac{1}{30}$
Instrument approach zones	—	—	$\frac{1}{40}$	$\frac{1}{40}$

NOTE: For turning zones in Class II, III, and IV airports—from the boundary of the airport for a distance of $\frac{1}{2}$ mile away, there shall be no obstruction above 75 ft in height. From the half mile away to 2 miles, no obstruction shall protrude above a $\frac{1}{30}$ obstruction ratio up from the 75-ft height.

CHAPTER X

LIGHTING

HISTORY

The history of airport lighting is one of steady progress where the manufacturers and the engineers have engaged in a continual race to keep pace with the increasing requirements of the air-transportation industry. Trial-and-error methods have of necessity been used. At the present time, a great deal of research and experimentation is being carried on. New and improved equipment is constantly becoming available. This is particularly true regarding contact and approach lights. It behooves the engineer to consult with both the manufacturers of lighting equipment and C.A.A. officials prior to preparing lighting plans and specifications in order to be certain that he is aware of the latest developments in equipment.

During World War II, the need for standardization of lighting equipment as a wartime measure was recognized by the Government. A.N.C. specifications and practices set forth by a committee composed of representatives of the U.S. Army Air Forces, the Bureau of Aeronautics, U.S. Navy Department, and the C.A.A. were therefore adopted as standard for all airport lighting. The War Production Board allowed the manufacture of only such equipment as A.N.C. felt was necessary and to the specifications A.N.C. provided.

SPECIFICATIONS

For the information and assistance of lighting engineers, the C.A.A. has prepared standard specifications covering all airport-lighting equipment. These specifications are compiled in C.A.A. Airport Division Specification 606 entitled "Standard Specifications for Airport Lighting—Part I—Equipment and Materials."

This text will outline the general requirements for lighting equipment. For detail requirements, the reader is advised to consult the C.A.A. publication referred to and material furnished for guidance by the equipment manufacturers. The history of airport lighting indicates that very few equipment specifications can be expected to remain current for any appreciable length of time because of continual improvements.

AUTOMATIC CONTROL DEVICES

The isolated location of some lighting facilities, and in many instances the desire to keep operating expenses at a minimum, make the use of automatic control devices necessary. Such devices turn lights on and off according to a predetermined time schedule, or cause the lights to burn during all periods where conditions of visibility are below set minimums.

Electric Time Switches

Whenever time is the factor governing the period of operation of any airport-lighting facility, an electric time switch can be used.

Electric time switches have proved to be very dependable and are manufactured by several reputable firms. Single-throw switches are available up to 60 amp, and double-throw up to 40 amp. These switches are obtainable with one, two, or three poles for operation on alternating or direct current. As many as three automatic operations every 24 hours can be arranged for with some types.

In instances where the time of operation has a definite reference to sunrise or sunset, the switches can be fitted with an astronomic dial. The mechanism used in connection with this dial automatically advances or retards the time of operation so that it maintains a predetermined relationship to either sunrise, sunset, or both.

Light-Sensitive Switches

The automatic operation of some types of lighting equipment during daytime periods when the light intensity is below prescribed levels is highly desirable. The type of lighting equipment usually involved is that which can not be operated manually in an economical manner. Remote obstruction lights, approach-light lanes, or any light whose operation would require a control line of excessive length or require the employment of a full-time caretaker for such control can be considered in this category.

WIRING METHODS

Low maintenance costs, dependable operation, and the effectiveness of an airport-lighting system depend to a large extent on the use of proper wiring methods at the time of installation. Since the degree of safety of night operations and the regularity of night schedules are dependent to such a large extent on the effectiveness of the airport lighting system, the workmanship, materials, equipment, and design must be the very best obtainable. Repairs and maintenance of poorly installed lighting systems have been found to be troublesome, expensive, and unsatisfactory. Local codes and utility-company practices should always be complied with and their requirements exceeded if considered necessary.

Multiple Circuits

As the name implies, multiple circuits require two or more conductors. A simple multiple circuit has two insulated conductors, usually carrying approximately 110 v, with the lighting equipment connected across the two.

A more efficient multiple system, referred to as a three-wire 110–22-v circuit, requires two insulated conductors, and one conductor which may either be bare or insulated. The two insulated conductors usually carry 220 v and the third conductor is a grounded neutral. One side of the lighting equipment is connected into one of the 220-v conductors and the other side to the neutral conductor to obtain 110 v. The three-wire circuit gains its efficiency due to the 220-v potential having a lower line loss for the same connected load than 110 v. A requirement of this system is that approximately equal loads be connected on each side of the neutral conductor.

Multiple circuits can use high voltage if individual transformers are provided for each lighting unit.

Multiple circuits can be fed from either end or can be fed from a centrally located point. Twelve thousand feet is usually the maximum allowable length for a multiple circuit. The generally accepted standard of not allowing a voltage drop in excess of 5 per cent of the input voltage is another limiting factor on the length of multiple circuits.

Multiple circuits have the following advantages:

1. No voltage-regulating equipment is required.
2. There is no high-voltage danger involved.
3. Standard lamps can be used.
4. Insulation requirements are kept at a minimum.
5. Short circuits seldom destroy fittings.
6. They are usually cheaper for circuits under 12,000 ft.

Multiple circuits have the following disadvantages:

1. The amount of copper and the number of conductors increase the cable cost.

2. Voltage drop requires lamps suited for the several different voltages to be used.
3. The restriction of the length of circuits requires extra cable to feed several circuits.

Series Circuits

A series circuit requires only a single conductor, and all lighting equipment is connected in series along the one conductor. The two ends of the conductor terminate in a runway-selector relay cabinet. These two ends are connected through a series protective relay to a constant-current regulator.

The principle of operation of a series circuit is that the constant-current regulator varies the voltage input to the circuit in relation to the connected load so that the amperage remains constant. For airport circuits the current is maintained at 6.6 amp. As series lamps can operate over a wide range in voltage and maintain the same luminosity as long as the current is constant, it can be seen that the number of lamps in a circuit can vary immensely.

Ohm's Law is expressed as $E = IR$—E being volts, I being current in amperes, and R being resistance in ohms. Assuming I to be constantly 6.6 amp, the constant-current regulator must vary E directly with the increase or decrease in R brought about by changes in the connected load.

Should an open circuit occur, R will immediately become very high, causing E to rise to the full capacity of the regulator. A series protective relay is connected into circuit ahead of the regulator. It opens the remote-controlled oil switch and protects the equipment from damage of high voltage resulting from an open circuit.

Each lamp socket is equipped with a protective device called a film cutout which prevents the burning out of a light from creating an open circuit. A film cutout is a thin disk about ½ in. in diameter. It is a nonconductor of electricity from one side to the other due to a thin film of insulating material. A film cutout is installed at each light fixture as an insulator between two spring clips in such a way that upon the lamp's failure the current melts the film, thereby closing the circuit. It can be seen that as a light burns out, the circuit resistance is reduced, and the voltage is lowered. Conversely, adding lamps to the circuit increases the resistance and therefore the voltage.

Series or multiple branch circuits can be taken off of the main series circuit by the use of series-to-series or series-to-multiple transformers.

Series circuits have the following advantages:

1. Line losses are kept at a minimum.
2. Longer circuits can be employed.
3. Cable is less expensive.
4. Constant current maintains desired brilliance.
5. Control of brilliance can be effected.
6. Grounding on one or more units will not put the entire circuit out of service.
7. They are usually cheaper for circuits over 12,000 ft.

Series circuits have the following disadvantages:

1. The high voltages are dangerous.
2. They require considerable control equipment.

Cable

Airport-lighting circuits are run underground. Such construction is necessary as any type of above-ground line for boundary, range, or contact lights would constitute a hazard.

Multiple circuits generally require parkway cable, lead-covered, and armored with flat steel tape. It is false economy to use conductors so small that they result in excessive line losses. Normally cable used for multiple circuits is insulated for 600-v service. If soil conditions are such that steel armor will corrode, nonmetallic armor or rubber-sheathed cables should be used. Federal Specification JC-106 may be used to advantage in specifying insulation, and JC-121 in specifying lead and armored cable. Cable conforming to the C.A.A. standard airport-lighting specifications is preferable to most commercial types of cable for airport uses.

Series circuits can use parkway or rubber-sheathed cable. It is recommended that the conductor be not less than No. 8 gauge. The insulation should be sufficient to protect against 3000 v.

Cable runs must be carefully laid to avoid damage to the armor or insulation. In rocky soils the cable should be laid in selected material so that the cable does not come into contact with sharp stones. The depth to which the cable is buried should be sufficient so that it can not be damaged by airplanes or equipment which may pass over it. A minimum depth of 18 in. on airport property and 36 in. off airport property or under roadways is recommended. When cable runs cross each other, 10-in. vertical separation should be maintained.

The safest method of laying cable is to dig a trench of sufficient width so that the cable can be unreeled alongside the trench and lifted into the trench easily. Cable should never be pulled, but always unreeled so as to avoid the strain tension imposes. Cable plows which have overcome most objectionable features previously associated with such equipment are being developed. A cable plow has the desirable feature of eliminating the mess and hazard of open-ditch construction, however there is no control of material such as sharp stones which might puncture the insulation and later cause a ground.

A creosoted plank placed 8 in. over the cable provides protection against mechanical damage and prevents damage to the cable should it have to be dug up. A creosoted plank should always be placed over a loop of cable which is buried to provide slack for future connections. Suitable markers should be installed along cable runs so that they can be easily located. Such a marker should be placed at every bend in a cable run. The importance of marking cable runs can hardly be overemphasized.

Junction Boxes

Underground splicing of cable should be avoided whenever possible. Cable should not be spliced between lights as splices are often a weak spot in any cable run. Wherever splices must be made, careful workmanship and high-quality materials and equipment are essential. Every underground splice should be recorded on the "as built" plan and plainly marked on the ground.

Underground Duct Conduit

Wherever cable runs across roadways, airport pavements, areas likely to be paved in the future, ditches, streams, or any area in which it will be difficult or expensive to reach the cable for alteration or repair, the cable should be placed in duct or conduit. All ducts under runways, taxiways, or aprons should be incased in concrete with the top of the concrete envelope 24 in. below finished grade. All such ducts or conduits should be provided with pull wires and sealed at the time of installation to facilitate placing the cable and to prevent the ducts from filling with dirt. Ducts should be laid so as to slope toward manholes, handholes and duct ends. Slope should be at least 3 in. per 100 ft. (Refer to Fig. 10–1.)

Any approved electrical duct material may be used. The inner diameter of the duct should not be less than 3 in. for one cable and larger if sufficient additional cables are to be run in the same duct. The best practice is to provide a separate duct run for each circuit. Multicelled terra cotta duct is recommended where more than two cables are to be run at the same crossing.

Metallic conduit, processed to be rustproof, is recommended where severe loads will be imposed above the cable or where less than 12 in. of cover can be provided.

Building Circuits

Normal inside-wiring methods, as required by national electric or local code, will generally suffice for inside wiring on airport installations. The necessity for excellent construction is again stressed because the safety of the life and property involved in night operations depends on reliable effective use of the airport lighting system.

Pole and Mast Fittings

Figures 10–2 and –3 illustrate the common type of pole and mast fittings.

AIRPORT BEACON

The purpose of the airport beacon is to provide a light of high intensity with peculiar characteristics which can be seen by a pilot a very considerable distance from the airport. The peculiar characteristic of the light enables the pilot to identify it as an airport beacon. This characteristic is obtained by having the beacon rotate and by using a color screen to make one beam of the beacon green and the other clear. A flashing-code beacon is often used to supplement the rotating beacon when an airport rotating beacon is installed more than $1\frac{1}{4}$ miles from the airport.

In order that the beacon may be as plainly visible as possible it should be mounted on the highest point in the vicinity of the airport. The high point may be a near-by hill. If the beacon is placed on a near-by hill, an auxiliary or flashing beacon should be installed on the airport if the hill is any appreciable distance from the airport. Ordinarily, the beacon is mounted on top of a building or on a steel tower. Figures 10–4,–5, and –6 illustrate a typical tower installation.

A beacon should never be placed where it forms an obstruction, never at the end of a runway, and if at all possible 1000 ft from any runway center line. It is often possible, however, to place the beacon where it will mark an existing obstruction.

A beacon consists of a searchlight type of projector rotated about its vertical axis by an electric motor. Two types of rotating beacons are in general use. One is a single-ended 24-in.-diameter beacon having a beam intensity of at least 1,000,000 cp. The other is a double-ended 36-in.-diameter beacon, each end of which projects a beam having a light intensity of at least 1,000,000 cp. (Refer to Fig. 10–7.)

Most beacons weigh approximately 500 lb and are equipped with two 1000-w lamps and an automatic lamp changer.

FLASHING CODE BEACON

A flashing-code beacon can be used for several different purposes. It is an identification type of light whose versatility comes from the fact it can combine any desired color with any desired code flashing. The extreme importance of this type of beacon in marking obstructions is brought out in Chapter IX. In airport lighting this beacon will generally be used as an auxiliary to the rotating beacon.

A code beacon is designed to throw light in all horizontal directions. Figure 10–8 shows the details of its construction. It uses two 500-w lamps to produce 5000 cp. The code-flasher mechanism is motor driven and usually is mounted remotely. The code signal assigned to give an identification may be one or more letters in International Morse Code. Assignment of code signals is made by the C.A.A. to avoid duplication.

TOWERS, MASTS, AND POLES

It is essential that every light in an airport lighting system convey the proper information to the pilot. Lights marking obstructions are expected to show not only the location of the obstruction, but also its height. As has been stated, beacons should be visible for the greatest possible distance. These requirements make it necessary that towers, masts, or poles be used so that the light may be placed at the proper elevation. Whichever method is used it must be possible for maintenance personnel to reach the light for servicing by the use of steps or ladders. Clean, well-compacted earth is usually sufficient to hold towers, masts, or poles erect in place. Gravel or concrete backfill can be used if soil or service conditions warrant it.

Poles

Wood poles are generally used for heights up to 50 ft. above ground. Such poles should have a minimum tip diameter of 6 in. and be firm and free from rot or excessive splitting. Unless the pole is of cedar, chestnut, or locust, it should be creosoted to insure its durability. Due to the fact that creosoted poles are difficult to paint, the practice of creosoting only that portion of the butt which will be underground is followed extensively. Poles should be carefully specified and inspected. Long poles require skillful handling to prevent breaking or cracking. Normal practice is to bury poles up to 25 ft in length 5 ft in the ground. Poles over 25 ft in length are buried to a depth equal to $\frac{1}{8}$ of their overall length. Pole steps, placed on 18-in. centers starting 3 ft above ground, are recommended for ease in servicing. Local power-company practice is always a good guide for pole installation.

Masts

Steel masts are generally used for heights in excess of 50 ft above ground level. Masts are usually square and of lattice construction. Masts are set in the ground in the same manner as are poles.

Towers

Steel towers are used almost entirely for mounting rotating or flashing beacons. The type of tower in general use mounts a platform approximately 7-ft square and is fitted with a ladder. The ladder on high towers should be enclosed in a cage as a safety measure. Most towers are made of galvanized iron and are fabricated in the following lengths: 51, 62, 75, 82, 91, and 104 ft.

Wind-cone fittings are manufactured for installation on steel towers. Their use is not recommended due to difficulty in replacing the fabric wind cone.

Wood towers can be used, but are not recommended.

BOUNDARY LIGHTING

The purpose of boundary lighting, also referred to as perimeter lighting, is to outline for night operation the extreme limits of the usable portion of airport landing strips. The proper painting of boundary-light cones serves also to outline the area for daytime operations. Boundary lighting is the oldest form of airport lighting.

Basic Design Principles

Boundary lights should be spaced as nearly as possible 300 ft apart. The spacing should not exceed 300 ft. It is desirable to have the lights spaced evenly and directly across from each other wherever a strip is being outlined. Lights should be placed with as few bends as possible in outlining the area. The engineer should bear in mind that boundary lights are to outline the airport in such a manner that it and its shape are readily distinguishable.

No obstructions should be allowed inside the area outlined by boundary lights except navigational aids such as wind indicators or glide-path buildings. Boundary lights should be approximately 10 ft inside of fences or toes of slopes.

Clear, green, and red colored globes are used on boundary lights with each color indicating a location or condition. A clear light indicates the boundary along the side of the airport where no unusual conditions are to be encountered. Green lights are used to mark the ends of runways or desirable landing areas and such lights correspond to range lights. Red globes are used in connection with hazardous areas. Where the boundary of an airport is flanked by hazardous obstructions it is often the practice to supplement the obstruction lights with red boundary lights. The use of colored globes makes it possible to change the color to correspond to changing conditions.

Boundary lights are always fed by underground cable and the circuit may be either multiple or series.

A boundary light is usually mounted on sheet-metal cones, the base having a diameter of approximately 30 in. The top of the cone should fit the lamp holder. Thirty to 36 in. is the normal height above ground. The height may be varied to suit local snow or vegetation conditions.

A tip-over type of boundary unit is used in either a series or multiple circuit. Figure 10–9 illustrates the details of a series boundary unit.

Controls

The switches controlling the operation of the boundary system should be located in the airport-traffic control tower wherever a tower is provided. If the airport is not equipped with a control tower the controls should be located where they are convenient to the field attendant. An electric time switch should be employed where the lights are to be operated on a regular nightly schedule.

CONTACT LIGHTS

Purpose

Contact lights are flush marker lights placed in the edge or adjacent to paved runways to assist the pilot in taking off and landing. The word contact is used to describe the lights because they are for the purpose of providing the pilot with a visual aid which will enable him to properly contact the runway. The use of a separate circuit for each runway allows the contact lights to be operated only on the runway in use. This is done to give the pilot a positive indication of the proper runway for landing and take-offs. The lighting of more than one runway of a Class IV or V airport would in some cases overload the constant-current regulator. The obstruction lights in the approaches and the range lights for each runway are connected into that runway's contact-light circuit and so are always operated only in conjunction with it.

Equipment

Contact lights may be either flush marker lights as shown in Figs. 10–10 and –11, or marker lights mounted on a pedestal.

Most airport-lighting systems installed prior to 1946 have used the flush marker type. The pedestal type of light shown in Figs. 10–12 and –13 is being developed to overcome difficulties which pilots have experienced in using the flush type of light. Contact lights, being in the development stage, will undoubtedly be improved and modified continually for some time to come.

Layout Plan

The flush marker lights should be installed in concrete pads along the edge of runway, spaced approximately 200 ft on centers. The end lights should always be opposite the end of the pavement. The light pad should be similar to the one shown in Fig. 10–10 as this design affords protection to the light against damage by snowplowing and mowing equipment.

The height above ground and the distance away from the runway for pedestal-type lights must be such that the light will not be hit by aircraft wings or propellers. The light pedestal is designed to break before the light can materially damage an airplane if a collision occurs.

Contact lights are placed in pairs with the two lights directly across the runway from each other. Proper spacing of lights will require considerable juggling where one runway is intersected by one or more additional runways. Two-hundred-foot spacing should be maintained as nearly as possible. The engineer must bear in mind that since only one runway is lighted at a time it often proves necessary to have lights serving different runways quite close together at runway intersections.

Contact lights can be fitted with split filters so that the light, as viewed from one direction, has a different color than that which is seen from the opposite direction. The usual practice is to use split filters on all lights within 1500 ft from the end of a runway. Looking toward the end of the runway, these lights are amber in color to warn the pilot that he is within 1500 ft of the end of the runway. These same lights, viewed from the end of the runway and looking toward the other end, are clear.

Control

Since the contact lights on only one runway are in operation at a time, the runway which is lighted must be the one that most nearly coincides with the wind direction. Satisfactory operation therefore requires controls so located that the operator can select the proper runway each time there is a change in wind direction. This requires an accurate knowledge of the wind direction.

The best practice is to combine all airport-lighting controls into one control panel, the usual size of which is approximately 14 in. square. Figure 10–14 shows the type currently used by C.A.A. This control panel, where used in conjunction with proper relay and selector equipment, allows the operator to select not only any desired runway, but also any one of five degrees of brightness. Each of the toggle switches at the left side of the panel is labeled to correspond to the equipment it controls.

The control panel should be mounted in the airport-traffic control tower wherever one is provided. At airports where no tower is provided, the controls should be conveniently located so that they may be operated by such personnel as are on duty. It is desirable that the person operating the controls be able to see the lights as a check on their operation. In any event, the operator must have positive knowledge of the wind direction.

The following difficulties have been experienced in using the flush marker type of contact lights:

1. Their visibility is often decreased due to high grass, snow, and blowing sand.
2. They are easily broken by airport maintenance equipment such as snowplows, mowing machines, and trucks. The wheels of heavily loaded airplanes will also break them.
3. The lights are difficult to keep moistureproof.

STRIP LIGHTING

Purpose

Strip lighting also serves the purpose of outlining for night operation the limits of the usable portions of the airport. Strip lighting is used where this area is in the shape of one or more landing strips, rather than a larger irregular shaped area. The purpose is to outline the limit of each individual landing strip by using a separate circuit for each such strip, as is done with contact lights.

Equipment

Cone types of lights are used in strip lighting. They may be installed in either multiple or series circuits.

Layout Plan

Strip lights are placed in pairs with the two lights directly across the strip from each other. The lights should be spaced as nearly 300 ft apart as possible.

Control

The principle of operation and control of strip lighting is identical to that described for contact lighting. Obstruction lights are also grouped and connected into the applicable circuit in the same manner.

RANGE LIGHTS

Purpose

Range lights are used in all types of lighting systems to indicate the location of the center of each end of a landing strip or paved runway. Confusion as to the direction of a landing strip or runway is avoided by placing the same distinctive arrangement of range lights at each end so that the pilot can easily pair them up. Since each airport usually has more than one strip or runway, the same arrangement of range lights can not be used for more than one runway.

Layout

Two range lights spaced 50 ft apart generally comprise the basic unit, and the best runway is marked by placing a basic unit at each end. A group of three range lights spaced 50 ft apart is then used on each end of the next most important runway. The process of adding one light to the group is continued until all runways are taken care of.

Whenever possible each line of range lights should be at right angles to the center line of the runway it serves. It is normal practice to place range lights back 75 ft from the end of a paved runway if terrain will permit.

Whenever an airport has both boundary and contact lights, the range lights should be connected into the contact-light circuit.

Equipment

Where range lights are installed adjacent to or very close to the end of the runway pavement, flush marker lights are used. If cone lights will not prove to be a hazard, they may be used for range lights.

TAXIWAY LIGHTS

Taxiway lights are similar to contact lights in nearly every respect, except that they are blue in color. They are installed for the purpose of guiding the pilot while taxiing at night. These lights may be spaced as far as 200 ft apart and are necessary only on one side of the taxiway.

OBSTRUCTION LIGHTS

Purpose

The purpose of an obstruction light is to provide a pilot flying at night with a visual means of knowing the location and height of a hazardous obstruction. A group of obstruction lights, with the lights spaced approximately 150 ft apart, serves the purpose of marking an obstruction which extends over a large area, as is the case with pole lines, woods, and large buildings.

Basic Design Principles

A pole, mast, or tower may be used to secure the proper elevation so that the light is approximately 1 ft higher than the obstruction it marks. In many instances, the light fitting may be attached directly to the obstruction, thereby eliminating the need for a pole or mast. It is essential that the light be at least equal in height or preferably slightly higher than the obstruction, and located as close to the obstruction as circumstance will permit.

Obstructions greater than 50 ft in height should be marked at more than one level. The requirements for marking towers, etc., given in Chapter IX are also applicable to such obstructions.

Obstruction lights may be fed from underground cable or overhead lines. It is usually advisable to use overhead lines wherever the line is cheaper and does not, itself, constitute a hazard. Underground cable has the advantage of not being unsightly or easily damaged by wind or ice.

Multiple or series circuits can be employed for obstruction lighting. Where a series circuit is used on field lighting, the obstruction lights are not connected directly into the series light circuit, but are fed by use of a series-to-series or series-to-multiple isolating transformer.

Where contact or strip lighting is installed, installation, maintenance, and operating costs can be reduced by arranging the airport wiring so that only the obstruction lights in the approaches to the landing strip or runway in use are lighted at one time. This is done by segregating the obstruction lights in each approach zone and connecting them into the appropriate field circuit by use of isolating transformers. In this manner, the field circuit controls operate the proper obstruction lights. Obstructions which can be considered a hazard to operations on more than one runway are usually placed on a separate circuit if they are close to the control point. More than one light, each connected into a different field circuit may be needed to mark some obstructions.

The following A.N.C. Obstruction Marking Policy dated July 18, 1945, has been approved and formally accepted by the Administrator of the Civil Aeronautics Administration:

ARMY-NAVY-CIVIL UNIFORM REQUIREMENTS FOR LIGHTING OBSTRUCTIONS TO AIR NAVIGATION

In order to standardize the lighting of hazards to air navigation, the Army-Navy-Civil Committee on Aviation Ground and Seadrome Lighting Equipment and Installations, composed of representatives of the U. S. Army Air Forces, the Bureau of Aeronautics, U. S. Navy Department, and the Civil Aeronautics Administration, concurs in the following requirements which shall apply to existing and future installations:

A. *Basic Requirements*

1. Objects on that part of the usable landing areas used or intended to be used for landing, take-off, or maneuvers of aircraft that constitute a hazard to aircraft engaged in normal ground or air maneuvers shall be considered obstructions and shall be marked with red lights placed as outlined herein.

2. All objects in the vicinity of usable landing areas that rise above any of the surfaces defined below, except as hereinafter noted, shall be considered obstructions and shall be marked with red lights placed as outlined herein.

a. Horizontal Surface. A surface 150 feet above the nearest limit of the usable landing area and within two miles of that limit.

b. Approach and/or Take-off Surface. A section of a plane of 1:40 inclination delimited by vertical planes bounding the approach area all defined as follows:

(1) The approach area is an area on the ground extending from the end of the runway for a distance of 2 miles into the approachway, and symmetrical about an axis coincident with respect to the extended center line of the runway. Where terrain or operational conditions so require, the axis of a non-instrument approach area may deviate from the extended runway center line.

(2) For instrument runways the lateral dimensions of the approach area per-

pendicular to the extended center line of the runway shall be 1000 feet at runway end and 4000 feet at approach end.

(3) For all other runways the lateral dimensions of the approach area perpendicular to the extended center line of the runway shall be runway width at runway end, and runway width plus 2000 feet at approach end, except that in no case shall the width at the runway end be less than 500 feet and the width at the approach end be less than 2500 feet.

(4) Stations of the armed Services charged with a particular tactical mission may be authorized by the Chief of the respective Service for the period of accomplishment of the mission to make certain variations in the above approach surface definitions.

(5) The inclination of the approach plane to landing areas not used by commercial air carriers or the military Services but used only for private flying or training may be increased when specifically authorized by the Chief of the respective Service.

c. Transitional Surfaces. The approach surface and the usable landing area surface shall be joined to the horizontal surface by transitional surfaces sloping upward and outward from the approach surfaces and from the boundary of the usable landing area, except that part of the landing area in common with the approach area. The slope of these transitional surfaces shall be 1:7.

(1) Usable Landing Area. The usable landing area is that part of a landing area that is used or intended to be used for actual landing and take-off of aircraft. In no case shall the width of the usable landing area with respect to a runway be considered less than the width of the approach area at the ends of that runway.

3. Objects which are not considered obstructions according to the foregoing requirements shall not be marked unless specifically authorized for each installation by the Chief of the Agency having jurisdiction.

B. *Light Arrangement*

1. The arrangement and number of obstruction lights in either the vertical plane or in the horizontal plane passing through the elevation to be marked shall be such that the obstruction is defined from every angle of azimuth.

a. Vertical Arrangement

(1) Unless otherwise provided in this paragraph, a light or lights shall be placed at the top of all obstructions. The top light may be omitted from all obstructions outside of the usable landing area that are less than 30 feet high above the ground surrounding them, unless these obstructions are located within the approach area less than one mile from the landing area. The top light shall be placed at the highest point or on the highest edge as applicable, unless the obstruction is a chimney or other structure of like function, in which case the obstruction lights shall be placed approximately six feet below the top.

(2) Intermediate Lights. When the top of the obstruction is more than 150 feet above the level of the surrounding ground, an additional light will be added for each additional 150 feet or fraction thereof. Additional lights will be equally spaced between the top light and the ground level. Any

such additional light position shielded in all directions by other objects shall have the shielded lights omitted.

b. Horizontal Arrangement

(1) Horizontally extended obstructions having a projected length parallel to the nearest edge of the usable landing area of 75 feet or less, above an obstruction marking surface as defined in Section A, shall have the top marked at approximately the center of the point or edge highest above the obstruction marking surface. If more than one edge is of equal height above the obstruction marking surface, the edge nearest the usable landing area shall be selected for marking.

(2) Horizontally extended obstructions having a projected length parallel to the nearest edge of the usable landing area of more than 75 feet, or an actual length of more than 300 feet above an obstruction marking surface as defined in Section A, shall have the top marked at each end of the length on the edge highest above the obstruction marking surface. In addition, an obstruction light shall be placed at the highest point above the obstruction marking surface between the end lights, if any such intermediate point of greater height exists. If more than one edge is of equal height above the obstruction marking surface, the edge nearest the landing area shall be selected for marking. An additional obstruction light shall be added for each 150 feet or fraction thereof, the projected length exceeds 150 feet, or for each 300 feet or fraction thereof, the actual length exceeds 300 feet, whichever results in the greatest number of lights. Such additional obstruction lights shall be spaced approximately at equal intervals between end lights positioned as above.

(3) Intermediate vertically spaced lights required by paragraph B1a(2) shall be installed to comply with the horizontal arrangement required by paragraph B1b, and shall be, insofar as practicable, in the plane perpendicular to the nearest edge of the usable landing area that passes through the corresponding top light.

c. In no case shall the pattern of the obstruction lights be such that they will be confused with any standardized pattern of lights devised for landing aids.

C. *Standard Equipment*

1. Obstruction lights to be installed in conformance with the above criteria shall be manufactured in accordance with Army-Navy Aeronautical Specifications.

2. Where obstruction lights manufactured in accordance with Army-Navy Aeronautical Specifications are considered inadequate for the particular application, a suitable substitution of equipment will be made only at the direction of the agency having jurisdiction.

In advising his assistants of his acceptance of the policy, Administrator T. P. Wright commented in part as follows:

There seems to be no immediate need for a revision of Part 525 of the Regulations to make its terms of reference agree with those of the ANC Policy. Notification of construction will continue in accordance with past practice until suitable contour maps are available to permit use of the landing area as a reference plane. During the interim period, determination of need for obstruction lighting will be made by observations from the landing area or by the use of proper existing maps.

It is to be noted that objects not projecting through an obstruction marking surface may be obstruction lighted when deemed necessary by the Chief of the Agency having jurisdiction. In some cases, outstanding objects within two miles of the landing area, while not defined as obstructions by the policy, will require lighting. Based on studies of individual cases and the fact that lighting does not remove a hazard, we will continue to oppose construction of structures which are deemed hazards, regardless of the requirements for lighting.

Equipment

Figure 10–3 illustrates a typical installation which can be used with a wood pole or a steel mast. Double obstruction-light fittings are equipped with a throw-over relay so that only one light will burn at a time and if one lamp burns out the other lamp will light.

APPROACH LIGHTS

Purpose

Approach lights are intended for use in connection with landings made under instrument conditions, day or night. They assist the pilot in establishing contact with the ground, and enable him to line himself up with the runway on which he is to land. They are a necessary adjunct to any type of instrument-landing system.

C.A.A. Policy

Nearly all approach-light lanes in existence at commercial airports prior to 1946 have been installed, maintained, and operated by the C.A.A. It appears that the government will continue this policy, so it is unlikely that many engineers will be required to lay out or design approach-light systems. The engineer will, however, need to give consideration to the space required for such a system at the time the airport site is selected.

Basic Design Principles

Many pilots feel that a satisfactory approach-light system has not been developed at the time of this writing. A good many changes may therefore be expected in both the type of light used and the spacing of the lights. It is impossible to state at this time whether the final system will consist of one, two, three, or more lines of lights. The earlier systems have employed neon lights. Later developments indicate that high intensity types of lights may be desirable.

The approach-light lane is always located at the approach end of the instrument runway. It should be controlled from the same point where the other airport lighting controls are located, or from the C.A.A. Airways Communication Station, wherever one exists.

FLOODLIGHTS

Purpose

Floodlighting is employed to supplement the airport-lighting system. It can be used to illuminate the runways during landings and take-offs, to illuminate obstructions which it is not desired to mark by obstruction lights, or to illuminate apron and building areas.

Basic Design Principles

Illumination of runways by floodlighting must be done in such a manner as to avoid glare and blinding of the pilot. Wherever the use of floodlighting equipment for runway illumination is contemplated, it is recommended that a very careful study of all available information and equipment be made.

Obstruction Marking

The use of floodlighting to mark obstructions is often the least expensive and most practical method. Obstructions should be floodlighted to an intensity of 15 ft-c.

Apron and Building Lighting

Floodlighting the operational ramp and the terminal-building area is essential where any appreciable number of night operations are conducted. The lighting should be designed to give an even intensity of 0.5 ft-c without undue glare to pilots, passengers, or spectators. Wide-angle projectors mounted on the face of buildings or on poles best serve this purpose.

The floodlighting of the terminal building area serves several useful purposes. It allows expeditious handling of baggage and cargo, reduces the likelihood of thievery or vandalism, makes for easier walking in that area, and adds to the attractive appearance of the airport. A minimum light intensity of 2.0 ft-c should be provided in the building area.

Further study of apron floodlighting is being made with the purpose of developing a light which will illuminate both sides of the airplane. Such a light would facilitate baggage and cargo handling and at the same time reduce glare to a point where it is not objectionable to the pilot as he taxies the airplane into its loading position.

WIND-DIRECTION INDICATORS

Purpose

Positive wind-direction indication equipment is more important to a pilot at night than it is in the daytime because he does not have the advantage of visual indications such as blowing smoke and dust. Lighted wind cones, wind tees, and tetrahedrons are the types of equipment available. Their purpose is to convey to the pilot positive wind-direction information.

Equipment

The simplest and least expensive lighted wind indicator is the illuminated wind cone. Figure 10–15 shows an externally lighted wind cone. This type of wind cone has the advantage of being economical and easy to locate above objects which might disturb air currents so that a false indication would be given.

Lighted wind tees are used extensively. The tee's T shape is roughly that of an airplane, and it is pivoted so that it will turn with the wind. An airplane headed in the same direction the T-shaped indicator is pointed will be flying directly into the wind.

A tetrahedron is a free-swinging wind-indicating device whose main advantage is its size and visibility. Metal tubing is used to make a frame forming a tetrahedron 36 ft long, as shown in Fig. 10–16. The frame is covered with airplane fabric, doped, and painted. It is erected on a pivot so that the small end points into the wind. Its edges are outlined by incandescent lights or neon tubes. Auxiliary, motor-driven equipment is manufactured so that the direction of the tetrahedron may be controlled during periods of calm.

Control of a wind indicator's direction is desirable to eliminate the false indication which might result from gusts or turbulence. Control also allows a definite runway to be selected when the wind direction lies between two runways. The C.A.A. has installed the majority of controlled tetrahedrons on commercial airports. They are used in connection with airport-traffic control towers which C.A.A. operates at the request of the armed services.

Location

The location of a wind-indicating device must be carefully chosen if the indications are to be reliable and the equipment a minimum hazard to operations.

The site selected should be in an open area where the wind direction and intensity will be influenced as little as possible by woods, buildings, or higher terrain. The farther the indicator is located from such objects, the more nearly reliable will be the results.

It is often necessary to compromise between the desirability of reliable indications and the desirability of a site where the indicator is much more easily seen by the pilot. Under the best conditions of visibility, it is often difficult for a pilot who is not well acquainted with the airport layout to locate the wind indicator. Despite the desirability of keeping the airport area free from any hazardous object, it is often necessary to place the wind tee or tetrahedron in one of the turfed areas between runways.

TRANSFORMER VAULT

Purpose

The transformer vault consists of one or more rooms specially designed to house the switches, transformers, and control equipment used in airport lighting. It may be a separate building or space in one of the terminal buildings. The construction details of a transformer-vault building are discussed in Chapter XI.

Basic Design Principles

The transformer vault should be located within convenient reach of the source of power, and also at a point where circuits can be run to the runways, buildings, and obstructions conveniently and economically. It is recommended that the vault be used as the primary distribution point for all electrical energy used on the airport.

The floor plan of the vault may be arranged as desired. It is recommended, however, that the room into which the outside door opens contains no dangerously-high-voltage equipment. The one or more rooms opening off this room should be provided with metal doors that are always locked. It is also recommended that the airport lighting equipment be located as shown in Fig. 10–17 as this layout allows for the future installation of additional equipment.

Equipment

The equipment listed in Fig. 10–17 is all of standard manufacture. The capacity of the regulator assembly and distribution transformers will vary at different airports according to the connected or anticipated load. It is recommended that a distribution panel board containing enough circuits to handle possible expansion of the airport be secured.

Control

The controls for the airport lighting equipment should, as previously stated, be either in the control tower or some other conveniently located place. It will prove to be very convenient to have a duplicate set of control equipment installed in the transformer vault for use in testing and for emergency use if the main controls become inoperative. (Refer to Figs. 10–18 and –19.)

PROTECTIVE DEVICES

Purpose

Protective devices are installed in electric circuits to prevent damage to insulation and equipment as well as to prevent fires which might be caused by overheating or lightning.

Basic Design Principles

The main function of any protective device is to break the electrical circuit the instant the load on the circuit exceeds a predetermined value. This value is somewhat in excess of the normal operating peak load, but still within the safe operating limits of the wiring and equipment in the circuit. One protective device is usually installed in the incoming primary circuit so as to protect the entire system. This primary protection device is supplemented by numerous other protective devices, each in turn taking in a smaller unit of the system. The proper placing of protective devices will result in confining outages to only the circuit in which trouble occurs.

PAINTING

Purpose

The painting of boundary-light cones, poles, masts, towers, and wind-indicating devices serves to protect such equipment from deterioration. It also increases the visibility of such equipment during daylight.

Basic Design Features

It has been found that international orange, white, and black paint, when used in certain combinations, produces the best visibility. The use of alternate stripes or bands allows the contrast of international orange and white to be very effective. Black provides a good background for international orange or chrome yellow.

TRENDS

Airport lighting has until recently been designed solely for the purpose of assisting in night landings of aircraft operating under contact conditions. The development of radio landing aids and the wartime necessity for landing military aircraft under very restricted conditions of ceiling and visibility have greatly expanded the functions which airport lighting must serve.

The military services led the way in expanding the use of lighting facilities. They soon discovered that contact lights and approach lights as illustrated in Figs. 10–12 and –20 were inadequate as visible ground aids during periods of low visibility, either day or night. Both the Army and the Navy have carried on extensive research in this field, as has the C.A.A.

In general terms it has developed that an airport lighting system for a major terminal, where schedules must be kept, should be adaptable to all possible conditions. It must be capable of producing light signals of very high intensity during periods when the weather is described as zero-zero, and of producing signals of lesser intensity for periods of better weather conditions.

It must furnish the pilot visible ground aids which allow him to make the transition from instrument to contact conditions or vice versa with the minimum possibility of his losing his sense of attitude or alignment.

In order to attain this versatility the following features must be incorporated in the system:

1. Brightness control which will allow maximum required light intensity, but prevent glare, and insure the most economical operation. The brightness control should be calibrated so that it can be set according to visibility conditions prevailing rather than according to each operator's opinion.
2. Optical equipment which will eliminate stray light, thereby restricting the beam to such angles as are of use to the pilot. In addition to restricting the angle of the beam, this optical equip-

ment must also vary the light intensity as viewed from different angles so that the light appears to have equal brightness throughout its effective range. (See Fig. 10–21.)

3. Sufficient approach lights of proper colors so that the pilot can ascertain his position relative to the runway in the very shortest possible time. Once the pilot has descended to a sufficiently low altitude so that he can distinguish airport approach lights, he should not be required to again refer to cockpit instruments for altitude or alignment.
4. Runway lights of sufficient height not to be affected by snow, ice, weeds, sand, or similar field surface conditions. The light must incorporate a safety device to minimize the possible damage resulting from a collision involving an aircraft.
5. Obstruction lights of such intensity that they are as effective as the approach and runway lights under extremely poor visibility conditions. The characteristics of an obstruction light must be such that it can not be mistaken for an approach or runway light.
6. The approach lights must extend out from the end of the runway such a distance as to tie in with the instrument-system inner marker (approximately 3500 ft).
7. Approach lights should be placed on both ends of the runway so that they may serve in take-offs as well as in landings.
8. Approach lights must be easily distinguishable from runway lights.

Figures 10–12, –13, and –20 illustrate a high-intensity light suitable for approach or runway use. This type of light requires a two-conductor cable.

Idlewild Airport in New York City is being lighted with various units which have been developed recently. This project as well as several military projects are to be watched with interest as they should reveal the more desirable types of installations.

FOG DISPERSAL

Fog dispersal by means of heat generated from gasoline burned in special burners (fido) proved to be of immense value to the allies in the operation of airports in the British Isles. While it is known that aircraft can maintain a high operation rate under poor visibility conditions when this method of fog dispersal is used, it remains to be seen whether it is suitable for peacetime use. It appears to be in competition with both airport lighting and instrument-approach systems as neither were required in military operations where fido was used.

American engineers are conducting research projects employing sonic methods, liquid sprays, and screening to attempt to accomplish fog dispersal. Should any method of fog dispersal prove to be economically feasible and not too objectionable to near-by residents, it can revolutionize airport lighting and approach systems. It is a subject worthy of the engineer's interest.

NUMBERING AND MARKING RUNWAYS

Traffic-control instructions are very difficult to comply with, particularly at airports with which the pilot is not completely familiar, unless runways are clearly designated. A.N.C. Drawing 1100, which is reproduced in Fig. 10–22, furnishes the details which have been worked out in the solution of the problem of runway designation.

The paint used for runway marking should be similar to that used by state highway departments and municipalities for marking similar types of pavement. The composition of paints which have been used with satisfaction may be obtained from local highway authorities. Many paint manufacturers specialize in highway marking paints.

The reflective type of paint referred to on Drawing A.N.C.-1100 is not in general use. Information concerning this material may be obtained from Specification T-1290, Corps of Engineers, U.S. Army.

AIR MARKING

Experience has shown that air markings are a most effective and necessary aid to air navigation, particularly for the private or nonscheduled flier. Air markings are of great asistance to pilots in locating the airport after reaching the general locality. Airport management will be interested in air markings on the airport as well as those affording aid in reaching it.

Types of Markers

The C.A.A. has issued an "Air Marking Manual" which is available on request. Advice regarding air-marking problems is available through air-marking specialists employed by C.A.A. The following discussion is taken from this manual.

Seven general types of air markers are recommended for use as air navigation aids. They are:

1. The painted roof town marker.
2. Painted marker for sides of buildings and water tanks.
3. Painted highway marker.
4. Illuminated day and night marker.
5. Crushed stone or concrete marker.
6. Baked enamel or porcelain raised marker.
7. Landscape marker for parks and along highways.

Each marker should carry, as well as the name of the town, the latitude and longitude in degrees and minutes, the latitude and longitude to be separated by the meridian or north marker. If space permits, an arrow enclosing the name of the nearest hard surface runway airport with the number of miles at the head of the arrow should be included.

Figure 10–23 furnishes the details of a typical air marker.

The engineer or airport manager is advised to secure the manual for advice, specifications, and dimensions of air markers.

CHAPTER XI

AIRPORT BUILDINGS

BUILDINGS GOVERN IMPRESSION OF AN AIRPORT

Because buildings play such an important part in creating a favorable impression of an airport, extreme care must be taken to insure that the layout, design, and architecture are of the best.

The services and conveniences of the terminal facilities, together with the appearance of the buildings, are factors which will largely govern the kind of an impression that is made. These factors, plus the necessity for proper allocation of space and the planning of each building relative to future expansion, will be stressed throughout this text.

The ease and dispatch with which passengers secure the services to which they feel they are entitled will affect their opinion not only of the airport, but of air travel as well.

The public, and in particular the air traveler, will be impressed favorably or unfavorably with such features as the facilities for parking cars, checking baggage, and securing transportation; the service, quality, and kind of food and beverages which are available; the convenience and condition of sanitary facilities and rest rooms. The extent to which those personal services are available and maintained efficiently in terminals is all-important. Equally important is the fact that they are a source of worth-while revenue.

The tenants of airport buildings will react in the same manner as can be expected from the general run of building tenants. The degree of satisfaction they feel regarding the manner in which heat, light, ventilation, fireproofing, and other realistic conveniences are provided will sway their opinion. They will judge the space they occupy from the standpoint of its effect on the efficiency and economy of their operations.

PECULIAR ASPECTS

The problems encountered in the design of serviceable airport buildings differ from those common to usual building construction largely because of the size and operational characteristics of airplanes.

The equipment used in most forms of transportation is stored, serviced, and repaired at locations remote from the station or pier where passengers and cargo are loaded and unloaded. Consequently storage and servicing problems ordinarily do not complicate the design of the terminal facilities. Dispatching and control of such equipment is usually handled from another location. An airplane, however, in most instances, is stored, serviced, and repaired at the same airport from which it operates.

BUILDING-AREA LAYOUT

Size

The first step in the planning of the building-area layout is to determine as nearly as possible how much of the area will ultimately be required to accommodate the airport buildings. This determination is difficult and can only be based on the experience of other airports of the same class. However, postwar developments are expected to increase the activity at most airports to such an extent that present-day experiences can not be relied upon too much. Very active airports such as La Guardia and Washington National can serve as a guide.

Figure 11–1 illustrates a possible terminal building-area layout.

A trend is developing whereby the terminal buildings and associated structures are developed in a central location on the airport with the hangars placed around the airport in such locations as not to constitute hazardous obstructions. This plan as used at New York's Idlewild Airport is shown in Fig. 2–2. In any event the building-area layout plan must fit in with the future expansion provided for in the master plan.

One of the most important factors in relation to airport design is the proper location of the passenger terminal building. Too frequently in the past the terminal building has been closely flanked with hangars on either side. This makes it difficult, when traffic increases, to further enlarge the plane-parking area and to increase the number of loading gates. Therefore, the proximity of the hangars to the terminal building must be given careful consideration, and sufficient space allowed for probable expansion.

The crowded conditions existing at La Guardia Field and the Washington National Airport are examples of outgrown facilities. In neither instance can short-sighted planning be blamed. Air transportation has simply grown faster and to larger proportions than could possibly have been anticipated. The war has set the stage for what should prove to be an even more rapid growth.

At some of the larger terminals it may be necessary to go into a more or less radical plan now being given consideration, but which as yet has not been worked out in its fullest details. This plan contemplates having two terminals—one for incoming planes and one for outgoing planes, with an area between these two terminals for servicing, fueling, loading mail and cargo, and placing food on the plane. This plan will probably be modified if a terminal handles both terminating and through traffic. Such a plan is being given consideration for future operations at the Washington National Airport.

Some airport designs now provide for roadway access to the plane loading gates, so that passengers may be driven directly to and from their planes. This arrangement offers the advantage of relieving congestion, as passengers do not have to be funnelled through a single foyer and waiting room. A further advantage is that travelers are spared long walks through the administration building, and thence to their planes.

Separate levels for loading passengers and cargo have also been widely advocated. Mail, freight, and express would be handled by trucks at grade level, and the passenger deck above would be reached by ramps.

STRUCTURES INVOLVED

The number, size, and type of buildings will vary according to the airport's size and the type of operations carried on. For this reason the structures involved are listed under three headings, namely: buildings required for aeronautical operations; buildings required for nonaeronautical operations; and strictly revenue-producing buildings. The subheads indicate associated facilities or equipment.

Buildings Required for Aeronautical Operations

1. Administration or terminal building.
   a. Operational ramp.
   b. Canopied passenger walkways or concourses.
   c. Observation or promenade deck.
   d. Field-side fencing and passenger gates.
   e. Ramp service pits.
2. Hangars.
   a. Apron and outside service area.
   b. Shops.
   c. Offices.
   d. Stock rooms.

e. Gasoline storage.
f. Motor-vehicle storage.
g. Engine test cells.
3. Traffic control tower.
4. Crash, fire, and ambulance building.
a. Crash boat if airport is near water areas.
5. Radio equipment buildings.
6. Post-office building.
7. Express and freight building.
8. Warehouse and refrigeration building.

Buildings Required for Nonaeronautical Operations—Nonrevenue Producing

1. Structures and field-maintenance equipment building.
   a. Motor-vehicle maintenance and repair shop.
   b. Stock room and warehouse for maintenance supplies.
   c. Carpenter shop.
   d. Electrical shop.
   e. Plumbing shop.
   f. Paint shop.
   g. Machine shop.
2. Electrical substation and standby power-plant building.
3. Pump house.
4. Auxiliary water-supply reservoir.
5. Sewage pump house.
6. Central heating plant.

Nonaeronautical—Revenue-Producing Buildings

1. Garage and/or filling station.
2. Auto-parking areas.
3. Outside refreshment stands.
4. Employees' cafeteria and recreation building.
5. Air-freight warehouse and cold storage.
6. Aircraft and accessories sales exhibition building.
7. General office building.
8. Hotel.
9. Shopping center.

TERMINAL BUILDINGS

Normal airport business transactions such as ticketing passengers; handling of mail, baggage, and cargo; air-line operations; restaurants;

and administrative matters require building space in a central location. At small airports one building or even space in a hangar may suffice. At large terminals a group of buildings may be necessary to house these activities.

The main structure is ordinarily referred to as the administration building. The size of this structure will vary with the extent and volume of the activities it houses. This building normally provides space for air-line ticket and operational offices, fixed-base operator's offices, airport management, C.A.A. communications, airport-traffic control, weather bureau, post office, and concessions.

TERMINAL BUILDINGS—MAJOR TERMINALS

A major terminal is generally considered to be any terminal having as many as fifty scheduled air-line stops per day. Terminals which can be expected in the reasonably near future to approximate this number of operations per day should be considered to be in the major-terminal category. There will naturally be a good deal of difference in the scope of the requirements of various major terminals. This difference will require the engineer to carefully study the present and estimated future activities the terminal building will be called on to house. Personal flying and fixed-base operations have a place in the estimation of major-terminal building requirements. The tendency, however, is to segregate commercial air-line from personal flying in cities high up in the major-terminal class. The features to be provided must in every instance be modified by the needs of the particular airport.

Allowance for Expansion

Almost without exception, every terminal building constructed to date has proved to be inadequate. Many have been outgrown even before their construction has been finished. It is equally correct to say that very few terminal buildings have been located or designed so that they can readily be expanded.

Regardless of the size of either the airport or the community it serves, terminal buildings must be carefully located and designed. Experience clearly indicates that the original structure or group of structures must be considered the nucleus for future developments. Future expansion must be allowed to govern the design of foundations, bearing walls, floors, roofs, access roadways, and the size of ducts for bringing in public utilities.

When expanding airport facilities to meet increased traffic, lengthening the building along the axis parallel to the airport is the more desirable method. Additional floors or wings radiating from the main section may also prove satisfactory.

Segregation of Operations

The most satisfactory design principle developed so far for terminal buildings is the one which gives major consideration to operational problems. This plan has resulted in the segregation of operations by allocating an entire floor to a group of activities having similar functions or operating problems. The segregation principle can also be applied within individual floors to advantage. Where the grouping of similar activities is not carried out, it is often necessary to install duplicate servicing facilities such as loading ramps, access roads, and gates.

Basement

The terminal-building basement can be used to house building service units, but can seldom be used for any operational activity. It may prove impractical for some terminal buildings to have a basement. In such instances the service units must be housed elsewhere in the building, or in separate structures. A basement will be found advantageous wherever it is feasible.

Unless a central heating plant is installed to service all airport buildings, the basement provides an ideal location for the furnace and fuel storage. Air-conditioning equipment can also be accommodated in the basement.

As is pointed out in Chapter XIV, communications are essential to a great many airport activities. A major terminal will require a central location where all incoming circuits are wired into distribution panels. This room can be located in the basement if provisions are made to insure its being completely waterproof and sufficiently well ventilated so that it is not affected by dampness. Dampness will cause corrosion and other damaging effects to equipment.

Transformers and switching equipment for electrical service also require a centrally located space. Because of the fire hazard and the danger associated with high voltages it is recommended that the distribution equipment be housed in a separate building used exclusively for that purpose. However, terminal-building basements have been successfully used to house this equipment.

Basement space can be utilized for storage of materials not affected by dampness, such as janitor supplies and equipment, employees' toilets, and a great many other miscellaneous uses.

The existence of a basement in a terminal building simplifies a number of problems such as access to conduit runs, plumbing and heating pipes, and pneumatic tubes. Where a basement is not contemplated, it is recommended that an easily accessible working space of at least 3 ft be provided between the ground level and the bottom of the first floor and that this space be obstructed as little as possible.

Wherever it is planned to locate equipment in a basement, the manufacturer or public utility involved should be contacted to determine the advisability of such action and whether any special precautions need to be taken. Building codes should also be checked as they usually have regulations governing the conditions under which such apparatus may be installed.

Topography

Topography has an important bearing on the use which is made of the first and second floors. The Washington National Airport and La Guardia Airport illustrate two common conditions.

At the Washington National Airport, rather high ground exists on the side of the building away from the airport. The difference in elevation is approximately one story. This building has only one public entrance, which is at the higher-ground elevation, leading into what will be termed the first or lobby floor. There are ground-floor entrances at both ends of the building which are used for servicing purposes exclusively. Passengers and visitors are not allowed to visit any portion of the ground floor of this building except the passenger concourses leading to the loading gates. Figure 11–2 is a picture of the field side of this building.

At La Guardia Field the Administration Building is located on level ground. Provision is made on the side of the building away from the airport for a ground-level entrance. This entrance is used mainly by passengers and employees arriving at or leaving the airport by bus. Airline coaches pick up and deliver passengers either at the loading gates or in the rear of the building. The ground-level entrance is not used extensively by passengers arriving by taxicab or private car as a ramp to the first or lobby floor entrance is provided. Figure 11–3 is a photograph of this entrance which also shows the parking area and second-floor ramp.

The problem of properly describing the segregation of activities by floors in order to clarify the units to be allocated to certain floors is somewhat difficult. However, it is felt that this can best be accomplished by using the space distribution as is done at the Washington National Airport. The arrangement involved can be applied to terminal buildings at airports where the ground level is the same on both sides of the building as a ramp can be constructed to take the entrance-road traffic up to the lobby level.

Ground Floor

Considering this floor to be on the level of the airport or landing field, and following the principle of segregation of activities by floors, the ground floor naturally lends itself to housing all functions directly relating to loading and servicing the aircraft. Keeping such activities on the ground floor saves the work and expense of the handling which would be entailed on a higher floor.

The following listed functions normally operate most efficiently on this ground floor when not housed in a separate building.

Facilities Used Jointly by All Air-Line Operators

1. Air-line departing passengers' baggage room.
2. Air-mail post office.
3. Air express or cargo office.
4. Trucking concourse connecting all these facilities with proper exits and entrances to the field.
5. Employees' rest room and locker rooms.
6. Terminal-building employees' cafeteria.
7. Branch office of the weather bureau.
8. Packing room for concessionnaire handling meals aloft.
9. Small predeparture passenger waiting room or lobby with suitable toilet facilities and phone booths.
10. Private conference or reception room for important visitors.

Facilities Used by Individual Companies or Airport Management

1. Air-line operation manager's office.
2. Air-line operational quarters.
3. Air-line airplane-servicing units.
4. Air-line ground crews' quarters.
5. Air-line flight crews' quarters.
6. Gasoline and oil concessionnaire's office and service crews' quarters.
7. Airport guards' office.
8. First-aid room.
9. Air-conditioning equipment room.

10. Chief janitor's office.
11. Field-lighting equipment room.
12. Transformer room.
13. Electrical section chief's office.
14. Electrical section shops and small stock room.
15. Public-address-system equipment room.
16. Battery-charging room for battery pits.
17. Weather bureau's storage room for helium tanks.
18. Airport operation manager's office.
19. Itinerant ground crews' quarters.
20. Private or itinerant pilots' lounge.

First or Lobby Floor

Buildings from which two-level loading is contemplated, or which are constructed on the segregation principle, usually have this floor space allocated to functions for the use and accommodation of the public. Since concessions should be easily accessible to the public, space on this floor is desirable to a number of them. Ground-floor space is also satisfactory for a number of concessions at locations where this floor is available to the public.

Activities and Functions Well Served by Lobby-Floor Space

1. Main public lobby.
2. Air-line ticket counters.
3. Air-line traffic manager's office.
4. Passenger waiting room.
5. Air-line station manager's office.
6. Newsstand.
7. Coffee shop.
8. Soda fountain.
9. Drugstore.
10. Barbershop.
11. Bank.
12. Western Union.
13. Main phone booths.
14. Public toilets.
15. Gift and novelty shops.
16. Beauty parlor.

Wherever floor space is allocated as indicated above, it is mandatory that it be accessible to public and private transportation. One set of doors for arriving and departing traffic can be used. Experience at the Washington National Airport, however, has proved the desirability of having the entrance and exit doors separated. All such doors must be of generous proportions to avoid congestion.

An arcade in one wing of a terminal building to provide space for a large variety of stores or shops offers many possibilities for public service, as well as a worth-while revenue in locations where passengers, employees, visitors, and near-by residents constitute a potential source of business for such shops. Such an arcade would logically have entrances on the floors used by the public.

Second Floor

The second floor of the terminal building can be devoted entirely to concessions as is the case at La Guardia Field. It can furnish space for offices as well.

Concessions such as the main dining room, private dining rooms, and cocktail lounges take up more space than can usually be accommodated on the ground or first floors. They should be on the second floor overlooking the airport. Other types of concessions which do not rely for business on the display of merchandise are often pleased with second-floor space. Such concessions include the barbershop and beauty parlor.

If space on the second floor is to be allocated for activities other than concessions they should include the following:

1. Mezzanine overlooking lobby.
2. Airport management and accounts offices.
3. Clubrooms.
4. Air-line reservation offices.
5. Air-line offices.

Third and Higher Floors

The third and higher floors will in almost all instances be devoted to office space.

Government agencies such as C.A.A. Airway Communications, Airway Traffic Control, Air Carrier Inspection, General Inspection, Airport Service District Office, and the U.S. Weather Bureau function to the best advantage of all concerned when properly housed in the terminal building. These agencies have a considerable number of contacts with the flying public and therefore should be easily accessible. Terminal buildings over two stories in height should have elevator service.

The U.S. Weather Bureau will in nearly all instances require roof space for their instruments and so should be consulted when building plans are being prepared.

The allocation of a wing or one or more floors in the main building for hotel purposes may prove sound in instances where local schedules or local attractions warrant.

Traffic Control Tower

The requirements and structural details of the control tower are discussed in Chapter XII. This structure should, wherever possible, form the top floors of the terminal building.

Operational Ramps

Space for loading and servicing planes is required in conjunction with the terminal building. This operational ramp must be hard surfaced, preferably concrete, and properly graded and drained. To be effective it must be available for use in all kinds of weather. It must, of course, be accessible to the administration building so that passengers may be loaded easily and mail, baggage, and cargo trucked to and from the aircraft.

It is essential that the length and width of the ramp be adequate. Four hundred feet in width should be considered the minimum to allow aircraft to pass each other. The length must be sufficient to allow the maximum number of loading gates which will ultimately be required. One hundred and fifty feet is considered the minimum gate spacing. There should be no buildings such as hangars fronting on the terminal-building operational ramp.

Apron Fencing and Passenger Gates

Loading and unloading, other than for relatively small aircraft, require a segregation of passengers and cargo by the use of gates if any appreciable amount of traffic is to be handled. Another purpose served by the fence and gates is to keep the public off the apron and airport.

In the simplest form, passenger gates are merely gates in a fence along the building side of the apron. The fence is usually chain-link construction. Each gate is numbered with the number plainly visible by day and illuminated by night. It is desirable to have each gate served by a telephone and loud-speaker connected with the airport intercommunication system. Each gate should be floodlighted and have weatherproof electrical sockets available. The actual gate should be at least 8 ft in width and provided with a lock. There must be a paved walkway at least 12 ft wide on the terminal building side of the fence for use by baggage trucks and passengers. Local practice will determine whether or not this walkway also is fenced.

Canopied Walkway or Concourse

Air transportation can not be expected to enjoy the fullest possible measure of popularity as long as its use necessitates passengers taking a risk of being drenched by rain or otherwise disheveled by the elements during the trip from the terminal building to the plane. The extent of the risk taken can be reduced by placing a canopy over the walkway along the operational ramp. The most satisfactory construction is to incorporate the walkway into a permanently constructed concourse. Even this provision leaves the passenger some distance to walk without protection. This condition has led to serious thought being given to ways and means of providing shelter until the passenger reaches the door of the plane.

Two-level loading from the concourse, using some form of telescoping loading gangway, appears to offer the best solution. Varying heights aboveground of aircraft doors, the wartime scarcity of critical materials, and the lack of concourses where they could be used have retarded the development of such a gangway.

A concourse can be used for a variety of purposes such as providing space for ground crews, air-line station manager's offices, predeparture passenger waiting rooms, baggage and cargo storage, and, where required, by immigration and customs offices.

A properly designed concourse will permit the separation of roadways used for air-line transportation vehicles, baggage- and cargo-carrying vehicles, and vehicles operated by the general public. Figure 11–4 illustrates a possible concourse design. It will be noted that two ground-level roadways are provided; one inside the structure for cargo or baggage vehicles and one outside for use by the general public. A third roadway at first-floor level is provided for strictly passenger-carrying vehicles.

A concourse designed along lines similar to those shown in Figure 11–4 can be adapted to a variety of operational plans. Air-line ticket offices could be housed in the concourse, or passengers who purchase tickets at a downtown office can proceed directly to the concourse waiting room nearest the gate from which their plane will depart. Continuous shuttle service could be provided along the second-floor roadway at terminals where the concourse is quite long, in order to save passengers the long walk from the terminal-building lobby to the gate.

Ramp Service Pits

The capacity for handling traffic at any airport will depend not only on the number of gates provided, but also on how fast each plane can be serviced and loaded. The facilities provided in the ramp service pits are the governing factor in the length of time required for plane servicing.

It is normal practice always to park the aircraft in the same position with reference to the gate. This is accomplished by painting guidelines on the ramp. The pilot follows these lines, assisted by the signals of the ground crew. A turntable for pivoting the plane wheel on which the final turn is made facilitates parking planes equipped with tail wheels. This method is recommended as it reduces wear and strain on the landing gear and tire.

Ramp service pits are pits of various sizes built in the ramp, and equipped with a cover flush with the ramp surface. The covers must have sufficient strength to support the plane wheel load. Pits must be provided with a drain and should be as weatherproof as possible. More than one pit is required to provide complete plane servicing. The pits should be located so as to be in the most convenient position with reference to the parked airplane.

Applicable codes and local servicing policy will govern the number of pits required and the type of equipment which can be grouped together in one pit. Ramp service pits should provide for the following:

1. Gasoline, oil, and grease service.
2. Air conditioning for hot-weather use.
3. Hot-air heat for cold-weather use.
4. Pneumatic tubes to air-line offices.
5. Telephone to ticket and reservation offices.
6. Batteries or rectifier for starting and lighting.
7. Fire-extinguisher equipment.

The above list may be reduced if some of the servicing is otherwise provided for.

TERMINAL BUILDINGS—MINOR TERMINALS—AIRPARKS, ETC.

The terminal-building requirements for minor terminals, small airports, airparks, etc., will vary widely in scope. The activities to be provided for must be carefully assessed. A number of years will no doubt be required to determine the extent or rate of growth of personal or private flying, charter operations, and feeder-line service.

The same advice holds for this class of terminal building as does for the one to be provided for a major terminal. Present construction should be planned as the nucleus around which construction required by future growth can readily be added. Provision for future expansion must be constantly kept in mind when building plans are being prepared.

As with the major terminal, the smaller terminal should be made as attractive as possible to passengers, operation personnel, and the public. The possibility of concessions should be fully exploited by providing satisfactory space.

A considerable amount of office space may well be required. Governmental agencies, fixed-base operators, aircraft, and other interests connected with air travel will prefer space in the terminal building.

It is advised that communities attract aviation interests to their airport by providing a well-designed terminal building rather than to lag in air transportation and wait for traffic to reach a volume where such facilities will have to be provided. Buildings of low-cost temporary construction, located so as not to interfere with future permanent construction, can be resorted to where there is considerable skepticism as to the terminal's future. This course of action has much to be said for it if it is properly planned. It can help avoid costly mistakes in permanent construction.

HANGARS—MAJOR TERMINALS

The features and requirements of a complete hangar for major-terminal operation will be described. By varying the size of the building and reducing the activities it houses to a minimum, the hangar described can be made to fit into commercial use at rather small airports. Private hangars are discussed in a later section.

Purpose

Hangars are intended primarily to provide space for the storage, maintenance, and repair of aircraft. As aircraft have become larger and less susceptible to the damaging action of the elements the necessity for storing aircraft has decreased greatly. Conversely, the activities now carried on in large hangars have increased the need for space suitable for materials, storage, shops, offices, and employee conveniences.

The following list of facilities needed in an air-line maintenance hangar illustrates the purposes hangar space serves:

1. Propeller shop.
2. Engine test stand.
3. Propeller-grinding room.
4. Engine-control room.
5. Engine storage.
6. Nacelle shop.
7. Engine teardown.
8. Cylinder shop.
9. Engine assembly.
10. Sandblast machine.
11. Men's locker room.
12. Parts-cleaning room.
13. Machine shop.
14. Welding shop.
15. Airplane-overhaul workshop.
16. Electric shop.
17. Airplane-overhaul office.
18. Production control.
19. Superintendent of maintenance.
20. Drafting room.
21. Metal shop.
22. Tool crib.
23. Stock room, supplies.
24. Paint shop and dope room.
25. Heat-treating room.
26. Stock room, parts.
27. Receiving room.
28. Transformer room.
29. Fabric shop.
30. Compressor room.
31. Porters' room.
32. Radio shop.
33. Drawing room and office.
34. Radio machine shop.
35. Radio screen rooms.
36. Line maintenance—G.O.
37. Line maintenance and inspection office.
38. Fire extinguisher storage and repairs.

39. Instrument workshop.
40. Ladies' room.
41. Men's room.
42. Line maintenance workshop.
43. Carpenter storeroom.
44. Battery room.
45. Carpenter shop.
46. Stock room office.
47. Lunch counter.

Layout of Floor Space

The nucleus of the hangar is that space having a clear span and sufficient headroom to accommodate the largest aircraft which it is expected to house. This area is reserved for use of aircraft which are being stored, serviced, or repaired.

Some portion of the main hangar area may be utilized for shops or offices, but this is usually not good practice. It is more economical to provide such space in buildings of a lean-to or attached type on the rear or sides of the hangar as this space needs only normal headroom height. Such practice is shown in a number of the illustrations for this chapter. Space in buildings attached to the hangar makes for greater efficiency as the operations are more compact.

The amount of floor space allocated to each activity will vary with the needs of the organization using the hangar. It has often been the practice to construct hangars and then expect the tenant to fit his activities into the space provided. Since most air lines and large commercial operators have standard operational procedures, the tenant should be consulted regarding space layout whenever possible.

Utility Services

Aircraft maintenance and service requires convenient access to various utilities and services. These may consist of a combination of any one or more of the following:

1. Electrical services.
2. Water.
3. Compressed air.
4. Steam.
5. Vacuum lines.
6. Communications.
7. Pneumatic tubes.

8. Drain lines.
9. Overhead cranes or conveyors.
10. Fire-protection equipment.

Since the floor space must be kept unobstructed these utilities and services must be provided in service trenches, suspended from the ceiling, or located on the walls. For most efficient operation all three methods will probably be used. (Refer to Fig. 11–8.)

Service trenches will average about 3 ft square and should be provided with a cover consisting of short removable sections. Service-trench locations will depend on the type of operation involved, but since they are comparatively inexpensive, an adequate number should be provided.

Since most roof members lend themselves readily to supporting overhead installations, these features do not require too exact planning.

Lighting

Indirect lighting by inverted, high-voltage lighting fixtures has proved satisfactory. When the fixtures are directed upward toward a light-colored ceiling, an even illumination without glare or shadows can be obtained.

Service Apron

A service apron in front of the hangar and connected with the taxiway system forms an integral part of the hangar. This apron provides parking space for aircraft and can be used for a number of servicing operations. In many instances it will be desirable to provide service pits in the apron similar to those described for the loading apron. This apron should be at least 400 ft in width if possible.

Planes having wing spans of approximately 250 ft seem certain to come into common use. These planes, and even much smaller planes, are too large to be hangared except for major repairs. There is reason to believe that shelters for providing protection to mechanics and equipment will be developed to a point where the majority of routine servicing is done on the service apron. Figure 11–9 shows a C-54 being serviced at La Guardia Field using such shelters. Figure 11–10 is a photograph of a nose hangar used by American Export Airlines at La Guardia Field.

DOORS

The cost of hangar doors, either manually or mechanically operated, is a major cost of the structure. Considerable study must be given to the type of doors from the standpoint of operation and functional purposes. In small hangars of spans up to 60 ft, manually operated doors of the vertical-lift, canopy, and horizontal types have been successfully used. For the larger hangars, mechanically operated doors are the more efficient. Since heat losses occurring when the door is opened become an important factor, the speed of operation, size of opening, and efficiency of performance of doors must be integrated against their initial cost.

The popular types of hangar doors are the vertical-lift and the horizontal sliding doors. Either type, or a combination of the two, may be used. Doors of any type or dimension must, of course, be designed to resist maximum wind pressures.

It is believed that the vertical-lift door, preferably the folding-canopy type, is the better of the two from the standpoint of economy and efficient operation. Sliding doors, operating as they do on a guide rail at the ground or floor level, are at times subject to serious obstructions in the form of ice, snow, and other materials which interfere with their efficient and free movement.

Single doors, opening for the full height and width of the space, permit a very objectionable and costly heat loss. Sectional doors may be designed and operated so as to greatly minimize heat losses and still permit the entrance and exit of the smaller planes or equipment. This is done by opening only a single section or portion thereof.

The tail height of the larger planes will prove to be a far more critical dimension than that of a wing span when doors of uniform height are used. Doors for tail heights approaching 50 ft above the floor level present difficult design problems and are unduly costly to construct and operate because of the size and weight involved.

Designs of the future will probably be simplified and construction and operation costs reduced by the adoption of sectional doors having a center section of a height required by the tail, and side or end sections reduced in height to accommodate the wings. For such a plan, the center section could be designed for a vertical lift canopy type, and the side or end sections for the horizontal sliding type. In a typical door 50 ft by 300 ft this plan would result in a reduction of approximately 30 per cent in total door space.

CONCRETE HANGARS

The rapid advance in the design of airplanes has been a challenge to the structural engineer. The enormous wing span of modern aircraft has brought about many advances in the design of hangars to house these planes. Until recently it has been only in very rare cases that the building designer has had to cope with spans varying from 150 ft to 300 ft or more. To meet these new requirements it was necessary to look to the bridge engineer for inspiration.

Three Types of Construction

Two types of bridges that have been in common use for a long period of time furnished, at least in part, the answer to this new problem. The concrete rigid frame and the concrete arch have been built successfully in these long spans, and the task of adapting them to lighter live loads was a fairly simple one. The solution of the problem, however, was not confined to the rigid frame and the arch. Another type of concrete construction fitted perfectly into this picture. The "shell dome" had already been developed for a great many armories, auditoriums, and similar types of long-span buildings, both in Europe and America.

In more recent years, hangars for airplanes have been built using all three of these types of construction, each giving entire satisfaction. The selection of type should be determined by economics. This, of course, varies in every case. Local labor conditions, availability of materials, and foundation conditions all influence the selection of the proper type of structure.

Advantageous Properties of Concrete

Concrete is a plastic. The mention of this magic word "plastic" at once conjures up in the minds of almost everyone something new, something modern; yet for centuries this plastic—concrete—has been used in building construction. It was molded into structures before the eleventh century by the ancient Greeks and Romans, and many of these structures are standing today in Athens and Rome.

The modern trend in architectural design is that it should be functional, and that the structure be designed so that the grace and beauty of the structural members are the main architectural features.

Architects and engineers not previously familiar with the possibilities of monolithic concrete construction are greatly impressed with its flexibility and adaptability to every decorative as well as structural requirement. Whether it is molded, tooled, colored, or left with the form impressions exposed makes little difference if the design has been well conceived and intelligently handled.

Economical Features

Monolithic concrete construction has other attributes. It is economical to construct, produces a fire-safe building, has a low maintenance cost, and has great lateral stiffness in spite of the absence of complicated trusses and braces. The monolithic interlocking action of all parts of the structure included in the exterior and interior walls makes this type of structure safe against hurricanes, earthquakes, and gravity loads. The economy of this type of construction is greatly influenced by the design of the structure. By intelligent planning, both the structural members and the architectural detail can be so arranged that a maximum re-use of the forms is attained. Many buildings have been designed where forms have been made up in panels and these panels re-used as often as twelve times in the originally assembled form. This is the sort of intelligent use of material that produces economic structures. Elaborate ornamentation may be comparatively inexpensive if it is so detailed that the plaster molds against which the concrete is cast can be made from the same model.

To attain the maximum economy in concrete construction the goal should be repetition and more repetition. If the structure is correctly detailed and the proper quality of concrete specified for the conditions of exposure, the upkeep will be negligible. Proper specifications, laboratory tests, and control of the concrete make this a simple procedure.

Foundation Analysis

Beginning with a careful analysis of the soil, its character and load-bearing qualities are scientifically determined. In the design of rigid frames or arches, the character of the soil may determine whether the foundations should be tied together or left free. Rigid frames have been designed and built on both pile foundations and spread footings.

When the thrust at the top of the foundations in which piles are used is excessive, batter piles are sometimes driven to take this thrust. It is quite common, however, in both types to tie the foundation together with steel rods encased in concrete. In certain types of soils, keys may be cut under the spread footings thus eliminating the necessity for tying the foundation.

Choice of Frames

The rigid frames are usually haunched at the supports to provide sufficient concrete area to take the compression due to the negative moment and to provide additional effective depth which reduces the amount of reinforcing steel required at this point. When very large spans are used it is sometimes advantageous to use hollow rigid frames. These hollow frames greatly reduce the weight of the structure and therefore reduce the size of the footings or foundations. The increase in the amount of formwork and sometimes the increased height of the building, plus additional labor required to place the concrete in the frames, will often prove to be greater than the economies brought about by the use of hollow frames. Each individual case must be studied.

It is impossible to write a general expression or equation for the length of span at which the hollow frame will be more economical than the solid frame. Practically every factor of design and construction enters the picture. The foundation conditions and the cost of labor and material must all be taken into account and each case decided on its merit.

Stress Analysis

The engineer has a wide choice in the method of analysis. He may use one of the most popular, commonly known as "Moment Distribution." The fact that the members are haunched at the supports and therefore have a varying moment of inertia is not difficult to handle by this method. Many textbooks which go into this method very thoroughly are available. Tables for determining the physical constants are available. They greatly reduce the amount of work necessary to make a design for this type of structure.

Practically all hangars are built with the floor on the ground so that the floor design is no different than that of the runways. The only loads to be considered on the structure are the weight of the structure and the wind and snow loads.

An analysis is also made for stresses due to change in temperature and for sidesway caused by unsymmetrical loading. In calculating these stresses due to temperature change, it is necessary to include stresses due to shrinkage along with the stresses due to temperature variation.

The assembly of the reinforcement for rigid-frame bents can be so designed that it will form trusses from which the formwork may be hung, thus eliminating a great deal of shoring of the formwork. These trusses, of course, must be designed so that they are capable of carrying the weight of the forms and the dead weight of the concrete until the concrete is sufficiently set to carry its own weight plus the other loads to which the structure will be subjected.

In the door bent it is customary to keep a uniform depth. This can be done easily since the greater depth is made possible by extending the girder above the roof slab any desired height to form a coping. This gives a uniform soffit to which the large doors may be attached.

Many types of roof slab can be adapted for this kind of construction. Beam and slab, ribbed slabs with removable metal domes or permanent masonry fillers, or precast joists may be used. In all cases except the latter, the structural slab will provide sufficient lateral bracing, but in the case of precast construction it is usually found necessary to cast integrally with the frames a system of lateral struts which tie the frames together. Small struts at the quarter points of the spans will usually be sufficient. The precast joists and precast slabs, however, have two distinct advantages. One is that they form a much lighter weight of roof construction. The precast plank and joists can be made of light-weight aggregate which results in a concrete approximately one-third lighter than stone concrete. The other point in favor of the precast-roof system is that it eliminates the shoring and formwork necessary for the cast-in-place construction.

Buildings under 200 ft in length are seldom provided with expansion joints, while longer buildings should have at least one joint. The design of the structure, however, will greatly influence the location of expansion joints. In multiple-span construction these joints are usually located at the point of contraflexure for gravity loads, and there is no limit to the kinds of joint that can be made. There are rockers, rollers, curved plates, sliding plates, and many others. The main thing, however, to consider in designing these joints is to keep them simple and remember that the building is to be built by carpenters, masons, and laborers, not jewelers.

Besides designing a joint that will allow the building to adjust itself to the changes in temperature and so forth, it is also necessary to design a joint that is watertight. Here again, however, there are a number of simple methods that have been successfully used.

It will be readily conceded that there will be more movement due to temperature changes on the exterior frames than the interior. The end bay construction must therefore be designed so that this differential movement will not cause cracks and other damage to the structure. The movement is so slight that there is little danger of its causing failure to the structures. It could, however, cause unsightly cracks and a leaky roof unless the details of bearing of the slab and flashings are given the closest attention.

Within certain span limits the rigid frame offers many advantages and these should be thoroughly investigated before rushing into arch designs. Since the hangar, besides being a storage space for planes, is also a workshop, it is necessary to support loads such as cranes from the ceiling. These loads can readily be attached to the soffit of the frames without the introduction of an elaborate system of suspended construction required by arch design. In the case of the arch too, the roof must be much higher. This means that the number of cubic feet in the building is greatly increased and all of this unusable space must be heated.

Many hangars have been built on the principle of three-dimensional dome design. That is, they are designed for an action in space similar to the problems found in the cupolas of churches.

If properly designed, domed structures are very economical and offer an optimum of resistance for a body built from a given quantity of material. Using the stiffness of curved surfaces for a hangar construction is applying the advanced knowledge of economical plane design to stationary buildings.

Domed surfaces on roofs are mainly in compression and concrete is an economical material for such stresses. The outstanding features of the shell-dome roof construction are the monolithic character of concrete slabs and framing and, above all, the fact that these curved slabs are stiffened at intervals and along the edges.

From the illustrations it is apparent that, mainly, cylindrical surfaces (surfaces with curvature in one direction only) are used. Such "barrel shells" are supported on arches or along the walls and consist of concrete slabs with a thickness varying between 2½ in. and 5 in.

There are two types of barrel shells: the single longitudinal barrel and the multiple barrels. The first hangars were built of the multiple barrel type of shell, which is very suitable for spans up to 160 ft, with barrels about 30 ft to 40 ft wide, arranged in parallel formations and stiffened along the edges. With spans over 160 ft it becomes advisable to use the single barrel with the barrel arranged either at right angles to the door or parallel with the door.

The latter type is suitable for hangars with a depth up to about 120 ft and door spans of about 160 ft. The small ribs in the roof slab are stiffeners to prevent buckling, and actually do not carry the shell, which is suspended between the end walls and the large arch rib in the center of the building.

Larger door spans are best taken care of by locating the barrel at right angles to the hangar door. These have been built in monolithic concrete for hangars over 300 ft wide. Such structures can easily be extended in the direction of the barrel and are adaptable for either sliding or canopy doors. Crane rails can easily be hung to the arches and stiffener ribs.

The casual observer always thinks that shells are carried by the edge beams with a thrust action like that which carries an arched bridge on piers. Actually, the curved shell itself is playing a major role in the beam action between supports. Acting like a corrugated sheeting with the large depths of corrugations from crowning to springing, the curved shell possesses much more stiffness than the comparatively shallow edge beams. Most important is the fact that the arches are supporting such curved shells: first, the suspension from one or two end frames or arch frames; and, second, some supports along the edge beams. It can be recognized that if the supports along one edge beam become defective or less efficient, increased supporting action along the remaining sides will immediately come into play. An appreciation of this possible change in the stress distribution on shells is most important because it shows their advantage in case of damage to the roof. A hole which might be torn out of the structure would not mean a total failure, and the remaining parts would be able to stand up until repairs could be made. The curved shells are able to take up some of the functions of a destroyed stiffener beam. This applies not only for hits in the shell proper but it has been proved that even a local destruction of the carrying arches will not cause the collapse of the structure. The adjoining shell is able to bridge the gap between the severed ends of the arches, transmitting direct compressive stresses across, like a hinge of an arch bridge.

There is practically unlimited carrying power in a large shell which, in the case of emergency such as the entire removal of a support, would still prevent a final collapse. The example of a very high, thin wall supported on columns of comparatively narrow spacing, such as a slab on edge, will illustrate the excess carrying power of shells. If the wall is higher than the span, only the lower part of this wall will act as a bridge between the columns, and the upper part is merely dead weight. It is easily understood, however, that when doubling the span (by removal of one column) the depth of that lower part of the wall taking part in the bridging action will automatically increase in proportion to the span. The elimination of support in a high wall is therefore not as dangerous as it is for shallow members such as common trusses or girders. The same reasoning can be applied to concrete-shell roofs which compare with a series of slabs set partly on edge, and therefore behave like the high wall described above.

A curved shell also has the adaptability of acting as a cantilever beam beyond the supporting arch. This action will also help to prevent a collapse in case of emergency.

Should an explosion occur inside the hangar, the shell can take the shock because its shape and design are like those of a pressure vessel. Even local fires of extreme heat will not cause failure in such structures.

Prestressed tension chords for the arch frames and proper location of expansion joints eliminate the hazards of unequal settlement and secondary stresses, even under unfavorable soil conditions. The high factor of safety with concrete structures is recognized, as is also the opportunity of employing a large percentage of local labor during construction.

STRUCTURAL STEEL HANGARS

Structural steel hangar design does not vary sufficiently from standard building practice to warrant any extensive discussion in this text. This type of construction has been used extensively in hangar construction and has proved satisfactory. A hangar of this type is shown in Fig. 11–16.

HANGARS FOR PERSONAL AIRCRAFT

While a good percentage of personal aircraft will continue to be stored in large hangars, there are several reasons to believe that small hangars will become increasingly popular. The sense of privacy afforded by the individual hangars appeals to many owners. The small hangar has the practical advantages of decreasing the general fire hazard and eliminating the opportunity for careless handling or tampering which exists where aircraft are accessible to hangar visitors who like to push, pull, and poke. The owner of a plane which is stored in a private hangar is saved the inconvenience of delay and also the danger of collision often encountered in moving other planes in a large hangar to allow his plane to be removed. It is expected that all airports where private flying is allowed will have need for a large number of hangars for personal planes.

Fireproofing

The fire hazard connected with aviation gasoline and doped fabrics is generally recognized. While it may be considerably reduced in the future it is believed that the need for fireproof construction in all hangars will remain. For this reason fireproof construction using concrete, concrete blocks, masonry, or other fire-resistant materials is recommended. It is also recommended that all multiple hangars contain as many fireproof partitions as possible so that any fire will be localized to the bay in which it is located.

Layout

The private-hangar area should be served by aprons and taxiways, but should be somewhat removed from the area where commercial operations will be conducted. The area chosen needs to be easily accessible and capable of considerable expansion. It is difficult to predict the percentage of the population which will own personal aircraft in the future, but it is safe to assume that it will be many times the present rate.

Aircraft, being T shaped, allow a number of floor-layout designs which result in a minimum of waste space. Figures 11–17, –18, –19, and –20 illustrate several possibilities. The amount of space required by a small plane is greatly reduced if its tail can be raised so that the plane is tilted at about a 45-deg angle. Raising the tail is practical only for very light planes.

In order to accommodate a large number of planes it may be necessary to have several rows of hangars. These may be at right angles or parallel to the main taxiway. The distance between rows of hangars will need to be quite wide in order to allow two planes to pass. It must also be borne in mind that many owners will desire to wash, polish, or otherwise service their planes in front of their individual hangars. A clear distance of at least 150 ft is advised.

Wing span and length of the aircraft govern the floor-space layout. These dimensions vary considerably with different aircraft. It is considered advisable to construct for the larger rather than the smaller popular planes. Door span and hangar depth should be approximately 4 ft wider than the wing span and length of the aircraft for which the hangar is designed. A door height of 12 ft is generally considered adequate.

Hangar floors should be paved and should slope so that positive runoff of water is assured.

Design

The C.A.A. and others are giving special attention to the problem of providing low-cost groups of hangars built for rental to private owners so that each has his own plane space. In surveying the standard clearance requirements the conclusion has been reached that the maximum door size needed is approximately 42 ft in width and 10 ft in height. These dimensions are adopted for use in this study, but may be modified to suit local requirements.

In the design of this type of hangar, the engineer or architect is not confronted with new types of construction but may use any of the well-known systems of construction: the flat slab, the reinforced concrete beam and slab, or precast joists and precast plank. The exterior walls may be cast-in-place concrete or masonry. Interior columns will not interfere with the housing of planes or cause the mechanics working on them any inconvenience if the columns are properly arranged and the planes backed into the hangars so that the wingspread is in the first bay between the exterior wall and the first row of columns.

For planes requiring a larger door opening than the 42-ft width discussed above, the added width may be divided up between the columns. In this way considerably larger planes may be housed without greatly complicating the design problems, the construction, or the cost.

The square hangar and the rectangular hangar will require a door for each plane, but they have the distinct advantage of providing a private hangar for each individual plane by constructing concrete or masonry partitions enclosing each plane. This provides maximum protection against fire and will undoubtedly be recognized by fire-insurance companies and show a saving in cost over the open hangar. However, even if these partitions are omitted, doors for each individual plane are advantageous and may well prove to be worth the added cost. It means that each plane can be taken in and out of the hangar without having to move any of the other planes.

The oblong hangar has many of the advantages of the square hangar, the principal difference being in the lack of continuity in the structural members. This might add a small amount to the cost of the structure but the added cost would not be big enough to rule this type out if it fitted into the field layout more advantageously.

Octagonal, circular, and other geometrical shapes offer an opportunity to remove the planes without moving any of the other planes in the hangar. Such a hangar has only one door and uses a turntable to bring each plane into position. However, it would be impossible to partition off each plane stall and the cost of construction generally would be considerably higher, since it would be impossible to have any columns inside the structure. Individual doors and stalls can of course be made in an octagonal hangar only by creating a great deal of waste floor space.

Utilities

Small hangars will require electricity for lighting and for operating various kinds of tools and equipment. Water and sewer facilities are desirable but not a necessity. Heating is desirable but probably too expensive in cold climates. Provisions should be made so that heat by the use of coal, gas, or electric heaters can be supplied as the occasion requires.

EMERGENCY-EQUIPMENT BUILDINGS

The design of buildings to house airport emergency equipment poses no design problems other than those ordinarily encountered in this type of building. The location of the building or space requires careful consideration and planning. The emergency equipment should not take up space which would otherwise produce good revenue, but it should be in a central location. The building must be easily accessible by paved roadway to the taxiways and runways. There must be the least possible chance that aircraft on taxiways would prevent the equipment from reaching any part of the airport or any airport building.

Wherever the airport depends on a municipal fire department or ambulance service, adequate provision must be made for this equipment to reach the airport runways and taxiways readily.

The larger terminals will require an automatic fire-alarm system with display boards to indicate the location of the fire. Fire and crash alarms must be so arranged that they can be operated from the traffic control tower.

In many instances an auxiliary water supply will be required to supplement the supply available from water mains. This will be true where the airport is a considerable distance from the main pumping station and where large structural fires may occur.

POST OFFICE

The space where incoming and outgoing mail is separated and distributed presents layout problems different from those encountered at an ordinary post office. The problem is most complicated where several air lines operate out of the airport. There is good reason to believe the volume of air mail will require a separate building for this purpose.

The post-office building can be located at any convenient place on the airport and need not front on an apron or taxiway.

One building plan which appears to have merit provides for a rather long narrow building with a loading platform on both sides. All incoming mail, both from planes and the local post office is delivered on one side of the building, and all outgoing mail to planes and local post office leaves from the other side. Each air line has one or more incoming and outgoing loading gates. Incoming and outgoing loading space is also assigned to the local post office. This design facilitates handling of mail pouches by air lines and avoids the confusion and congestion that results when several air lines use a common loading gate.

In planning a building to handle air mail, allowance for expansion must be provided and the possibility of additional air lines using the airport at a later date recognized.

EXPRESS AND FREIGHT

The volume of express and freight handled by air-transportation companies can be expected to grow to a point where the present practice of using space in the terminal building for these activities will no longer suffice.

A building design similar to that described above for handling air mail has merit for use in handling express and freight. The idea of segregating incoming and outgoing shipments according to air lines is applicable. There is no reason for this building to front on a ramp or taxiway as long as it is accessible to them by road.

The part which refrigeration and warehousing may come to play in connection with air transportation is discussed in Chapter XV. It appears desirable to include these facilities in any building built to take care of express and freight shipments, or at least provide for their inclusion at a later date.

ELECTRICAL SUBSTATION

It is essential that every major terminal and any other airport having important schedules have a sufficient number of independent sources of power so that continuous operation of radio, lighting, and other electrical equipment is guaranteed.

It is recommended that an electrical substation be provided in a building suitable for housing transformers, switching equipment, and a standby engine-generator plant. This building should be centrally located and can be combined with the transformer vault described in Chapter X.

Wherever possible, power lines from two or more independent distribution lines should run to the substation. Automatic switching equipment should be provided to transfer the load to the alternate supply in case of outage of the main supply.

An engine-generator plant of sufficient capacity to carry the entire airport load should be connected into the power distribution system so that it will automatically take over the entire load in the event all sources of commercial power fail. Since the engine-generator must go into full-load operation almost instantaneously, time can not be allowed for it to warm up. This condition makes it mandatory to heat the building continuously or to provide thermostatically controlled electric heating elements in the engine cooling system.

CENTRAL-HEATING PLANT

For reasons other than the general benefits common to central heating of a group of buildings, this heating principle is most desirable for airport-building heating. The advantage as far as airport operation is concerned lies in the fact that the smoke and soot can be removed from the vicinity of the traffic control tower.

Where the traffic control tower is in a building having one or more chimneys there is a conflict between efficient furnace operation and unobstructed vision from the control tower. To secure a good draft the chimney usually has to be as high as the control tower and therefore constitutes an obstruction to vision. Any smoke from the chimney increases this undesirable condition. Another disadvantage in having a chimney near a control tower is that soot or oil smoke causes the windows to become dirty quite rapidly.

MISCELLANEOUS BUILDINGS

Local conditions pertaining to such services as sewage disposal, housing maintenance equipment, garage, employees' cafeteria or recreation building, office space, shopping facilities, and various forms of entertainment will determine what other buildings may be necessary. Few, if any, of these buildings present any special problems in their use on an airport and so are not discussed individually.

Local conditions often make it necessary to provide buildings remote from the airport to house radio receivers or transmitters. Buildings for housing radio facilities used in connection with instrument-landing systems are generally provided by C.A.A. If the airport management should have use for such buildings C.A.A. will gladly furnish current information and drawings.

At airports where maintenance is carried on by airport employees with airport equipment, storage buildings and various shops will probably be desirable.

The design of miscellaneous airport buildings should recognize the likelihood of considerable expansion in airport size or activities.

SNOW AND ICE REMOVAL

Wherever any appreciable volume of snow falls or ice forms, its removal presents a serious and costly maintenance and operational problem. The problem is particularly complicated where the paved areas have openings such as service pits and where gates and buildings interfere with the free and full use of snow-removal equipment.

Radiant heating from a system of pipe lines, installed beneath the pavement, which melts the snow and ice and evaporates the resulting moisture has proved practical for sidewalks, driveways, platforms, and floors. The installation costs of radiant-heating systems have been of interest to observers during the period of the development of the technique. Two factors, engineering and fabrication, have undergone slow but steady changes, with the result that the systems have become less costly as time went on.

The manufacturers of this equipment advocate its use as practical and economical for airport runways, taxiways, and aprons. The writers feel that removal of snow and ice by this method should be investigated, at least for aprons, passenger walks, and paved areas around buildings.

CHAPTER XII

TRAFFIC CONTROL TOWERS

PURPOSE

Whenever traffic in and out of an airport reaches any appreciable number of operations per hour, control of the activities of the aircraft, both on the ground and in the air, is necessary in order to avoid collisions and to speed up operations. Diversified traffic such as a mixture of air-line operations, student training, and local pleasure flights usually requires control even when the traffic count is much lower.

The people who exercise airport-traffic control are referred to as controllers. At airports where traffic control is in effect, it is a violation of the Civil Air Regulations for a pilot to fail to comply with the controller's instructions. Control is exercised over every aircraft within the area designated under the control tower's jurisdiction. This control includes taxiing instructions, take-off clearance, approval to vary from prescribed traffic pattern, designation of landing priority, collision course warning, and providing information as to traffic, airport surface conditions, and weather conditions. Aircraft equipped with two-way radio can take full advantage of the controller's services. Other aircraft have to rely on light-gun signals. A light gun is a spotlight which can be aimed at the pilot in much the same manner as a gun could be. It shows either red or green as desired. Green indicates approval of the next logical operation such as taxiing into position, taking off, or landing. A red light means danger or nonapproval of next logical operation. The pilot acknowledges receipt of the light signal by rocking the airplane slightly.

It is readily apparent that the person controlling traffic must be able to see and contact not only the aircraft being controlled, but also all other aircraft in the immediate vicinity. The purpose of the traffic control tower is to provide working space for the controller in carrying out his duties.

LOCATION REQUIREMENTS

The necessity for the controller to be able to see all aircraft operating on or in the immediate vicinity of the airport makes proper location of the tower the prime requirement.

From an ideally located tower, the controller can see all aircraft on the airport taxiways, aprons, and runways. He also has full view of the approaches and turning zones of the airport. He is in a position to see every aircraft which in any way has a bearing on the control he exercises.

The ideal tower must therefore be higher than any near-by structure which could limit the controller's vision. It must also be centrally located and so placed that lower structures do not cut off the controller's view of any portion of the runway, taxiway, apron, or approaches.

Since the terminal building is also usually centrally located, it very often works out that the control tower can form the upper stories of this building. In many instances, however, special control-tower structures will be necessary or desirable.

STRUCTURAL REQUIREMENTS

Vision

Unobstructed vision takes precedence over all other requirements. The sides of a control tower are, therefore, as nearly as possible made up entirely of glass. Unobstructed vision means not only freedom from objects in the controller's line of sight, but also freedom from all forms of reflections, distortion, or other optical defects.

Temperature and Ventilation Control

When provisions have been made for clear vision, the factors which affect the controller's operating efficiency are next in importance. Temperature control combined with ventilation affects the controller's comfort to the largest extent. It must be realized that controllers work under more than a normal amount of strain and under conditions which require clear, quick thinking along with prompt, accurate decisions. To allow a controller to work with confidence and ease, his surroundings must be conducive to physical comfort and good health, and working space best suited for this must be provided.

Noise Level

A controller is constantly alert. He scans the area around the tower continually, at the same time listening for radio contacts which may come to him over any one of several radio receivers. Noises which can distract his attention or interfere with his receiving calls on the radio must be kept to a minimum. A low noise level can be taken as the requirement next in importance.

Equipment Location

The equipment, such as radio receivers, transmitters, wind instruments, light gun, and lighting controls, which is furnished for the controller's use, determine to a large extent how well he performs his work. The convenience with which the controller can reach this equipment both for use and repair is also an important factor in his operating efficiency. Proper equipment layout is considered the next requirement.

Ease of Access

The number of controllers on duty at any time may vary from one to several. A variety of causes may make it imperative that the controller leave his post of duty. He will no doubt use good judgment as to the actual time he leaves, but in every case it will be imperative that he return as soon as possible. For the controller's efficient operation and the general convenience of all people who have occasion to visit the tower, it should be easily accessible. It should be as convenient to toilets as can be arranged. At present many controllers are women. This makes it even more important that steep stairs, exposed ladders, and the like be avoided.

Office Space

The operation of a control tower is usually under the supervision of a chief controller. Many records have to be kept, conferences held, people interviewed, and matters pertaining to traffic control handled by the chief controller. These activities require office space separate from the tower, but closely associated therewith. Convenient office space for tower purposes is a requirement either of the tower structure or the building of which the tower is a part.

Efficient Lighting

The interior lighting of a traffic control tower differs from ordinary office lighting because the controller must have, as nearly as possible, perfect lighting for his paper work, operation of controls, and reading of instruments, while at the same time he must be able to look through the tower windows without having his vision impaired by glare or reflections. Consideration is being given to using recessed lighting so that transparent paper instead of ordinary opaque paper can be used. Lighting engineers are making a good deal of progress in this field. The engineer should always provide the most modern type of tower lighting which has found general acceptance.

SEPARATE TOWER STRUCTURE

C.A.A. Experience

The C.A.A. has constructed and operated several airport-traffic control towers in instances where they were specifically requested to do so. Their experience in developing a satisfactory tower structure provided much information of value, as the latest design incorporates all the features actual operation showed to be desirable.

C.A.A. selected each site for their towers only after giving careful consideration to the vision a standard 52-ft-high tower in that location would afford the controller. They also considered the possible hazard the tower would create, the ease with which the site could be reached, the cost of extending a road and public utilities to the site, and the site's relation to future airport expansion.

It was decided that a structure, five stories in height would be accepted as standard. Figure 12–1 is a photograph of the tower constructed.

The first floor is designed to provide room for the heating unit, coal-bin, stand-by engine generator, and storage room. The lobby portion can be used for office space.

C.A.A. generally uses the second floor for the maintenance shop and the third floor for the chief controller's office. The fourth floor provides space for the men's and women's toilets and the equipment room. The control tower itself constitutes the fifth floor.

The uses made of the various floors can be changed to suit local conditions. It is advised, however, that the equipment be kept on the fourth floor as it is more readily accessible to the controller on duty for emergency repairs.

The main criticisms of this particular structure are that it is not fire-proof, has no provision for a fire escape, and the tower portion is difficult to heat and ventilate. Masonry construction and an outside fire escape would go far to eliminate the fire hazard.

Open Steel-Tower Type

In a number of instances control towers have been mounted on top of open-framework steel towers. These have usually been temporary expedients. It should be apparent that this type of structure does not lend itself readily to meeting several of the requirements connected with the physical comfort of the controller, or for office space. Such a structure is not recommended. A properly designed enclosed steel tower can, however, prove satisfactory.

TOWER INCORPORATED IN TERMINAL BUILDING

Advantages

There are many advantages to be gained by having the control tower form an integral part of the terminal building.

Among these advantages are:

1. Controllers are in close proximity to the airport management, C.A.A. communications, and U.S. Weather Bureau if these agencies are also housed in the terminal building.
2. Tower construction can usually be more stable and therefore less liable to damage by high winds.
3. Terminal building heating is usually steadier and more dependable, and advantage can be taken of any air-conditioning facilities of the building.
4. Cost of construction is lower, owing to the terminal building forming the lower floors.
5. Space that a separate structure would occupy could be used for other purposes.

DETAILS OF CONSTRUCTION

General

The glassed-in operating quarters and the equipment room immediately below should be constructed in much the same manner, regardless of whether a separate structure or the terminal building is used. This is true because most of the actual operation problems are concentrated in these two floors.

Glass Portion

The accuracy of the image received by a person looking through $\frac{1}{4}$-in.-thick plate glass is affected by several different properties of the glass.

Distortion occurs if the glass contains faults which cause the light waves to be transmitted in an uneven manner. The plate glass used must therefore possess the best possible optical characteristics. Glass used in a control tower must be specially selected, clear glass with good optical qualities; run-of-the-mill plate glass should not be used.

High-quality glass is not only important to prevent accidents which might occur through faulty vision, but also to prevent deterioration of the controller's eyesight from eyestrain.

A difference of opinion exists as to the value of using tinted glass. The advocates of tinted glass contend that eyestrain during periods of bright sunlight is lessened, glare from all sources is reduced, and the filtering effect improves the quality of the image seen, under all conditions. Those people who are opposed to the idea of tinting point out that any coloring whatsoever cuts down the amount of light transmitted, with resulting decrease in vision. Most controllers appear to favor tinting while people relying on scientifically conducted tests favor clear glass. The use of curved glass should be avoided.

Since reflection of any kind is confusing to the controller it must be avoided as far as is possible. Tilting the glass outward at the top in the amount of approximately 3½ in. per vertical foot is the most effective means so far employed.

Some towers have the glass sloping outward for about three-fourths of the tower height with the top one quarter sloping inward at a sharp angle. It is the general consensus that this design is much less desirable than is a constant outward slope the full height of the glass. Access to the tower roof is necessary as wind instruments are usually located there. This can usually be provided far more easily if the glass has a constant slope.

Many towers have been constructed with hinged glass windows. This was done to provide ventilation and to lessen the difficulty of window washing.

This method of installing the glass has several bad features and should not be used. Hinged windows are very difficult to control if opened when the wind has any appreciable velocity. The large glass windows break easily if allowed to slam. The glasses are costly and difficult to replace. It can be readily appreciated that the tower personnel and equipment have reduced protection from wind, rain, and temperature during the period required to replace a broken glass. Hinges and catches capable of holding the large glass deteriorate rapidly, making tight joints difficult to maintain, with drafts and water leaks resulting. Falling glass from a broken control-tower window is very dangerous to anyone who may be in its path.

Nothing can be done to control the transmission of heat by the glass portion of the tower unless two thicknesses of glass with a vacuum air space between them are used. This practice is recommended wherever funds are available.

Roof

The tower roof, the highest platform in the vicinity, provides a perfect place to install wind-recording instruments. The roof must therefore be accessible for installation and maintenance of these instruments. Access is usually provided by an outside ladder permanently installed on the side of the tower away from the airport.

Since the roof must support the live load of one or more persons working there, it must be structurally capable of carrying this load and must have safety devices to prevent workmen from falling off.

Pipe railing, supports for wind instruments, wiring fixtures, and similar equipment require a type of roof to which such things can be rigidly bolted in order to withstand wind vibration. Provision must also be made in the roof for wiring ducts to accommodate the wiring for wind instruments. A steel plank roof provides a practical solution to these problems at a low weight per square foot.

A great deal of heat can be transmitted by the tower roof, causing excessive heat in the summer and a waste of heat in the winter. It is therefore very essential that the roof be insulated by every means possible. A combination of a layer of insulating material and a dead-air space is recommended. Proper insulation will prove economical as far as heating and temperature control is concerned and will improve the controller's efficiency by avoiding physical discomfort.

Where air conditioning is not to be provided, the roof must contain a ventilator. The ventilator should be designed to house an exhaust fan of sufficient capacity to insure a frequent change of air during periods of intense heat. The ventilator must be of the louvre type covered with a fine-mesh wire screen.

Tower roofs should never be supported by columns. Columns interfere with vision and restrict the operating space.

The importance of soundproofing has been previously pointed out. To accomplish satisfactory soundproofing the ceiling must be covered with acoustical tile.

Floor

In addition to the strength to support its load, the tower floor must provide wiring ducts to allow a large variety of equipment to be connected. It must also provide a surface which keeps the noise level as low as possible and which can be easily cleaned. A steel-plank floor covered with a good grade of linoleum is recommended.

Walls

Almost every tower design will call for a small section (approximately 3 ft) of vertical wall below the glass portion.

The vertical section of wall should carry out the same degree of insulation and soundproofing as was recommended for the ceiling. Where air conditioning is not to be installed, screened louvres must be installed in this section of wall to provide ventilation.

Heating and Ventilation

It has previously been indicated that proper heating and ventilating are extremely important as well as difficult to obtain. Year-round air conditioning with humidity control is recommended. In considering expenditures for control-tower construction it must be borne in mind that the tower is the nerve center of the airport, with people's safety constantly depending on the accuracy of the controller's operations.

Aside from the fact that air conditioning and humidity control are perfect as far as the controller's comfort is concerned, they also eliminate a great deal of dust and fogging up of the tower windows.

Any type of dry heat, such as hot-air or electric space heaters, is harmful to the controller's health and is therefore undesirable. Some provision must be made to provide moist heat.

Since floor space in the tower is needed entirely for equipment and operations, radiators built into the wall must be used. It is recommended that radiators be installed on the two sides of the tower which are at right angles to the field. Radiators that are placed in the front of the tower are not effective because this space is usually taken up by the control desk.

If floor openings are used, the location of the openings must be carefully chosen as they may easily interfere with operations or be covered over by equipment.

Window Washing

In the design of a traffic control tower there are several other provisions which are desirable, if not mandatory.

Washing the tower windows should be made as easy as possible. No special provisions are necessary if the glass section starts only ten to twelve feet above a building roof. A walkway must be provided if the windows can not be reached by long-handled washing tools.

Water Coolers

In line with providing for the controller's comfort the installation of an electric water cooler is recommended. This equipment requires the extension of water and sewer line to the tower floor.

Special Toilets

In many instances control towers must be as high as 80 ft above the ground to meet visibility requirements. Walking up steps to such a height is a considerable strain on anyone not in excellent physical condition. Making one or two trips daily up and down such a flight of stairs may not harm a person in good health. However, if such a trip must be made to reach the toilet facilities, the strain over a period of time may easily be dangerous to the controller's health.

Whenever possible, control towers of excessive height should be served by elevators. Regardless of whether an elevator is provided, toilet facilities should be within one, or at most two, floors of the tower.

Sectional Construction

There may be many reasons which dictate that the terminal building be constructed a considerable length of time before the control tower is erected. It may also happen that an outgrown terminal building having a control tower may be replaced with a new structure which provides a more desirable tower location. In either instance a prefabricated tower structure will prove advantageous.

Where the tower is to be constructed some time after the terminal building is completed, it is recommended that the terminal-building plans include the tower. A specific tower should be chosen and all provisions made so that the minimum amount of building alteration will be required when the tower is added.

Required Equipment

The following controls and equipment are located in the operating floor of the tower:

1. Runway lighting controls.
2. Wind-velocity and -direction instruments.
3. Clock.
4. A varying number of radio loud-speakers.
5. Three voice recorders.
6. Time stamp.

7. Telephones.
8. Fire extinguishers.
9. Microphones.
10. Altimeters.
11. Radio monitor equipment.
12. Flight-progress board approximately 5 ft by 4 ft.
13. Light gun.
14. Efficient interior lighting.
15. Thermometers.
16. Crash alarm equipment.
17. Water cooler.
18. Searchlight controls.

The majority of the operating equipment can be reached most easily by the controller if it is mounted on a desk which extends along the field side of the tower and runs about halfway back on the two adjoining sides.

Wiring

From the list of equipment given above, it can be seen that careful consideration must be given to both floor and roof ducts and to conduits running up to the tower. New equipment is constantly being added, making it mandatory that ample space ducts and conduits be provided.

Antenna

Both receiving and transmitting antennas must be readily accessible to the tower. These may be remote or may be installed on the building roof. Tower plans must take these antennas into consideration.

EQUIPMENT ROOM

It is recommended that the equipment room be square or of the same shape as the tower, and that it form the story immediately below the tower. This room is almost always necessary to gain height for the tower.

The equipment room can be used to provide toilet space as well as space for transmitters, air-conditioning units, and storage.

SIZE

Towers 14 ft square are proving to be ample in size for present operating conditions. It is possible that the use of radar and the development of approach control may require more operating space in the future.

When a tower is designed it is recommended that the architect consult C.A.A. and the managers of other airports for their opinions.

C.A.A. ASSISTANCE

Providing for radio aids is a highly specialized field of endeavor. C.A.A. has personnel who are making this a life work. The best advice that can be given an engineer is to call on C.A.A. for information. No airport is too small to warrant a study of its radio facility problems. With the increased use of airplanes, traffic control and navigation will prove to be equally important to personal flyers and to air-line pilots.

CHAPTER XIII

RADIO AIDS

GENERAL

The ultimate success of air transport will to a large extent depend on the use of radio aids to air navigation. Excellent engines, structural refinements, luxurious appointments, high-lift or high-speed wings, safety devices, fine airports—all these things mean little if aircraft cannot operate on reasonably consistent schedules. Dependable scheduled operation is just now being attained, with radio aids entirely responsible for the consistency attained to date.

Operating under instrument conditions, or on top of an overcast without radio aids, a pilot can keep his craft on an even keel and maintain any desired altitude, but it is unlikely that he knows his exact position with a sufficient degree of certainty. Dead reckoning allows the pilot to hazard a reasonable guess as to his whereabouts, with the accuracy of his guess depending entirely on his skill as a navigator. Celestial navigation can be more accurate than dead reckoning but requires too much in the way of skill, operating equipment, and opportunity for observations to have a completely practical usage in ordinary instrument flying.

Radio aids allow a pilot to locate himself in a variety of ways. They make it possible for him to navigate accurately to any desired location which is served by proper radio aids, and on reaching his destination, to descend through the overcast and make a safe landing even with very limited ceiling and/or visibility. There is every reason to believe that when radar equipment is removed from the restricted list, landings will be made under practically "zero zero" conditions.

It is felt that a discussion of radio aids will help the engineer, as he should know what equipment is available, how it can be secured, and what provisions he should make in order that space will be available for its installation and control. Careful consideration should be given to insure the provision of at least the minimum number of radio aids as well as to utilize to the fullest practical extent those aids already in existence.

OPERATIONAL CHARACTERISTICS

No attempt will be made to explain the theory of operation of the radio aids described herein. An endeavor will be made, however, to describe briefly the operational characteristics of each facility in order that the engineer will be aware of the service each aid renders.

Federal airways radio facilities at present operate on a number of frequency bands.

The intermediate frequency radio ranges operate on frequencies in the band between 200 and 400 kc. Aircraft automatic-direction-finding equipment operates between 200 to 1600 kc, whereas ground azimuth indicators operate in the medium-high-frequency bands or 3 to 10 megacycles.

Very-high-frequency operations are carried on in the frequency range between 75 and 335 megacycles. Radio waves of these frequencies have many of the characteristics of light waves, as they are similarly reflected or refracted and travel a line-of-sight path. A mountain, hill, trees, or other obstructions which might exist in the vicinity of a VHF radio station, or along the path of the course, can cause operational difficulties for two reasons. First, the obstruction may reflect the waves so as to superimpose the reflected waves upon the direct waves giving erroneous signal indications or false courses. This is particularly true where the waves are used for producing visual and aural range courses. Second, when the obstruction is between the radio station and the aircraft receiver and is high enough to produce a signal shadow, it will be impossible for the pilot to receive sufficient signal to operate the receiver. Neither of these difficulties is pronounced in the intermediate frequency band. The phenomena of course bends, dead spots, and multiple courses are also found in the 200- to 400-kc band. The multiple structure of the courses in the lower wave lengths may be found to cover a much broader angle than in the VHF.

FEDERAL AIRWAYS AIDS

To date it has been the policy of the federal government to install, maintain, and operate all the radio aids discussed herein, with the exception of the radio transmitter stations used for ground-to-air communications by air-transport companies and municipally operated airport-traffic control towers. Regardless of which agency provides and operates the aid, its most efficient use will in very many instances be impossible unless the engineer makes certain that a suitable site for each such facility is available and meets at least the minimum requirements. This can best be done by making definite provisions for such aids as he feels the particular airport will require, going so far as to purchase or secure options on possible sites. As will be pointed out later, some of the most important aids must be located in a definite relationship to airport runways. The engineer should consult C.A.A. Airway Engineering Division or Communications Operations Division personnel for advice on all matters regarding aids to air navigation, as these divisions of the C.A.A. ordinarily survey, select sites, install equipment, and maintain all such aids for Federal Airways, and are in the best position to make recommendations.

VHF, APPROACH AND LOW-POWER FAN MARKERS

A VHF fan marker is a radio aid, the value of which has been proved over the period of the last six or seven years. These markers, as the name implies, are used to mark a definite location and may be used for a variety of purposes. The most extensive use of fan markers is to provide or augment a radio fix along an airway or along the path of an instrument approach to an airport.

A Civil Airway is defined as: "A path through the navigable airspace of the United States identified by an area on the surface of the earth, designated or approved by the Administrator as suitable for interstate, overseas, or foreign air commerce."

A radio fix is defined as: "A geographical location designated by the Administrator on a Civil Airway above which the position of an aircraft in flight can be accurately determined by means of radio only (such as a cone of silence over the radio range, 'Z' marker, fan-type marker, or intersection of radio range on-course signals)."

A fan marker can also be used to mark any desired location such as a danger area or a hazardous obstruction.

It is logical to assume that nearly every airport where instrument operations are to be expected will sooner or later have one or more VHF fan markers installed for any one of several purposes. This facility is being discussed prior to the navigational and landing-system aids as it usually is used in conjunction with both.

Figure 13-1 shows typical plot layouts required for fan-marker installations using standard C.A.A. equipment. The site must be accessible for maintenance, available to commercial power, and, if convenient, to telephone lines. The telephone lines are sometimes used for control and monitoring purposes.

Surrounding obstructions play a big part in the proper operation of a fan marker. Figure 13-1 gives the allowable vertical angle from the counterpoise level to obstructions in various quadrants.

A VHF fan marker emits radio energy in such a manner that its radiation is confined essentially to an elliptical pattern, the actual size of which is determined by the output power of the marker transmitter and the radio-frequency sensitivity of the aircraft receiver. The audio or modulating frequency of the transmitter can be varied so that various markers in the same locality can be identified, not only by the transmitting at regular intervals of identifying signals, but also by the tone of the signals. Aircraft-marker receiver equipment is provided with audio-frequency filters so that a certain audio frequency will light one color light, while a tone of another frequency will light another color. It will be seen, therefore, that a pilot with proper receiving equipment can identify a marker in three ways: namely, the tone, the identifying signal, and the color of the light the marker lights on the instrument panel.

High-powered VHF fan markers, used mostly to provide airways radio fixes, operate on 100 w of output power and produce an elliptical pattern having a major axis approximately 12 miles long and a minor axis 3 miles long at 5000-ft altitude above the marker, with major axis being perpendicular to line of flight, providing the receiver in the aircraft has been adjusted to certain standards.

Low-powered VHF fan markers are used to augment radio fixes, to mark obstructions, and for distance indicators in connection with instrument-landing systems. They operate on approximately 5 w of output power and produce either a circular or an elliptical pattern depending upon the design of the antenna system.

Boundary markers are used exclusively in instrument-landing systems, and are designed to let the pilot know he is approaching the end of the runway; therefore, to serve its purpose the pattern must be very small. A pilot using this facility will usually be from 50 to 100 ft above it and should be able to receive it for only a very brief period while traveling at 120 mph.

A "Z," or station location marker, is similar in principle to the low-powered fan markers, and is used to augment or take the place of the cone of silence above the range. Its radiation pattern is nearly conical, becoming somewhat wider in diameter as altitude above the station increases, but always very local in scope. A "Z" marker, with proper receiver setting, can be heard only in a very limited area. "Z" markers are installed at all radio range stations to provide the pilot a positive "over the station" position check.

COMPASS-LOCATOR STATIONS

Compass-locator stations provide additional aids which can be used to supplement instrument approach facilities or radio ranges. A compass-locator station, or homing beacon, is a standard low-frequency C-W radio transmitter, radiating a continuous carrier, and modulated for identification. It is provided for the express purpose of allowing pilots to "home" on it with automatic direction finding (ADF) radio-receiving equipment. Each station has a designated identification signal which is repeated at frequent intervals. DF receivers allow the pilot to home on any radio station he can receive, which is transmitting on frequencies between approximately 200 kc to 1000 kc. Therefore, all commercial broadcast stations and low-frequency simultaneous radio-range stations may serve as compass-locator stations. The principal objection to using commercial broadcasting stations is that they do not identify themselves often enough to allow the pilot to constantly check the station he is homing on, and further, they seldom operate over a 24-hr period. A compass locator station may be simply a vertical antenna top loaded approximately 20 ft high and supported on two or three poles together with a small building for housing the transmitter equipment. A plot 10 ft by 300 ft will be adequate for the building and poles.

RADIO RANGES—LOW FREQUENCY

The most important radio aid to air navigation up to the present time has been the radio range, operating on low (200–400-kc) frequencies. Four courses or beams emanate from the station, each course forming a highway of the sky. The courses are usually more stable when they all lie at 90 deg with respect to one another. They are sometimes, however, squeezed to within about 40 deg of each other when necessary.

Along the center of the course a constant tone signal is audible, broken every 30 sec for the transmission of the identification signal of the range from which the signals emanate.

An N-signal (dash dot) is heard in two of the opposite quadrants formed by the courses, with an A-signal (dot dash) heard in the other two.

The A and N signals are keyed so that their respective figure of 8 patterns interlocks to form the constant-tone signal at all points where their two fields are of equal strength. Directly over a range station, a cone of silence exists where no tone signal can be heard. This cone of silence together with the "Z" marker affords definite position checks.

After proper training a pilot can tell, by the comparative strength of the two A- and N-tone signals, a great deal about his direction with reference to the range station. By working an orientation problem, he can place himself in any desired position relative to the range station. Radio ranges are particularly useful for instrument let-down or approach procedures.

The usefulness of a radio range, as far as instrument landings and take-offs on an airport are concerned, depends very largely on its location with reference to the airport runways. The ideal location is for the range to be on a projection of the center line of, and between 3 and 4.5 miles from, the down-wind end of the runway used the largest per cent of the time during periods of low ceiling and visibility. One course, or leg, of the range is then directed down the center of the runway with the reciprocal course 180 deg from the runway course. With this orientation the pilot can approach the range on the reciprocal leg and let down on the leg coinciding with the runway without lateral maneuvering or changing his gyro heading. Figure 13–2 illustrates an excellently located radio range, particularly so since bad-weather winds are from the northeast in this area.

There are two types of low-frequency radio ranges, differentiated by the type of antenna used for radiation and service. As the characteristics of the two types of antenna vary, each will be discussed.

Adcock Antenna

Adcock antennas are 135-ft, base-insulated, steel towers. Five of these are used in a simultaneous radio range as shown in Fig. 13–3. One tower is set on each corner of a square plot, the diagonal dimension of which is usually 600 ft. These are the antennas from which the field patterns are generated and interlocked to produce the four courses. The fifth tower is set in the exact center of the plot. It is used for voice broadcasting simultaneously with the transmission of range signals. Voice broadcast is transmitted on a carrier frequency differing in frequency by 1020 cycles from the side bands used to produce the range courses. This allows the pilot to listen to either one or both at the same receiver setting by the use of filters in the aircraft receiver.

The signals from a tower type of station can be relied upon to be more stable at night than loop ranges, owing to their transmission of a vertically polarized electric field. It happens, however, that the presence of near-by mountains, large metallic structures, or power lines may cause the courses to appear to bend or break up into multiples. This type of station is always used where maximum coverage is desirable.

A square plot, 600 ft on a side, is considered a minimum size on which a tower station should be erected if proper coverage is to be provided. The range courses are most stable and the maximum operating efficiency is obtained when the towers are located so that the range courses pass as nearly as possible directly through the towers. Ideal conditions can be obtained when courses are 90 deg apart. Inherent instability is slightly more pronounced when the courses are to be squeezed but this instability can usually be corrected in the tower circuits. "Optimum setting" need concern the engineer only when property for a range site is very expensive or very limited in size. The rule to be followed to secure "optimum setting" is: The average azimuth of the four courses is determined and 45 deg added to the result to obtain the azimuth of the line running through two diagonal towers. The other two towers are set along a line at right angles to this line.

A radio-range plot must be reasonably level and should allow a minimum clearance of 200 ft between any tower and obstructions such as trees, buildings, power lines, telephone lines, or other large obstructions. Power and telephone service for the operation of the facility must be brought the last 200 ft by means of an underground cable. The difference in elevation between any two towers must not be more than 20 ft.

Loop Antenna

The loop type of range uses seven poles 52 ft aboveground for supporting the range and the voice-broadcast antenna systems. (Refer to Fig. 13-4.)

This type of station, like the tower type, can be used to provide airways courses, instrument approach courses to the airport, or a combination of both. Its effective range is normally considerably less than the tower type over the same terrain. A loop type of station is often referred to as a localizer.

The horizontal component of the rectangular loop antenna is of no value, as the useful course signals radiate from the vertical component. The loop type of station has one serious disadvantage in that its courses may be unstable beyond a distance of 20 or 25 miles at sunrise and sunset. Course swinging and fading is attributed to the reflection of energy radiated from the horizontal component of the loop by the earth's several ionized Heaviside layers, which are variable in height and density, particularly at sunrise and sunset.

A square plot at least 330 ft on a side is required for an efficient loop station. The same requirements as for the tower type of station apply in regard to reasonably level ground, and proximity to power line, telephone lines, hills, mountains, and large metallic structures. Greatest efficiency is obtained by optimum setting of the four corner poles.

RADIO RANGE—VHF

Probably the greatest objection to intermediate-frequency radio ranges is the fact that the frequencies on which they operate are subject to static interference. Because of this objection the present trend is toward ranges operating on very high frequencies between 107 and 111 megacycles. (Refer to Fig. 13–5.) This frequency band is to all intents and purposes free from atmospheric interference such as rain and snow static.

The similarity of the action of VHF radio waves to the action of light waves makes the presence of near-by obstructions such as hills, buildings, trees, and mountains much more likely to affect the operational features than would be the case with an intermediate frequency facility.

VHF radio ranges can be any one of three types, namely, two courses aural; four courses—two aural, two visual; or omnidirectional. Several airways have been equipped with ranges having two aural and two visual courses. VHF ranges are still in the development stage and are constantly being improved.

INSTRUMENT-LANDING SYSTEMS

Instrument-landing systems are considered to be of the utmost importance; therefore, it is felt the engineer should have this aid definitely in mind at the time the airport site is selected as well as when the airport runway, taxiway, and building layout is under consideration. Present experience indicates instrument-landing systems have reached a stage where they can be completely relied upon to allow a pilot to make a safe landing under conditions of very limited visibility and ceiling.

Four, and in some instances five, separate VHF transmitting stations comprise an instrument-landing system. These are designated as the

(1) localizer, (2) glide path, (3) boundary marker, (4) middle marker which is optional, and (5) outer marker.

Localizer

The localizer provides lateral guidance. It is essentially a two-course VHF radio range with the two visual courses on reciprocal headings. A zero-center cross-pointer indicator on the aircraft instrument panel provides the guidance for the pilot.

The localizer site must be located exactly on the prolonged center line of the runway it is to serve. The localizer is always placed on the opposite end of the runway from the direction instrument approaches are to be made, as all such approaches are toward the localizer. The structure housing this facility extends a minimum of 8 ft aboveground, so must be located far enough from the runway that it does not constitute an obstruction.

The line-of-sight characteristics of VHF radio waves make it necessary for the location of the antenna of the localizer to bear a definite relationship with respect to the runway elevation. Satisfactory operation is accomplished by designing the antenna structure so as to compensate for the difference in elevation between the far end of the runway and the localizer. Placing the localizer too far from the runway results in the course across the airport possibly becoming wider than the runway. This is undesirable as the pilot must be certain he is over the runway when he receives the on-course signal. Location of the localizer is therefore affected by the length and width of the runway.

Due to the critical behavior of VHF radio transmission, it is almost impossible to predict how accurately a localizer will operate from any given location. It is, therefore, standard policy to try out a site by the use of portable equipment prior to its acceptance. The Air Navigation Facilities Service of C.A.A. has this test equipment which can usually be secured for test purposes.

Glide Path

The glide path provides vertical guidance so that the pilot may maintain proper elevation as he approaches the runway along the localizer beam.

The glide-path site must be to one side or the other of the runway to be served, and is usually located on the airport property. It must be approximately 400 ft from the center line of the runway and approximately 750 ft to 1000 ft from the end of the runway farthest from the localizer. The engineer in planning his building layout, should take the glide-path location into consideration. The glide-path equipment is housed in a building 8 ft by 12 ft by 10 ft high.

Boundary Marker

As the name implies, this facility marks the boundary of the airport runway. It is a low-powered marker located as nearly as is practical to the end of the runway opposite the localizer.

The equipment stands approximately 4 ft above the ground. The elevation of the site is of little importance. Near-by obstructions should be avoided.

Middle and Outer Markers

These markers provide reference points along the localizer beam which permit the pilot to determine how close he is to the end of the runway. They are essentially low-powered fan markers and have all of the usual characteristics. All previous instructions as to plot sizes and near-by obstructions apply.

Compass-locator stations can be combined with each of these two markers to advantage. The combination of the marker and compass locator provides for very positive position determination over the site and also allows a DF receiver to be used in the approach procedure. Figure 13–6 shows a compass-locator station installed on a marker plot.

RADAR

It can only be said at this time that radar has developed to a point where it is definitely expected to have an important place in instrument approaches and traffic control.

Selection of sites for radar equipment will follow the same general pattern as for VHF equipment. So far as can be told at this time, no special provisions for installing this equipment need be made other than line-of-sight operation over the field to be used.

REMOTE CONTROL

Strowager switches similar to those operated by dial telephones are used to control the operation of radio facilities. Turning on tower obstruction lights, changeover from one transmitter to another, and a number of other operations which would otherwise have to be performed manually can be performed remotely in this manner. Voice broadcast over radio-range stations originates in the remote-control quarters at the airport. All such remote control utilizes telephone circuits usually furnished by the local telephone company.

C.A.A. radio facilities are operated by Airways Communication Station personnel or C.A.A. Airport Traffic Controllers. Control quarters are usually located in the administration building and are discussed in detail in the chapter on Buildings.

AIR TRAFFIC CONTROL

Aircraft operating within a prescribed distance of a controlled airport are subject to instructions issued by airport or airway traffic controllers. Such control relies almost entirely on radio aids for its effectiveness. The most efficient use of radio aids depends on the proper location of these aids with respect to airport runways. It is felt, therefore, that students of airport location and design must consider it as mandatory that they become familiar with the use of radio aids as they pertain to traffic control.

Traffic-control procedures use radio as follows:

1. *Two-way radio* for communication with pilots.
2. *Radio fixes* for position reporting, holding, and stacking.

Holding is an operation where the pilot flys back and forth within a designated area without visual reference to the ground, using the course of a radio range or localizer for lateral guidance and a radio fix to establish one end of the pattern. Figure 13–7 shows a typical holding pattern.

Stacking is the simultaneous holding of several aircraft in the same area, with vertical separation relied on to avoid collisions. Each aircraft in a stack is assigned an altitude, usually 1000 ft above or below the adjacent aircraft in the stack. When the plane on the bottom of the stack is directed to proceed toward the airport, thereby vacating the altitude it held in the stack, the planes above are stepped down as each of the lower altitudes is vacated.

3. *Radio ranges and instrument landing systems* for navigation along a known path or for instrument approaches to an airport.

An instrument approach is a flight operation executed without visual reference to the ground preparatory to landing at an airport under instrument weather conditions. In executing this maneuver, the pilot depends entirely on radio aids for determining his location with reference to the airport runway he is approaching. The pilot can use his barometric altimeter, his radio altimeter, or the glide-path beam to maintain the proper rate of descent during the instrument approach. If the pilot has not established visual contact with the ground by the time he has descended to a prescribed minimum altitude, he pulls up again, which procedure is termed a missed approach.

Radio Aids for Instrument-Operation Airports

Where instrument operations are to be carried on at two or more airports in close proximity to each other, the following rules apply:

1. The location of radio aids and the traffic-control plan for the area should be carefully worked out before airport sites are selected.
2. None of the airports involved should be located within the instrument approach zone of any other airport or within a 15-mile extension of such instrument approach zone.
3. The radio aids should be located so that the center line of the stacking area for each airport has at least 8 miles lateral separation from the center line of the stacking area for any other airport.
4. The bearing of all instrument runways involved should be as nearly the same as possible.

Possible Restrictions

In instances where the above rules are not followed, restrictions which will materially reduce the capacity of the airports involved during instrument weather conditions are almost certain to be imposed. It is entirely possible that in trying to locate radio aids so as to allow instrument approaches to be made to each of several airports, the actual capacity of all of the airports combined will be less than would otherwise be the normal capacity of one large airport.

A violation of rule 2 results in instrument approaches, take-offs, or pull-outs on missed approaches having to be made over the other airport or in the zone which its instrument traffic would normally use. The chance of collision unless operations are restricted is obvious.

A violation of rule 3 results in a merging of stacking areas for two airports. This reduces the capacity of each airport by more than one-half due to complicated handling procedures.

A violation of rule 4 results in a crossing of approach paths. Approach paths which cross within approximately 15 miles of either airport result in insufficient lateral separation for stacking areas or unsafe lateral separation for missed approaches or instrument take-offs.

Most air-line pilots definitely prefer to land directly into the wind. Cross-wind landings are becoming much more feasible, but they still entail an element of possible damage to the aircraft. This possibility is somewhat increased in making cross-wind instrument landings.

It is considered impossible to overestimate the importance of radio aids and traffic control procedures in connection with any airport, and particularly where other near-by airports are involved.

CHAPTER XIV

COMMUNICATIONS

PURPOSE

The need for communication facilities at an airport seems to remain at a low level so long as the flight operations are mostly local in character. Local telephone service usually proves sufficient in such a case.

As soon as air-line operations or any appreciable amount of cross-country flying starts, the need for communication facilities expands out of all proportion to the increase in traffic. For this reason the engineer must carefully evaluate both present and future needs for communication facilities and make provision for their installation.

Communication facilities are needed to handle the airport administrative matters such as telegrams and telephone calls. They are also needed for a large variety of purposes connected with the safety, dispatching, and control of aircraft. Weather information is received and disseminated, control instructions issued and acknowledged, flight plans filed and approved, flight advisory service given, reservations made; all these and many more things are accomplished through communication facilities.

Communications are accomplished by the use of landlines and by the use of two-way radio. Intercommunication between offices and between buildings is often handled best by the use of pneumatic tubes.

LANDLINES

Local Circuits

The engineer in making up his duct layout for the airport will be concerned with local landline circuits. These circuits will, in part, be provided by public utilities companies and, in part, by the airport.

Local landline circuits are needed for the following purposes:

1. Intercommunication between buildings.
2. Fire-alarm system.
3. Crash warning system.

4. Loud-speaker system.
5. Gate phones.
6. Interphone and teletype drops.
7. Lighting controls.
8. Remote antennas.

Long-Line Circuits

Teletype machines and interphones connected into a network linking several cities use long-line circuits. There is no physical difference between local and long-line circuits. The engineer's primary concern with long-line circuits will be to provide for the required number of circuits being brought into the main distribution point on the airport.

Construction Problems

Airport communications create no unusual construction problems, but do make it necessary for the engineer to plan carefully for underground duct layouts and conduit runs in buildings.

The first requirement is adequate space in the room which will be used for distribution and switching equipment. A room at least 20 ft square is recommended even though this is a much larger size than present requirements indicate to be necessary. Moving terminal equipment is very expensive and that cost can ordinarily be avoided by the careful planning of the size and location of the space involved. It is to be borne in mind that the activities of the airport can be expected to continue to grow for many years to come and that switchboard or automatic-posting equipment may be needed eventually.

It is highly desirable to bring communications lines into the distribution point by underground cable. To save the cost of having to tear out pavements or disturb turf areas, adequate underground ducts, numbering at least four, should be run into the terminal room.

The duct layout within the terminal building and any other building which may be used for operational or control purposes must be determined on the basis of future expansion. It is quite possible that any room in buildings of this type may sooner or later require teletype, interphone, or pneumatic-tube service.

Efficient communications require that the noise level be kept to a minimum. Soundproofing materials should therefore be used on the walls and ceilings of rooms where communications activities are likely to be conducted.

Estimating the Number of Circuits

Making ample provision for future expansion has been stressed throughout this text. The same advice applies to communication-facility circuits. Spare ducts and conduit cost very little when they are installed prior to the completion of the pavement and buildings. They are very expensive to install in locations where so doing requires the tearing up and replacing of pavements, building walls, or floors.

The master plan is of great assistance in estimating ultimate needs. Present needs can be estimated by consulting all of the companies who will have offices on the airport.

The following is an estimate arrived at for one terminal building serving five air lines, C.A.A. communication station, U.S. Weather Bureau, U.S. Post Office, and the Railway Express:

1. Federal Agencies—12 long line, 2 local lines.
2. Municipality—10 pairs—local.
3. T.W.A.—4 long line, 7 local.
4. E.A.L.—5 long line, 7 local.
5. A.A.—8 long line, 4 local.
6. U.A.L.—6 long line, 5 local.
7. Telephone Company—11 pairs, local.

To allow for expansion it was decided to run a 100-pair cable to this airport and provide ducts for bringing in additional cables should they be required later.

RADIO

Two-way radio communications will be carried on by each air line, C.A.A. Airways Communication Station, and traffic control tower.

Local Antennas

Local antennas are those so located that the leadin goes directly to the receiver or transmitter.

Local antennas are strung between uprights or are vertical antennas of the whip type. Local antennas are usually unsightly and they often pick up or cause local interference. Local receiving antennas have the advantage of being economical to install and operate.

Since the number of receiving antennas usually far exceeds the number used for transmitting, local antennas may be used for receiving, and remote antennas for transmitting.

Remote Antennas

Remote antennas are located a considerable distance from the point where the operator is stationed.

Remote-receiver antenna sites are chosen for their freedom from sources of interference such as power lines, telephone lines, engine warm-up stands, or electrical equipment.

Remote transmitter sites are chosen a sufficient distance from the airport so that they can not interfere with radio reception.

CHAPTER XV

MANAGEMENT AND OPERATION

The methods of management and operation which are described in this chapter are those which are considered essential and applicable for the larger terminal airport. Such an airport is usually operated independently of other city, county, or state departments, although various facilities may be provided for airport use by such departments. From the over-all treatment of the subject, it is possible for each locality to determine the procedures which are applicable to its airport problems. Several of the functions which will be discussed are not necessary for the smaller airport.

MANAGEMENT

Effective airport management requires a well-planned organizational set-up wherein each employee's functions and responsibilities are clearly set forth and defined. Inasmuch as the Washington National Airport exemplifies a large terminal, where all types of problems have been encountered and satisfactory solutions arrived at, its operational structure is offered as a guide.

Organization Chart

The Washington National Airport organization chart is shown in Fig. 15–1.

This chart is rather extensive because of the prominence and size of the airport. The lines of authority are clearly drawn. The small number of people reporting directly to the airport administrator is to be noted.

Functions of Various Offices

Having arrived at a satisfactory organization chart, the next step is to set forth the functions and duties of each of the offices shown on the chart. Overlapping of functions must be avoided as this results in friction and inefficiency. The same principles which have been found to be successful in the management of large private enterprises should be incorporated in airport management.

The functions, duties, and responsibilities of the various units shown in the Washington National Airport organization chart as set forth in C.A.A.'s Administrative Order No. 36, September 10, 1945, follow.

Office of Airport Administrator

Administers, controls and provides for the care, operation, maintenance and protection of the Washington National Airport in conformance with general policies and standards established by the Administrator of Civil Aeronautics. Inspects the work and performance of the Branches comprising the Airport organization for conformance with requisite standards of operation and competency. Develops future planning of the Airport's facilities. Negotiates with air carriers and others for use of the Airport and its facilities, and with concessionaires to provide proper services required by air carriers, the public and Airport users. Provides consulting advice, exchanges information with foreign and domestic visitors to the Airport and maintains liaison with state, municipal and other public officials and bodies, private aeronautical and civic organizations, airport operators and others concerned with or interested in airports.

Airport Traffic Control Tower
(Office of Airport Administrator)

1. Controls air traffic at the airport and operates approach control of air traffic in this area.
2. Prepares or assists in the preparation of airport traffic rules and traffic patterns.
3. Maintains control record of arrivals and departures of aircraft at the airport.
4. Reports alleged violations of air traffic regulations and irregularities resulting from non-observance of standard procedures.
5. Maintains liaison with military airports within the control zone, on matters relating to airport traffic and approach control.
6. Operates crash alarms and crash and stand-by phones.

Protection Services
(Office of Airport Administrator)

1. Maintains and operates the First Aid Room and renders first aid to airport employees and public visiting the airport.
2. Records and reports accidents and injuries to persons on the airport premises; prepares other related reports.
3. Guards and polices the airport buildings and grounds; enforces police, fire and traffic regulations and protects life and property.
4. Operates fire, crash and rescue truck, ambulance and crash boat; performs firefighting, rescue and emergency aircraft stand-by services with this equipment.

5. Takes fingerprints of personnel working at the airport for checking with the F.B.I. and initiates appropriate action based on reports of searches of fingerprints.

Business Management Branch
(Office of Airport Administrator)

Conducts the general business management activities of the Washington National Airport, involving the following functions:

1. Advises the Airport Administrator and operating officials on administrative and business management activities and problems.
2. Reviews contract performance of concessionnaires and other airport users; recommends remedial action as required.
3. Maintains accounting records; performs administrative audits; receives and deposits, collections and other receipts.
4. Provides general office services, including telephone switchboard service and procures materials, supplies and services for the airport.
5. Conducts the personnel management functions of the airport (except classification of positions).
6. Provides information services to the public.
7. Maintains liaison as required in the performance of foregoing functions.

Cashiers Unit
(Business Management Branch)

1. Conducts all cash transactions for the airport including collections and deposits, the maintenance and accountability of an advance of funds from the U.S. Treasury, and the making of change.
2. Conducts paid tours of the building and gives lectures on various points of interest in and around the airport.
3. Reads and records sales data from cash registers of concessionnaires.
4. Audits trip reports of taxicab concessionnaire.

Accounts Section
(Business Management Branch)

1. Maintains allotment and other accounting records; maintains accounting control of funds, obligations and expenditures.
2. Audits financial records of the cashier unit; prepares and submits bills to concessionnaires and lessees at the airport.
3. Schedules vouchers for payment; receives, schedules and deposits collections and miscellaneous receipts from concessionnaires and other airport users.
4. Performs administrative examination of vouchers of all classes, including contract vouchers, travel and transportation vouchers; certifies such vouchers for payment.
5. Prepares periodic summaries of allotment ledger transactions.

6. Operates turnstiles controlling public access to observation platforms and handles the collections therefrom.

Personnel Section
(Business Management Branch)

1. Recruits, interviews and recommends personnel for appointments; reviews proposed personnel actions for conformance with applicable standards, policies and regulations; effectuates actions approved by the Airport Administrator and transmits other actions for Washington Office approval and effectuation.
2. Maintains individual employment, leave and retirement records and prepares required reports.
3. Compiles information necessary for the preparation of regular, supplemental and force account payrolls.
4. Maintains personnel files of employees and applicants.
5. Directs and coordinates activities in connection with airport efficiency rating program.
6. Interprets and applies laws, rules, regulations, directives and decisions affecting personnel administration.
7. Maintains records of War Savings Bond allotments and payroll bond deductions; orders and distributes bonds.

Procurement and Office Service Section
(Business Management Branch)

1. Procures, by contract and otherwise, property, equipment, supplies and services requisitioned for the conduct of airport operations.
2. Advises and assists operating officials in formulation of technical specifications for procurement and for construction work, as requested.
3. Performs office service functions; furnishes inter-office messenger services; receives, sorts, distributes and collects mail.
4. Maintains and operates airport warehouse; assumes custody of reserve property, equipment and supplies, and issues such materials to operating services, as required.
5. Coordinates procurement requests for property with stocks on hand and available elsewhere from C.A.A.
6. Maintains records of accountable property.
7. Issues bills of lading and advises operating officials on matters pertaining to transportation and shipping.
8. Maintains operating and service records of official automobiles, trucks and automotive equipment.

Telephone Section
(Business Management Branch)

1. Operates the telephone switchboard for the airport.
2. Maintains records of calls; prepares reports as required.
3. Provides general information to public when information counter is closed.

Engineering and Maintenance Branch
(Office of Airport Administrator)

1. Directs and coordinates planning, engineering, construction, installation and over-all maintenance work of the airport, including buildings, hangars, landing field, roadways, grounds and plant facilities.
2. Maintains airport electrical facilities; engineers and constructs special airport electrical apparatus.
3. Maintains and operates the central heating plant and air-conditioning system; provides stand-by electric generator facilities.
4. Provides janitorial and general cleaning services.
5. Designs, engineers and constructs auxiliary structures, maintenance equipment and installations.
6. Directs the handling, placing and movement of itinerant aircraft, other than at landing and take-off; provides various service facilities for public and private aircraft, including flight clearance service.
7. Inspects work and performance of the sections comprising the Branch for conformance with requisite standards of operation and competency.
8. Maintains liaison as required in the performance of the foregoing functions.

Operations Section
(Engineering and Maintenance Branch)

1. Controls and directs the parking and movement of itinerant aircraft when not under the direction of the control tower.
2. Maintains records of itinerant aircraft arrivals and departures; collects fees for aircraft parking and for services furnished by the Washington National Airport.
3. Assists pilots in filing of flight plans and in securing flight clearances, provides various service facilities to public and private aircraft users.
4. Services and maintains the loading apron and turntables; services battery pits, pneumatic tube system and air-conditioning system on the apron; performs inspections and tests of apron facilities and makes repairs as required; performs other services necessary to the general upkeep of the loading and unloading areas.
5. Makes daily inspections of all runways, taxiways and apron surfaces to assure their safe condition for use.

Construction and Maintenance Section
(Engineering and Maintenance Branch)

1. Maintains airport buildings, hangars, roadways and airport grounds including the landing areas.
2. Performs regular inspections of airport structures, mechanical devices, automotive equipment, roadways and grounds to insure satisfactory condition; services and makes necessary repairs or initiates remedial action as required.

3. Plans, develops and constructs auxiliary structures, maintenance equipment and installations; recommends improvements and changes to existing structures and equipment based on maintenance experience.
4. Performs major overhaul, modification and repair of equipment including automobiles, trucks, scooters and other automotive equipment.
5. Operates a paint shop, machine shop and carpenter-cabinet making shop.
6. Removes snow, sands and otherwise conditions runways, taxiways and aprons in inclement weather.
7. Recommends items and quantities of appropriate stocks used by the section to be maintained in the airport warehouse and the shops and recommends the declaration of equipment or materials as surplus.

Janitor Section
(Engineering and Maintenance Branch)

1. Performs cleaning services of public and private areas in the terminal building on a twenty-four hour basis.
2. Operates floor cleaning, waxing and polishing machines; applies special preparations to terrazzo floors.
3. Provides towels and other sanitary services in lounge and rest rooms.
4. Cleans windows and glassed areas in the terminal building.
5. Requisitions items of supply needed in the performance of the foregoing functions.

Electrical Section
(Engineering and Maintenance Branch)

1. Distributes electric energy for light and power through cubicles and transformers to all users at the airport, including terminal building, hangars, Army Air Forces buildings and Public Roads buildings.
2. Inspects airport field lighting facilities and equipment to insure safety and satisfactory conditions; services and makes necessary repair or initiates remedial action as required.
3. Maintains and services transformers, relays, power lines, underground cables, motors, cubicles and other electrical equipment; plans for and installs electrical motors, wiring and equipment, including the laying of high voltage cable and of related facilities.
4. Installs, inspects and maintains radio and communication facilities and equipment at the airport except that used in air traffic control.
5. Makes periodic inspections of the fire alarm system in the hangars and terminal building and repairs system as required.
6. Inspects electrical installations in the hangars and terminal building to insure proper functioning and conformance to standards; makes necessary repairs or initiates remedial action as required.
7. Recommends improvements in facilities on the basis of maintenance experience.
8. Plans, designs, tests and constructs special electrical apparatus required at the airport.

9. Recommends and requisitions items and quantities of appropriate stocks used by the section to be maintained in the airport warehouse and recommends the declaration of equipment or materials as surplus.

Utilities Section
(Engineering and Maintenance Branch)

1. Maintains and operates the central heating plant, manufacturing and distributing steam for heat and power to all buildings on the airport, including terminal building, hangars, Army Air Forces building and Public Roads buildings.
2. Installs or arranges for installation of heating, plumbing and sanitary system for auxiliary structures and installations.
3. Provides hot water for sanitary and commercial usage throughout the airport.
4. Performs regular inspections of the heating plant, steam pipe lines, condensors, meters, valves and other facilities to assure proper functioning; services and makes necessary repairs or initiates remedial action as required.
5. Maintains and operates the fire pump station supplying water for the deluge and sprinkler systems in the hangars; maintains the fire reservoir and emergency gas driven fire pumps.
6. Inspects the operation and makes periodic tests of the fire lines, fire plugs, sprinkler and deluge systems and maintains the entire system on the airport to insure proper fire protection.
7. Operates gas motor driven generators providing stand-by electrical service.
8. Maintains and services the sewage disposal plant, sewer lines and storm drains.
9. Operates and services air compressors and lines supplying compressed air in the hangars.
10. Maintains the pneumatic tube communications system and makes repairs as required.
11. Operates and maintains the air conditioning system for the terminal building; services the drinking water coolers on the airport.
12. Inspects and maintains airport plumbing system and water supply.
13. Recommends improvements in facilities on the basis of maintenance experience.
14. Recommends and requisitions items and quantities of appropriate stocks used by the section to be maintained in the airport warehouse and recommends the declaration of equipment or materials as surplus.

Airports as Business Ventures

It is readily seen from the functional descriptions pertaining to each unit that there are many diversified fields covered by airport management. In some respects it is similar to the management and operation of a small city. However, it is distinctly different from a strictly municipal operation, such as a city, in one respect. The airport should be operated as a self-sustaining business proposition wherein the income should at least carry the entire maintenance cost of the airport and if possible take care of the interest on the investment.

Budgeting

Because of this difference, it is necessary that the budget covering the operational expenses be broken down into the amounts to be allocated to each of the various units, and then upon the actual receipt of this appropriation to require each unit to operate within its allotments. Each unit chief should be made to realize that his particular unit is to be carried on in a businesslike manner so that the airport will be properly maintained and operated at the lowest possible cost. If a unit chief does not assume this responsibility, it can readily be seen that it will be impossible to keep expenditures within the limits of the unit's allotment of funds.

Cost Accounting

The method of cost accounting can well be patterned after a system which has proved to be satisfactory in private enterprise or which will tie in with the system used by the owner. The system should incorporate reports which will allow management to know at all times what the costs of maintenance and operation are.

REVENUE PRODUCING MEASURES

Management's Responsibility

Airport management covers such a large field of endeavor that the manager must be alert and aggressive if the airport is to operate efficiently and on a paying basis. Management must be continually on the lookout for new ideas and new thoughts which can be put into actuality as income producers.

Management must be in a position to determine reasonable rates and fees to be charged for the use of space and airport facilities. The charges must not be excessive as fair profits are required by airport tenants and operators in order for them to maintain high standards and efficient operations.

The tenants and airport operators will make many requests to management for improved facilities, special privileges, and changes in operational procedures. These requests require management to be familiar with the problems involved to such an extent that the decision rendered is fair. Management must see to it that the real needs of the tenants and operators are met without the necessity of the airport operating at a loss.

It is felt by the writers that the largest amount of income to an airport should come from nonaviation activities if possible. Aviation activities supply the interesting feature of an airport and, therefore, should be given every possible opportunity to grow and expand.

Operating on the basis that an airport is a revenue-producing business venture requires management to take all of the necessary measures to insure maximum income from the airport facilities and concessions. Conversely, expenses must be kept at the lowest level which will allow safe normal operation. The more common, as well as potential sources of revenue are discussed hereunder.

Miscellaneous Facilities

One of the most obvious sources of revenue is the rental of space in the terminal building for concessions. These concessions may include a newsstand, drugstore, barbershop, soda fountain, bank, phone booths, beauty parlor, and gift or novelty shop.

The rental for this type of space should be the maximum which the potential business opportunities warrant. A detailed study of the maintenance cost of the building is advised. From this study the actual cost per square foot of floor space can be determined. All space available for rental should pay at least its proportionate share and in most cases should absorb a portion of the maintenance cost of areas such as lobbies, passenger concourses, hallways, and rest rooms. In many instances negotiations or competitive bids prove to be the fairest way in which to establish space rates.

Aviation Gasoline Sales

The distribution and sale of aviation gasoline is a matter with which all airport managers are concerned. It can be one of the largest and most dependable sources of income.

The merits of various methods of gasoline distribution and sales are frequently discussed by airport managers and owners. Part of this group feels that revenue should be secured from the gasoline concession by charging a fee on each gallon of gasoline sold. This practice is frowned upon by both the air lines and private operators as they feel that such a fee is, in effect, an additional gasoline tax. The practice is in quite general use, however.

Another method is that of awarding the concession to the company submitting the highest bid for the privilege of exclusive rights to sell gasoline on the airport. This practice has a good many features which make it desirable.

Some airport managers argue that the airport management should handle the gasoline distribution themselves as it is felt that the largest revenue to the airport from this concession could be secured in this way. However, because of the large cost of maintenance of such a system, the shrinkage of gasoline, and the increased personnel needed to handle distribution, the writers feel that it is best for the oil companies to handle gasoline distribution. They are much more familiar with the handling of gasoline and oil and have far more experience in this field.

The air lines usually feel that the airport should not secure revenue from the sale of gasoline and that the air lines should be permitted to buy from whatever company they choose. One reason for this is that each air line usually has a contract for servicing its planes all along the line of operation. Some air-line officials have expressed the opinion that this revenue to the airport should be secured from possibly higher landing fees or other fees charged the air lines so that the same income would be received by the airport. This would be satisfactory if all the air lines agreed, but it is doubtful whether they would be willing to have the other fees increased to make up for the difference.

Some oil companies feel that one company should not have the sole right of gasoline sales and distribution at a large terminal, as they feel this is giving a monopoly to one company. It is felt, however, that with the large number of terminal airports which will have heavy traffic, an equitable distribution of contracts among the different oil companies will be the result.

This subject has been dealt with at quite some length because it is a controversial subject in airport management and there are good and bad points connected with each of the various ideas which have been developed in relation to this particular concession.

Landing and Ramp Fees

Among other revenues which may be received by the airport from the aviation activities of air lines or other commercial operators should be the fee charged for the use of the landing area itself, as well as the ramp area and gate facilities.

The matter of fees charged for landing-area usage has also been a very controversial one, and there has been much discussion in regard to rates to be charged the air lines operating from the various airports so that these rates would be as nearly uniform as possible. Again, the air lines should not be overcharged for this facility. The trend seems to be that of charging on a gross-weight basis for an airplane using the landing area. It seems that this is a fair way of attacking the problem. The heavier the plane that uses the airport, the greater is the expense involved in maintaining the runways and the larger the investment required in constructing these runways to withstand the heavier weights.

While the rate should be reasonable for the aircraft using the airport, it should be based on consideration given to the actual maintenance cost of the landing field itself. The features which should be considered in determining the maintenance cost are: periodic seal coats for asphalt pavements and filling of expansion joints in concrete pavements; cost of maintenance of turfed areas, which requires mowing, fertilization, and rolling; the striping or painting of traffic lines on the runways, taxiways, and aprons; the maintenance and actual cost of energy used in the operation of the night lighting system; the daily inspection of runway surfaces in order to keep them free from any debris such as nuts, bolts, and other articles which continually are falling on the runway surface; snow-removal cost; maintenance of drainage system; operation of the control tower if same is handled by the airport itself and not operated by the federal government; and cost of operation of fire and crash equipment. Of course, in considering these maintenance costs both personnel and materials to carry out this work should be included.

Private or Itinerant Aircraft Service Fees

Private airplanes, upon arrival, are shown a parking location by an attendant. The plane is tied down, the pilot and his passengers, together with the baggage, are transported from the plane to the terminal building. Upon departure the same service is given. For this service, a reasonable fee should be charged and the amount of the fee based upon the size of the airplane. The same charge should be made for any part of a 24-hr period. There should not be a landing fee for any private plane merely visiting the airport for a short period of fifteen minutes or so, wherein a passenger might be let off.

Office Space for Aviation Activities

The revenues which can be derived from air lines in the terminal building are those for office space, ticket counter space, traffic offices, baggage handling areas, operational quarters, reservations office, and crew quarters. Also, space can be rented in the terminal building for air express and air-mail postal facilities. These rates are usually based upon a per square foot figure on a per annum basis and are variable in relation to the location used in the terminal building.

A controversial issue in relation to rental of space in the terminal building is the space used by the federal government for such facilities as Airways Communications, Airway Traffic Control, Weather Bureau, and both Scheduled Air Carrier and General Inspection Services. In order for the federal services to pay rental for such space it would require Congress to consider the appropriation of funds for that purpose, and up until the present time, Congress has not done so except where such funds have been provided the C.A.A. for the rental of space for the inspection services.

The appropriations committees of Congress have considered the government services as necessary to the operation of an airport, and therefore, it was to the advantage of the airport itself to have these services located on the airport. It has been the stated policy of Congress that the management should supply the space required by these services at no charge. The government, in many instances, will approve payment of light, heat, power, and janitor service required by its offices. It has been the feeling of many airport managers and owners that the federal government should pay for the space used, as in many cases a considerable area is required, and in some of the smaller airports it amounts to a large percentage of the space of the entire building.

This controversial issue undoubtedly will be settled in the not too distant future.

Hangar Rental

Since the air lines and commercial operators provide the services which bring business to the airport, it is felt that hangar space rentals should be as reasonable as possible and not to be considered a source of actual profit.

Therefore, it is felt that an equitable charge for hangar facilities would be one which is based upon the amortization of the cost of the hangar over a period of 25, 30, or 40 years, payment of interest on the investment balance, and the cost of maintenance. Hangar maintenance can either be supplied by the airport or by the air-line companies or fixed-base operators using these facilities. This charge is no different than if an air line or fixed-base operator constructed its own hangar building.

Also, the privilege should be given to the air line or fixed-base operators to construct their own hangars by leasing or purchasing the land on which the buildings are to be constructed. The lease or deed should stipulate that the architectural and utility features of such hangar buildings should conform with the standards of the airport so that the type of building would fit in with the airport as a whole.

In other words, this particular feature, as it relates to airport income, should produce a revenue sufficient only to carry the operating and construction cost if the building is built by the airport.

Food Concession

Another concession which should be very lucrative to an airport, and which in the majority of airports as they exist today has been overlooked, is that of the food or restaurant concession. If properly handled this concession can produce a very large part of an airport's income.

By providing an attractive dining room with the best view possible overlooking the airport with its flying activities, there can be developed a food serving facility which has one of the best and most interesting "floor shows" that can be supplied and which costs the food concessionnaires absolutely nothing.

If a very attractive dining room can be combined with excellent service and the highest grade food it is possible to secure, experience has proved that a large volume of sales can be expected. Even the smaller airports should not overlook this particular feature. Many times, if such services are provided, the general public will drive to the airport merely to partake of good food and to enjoy an attractive environment. These people who do come to the airport for the food service very often will become actively interested in flying itself, which results in benefit to the entire airport.

When facilities have been provided which will attract the highest type of food concessionnaire, then bid proposals should be put out on this concession. The highest bid received from a qualified food concessionnaire should be accepted. The writers favor contracting for food concessions on the basis of the airport receiving a fixed percentage of the gross sales.

In addition to the main dining room, auxiliary food service should be provided in the terminal building, such as a coffee shop, employees' cafeteria, soda fountain, etc. As an example of the extent to which it is feasible to provide food concessions, attention is called to the Washington National Airport where there are the Terrace Dining Room which is the main dining room, a Coffee Shop, a Terminal Employees' Cafeteria, a Hangar Cafeteria, and a cafeteria in one of the office buildings, as well as soda-fountain service, hangar luncheon-counter service, and an outdoor refreshment stand. The revenue from these facilities is the second highest of all revenue-producing features at this airport, and in 1944 exceeded $113,000, which will give some idea of what these facilities will do.

Providing meals aloft to the various air lines is also a function of the food concessionnaires at several airports.

The airport management should not be content when it has signed a contract with a food concessionnaire, particularly if the revenue to the airport is on the basis of a percentage of the gross business done by the concessionnaire. If the food concession is handled on this basis and the management feels that from then on it has no further responsibility in relation to the food operations, the income to the airport may fall far short of what it should be. The concessionnaire may not provide the finest food and service possible to obtain, and therefore it is up to the management to keep a very accurate check on these operations in order that this business may be kept at the highest level possible. The management should endeavor to bring more and more business to this particular concessionnaire through special events and good publicity.

The above policy has been carried out at the Washington National Airport and there has been a steady increase in the income from the food concession, year by year, until it has reached the amount mentioned above. It is expected that as time goes on this income will still further increase if the standards are kept to the highest.

Advertising Contract

Another source of income is a contract with an advertising concern granting to them the exclusive rights to display or publish advertising matter on the airport premises. It is recommended that this contract provide that the airport receive a certain percentage, arrived at by negotiations or bidding to insure competition, of the gross income from this business.

Posters, display cases, show cards, and diorama signs are the more common sources of income.

A properly designed arrival and departure board can render a service for which the air lines are willing to pay, and at the same time provide space for special forms of advertising. The arrival and departure postings are made by the advertising contractor, usually in consideration of a set rate per line. Such a board can incorporate an electrically illuminated sign furnishing the latest news, advertising items, and notices of interest to the public.

The publication of an airport newspaper supported by advertising has proved highly pleasing to users of the Washington National Airport. The distribution of this paper is made in the terminal building to the general public, arriving and departing air-line passengers, ground-transportation passengers, and some 8000 field employees. Requests for copies of this paper have come from people throughout the entire United States and from various foreign countries.

Promenade Deck

Another source of income, which may be either a part of the terminal building or connected with it, is a promenade terrace or deck. The use of turnstiles reduces the cost of collecting entrance fees to a minimum. This feature has proved highly successful both at Washington National Airport and LaGuardia Field, and could be of considerable value in producing income at other airports. This might be most valuable at the larger terminals, but if properly handled should have good possibilities of success at the medium-sized airports.

Ground Transportation

A good income can be secured from the ground-transportation concession. The concessionnaires are given exclusive rights to the transportation of passengers between the terminal building and the adjacent city or suburban areas. This type of concession is usually handled on a percentage of the gross, including a clause fixing a minimum annual payment.

Parking

The trend at the present time is toward suitable parking areas under proper supervision of attendants, where a reasonable parking charge can be made. Proper handling of such a parking service should include free parking for a certain period of time for persons bringing friends who are departing by plane or who are meeting passengers upon their arrival. A control on this free parking service could be carried out by having a parking slip stamped by the particular air line on which the passenger is departing or arriving. Also, free parking could be allowed to patrons of the restaurant or eating facilities by having the slip stamped by the concessionnaire. In other words, those coming to use airport services from which some income is derived would be given free parking for a suitable length of time. However, if the car were parked in excess of this period it would naturally be assumed that the party would be enjoying merely the airport in general and should pay for such parking.

Also, it is felt that the majority of employees at an airport would be willing to pay a nominal sum, on a monthly basis, for daily parking of their cars if they were sure their cars would be protected by attendants on duty. It has too often been the experience where large, unattended, free parking areas are provided that there are numerous instances of theft, vandalism, and damage by other cars. The cost of providing dependable attendants makes it economically unfeasible to provide this service for free parking areas.

Garage

An airport garage may offer an excellent source of revenue. If the airport has a large number of employees as well as a large passenger traffic, a garage is worth while from an income standpoint, and may also provide a much needed service. An airport is usually some distance from the center of the metropolitan area where garage service is available, and therefore it would be of great service to the employees as well as passengers if they could leave their cars in a garage for repair service during their period of employment or while away on a trip. Therefore, particularly at the larger terminals where the employees number into the thousands, it is readily seen that the potential volume of business is very great. In such a garage all types of automobile servicing as well as automobile accessories, gasoline, oil, etc., should be available. Here again, such a concession could be entered into on the basis of the airport receiving a percentage of the gross business.

Hotel

A hotel is another means of increasing the airport income in localities where such a service would be desirable. An airport hotel should be a combination of apartments and transient rooms. Properly arranged apartments will supply the needs of certain airport employees, particularly those subject to call, some air-line pilots, and possibly some types of businessmen. The transient rooms should prove useful to a variety of people, particularly passengers and businessmen with a long wait between planes. It is felt that the hotel would be of real service to the flying businessman and in many cases would save him a considerable amount of time which would otherwise be consumed by going into the city from the airport and returning later the same day to make a plane connection.

In connection with the airport hotel it may be feasible to include a swimming pool which, if properly operated, can produce a good income.

Recreational Facilities

Recreational facilities should be considered from the point of view of serving airport employees as well as in connection with producing revenue. The income from recreational facilities may not be large, but their value in attracting the public to the airport is considerable.

Management should consider measures to provide space for bowling alleys, badminton courts, handball courts, ping-pong tables, and a small auditorium. Where an airport is large enough to require a separate building to house airport employees' lockers and cafeteria, the second story of this building can well provide space for recreational facilities. A small auditorium for meetings, dances, and banquets should be incorporated in the recreational space. Providing for the above activities tends to further the likeness of the airport to a small city within itself.

Shopping Center

Again, because an airport is usually located outside of the business area of a community, a complete shopping center could very readily be included at a major terminal. Airport employees often find it difficult to do shopping after their working hours because of the time needed to go from the airport into the shopping centers. In most cities they find the shopping areas closed at the time they leave work, except on certain days. If the airport employees together with the people residing in the airport area comprise a large enough population, a shopping center in connection with the airport may prove profitable and of service to employees and air-line passengers.

Exhibition Building

A source of revenue which may not have been considered by airport management in the past is a building wherein the latest ideas pertaining to aircraft accessories could be placed on exhibit. In this building the latest development in accessories, radios, motors, and even small aircraft could be displayed. Such a building should be of one-story construction with interior courts where people could wander through the exhibition area. This type of space could demand a very good rental and would be another means of building up the over-all airport income.

OPERATIONS

Management's Responsibility

In the operation of an airport, management is usually held responsible for maintaining the airport and its appurtenances in a safe, usable condition; establishing satisfactory operating procedures; providing protection for life and property; providing first aid; recommending airport improvements; and accounting for funds.

The efficiency of management's operation of the airport will be reflected in many ways. The degree of efficiency with which the air lines and the private operators conduct their activities depends to a large extent on the condition of the facilities they use. If management enforces safe operating procedures the accident rate is usually low. Satisfactory operation will in most instances attract business and result in increased revenues and lower operating costs.

A good deal can be learned about airport operation by studying the functional description, given previously in this chapter, for units of the Washington National Airport.

Landing-Area Maintenance

The scope of operations problems which will be encountered at a given airport will depend largely on the nature and volume of air traffic. Every airport, however, has its landing-area maintenance and traffic-pattern problems.

Landing-area maintenance is considered to include all activities required to keep any area, which may possibly be used by aircraft, in a usable state of repair. Runway pavements, taxiways, aprons, service ramps, turfed areas, approaches, and drainage structures are included in this category.

Frequent inspection is required to insure that paved areas are free from debris and to discover any early indications of deterioration of pavement or pavement drainage failure.

Constant attention is required to keep turfed areas free from washes, and to keep the turf properly cut. Some reseeding is usually required from time to time.

There is a universal tendency to neglect this operational problem as most pavements and turfed areas will stand a great deal of abuse. Ordinarily it is false economy to delay needed repairs to the landing area, and this practice often allows hazardous conditions to prevail over long periods of time.

Traffic Control

Traffic control is ordinarily thought of as the control exercised by control-tower operators. Even at airports which are not equipped with a control tower, traffic control is an important function of management. Local traffic rules and traffic patterns for various wind conditions must be established. Ground signals must be arranged to indicate prevailing conditions. It is usually a function of management to carry out the intent of the Civil Air Regulations and to report violations.

The C.A.A. operates a number of control towers throughout the United States, but in each instance they do so at the specific request of the armed services and with funds turned over to them by such military agencies. Where the tower is operated by the airport it is necessary to hire a chief controller and a ranging number of controllers and assistant controllers. These employees usually work under the direct supervision of the airport manager. It is the duty of the controllers to control all traffic within the airport traffic zone. This includes giving all instructions for landings, take-offs, and taxiing, the assignment of gates, and the directing of incoming planes to parking areas. Efficient management will handle traffic in such a manner that all safety standards are observed without creating friction or ill will in the issuance of instructions.

Airport Lighting

The operation of an airport lighting system so that continuous service is rendered all night requires someone in constant attendance to operate runway selector equipment. The services of the attendant, unless handled by traffic control tower or C.A.A. Communication Station personnel, taken together with charges for electrical energy amounts to a sizable sum each year. This cost can not be avoided for the large terminals having a number of night operations. Proper management can, however, reduce this cost for the other airports by having the lights operated by reliable night watchmen, night police, or resident caretakers on an on-call basis.

For busy terminals, the inspection of lighting equipment, replacement of necessary electrical parts and equipment, and checking transformers and relays requires the full-time attention of an electrical unit. This maintenance is a 24-hr operation as a major portion of the work must be done in the daytime to insure that the lighting system is in proper condition for night operations. First-class maintenance of circuits and equipment will reduce current losses due to dampness and partial grounding.

Buildings and Hangars

Airport management, in the operation of the terminal building, finds itself in about the same position as does any other landlord. Heat, light, toilet facilities, and janitor service are the main concerns. Bearing in mind that airport buildings largely govern the visitors' reaction to the airport, good management will devote a fair percentage of its time to building maintenance and repair.

Efficient management will not be content just to have rented the building space, but will also make every effort to insure that the service rendered in rented space will be up to the airport standard so that it is not only a credit to the airport but also does its share to attract visitors and business.

It is advised that airport management study the practices which have proved successful in the operation of public and private buildings and adopt such of these practices as are suitable. Airport management will be faced with the problem of allocating space to various tenants. In this connection it will need to know the importance to the airport of each function requiring space. Choice space must be reserved for the more important functions. Lease agreements should be drawn with the idea in mind that as the airport's activities expand, revisions and reallocations of space may become desirable. Management must anticipate the need for additional space and make provisions for it well in advance of the actual date it is needed.

First Aid

The possibility of accidents involving aircraft or other forms of transportation or equipment on the airport must be recognized and every precaution taken to reduce this possibility and to minimize the consequences of those accidents which do happen.

Efficient first aid requires trained personnel and special equipment. At the larger airports it is common practice to have fire-fighting and ambulance equipment stationed on the airport ready for instant use. Finances will govern, to a large extent, the equipment which can be made available, whereas merely taking advantage of gratuitous services is usually the principal factor in training personnel in first aid methods.

It is recommended that one or more rooms be equipped for emergency use and that all airport personnel be required to become proficient in the use of first-aid appliances and techniques.

While most airports will come within the jurisdiction of some municipal, county, or state safety agency, it is management's responsibility to make the airport operation as safe as possible by providing every possible safeguard to life and property.

Protection Service

Airport protection service may be provided in a number of different ways. It may be considered as a part of the duties of some regularly constituted police force, or it may be provided by airport employees. It is common practice for members of the protection service to perform other duties in connection with maintenance or service as well as those of a policing nature. One of the prime functions of the protective service is to see that unauthorized vehicles or persons do not get out on the actual landing area.

Warehousing

It is believed that warehousing of freight and express will become a very important function of airport management. It is possible that each interested air line may provide its own warehousing facilities, but it seems more logical for the airport to provide this service. Refrigeration in connection with storing perishable goods is assuming increasing importance in other fields. There is every reason to believe that a fair share of air transportation's income will eventually be derived from rapid handling of high-grade foods and this will surely involve warehousing and refrigeration.

There now exists a limited need for airport warehousing to store maintenance supplies.

Cost Accounting

Referring again to the Washington National Airport organization chart, an accounts section is set up under the business management branch for the handling of all accounts pertaining to the airport operations. It is the responsibility of this section to record all receipts from various concessionnaires, make charges to all the tenants, and prepare the proper billing for all these items. A contracts and service section also operates under the business management branch. It prepares bid proposals for all contracts and supervises the awarding of all contracts. This branch handles all bills payable and receives and records all monies handled by the airport manager. The personnel section handles all airport matters pertaining to personnel and the preparation of all pay rolls of the airport personnel. This office makes a complete annual report on all the income-bearing features as well as an over-all annual expenditures report. The records of this branch are used in the preparation of the annual budget for securing the appropriation on which the airport will operate.

Should an airport be operated so that it would have the right to spend its income, the entire bookkeeping system for such an airport would be carried on by an airport accounting staff. However, in the majority of the cases, airports are operated by a municipality or a state—or in the case of Washington National Airport by the federal government—an annual appropriation is received, and the income or receipts are turned over to the general treasury of the municipality, state, or federal government. It is believed that it would be beneficial to change this practice so that the actual income of an airport could be used in the expense of its operational needs and, therefore, operated in the same manner as a private corporation. It is felt that this system would be more satisfactory because it would put the airport operation on much more of a business basis. If this were done it would only be necessary at the start of airport operation for the municipal, state, or federal government to appropriate the difference between the income and operating expenses until the airport could build up its income and pay its own way.

The functions of the accounts section are very important as the records of this office advise the management as to the actual financial conditions of the airport.

Telephone Switchboard

At the larger airports it is necessary to operate a switchboard and to keep records of all telephone calls which involve billing of charges to the various tenants or users. This section must operate on a 24-hr basis with three 8-hr shifts a day.

Engineering Section

Another important unit which has not been mentioned previously, and too often is not included in an airport setup, is an engineering section which would carry out all engineering work in relation to actual airport construction in the first place and then supervise all further extension and improvement of the airport itself. This section should include qualified civil engineers and draftsmen. Most frequently this work is handled by a city or state engineering department or by another branch of the federal government as is the case at the Washington National Airport, but it is felt that more economic and efficient construction work could be carried out if the airport itself had an engineering section.

It is necessary, however, that the management have proper knowledge of engineering because of the many construction and maintenance problems which arise at an airport. The management should be qualified to review and supervise any engineering in the original construction or additional construction.

Repair Shops

Repair shops operated by airport employees may prove valuable in airport maintenance.

Passenger cars, scooters, mowing equipment, snow-removal equipment, gasoline motors, and equipment used in connection with auxiliary fire pumps and stand-by electrical equipment can often be repaired to advantage in such a shop.

Building and lighting maintenance often make a carpenter shop, plumbing shop, or electrical shop almost a necessity.

SUMMATION

In summing up this entire chapter it can be readily seen that the owner of any airport—private, municipal, state, or federal—must give serious consideration to the selection of personnel to carry on management and operation. The many fields which are covered require experience and judgment in handling the multitudinous problems which arise. Because management is called on to deal with all kinds and varieties of individuals, it must have skill in handling personnel and experience in dealing with the general public. The proper handling of important personages who visit the airport requires tact and diplomacy. Management must be in a position to answer requests for information and advice which may be received from other communities and possibly from representatives of foreign governments. This will be particularly true during the period where many communities which have never before undertaken this kind of an operation are preparing their air transportation facilities. The interchanging of ideas and the discussion of common problems by various management groups, together with the desire to constantly improve the methods of airport operation and management are some of the more important steps which management can take to assist in expediting the growth of air transportation.

CHAPTER XVI

ZONING

The rapid growth of air transportation together with the attendant increase in the number of airports constructed has accentuated the need for legislation dealing with the legal problems peculiar to aviation. The use of airplanes is such a comparatively new form of transportation that there are not too many precedents established which can be used for making decisions.

Legislation to prevent the creation or establishment of airport hazards and the elimination or marking of existing hazards is somewhat complicated by the fact that a potential hazard may or may not constitute an actual hazard when investigated from an aeronautical point of view.

The National Institute of Municipal Law Officers and the C.A.A. have devoted a great deal of study to the matter of drafting a model airport zoning act. The fifth model act drafted and recommended by one or the other or both follows. (Footnotes are not included.)

AN ACT TO EMPOWER MUNICIPALITIES AND OTHER POLITICAL SUBDIVISIONS TO PROMULGATE, ADMINISTER, AND ENFORCE AIRPORT ZONING REGULATIONS LIMITING THE HEIGHT OF STRUCTURES AND OBJECTS OF NATURAL GROWTH, AND OTHERWISE REGULATING THE USE OF PROPERTY, IN THE VICINITY OF AIRPORTS, AND TO ACQUIRE, BY PURCHASE, GRANT, OR CONDEMNATION, AIR RIGHTS AND OTHER INTERESTS IN LAND; TO PROVIDE PENALTIES AND REMEDIES FOR VIOLATIONS OF THIS ACT OR OF ANY ORDINANCE OR REGULATION MADE UNDER THE AUTHORITY CONFERRED HEREIN; AND FOR OTHER PURPOSES. (BE IT ENACTED, etc.)

Section 1. Definitions. As used in this Act, unless the context otherwise requires:

1. "Airport" means any area of land or water designed and set aside for the landing and taking-off of aircraft and utilized or to be utilized in the interest of the public for such purposes.

2. "Airport hazard" means any structure or tree or use of land which obstructs the airspace required for the flight of aircraft in landing or taking-off at an airport or is otherwise hazardous to such landing or taking-off of aircraft.

3. "Airport hazard area" means any area of land or water upon which an airport hazard might be established if not prevented as provided in this Act.

4. "Political subdivision" means any municipality, city, town, village, borough or county.

5. "Person" means any individual, firm, co-partnership, corporation, company, association, joint stock association, or body politic, and includes any trustee, receiver, assignee, or other similar representative thereof.

6. "Structure" means any object constructed or installed by man, including, but without limitation, buildings, towers, smoke-stacks, and over-head transmission lines.

7. "Tree" means any object of natural growth.

Section 2. Airport Hazards Contrary to Public Interest. It is hereby found that an airport hazard endangers the lives and property of users of the airport and of occupants of land in its vicinity, and also if of the obstruction type, in effect reduces the size of the area available for the landing, taking-off and maneuvering of aircraft, thus tending to destroy or impair the utility of the airport and the public investment therein. Accordingly, it is hereby declared: (a) that the creation or establishment of an airport hazard is a public nuisance and an injury to the community served by the airport in question; (b) that it is therefore necessary in the interest of the public health, public safety, and general welfare that the creation or establishment of airport hazards be prevented; and (c) that this should be accomplished, to the extent legally possible, by exercise of the police power, without compensation. It is further declared that both the prevention of the creation or establishment of airport hazards and the elimination, removal, alteration, mitigation, or marking and lighting of existing airport hazards are public purposes for which political subdivisions may raise and expend public funds and acquire land or property interests therein.

Section 3. Power to Adopt Airport Zoning Regulations.

1. In order to prevent the creation or establishment of airport hazards, every political subdivision having an airport hazard area within its territorial limits may adopt, administer, and enforce, under the police power and in the manner and upon the conditions hereinafter prescribed, airport zoning regulations for such airport hazard area, which regulations may divide such area into zones, and, within such zones, specify the land uses permitted and regulate and restrict the height to which structures and trees may be erected or allowed to grow.

2. Where an airport is owned or controlled by a political subdivision and any airport hazard area appertaining to such airport is located outside the territorial limits of said political subdivision, the political subdivision owning or controlling the airport and the political subdivision within which the airport hazard area is located may, by ordinance or resolution duly adopted, create a joint airport zoning board, which board shall have the same power to adopt, administer and enforce airport zoning regulations applicable to the airport hazard area in question as that vested by subsection (1) in the political subdivision within which such area is located. Each such joint board shall have as members two representatives appointed by each political subdivision participating in its creation and in addition a chairman elected by a majority of the members so appointed.

Section 4. Relation to Comprehensive Zoning Regulations.

1. *Incorporation.* In the event that a political subdivision has adopted, or hereafter adopts, a comprehensive zoning ordinance regulating, among other things, the height of buildings, any airport zoning regulations applicable to the same area or portion thereof, may be incorporated in and made a part of such comprehensive zoning regulations, and be administered and enforced in connection therewith.

2. *Conflict.* In the event of conflict between any airport zoning regulations adopted under this Act and any other regulations applicable to the same area, whether the conflict be with respect to the height of structures or trees, the use of land, or any other matter, and whether such other regulations were adopted by the political subdivision which adopted the airport zoning regulations or by some other political subdivision, the more stringent limitation or requirement shall govern and prevail.

Section 5. Procedure for Adoption of Zoning Regulations.

1. *Notice and Hearing.* No airport zoning regulations shall be adopted, amended, or changed under this Act except by action of the legislative body of the political subdivision in question, or the joint board provided for in Section 3 (2), after a public hearing in relation thereto, at which parties in interest and citizens shall have an opportunity to be heard. At least 15 days' notice of the hearing shall be published in an official paper, or a paper of general circulation, in the political subdivision or subdivisions in which is located the airport hazard area to be zoned.

2. *Airport Zoning Commission.* Prior to the initial zoning of any airport hazard area under this Act, the political subdivision or joint airport zoning board which is to adopt the regulations shall appoint a commission, to be known as the airport zoning commission, to recommend the boundaries of the various zones to be established and the regulations to be adopted therefor. Such commission shall make a preliminary report and hold public hearings thereon before submitting its final report, and the legislative body of the political subdivision or the joint airport zoning board shall not hold its public hearings or take other action until it has received the final report of such commission. Where a city plan commission or comprehensive zoning commission already exist, it may be appointed as the airport zoning commission.

Section 6. Airport Zoning Requirements.

1. *Reasonableness.* All airport zoning regulations adopted under this Act shall be reasonable and none shall impose any requirement or restriction which is not reasonably necessary to effectuate the purposes of this Act. In determining what regulations it may adopt, each political subdivision and joint airport zoning board shall consider, among other things, the character of the flying operations expected to be conducted at the airport, the nature of the terrain within the airport hazard area, the character of the neighborhood, and the uses to which the property to be zoned is put and adaptable.

2. *Non-conforming Uses.* No airport zoning regulations adopted under this

Act shall require the removal, lowering, or other change or alteration of any structure or tree not conforming to the regulations when adopted or amended, or otherwise interfere with the continuance of any non-conforming use, except as provided in Section 7 (3).

Section 7. Permits and Variances.

1. *Permits.* Any airport zoning regulations adopted under this Act may require that a permit be obtained before any new structure or use may be constructed or established and before any existing use or structure may be substantially changed or substantially altered or repaired. In any event, however, all such regulations shall provide that before any non-conforming structure or tree may be replaced, substantially altered or repaired, rebuilt, allowed to grow higher, or replanted, a permit must be secured from the administrative agency authorized to administer and enforce the regulations, authorizing such replacement, change or repair. No permit shall be granted that would allow the establishment or creation of an airport hazard or permit a non-conforming structure or tree or non-conforming use to be made or become higher or become a greater hazard to air navigation than it was when the applicable regulation was adopted or than it is when the application for a permit is made. Except as provided herein, all applications for permits shall be granted.

2. *Variances.* Any person desiring to erect any structure, or increase the height of any structure, or permit the growth of any tree, or otherwise use his property in violation of airport zoning regulations adopted under this Act, may apply to the Board of Adjustment for a variance from the zoning regulations in question. Such variances shall be allowed where a literal application or enforcement of the regulations would result in practical difficulty or unnecessary hardship and the relief granted would not be contrary to the public interest but do substantial justice and be in accordance with the spirit of the regulations and this Act; Provided, That any variance may be allowed subject to any reasonable conditions that the Board of Adjustment may deem necessary to effectuate the purposes of this Act.

3. *Hazard Marking and Lighting.* In granting any permit or variance under this Section, the administrative agency or Board of Adjustment may, if it deems such action advisable to effectuate the purposes of this Act and reasonable in the circumstances, so condition such permit or variance as to require the owner of the structure or tree in question to permit the political subdivision, at its own expense, to install, operate, and maintain thereon such markers and lights as may be necessary to indicate to flyers the presence of an airport hazard.

Section 8. Appeals.

1. Any person aggrieved, or taxpayer affected, by any decision of an administrative agency made in its administration of airport zoning regulations adopted under this Act, or any governing body of a political subdivision, or any joint airport zoning board, which is of the opinion that a decision of such an administrative agency is an improper application of airport zoning regulations of concern to such governing body or board, may appeal to the Board of Adjustment authorized to hear and decide appeals from the decisions of such administrative agency.

2. All appeals taken under this Section must be taken within a reasonable time, as provided by the rules of the Board, by filing with the agency from which the appeal is taken and with the Board, a notice of appeal specifying the grounds thereof. The agency from which the appeal is taken shall forthwith transmit to the Board all the papers constituting the record upon which the action appealed from was taken.

3. An appeal shall stay all proceedings in furtherance of the action appealed from, unless the agency from which the appeal is taken certifies to the Board, after the notice of appeal has been filed with it, that by reason of the facts stated in the certificate a stay would, in its opinion, cause imminent peril to life or property. In such cases proceedings shall not be stayed otherwise than by order of the Board on notice to the agency from which the appeal is taken and on due cause shown.

4. The Board shall fix a reasonable time for the hearing of appeals, give public notice and due notice to the parties in interest, and decide the same within a reasonable time. Upon the hearing any party may appear in person or by agent or by attorney.

5. The Board may, in conformity with the provisions of this Act, reverse or affirm wholly or partly, or modify, the order, requirement, decision, or determination appealed from and may make such order, requirement, decision, or determination as ought to be made, and to that end shall have all the powers of the administrative agency from which the appeal is taken.

Section 9. Administration of Airport Zoning Regulations. All airport zoning regulations adopted under this Act shall provide for the administration and enforcement of such regulations by an administrative agency which may be an agency created by such regulations or any official, board, or other existing agency of the political subdivision adopting the regulations or of one of the political subdivisions which participated in the creation of the joint airport zoning board adopting the regulations, if satisfactory to that political subdivision, but in no case shall such administrative agency be or include any member of the Board of Adjustment. The duties of any administrative agency designated pursuant to this Act shall include that of hearing and deciding all permits under Section 7 (1), but such agency shall not have or exercise any of the powers herein delegated to the Board of Adjustment.

Section 10. Board of Adjustment.

1. All airport zoning regulations adopted under this Act shall provide for a Board of Adjustment to have and exercise the following powers:
   a. To hear and decide appeals from any order, requirement, decision, or determination made by the administrative agency in the enforcement of the airport zoning regulations, as provided in Section 8.
   b. To hear and decide any special exceptions to the terms of the airport zoning regulations upon which such Board may be required to pass under such regulations.
   c. To hear and decide specific variances under Section 7(2).

2. Where a zoning board of appeals or adjustment already exists, it may be appointed as the Board of Adjustment. Otherwise, the Board of Adjustment shall

consist of five members, each to be appointed for a term of three years by the authority adopting the regulations and to be removable by the appointing authority for cause, upon written charges and after public hearing.

3. The concurring vote of a majority of the members of the Board of Adjustment shall be sufficient to reverse any order, requirement, decision, or determination of the administrative agency, or to decide in favor of the applicant on any matter upon which it is required to pass under the airport zoning regulations, or to effect any variation in such regulations.

4. The Board shall adopt rules in accordance with the provisions of the ordinance or resolution by which it was created. Meetings of the Board shall be held at the call of the chairman and at such other times as the Board may determine. The Chairman, or in his absence the acting chairman, may administer oaths and compel the attendance of witnesses. All hearings of the Board shall be public. The Board shall keep minutes of its proceedings, showing the vote of each member upon each question, or, if absent or failing to vote, indicating such fact, and shall keep records of its examinations and other official actions, all of which shall immediately be filed in the office of the Board and shall be a public record.

Section 11. Judicial Review.

1. Any person aggrieved, or taxpayer affected, by any decision of a Board of Adjustment, or any governing body of a political subdivision or any joint airport zoning board which is of the opinion that a decision of a Board of Adjustment is illegal, may present to the __________ court a verified petition setting forth that the decision is illegal, in whole or in part, and specifying the grounds of the illegality. Such petition shall be presented to the court within 30 days after the decision is filed in the office of the Board.

2. Upon presentation of such petition the court may allow a writ of certiorari directed to the Board of Adjustment to review such decision of the Board. The allowance of the writ shall not stay proceedings upon the decision appealed from, but the court may, on application, on notice to the Board and on due cause shown, grant a restraining order.

3. The Board of Adjustment shall not be required to return the original papers acted upon by it, but it shall be sufficient to return certified or sworn copies thereof or of such portions thereof as may be called for by the writ. The return shall concisely set forth such other facts as may be pertinent and material to show the grounds of the decision appealed from and shall be verified.

4. The court shall have exclusive jurisdiction to affirm, modify, or set aside the decision brought up for review, in whole or in part, and if need be, to order further proceedings by the Board of Adjustment. The findings of fact of the Board, if supported by substantial evidence, shall be accepted by the court as conclusive, and no objection to a decision of the Board shall be considered by the court unless such objection shall have been urged before the Board, or, if it was not so urged, unless there were reasonable grounds for failure to do so.

5. Costs shall not be allowed against the Board of Adjustment unless it appears to the court that it acted with gross negligence, in bad faith, or with malice, in making the decision appealed from.

6. In any case in which airport zoning regulations adopted under this Act,

although generally reasonable, are held by a court to interfere with the use or enjoyment of a particular structure or parcel of land to such an extent, or to be so onerous in their application to such a structure or parcel of land, as to constitute a taking or deprivation of that property in violation of the Constitution of this State or the Constitution of the United States, such holding shall not affect the application of such regulations to other structures and parcels of land.

Section 12. Enforcement and Remedies. Each violation of this Act or of any regulations, orders, or rulings promulgated or made pursuant to this Act, shall constitute a misdemeanor and shall be punishable by a fine of not more than $______ or imprisonment for not more than ______ days or by both such fine and imprisonment, and each day a violation continues to exist shall constitute a separate offense. In addition, the political subdivision or agency adopting zoning regulations under this Act may institute in any court of competent jurisdiction, an action to prevent, restrain, correct or abate any violation of this Act, or of airport zoning regulations adopted under this Act, or of any order or ruling made in connection with their administration or enforcement, and the court shall adjudge to the plaintiff such relief, by way of injunction (which may be mandatory) or otherwise, as may be proper under all the facts and circumstances of the case, in order fully to effectuate the purpose of this Act and of the regulations adopted and orders and rulings made pursuant thereto.

Section 13. Acquisition of Air Rights. In any case in which: (1) it is desired to remove, lower, or otherwise terminate a non-conforming structure or use, or (2) the approach protection necessary cannot, because of constitutional limitations, be provided by airport zoning regulations under this Act; or (3) it appears advisable that the necessary approach protection be provided by acquisition of property rights rather than by airport zoning regulations, the political subdivision within which the property or non-conforming use is located or the political subdivision owning the airport or served by it may acquire, by purchase, grant, or condemnation in the manner provided by the law under which political subdivisions are authorized to acquire real property for public purposes, such air right, avigation easement, or other estate or interest in the property or non-conforming structure or use in question as may be necessary to effectuate the purposes of this Act.

Section 14. Severability. If any provision of this Act or the application thereof to any person or circumstances is held invalid, such invalidity shall not affect the provisions or applications of the Act which can be given effect without the invalid provision or application, and to this end the provisions of this Act are declared to be severable.

Section 15. Short Title. This Act shall be known and may be cited as the "Airport Zoning Act."

Section 16. Repeal. All acts or parts of acts which are inconsistent with the provisions of this Act are hereby repealed.

Section 17. Effective Date. This Act shall take effect ________.

The National Institute of Municipal Law Officers published in August, 1944, *Airport and the Courts* which presents a comprehensive survey of court decisions and legal writings and is recommended for study.

APPENDIX 1

GLOSSARY OF TERMS

Airport. A landing area used regularly by aircraft for receiving or discharging passengers or cargo.

Airport beacon. A beacon located at or near an airport for the purpose of indicating the location of the airport. An airport beacon produces alternate clear and green beams.

Airport lighting. The application of lights or floodlighting as air navigation facilities at airports. Airport lighting includes airport beacons, boundary lighting, range lighting, approach lighting, contact lighting, obstruction lighting, traffic control lighting, and floodlighting.

Airway beacon. A beacon, other than an airport beacon located on or near an airway and used for the purpose of indicating the location of the airway. An airway beacon produces alternate clear and red beams.

Approach zone. The area leading from the end of each landing strip within which the approach paths should be kept clear of obstructions. Specifically, commonly considered as a zone increasing gradually in width from 500 feet at the end of the usable portion of a landing strip to 2500 feet at a distance of 2 miles from the center of the landing area.

Approach light. One of a group of lights located outside of a landing area to indicate the projection of a runway or landing strip.

Apron. The portion of an airport, usually paved, immediately adjacent to hangars and other buildings, used for parking, loading, and unloading of aircraft.

Beacon. A light used to indicate a geographical location, producing high power beams directed slightly above the horizontal, and rotated to produce flashing lights to an observer.

Boundary light. One of a series of lights used to indicate the limits of the landing area or a landing field.

Calm. The absence of appreciable wind. Generally considered as 3 miles per hour or less.

Ceiling projector. A device designed to produce a well defined illuminated spot on the lower portion of a cloud for the purpose of providing a reference mark for the determination of the height of that part of the cloud.

Civil airway. A path through the navigable air space of the United States, identified by an area on the surface of the earth designated or approved by the Administrator as suitable for interstate, overseas, or foreign air commerce.

Code beacon. A beacon having the characteristics of a code light.

Contact light. One of a series of marker lights, set substantially flush in the ground along a runway, for the purpose of indicating the location of the runway, and assisting aircraft to land and take off. Contact lights are clear along the entire length of a runway except the final fifteen hundred feet, which are yellow and white.

Control panel. A master control panel, usually located in an airport control tower, equipped with light switches and indicating devices for the control of airport lighting.

Control tower. An establishment properly situated and equipped to allow an operator thereof to adequately control air traffic in the immediate vicinity of the airport on or adjacent to which such airport tower is located.

Control zone. The air space above an area within a circle with a radius of 3 miles drawn from the center of a control airport: Provided, however, that if a radio directional aid station designed to direct air traffic to the control airport is more than 3 miles from the center thereof, then the control zone is extended above an area one-half mile on each side of a line projected from the center of such airport to such radio aid.

Course. The direction over the surface of the earth, expressed as an angle with respect to north, that an aircraft is intended to be flown. It is the course laid out on the chart or map with respect to true north unless otherwise designated. Abbreviation: C. All courses are measured from north through east to 360°.

Floodlight. A projector designed to be arranged to illuminate a surface.

Instrument landing. A landing in which the landing area is approached and the aircraft brought properly to rest upon the ground through the use of radio communication and of instruments installed upon the aircraft.

Landing area. Any locality, either of land or water, including airports and intermediate landing fields, which is used, or intended to be used, for the landing and take-off of aircraft, whether or not facilities are provided for the shelter, servicing, or repair of aircraft, or for receiving or discharging passengers or cargo.

Landing light. A device designed for use abroad an aircraft to illuminate a ground area from the aircraft.

Landing strip. A portion of the usable area of an airport, generally 500 feet or more in width, which in its natural state or as the result of construction work is suitable for the landing and taking off of aircraft under all ordinary weather conditions. The term "runway" is frequently incorrectly used for landing strip.

Obstruction light. A red light which indicates the presence of a fixed object that is dangerous to aircraft in motion.

Range light. A marker light having a distinctive characteristic to indicate the ends of a landing strip or runway. Range lights are green lights, located in groups at the ends of runways or landing strips.

Runway. The paved surface of an airport used for the landing and taking off of aircraft.

Taxiway. A paved or unpaved strip over which aircraft may taxi to and from the landing area, runways, or aprons of an airport.

Taxi lights. Flush-type lights spaced evenly along the edges of taxiways to guide ships taxiing at night. Taxi lights are blue in color.

Wind Cone. A tapered fabric sleeve pivoted on a standard to indicate the wind direction.

Wind direction. The true direction *from* which the wind blows.

Wind rose. (1) A diagram showing the relative frequency and sometimes also the average strength of the winds blowing from different directions in a specified region. (2) A diagram showing the average relation between winds from different directions and the occurrence of other meteorological phenomena.

Wind tee. A lighted wind indicator having the form of a tee in a horizontal or slightly tilted plane. A wind tee is marked by green lights.

APPENDIX 2

REPORT OF COMMITTEE ON FLEXIBLE PAVEMENT DESIGN *

METHODS OF DESIGNING THICKNESS OF FLIGHT STRIPS AND AIRPORT RUNWAYS FOR WHEEL LOADS EXCEEDING 10,000 LB.

A. C. BENKELMAN, *Chairman*

FRED BURGGRAF
M. D. CATTON
T. V. FAHNESTOCK
A. T. GOLDBECK
B. E. GRAY
C. A. HOGENTOGLER
W. S. HOUSEL
PREVOST HUBBARD
GEORGE E. MARTIN
L. A. PALMER
M. G. SPANGLER

SYNOPSIS

Present construction practices disclose that there is a wide divergence of opinion among engineers concerning the problem of design of airport runways.

This paper describes the methods of design that are at present in use and outlines a method based on large-scale loading tests of trial pavement sections.

Three sections of pavement are constructed on a prepared section of the subgrade. The thickness of one of the sections is that estimated to be necessary for the wheel loads in question by any desired method, such as used by the Army, the Navy or by the use of soil bearing test data. The thickness of the second section is 50 per cent greater and of the third 30 per cent less than that estimated. These are tested using a repetitional method of loading. The thickness necessary to support the design load for a specified deflection is obtained by plotting the thicknesses of the trial sections against the recorded deflections.

The report stresses the fact that the success of the method is largely dependent upon the correct evaluation of the load bearing test data. It is pointed out that in many cases, due to inadequate construction compaction of the subgrade and pavement courses, a large portion of the initial load settlement may be due to mere consolidation of the component parts of the structure. The method makes it possible to consider the total settlement or only that portion of the settlement which is of primary importance as far as the ultimate load carrying capacity of the structure is concerned.

For runways and flight strips designed for wheel loads of not over 10,000 lb. the thickness values published in Wartime Road Problem No. 8 "Thickness of Flexible Pavements for Highway Loads" are recommended. However, wheel loads far greater than those accommodated by highways must often be considered. Records of experience with flexible pavements under such wheel loads are limited. Although many airports have been built recently it will be some time before the lessons they have to teach will become apparent. In the meantime it is necessary to build as best we may in the light of highway experience, research and theoretical considerations.

Three methods are described in this report.

1. The Office of the Chief of Engineers of the War Department determines thickness by using the California bearing ratio test in conjunction with curves for various wheel loads extended from those developed for highway loading.

* Highway Research Board, *Proceedings, Twenty-third Meeting, 1943*, pp. 90–100.

2. The Bureau of Yards and Docks, U. S. Navy, bases design upon the results of field loading tests on specially constructed trial pavement sections.

3. A method is proposed by the Committee which also utilizes field loading tests on trial pavement sections. It differs from the Navy method in procedure although not fundamentally.

There are several other solutions which have been proposed on the basis of research. They include:

A method of design advanced by W. S. Housel.[1]

A method of design used by the Omaha Testing Laboratories.[2]

A method based on the theory of elasticity.[3]

A method based on the cone soil bearing test developed in North Dakota.[4]

A method devised by Prof. M. G. Spangler.[5]

A method based on determination of bearing value by means of tests on bearing blocks.[6]

APPLICATION OF CALIFORNIA BEARING RATIO TEST TO AIRPLANE RUNWAY DESIGN [7]

The California bearing ratio method as used by the U. S. Engineer Department is an empirical method based upon an extension of data secured by studies of the service behavior of highway pavements. The ability of the subgrade to support load is expressed by a soil bearing value, termed the bearing ratio. Values of the bearing ratio were correlated with those thicknesses of pavement which had given satisfactory service in California under light and medium-heavy traffic. Thicknesses corresponding to different values of the bearing ratio were then extrapolated for wheel loads up to 75,000 lb. The method of extrapolation was based in part upon the elastic theory and in part upon such information as was available concerning load distribution or the angle of spread of the load through flexible pavement structures.

In design the bearing ratio is determined and the thickness for the design wheel load corresponding to the bearing ratio is obtained from the curves of thickness. The thickness thus determined is used for design of runways. To compensate for increase in stress due to vibration of slow moving or warming up

[1] "Design of Flexible Surfaces," *Proceedings*, Twenty-third Annual Highway Conference, University of Michigan, 1937; "Design of Flexible Pavements," Vol. 13, *Proceedings*, Association of Asphalt Paving Technologists.

[2] W. H. Campen, discussion on "Soil Tests for Runway Pavements," *Proceedings*, Highway Research Board, Vol. 22, p. 173 (1942).

[3] L. A. Palmer and E. S. Barber, "Soil Displacement Under a Circular Loaded Area," *Proceedings*, Highway Research Board, Vol. 20, p. 279 (1940).

[4] Keith Boyd, "An Analysis of Wheel Load Limits as Related to Design," *Proceedings*, Highway Research Board, Vol. 22, p. 185 (1942).

[5] M. G. Spangler, "The Structural Design of Flexible Pavements," *Proceedings*, Highway Research Board, Vol. 22, p. 199 (1942).

[6] A. T. Goldbeck, "A Method of Design of Nonrigid Pavements for Highways and Airport Runways," *Proceedings*, Highway Research Board, Vol. 20, p. 258 (1940).

[7] Chapter XX, Engineering Manual, Office of Chief of Engineers, War Department. Also, O. J. Porter, Foundations for Flexible Pavements, *Proceedings*, Highway Research Board, Vol. 22, p. 100 (1942). Also, T. A. Middlebrooks and G. E. Bertram, "Soil Tests for Design of Runway Pavements," *Proceedings*, Highway Research Board, Vol. 22, p. 144 (1942).

planes, the U. S. Engineer Department recommends that the wheel loads for design of turn-arounds, warm up areas, hardstandings, taxiways and aprons be increased by 25 per cent. For stub end taxiways, portions of peripheral taxiways used infrequently, surfaced-all-over fields and designed shoulders, the thickness is made 80 per cent of that for runways.

The method takes into consideration the fact that stresses imposed by the surface load decrease in unit intensity as thickness increases. As a result, the structure may be composed of layers of material having successively less support in the lower portion of the composite structure.

TRIAL SECTION METHOD USED BY U.S. NAVY [8]

In this method the thickness is determined from loading tests made upon trial sections of the pavement. The sections are constructed upon a representative area of the subgrade prepared in accordance with specifications governing the project. An initial section is built, the thickness of which, exclusive of surface course, is equal to the radius of the equivalent circular tire imprint area for the design load in question. This section is then incrementally loaded through a circular bearing block until the design load is reached. If the recorded deflection exceeds 0.2 in., the assumed design value, the trial section is too thin and if it is less than 0.2 in. it is too thick.

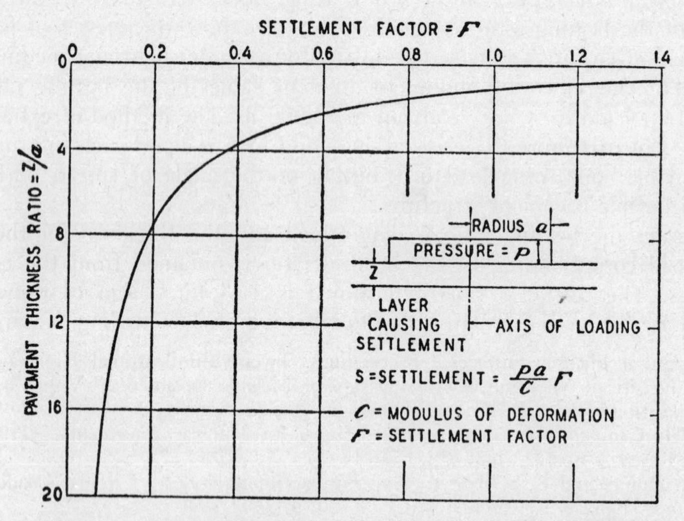

FIG. 1. Settlement under Center of Uniform Circular Load.

From the thickness, load and deflection values of this trial section, the necessary thickness to give 0.2 inch deflection is computed from the formula:

$$S = \frac{pa}{C} F \tag{1}$$

[8] U.S. Navy Department, Bureau of Yards and Docks, "Procedure for Determination of Thickness of Flexible Type Pavements."

Wherein:

S = pavement deflection, in.
p = contact pressure, lb. per sq. in.
a = radius of contact area, in.
C = modulus of vertical deformation.
F = settlement factor (from Fig. 1).
Z (Fig. 1) = thickness of section, in.

Values of S, p, a and F from the first trial section are substituted in formula (1) and C, the modulus of vertical deformation, is determined. The settlement factor F is taken from Figure 1, for $\frac{Z_1}{a}$ in which Z_1 is the thickness of the first trial section and a is the radius of contact area.

Assuming that C is constant, the formula is again solved, this time for the settlement factor (F), corresponding to the value of C as determined and S = 0.2 in. For this value of F the thickness (Z_2), presumably corresponding to 0.2-in. deflection, is determined from Figure 1.

A second trial section is then built and tested of thickness Z_2. This will most likely be too thick since C tends to increase with pavement thickness and does not remain constant as assumed. If the measured deflection of the second trial section is appreciably less than 0.2 in. another computation should be made to determine a new value of C. For a closer approximation, the two values of C are averaged and this average value substituted in formula (1) with $S = 0.2$ inch to determine a new value of F and hence, from Figure 1, the required thickness.

PROPOSED TRIAL SECTION METHOD

The Committee proposes that design of overall thickness of flexible type pavements be made on the basis of load tests of trial sections as follows:

1. Estimate the thickness required on the subgrade at the site by any desired method, such as used by the Army, the Navy, or by the use of soil bearing test data.
2. Construct three trial sections; the first of the estimated thickness, the second of a thickness 50 per cent greater and the third 30 per cent less than the estimated value.
3. Make load bearing tests and measure the deflections under load of the three trial sections.
4. Determine the thickness necessary to support the design load as follows: First, plot the supporting value of the trial sections against the deflections; second, analyze these results as described under "Evaluation of Test Results" on page 305; third, plot the selected supporting values for the three thicknesses, to produce a curve showing the relation of thickness to support. In case it is necessary to extend the curve appreciably beyond the observed values in order to obtain the design thickness, it is recommended that a fourth trial section be built and tested to verify the results.

The success of the trial section method of design depends upon correct evaluation of the results of the load bearing tests. Methods for estimating trial thickness, for constructing test sections and for making load tests on trial pavement sections will be described.

When loads are vibrating as when an airplane is "warming up," a pavement is subjected to unusually severe conditions. Extra thicknesses and the selection of subbases of high stability, noncapillary material is recommended for this type of loading.

INITIAL ESTIMATE OF THICKNESS

Since the final selection of thickness is to be based upon actual full-sized load bearing tests, the initial estimate of required thickness is not a vital factor. It should, however, approximate the actual thickness as closely as possible.

The initial thickness may be assumed, as is done by the Navy Department method by using a value equal to the radius of the equivalent circular tire contact area, or it may be estimated by the California bearing test and curves or by one of the methods listed in footnotes 1 to 6 inclusive or by means of loading tests on the subgrade soil.

Estimate of Thickness by Load Tests

The estimated thickness is computed by the following procedure, after making load tests on trial pavement sections to determine the subgrade bearing value for use in formulas (2) and (3).

When the wheel load is carried on a single tire,

$$T = \sqrt{\frac{2P}{\pi M}} - \frac{1}{2}(L_1 + L_2) \tag{2}$$

T = required overall thickness of non-rigid pavement, inches.
P = maximum wheel load on single pneumatic tire, lb.
M = subgrade bearing value determined as described in a later paragraph.
L_1 = ½ major axis of ellipse of tire contact area, inches.
L_2 = ½ minor axis of ellipse of tire contact area, inches.

Dual Tires. When dual tires are used the effective tire contact area is assumed equal to the area of one tire plus that of the rectangle whose area equals the center to center tire spacing multiplied by the length of major axis of the tire contact area. Both formulas (2) and (3) for pavement thickness result from equating the load to the uniform pressure on the subgrade over an area defined by 45-deg. lines extended to the subgrade from this effective tire contact area. This uniform pressure is assumed to be one-half the bearing value of the subgrade.

$$T = \sqrt{\left(\frac{B}{2\pi}\right)^2 + C} - \frac{B}{2\pi} \tag{3}$$

T = required thickness of nonrigid pavement, in.
$B = 2S + \pi(L_1 + L_2)$
$C = \frac{2P}{M\pi} - \frac{2SL_1}{\pi} - L_1 L_2$
P = maximum wheel load supported on dual pneumatic tires, lb.
M = subgrade bearing value determined as described in a later paragraph.

$L_1 = \frac{1}{2}$ major axis of ellipse of tire contact area, in.
$L_2 = \frac{1}{2}$ minor axis of ellipse of tire contact area, in.
$S =$ center to center spacing of tires.

It will be noted that formulas (2) and (3) take into account the influences of tire dimensions, tire pressure and spacing of dual tires.

The tire contact area (sq. in.) = tire load (lb.)/tire inflation pressure (lb. per sq. in.) × tire load supporting factor. It is sufficiently accurate to consider the tire load supporting factor as 1.10.

The tire contact area is an ellipse which has a major axis equal approximately to twice the minor axis. Therefore, tire contact area $= 2\pi L_2^2$, from which L_2 and L_1 may be calculated.

In the case of airplane tires L_2 may be assumed, with sufficient accuracy, equal to $0.6L_1$. If dual tires are used on large planes of future design, the spacing of the tires may be such that a single tire load may govern the required pavement thickness and this possibility should be investigated by using both formulas (2) and (3).

Relation of Surface Course to Thickness Design

For wheel loads greater than 10,000 lb., only bituminous plant mix and bituminous penetration macadam are recommended.

Cold Laid Plant Mix Types. A 2-in. finished layer of cold laid plant mix will generally prove adequate. Little or no advantage is gained by making such surfaces thicker than this, as the additional load supporting value which they impart to the total structure is probably no more than that imparted by an equal thickness of well compacted dense graded mineral aggregate such as gravel, broken stone, or slag. In general, their use should be limited to wheel loads of not over 15,000 lb.

Penetration Macadam. Hot penetration macadam primarily employs a large one-sized crushed aggregate which controls its minimum thickness, usually 2½ in. It is placed ordinarily on gravel or stone bases and in estimating the thickness may be considered to have approximately the same structural strength per inch thickness. Unless constructed of very hard rock, such as trap, its use should be limited to maximum wheel loads of 25,000 lb.

Dense Graded Hot Mix Pavements. The minimum thickness of this type pavement surface for highway traffic is usually 2 in.

(a) On pavements where the torsional stresses imposed by heavy wheel loads making sharp turns are very great, thicknesses of dense graded hot mix pavements greater than 2 in. are advisable.

(b) Until more information is developed, it seems advisable to adopt a minimum thickness of 2½ in. of dense graded hot mix pavement for wheel loads between 15,000 and 25,000 lb.; a 4-in. minimum thickness for wheel loads of from 25,000 to 60,000 lb.; and a 5-in. minimum thickness for heavier wheel loads. For the purpose of thickness design estimate, each inch of dense graded hot mix pavement may be considered as the equivalent of not less than 2 in. of granular base material.

METHOD OF CONSTRUCTING TEST SECTIONS

Three test sections should be constructed, each not less than 20 ft. square. One section should be of the estimated total thickness and design. A second section should have a thickness 30 per cent less than the estimated total, and a third section 50 per cent greater than the estimated total. The entire structure should be embankment and the reduction or increase in total thickness should be accomplished by variation in the bottom portion of the pavement structure, which usually will be the subbase.

These sections ordinarily should be built as a continuous structure and to the same elevation above existing subgrade. The variation in thickness of the bottom portion of the sections should be adjusted by placing subgrade material above the existing subgrade level. Figure 2 shows the embankment and the necessary construction steps to produce an estimated total thickness of 30 in., with adjacent test sections 30 per cent less and 50 per cent greater. In all sections the bituminous wearing course is 4 in. and the base course 8 in. thick, for the particular example illustrated in Figure 2.

For ease of access to the sections, a ramp should be constructed at each end having a maximum grade of 6 per cent. The base course should extend 5 ft. beyond each side of the wearing course and at least 10 ft. beyond each end. Side slopes of the embankment should be approximately 2 to 1, with suitable drainage provided at the bottom of the slope.

Prior to constructing the embankment, the upper 6 in. of the subgrade, if it consists of fine grained silts and clays, should be scarified and recompacted at a moisture content about 2 per cent above the optimum as determined by the American Society for Testing Materials Tentative Method of Test for Moisture-Density Relations of Soils, D 698–42 T.[9]

During construction of the sections, subgrade material from adjacent areas should be hauled in and compacted, (with a like moisture content) for the purpose of raising the subgrade level as may be required for thickness adjustment of the sections.

Subgrade, subbase and base materials should be placed and compacted in layers not exceeding 6 in. thick. In the example (Fig. 2) thicknesses of 4½ and 5 in. have been selected as a matter of convenience during construction. Extreme care should be exercised to obtain uniform compaction throughout and suitable tests should be made to insure this result. Construction methods should conform to recognized standard practice in the locality where the work is being done. As a rule final compaction should be obtained by rolling. Tarpaulin or roofing paper of sufficient area should be provided to protect unfinished areas from rainfall.

Where subbase or base courses are placed which would ordinarily require application of water for bonding, this should be accomplished by pre-mixing water with the aggregate in the required amount, in order not to saturate the subgrade under the embankment through excess surface application.

[9] See also "maximum density," Standard Laboratory Method of Test for the Compaction and Density of Soil, American Association of State Highway Officials, T 99–38.

METHOD OF MAKING LOAD TESTS ON TRIAL PAVEMENT SECTIONS

Equipment

(a) Hydraulic jack assembly with ball joint attachment capable of applying and releasing the load in increments.

(b) Set of circular steel bearing plates, 1 in. thick, 12, 16, 20, 24 and 30 in. in diameter, machined so that they can be arranged in pyramid fashion to insure rigidity.

(c) Two dial gages capable of recording deflections of 0.001 in. up to a maximum of 1 in.

(d) Trailer or truck assembly to provide reaction load. Point of application of load to be at least 8 ft. from the nearest wheel.

(e) Deflection beam, 3 by 3 by $\frac{1}{4}$ in. steel angle, 16 ft. long, to rest upon supports located at least 8 ft. from the nearest wheel of truck or trailer.

Testing Procedure

Testing Objectives. In this discussion, deflection is defined as the lowering of the loaded area while still subjected to load. Settlement is the permanent lowering of the area after the load is removed.

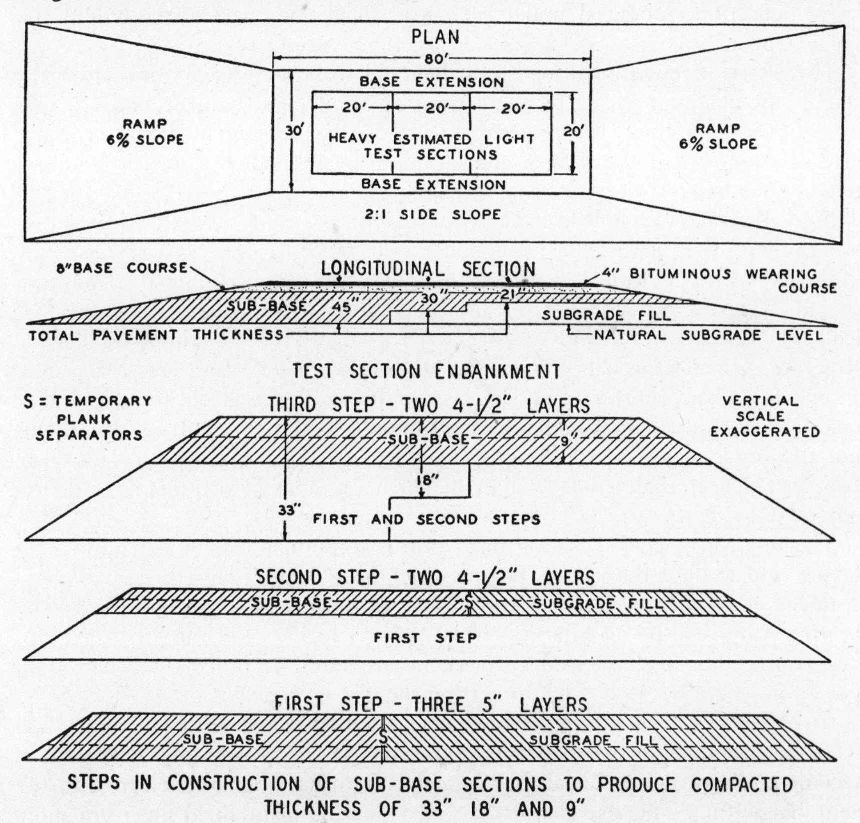

FIG. 2. Construction Details of Typical Pavement Test Sections.

Unless it is abnormally weak with respect to the load applied, a flexible pavement seldom fails upon the first application of load. The first load frequently compacts one or more courses of the pavement more thoroughly than the original construction compaction, thus developing greater resistance to subsequent repetitions of the load than is indicated by the initial settlement. Additional settlement produced by the second load application may be, and frequently is, very much less than the original settlement. A third load application will usually develop further settlement but, unless complete failure is imminent, the increment of settlement under the third repetition of load will be slightly less than that for the second repetition. Subsequent repetitions then show decreasing increments of settlement in an orderly manner which makes it possible to estimate total settlement for any number of repetitions. About four load repetitions are usually required to develop this information, which is graphically illustrated in Figure 3. In this illustration, cumulative settlements are plotted against four load applications which are spaced on a logarithmic scale. It will be noted that the cumulative settlements for the second, third and fourth applications are connected by a straight-line that may be projected to any desired number of load repetitions for the purpose of estimating total settlement for that number of loadings. Cumulative deflections produced under each load repetition may be plotted in the same manner.

The effect of repetitional loading is believed to be more significant from the standpoint of design than the mere determination of settlement under a first load application. Unless the structure fails, the initial settlement should be evaluated as a measure of the compaction produced by the first test load in addition to that obtained in the original construction.

From the single cycle load deflection curve on soil materials, a critical deflection of about 0.2 inch has been frequently selected as the basis of evaluating the load support of a flexible pavement placed upon the soil. Such assumption should, however, be corrected for additional compaction produced by the first load application on the soil itself, as well as upon the superimposed flexible structure. This is especially true in the case of design for wheel loads exceeding 15,000 lb., where the initial compaction under loading is likely to exceed that produced by construction equipment commonly used at present. A bituminous hot-mix surface course, such as recommended for the heavy wheel loads, may moreover deflect under one load to 0.5 inch or more before incipient failure occurs.

The following detailed testing procedure is recommended for the purpose of taking into account the various factors which have been discussed.

Recommended Procedure for Applications of Loads to Test Sections. (a) The bearing plate shall be set in a thin bed of plaster to insure bearing with the surface course. The smallest load that can be accurately recorded (less than 1 lb. per sq. in.) shall be applied before setting the dials at 0 deflection.

(b) All load increment applications shall be maintained until not more than 0.001 in. per min. increased deflection occurs. At this point, total deflection is recorded, after which the load shall be reduced to that originally selected for the zero dial setting. The zero dial setting load shall be maintained until not more than 0.001 in. per min. increased recovery occurs. The dial reading at this point shall be recorded as settlement.

(c) Four applications and releases of each load increment shall be made, as described in paragraph (b), before proceeding to the next increment of loading.

(d) While the selection of load increments may be varied according to the judgment of the engineer, the following procedure is recommended to develop the maximum amount of information with the minimum of effort: The first increment is selected by slowly applying load until an initial deflection of 0.1 in. is obtained or the design load reached, whichever occurs first. After this load has been applied and released four times, as described in paragraphs (b) and (c), the second increment is selected by increasing the load until initial deflection is either 0.1 in. greater than the last recorded deflection for the preceding increment, or the design load is reached, whichever occurs first. Successive load increments are selected in the same manner until the final deflection is approximately 0.5 in.

EVALUATION OF TEST RESULTS

Cumulative deflections and cumulative settlements for each individual load increment are first plotted on semilog paper as illustrated in Figure 3. The straight lines, connecting values for the second, third and fourth repetitions, may be extended to any desired number of repetitions, or from the slopes of the lines, deflections and settlements may be calculated for the desired number of repetitions.

A composite diagram may then be prepared from the test data, as illustrated in Figure 4. Here the design wheel load is assumed to be 37,000 lb. The initial settlement curve is plotted from settlements recorded for the first application

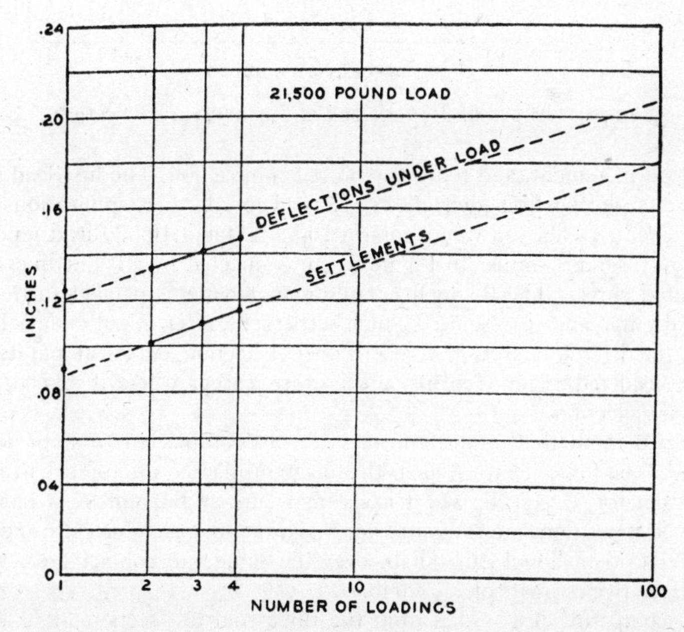

FIG. 3. Cumulative Deflections and Settlements Produced by Repetitions of the Same Load.

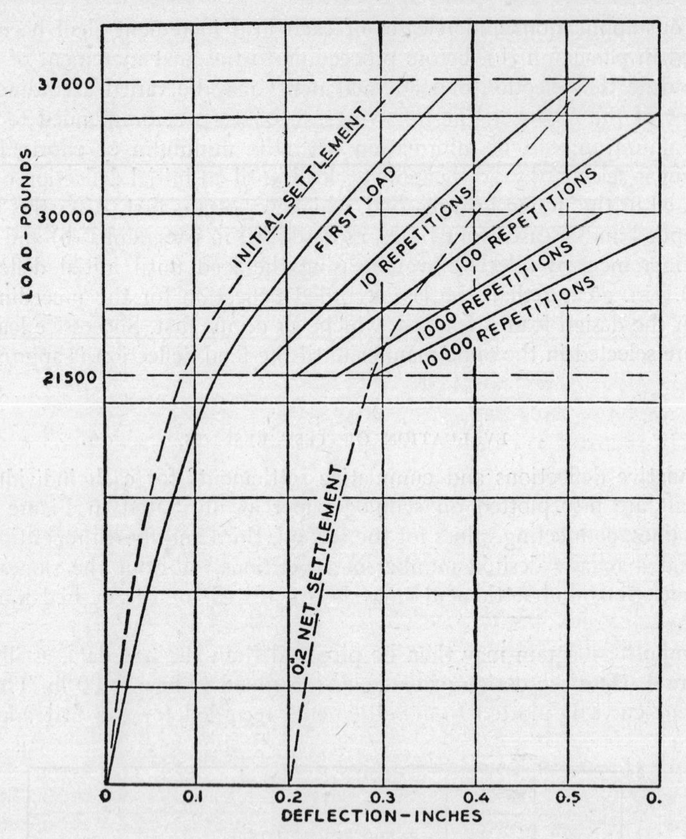

Fig. 4. Effect of Repetitions of Load upon Deflection.

of each load increment, and represents initial compaction. The first load application curve is plotted from deflections recorded for the first application of each load increment. Deflection values for 10, 100, 1000 and 10,000 load repetitions, taken from diagrams similar to Figure 3, are connected by straight lines instead of estimated curves. The 0.2-inch net settlement curve is parallel to the initial settlement curve and represents 0.2-inch settlement, after initial compaction has been obtained. It intersects the repetitional deflection curves at points which may be considered as representing safe loading, except where it exceeds a total of 0.5-inch deflection.

Bearing in mind that airport runways are rarely subjected to static loads repeated over the same identical area, this diagram may be interpreted to indicate a safe design for 37,000 lb. wheel loads on a runway but not on a taxiway. If 10,000 load repetitions are estimated for a taxiway, the same diagram indicates a safe wheel load of about 26,500 lb. over the same tire contact area, with an ultra conservative estimate of 21,500 lb.

When comparing test results from the three trial test sections, it is believed that the best evaluation of relative strength can be obtained by plotting all deflections for a given load from the initial settlement curve taken as zero, as illustrated by the 0.2-in. net settlement curve in Figure 4. In this way, the effect of initial compaction is eliminated and any differences due to unequal construction compaction minimized.

LOAD TESTS FOR SUBGRADE BEARING VALUE

The formulas for determining the thickness of trial sections of pavements for supporting heavy loads, require a knowledge of the subgrade bearing value. Obviously the amount of rolling of the subgrade, the weight and rigidity of the overlying surfacing and the subgrade moisture conditions influence the bearing value. Hence, the subgrade bearing value must be determined on the subgrade as it will exist under the pavement and not as it exists at the airport site when in an uncompacted and uncovered condition.

Preparation of Subgrade. The subgrade at the spot or spots selected for test should be prepared as described under "Method of Constructing Test Sections." The upper 6 in. should be scarified and recompacted using a moisture content about two per cent above the standard optimum, if the subgrade material consists of fine grained silts or clays. This procedure will bring the subgrade to approximately the moisture condition desired for making the load tests.

Placing Bearing Block. After preparation of the subgrade the spot selected for test should be carefully leveled and the bearing block bedded in place on a thin layer of plaster of paris. A double layer of 1-in. planks should be laid on the subgrade to form a platform about 8 ft. square, centered over the bearing block and having an opening at the center about ¼ in. larger in diameter than the bearing block. This platform should be loaded with sand bags so that the surcharge will serve to prevent lateral displacement of the surface of the soil adjacent to the bearing block during test. This weighted platform is intended to simulate the vertical restraining influence of the pavement surface.

Bearing Blocks. The bearing block should have approximately the same area as the contact area of the tire required for the design wheel load. If equipment is not available for applying sufficient load on the large bearing block which may be required, it is suggested that tests be made using three smaller blocks, 16, 20 and 24 in. in diameter.

Test Procedure. The test should be conducted with repeated loads using the method already described for loading the finished trial pavement sections; and the load necessary to produce a net deflection of 0.2 in., after the required number of repetitions, is taken as the bearing value. If necessary to use the three small bearing blocks instead of one approaching in size the tire contact area, a curve is plotted between the unit load which produces 0.2 in. net deflection and the perimeter-area ratio (= 2/radius). Finally, the unit load for the large block may be extrapolated from this curve which will be approximately a straight line with unit loads as ordinates and values for perimeter-area ratio (2/radius of block) as abscissas.

Use of Subgrade Bearing Value. Test sections for a runway which in service has relatively few load repetitions in a given spot can be designed with a subgrade bearing value determined at a net deflection of 0.2 in. after ten repetitions of load, whereas a taxiway may require the use of a bearing value resulting from a determination at 1000 or even 10,000 repetitions. A gross deflection of 0.5 in. should not be exceeded for bituminous surfaces and this requirement may possibly govern the bearing value rather than a net deflection of 0.2 in. under repeated loads.

GENERAL CONSIDERATIONS IN THE CONSTRUCTION OF FLIGHT STRIPS AND AIRPLANE RUNWAYS

It is recommended that generally subgrades and embankments be prepared in accordance with the A.A.S.H.O. standard specifications for materials for embankments and subgrades (Designation M 57–42) which utilizes data furnished by the Standard A.A.S.H.O. and A.S.T.M. compaction tests.

As a precaution against detrimental swell of the compacted soil, the upper layer (at least 1 ft.) should be compacted at a moisture content about two per cent above the optimum.[10] For embankments up to about 50 ft. high, the remainder should be placed at not less than 95 per cent standard density. Embankments exceeding 50 ft. high should be studied as special problems in soil mechanics and constructed by procedures selected to suit individual cases.

The subgrade should be inspected to insure that the specified compaction is obtained. A soft subgrade may affect adversely both the subbase and the base course. Lateral drainage ditches should be kept open during construction so that water is not trapped in the subgrade. If difficulty is encountered in drying out the subgrade, some insulation course should be used either to take up the excess moisture or blanket the soft undersoil. Stone screenings, sand, and in emergency even hay and straw may be used for this purpose and will provide firm bearing even during rain periods.

Base courses should be compacted to the designed density. Stabilization procedures requiring excess water for manipulation purposes should not be employed in areas subject to heavy or continuous rainfall. In case of unexpected wet weather, expediency may dictate change of design to the use of granular material containing the minimum amount passing the No. 200 sieve, as designated in the standard specifications [11] for base course materials.

Thorough mixing of stabilized base course materials is an essential requirement. Clay added in correct amounts but not properly dispersed through the granular materials may be as detrimental as too much clay. Use of a mixing plant is recommended to facilitate the production of good mixtures with the specified optimum moisture content.

Rolling should be continued until adequate compaction of base courses is attained. This is necessary in order that the proper density can be obtained in the bituminous wearing course. Frequent tests should be made to see that the correct density in all courses is being secured. Placement of the material in several layers will aid in securing this density. When bituminous wearing courses are placed in layers by mechanical finishers, joints between adjacent strips of one

[10] A.S.T.M. Tentative Method of Test for Moisture-Density Relations of Soils, D698–42 T. A.A.S.H.O., Standard Laboratory Method of Test for the Compaction and Density of Soil, T 99–38.

[11] A.A.S.H.O. Standard Specifications for Materials for Stabilized Base Course, M 56–42. A.S.T.M. Tentative Specifications for Materials for Stabilized Base Course, D 556–40 T. Highway Research Board, Wartime Problems No. 5, Granular Stabilized Roads.

layer should overlap joints in the layer beneath. In order to produce tight longitudinal joints between adjacent strips one man should be detailed to place extra needed mixture in any open or low area prior to initial rolling so that a uniform density is produced throughout.

DISCUSSION ON THICKNESS OF FLIGHT STRIPS AND AIRPORT RUNWAYS

MR. M. D. CATTON, *Portland Cement Association*: As mentioned by Mr. Benkelman in his formal presentation of the report of the Committee on Flexible Pavement Design, "Methods of Designing Thickness of Flight Strips and Airport Runways for Wheel Loads Exceeding 10,000 Lb.," the Committee was not in common agreement on some basic points influencing design. The Committee worked diligently for several months on this report, during which time all available data were carefully studied and analyzed. Even though common agreement could not be obtained on all points for a wartime bulletin, it was agreed that ". . . it is necessary to build as best we may in the light of highway experience, research and theoretical considerations" and to present a report for consideration.

The report describes three design methods:

1. That used by the Office of Chief of Engineers, U.S. Army.
2. That used by the Bureau of Yards & Docks, U.S. Navy, and
3. One proposed by the Committee.

A large number of airports have been built using methods 1 and 2, which are supplying experience records. However, the third method proposed by the Committee, does not have an extended experience background, which leaves several points to be verified by tests, research and experience.

As stated in the report: "The success of the trial section method of design (proposed by the Committee) depends upon correct evaluation of the results of the load bearing test." My comments refer particularly to the interpretation and evaluation of the examples of the load bearing tests given in the report.

The methods or procedures for making the test have many desirable features. However, some of the recommended interpretations require more background, in my judgment, than is available at present. For example, it is assumed (1) that the settlement produced by initial test loadings is confined largely to additional compaction in the base and subbase; and (2) that the settlement curve developed by four load repetitions may be used to develop settlement for as many as 10,000 repetitions of load or more. I do not believe that either of these assumptions is necessarily true.

Some loading data that I have seen show that initial settlement or deformation in the base is actually a measurement of incipient base failure. In these instances, at least, settlement from four load repetitions could not be projected to indicate settlement for a large number of loadings. Other test data show the same total static load deformation before and after 2000+ trips of a 33,000-lb. wheel load, but additional static load deformation after 5000+ loadings. These loading tests indicate that it is most difficult to predict a constant, orderly manner in which settlement and deformation data can be projected from a few loadings to any particular number of subsequent loadings.

As indicated above, a shortcoming in the procedure is that it does not permit differentiation between deformation in the subgrade, in the base and in the surfacing. In any case, any deformations due to consolidation of the subbase and base materials will vary with construction control on each job and must be segregated from deformations in other elements of the pavement structure to permit proper design.

I think another instance of misinterpretation of data exists where the statement is made that . . . this diagram (Fig. 4) may be interpreted to indicate a safe design for 37,000-lb. wheel loads on a runway . . . The fact that a total deflection of more than 0.5 in. is indicated after only 10 repetitions of load would lead me to speculate that rupture and failure would result from a few more loadings and that the diagram indicates the design is not safe for a 37,000-lb. wheel load.

In determining permissible deformations on flexible pavements in place, it is desirable to know the permissible deformations of each element in the structure with the lowest permissible deformation governing design. The subgrade will have a certain permissible maximum deformation before failure, the base course material itself will probably have an entirely different permissible deformation and the bituminous surface a still different permissible deformation. It is my judgment that in many cases permissible maximum deformations or deflections will be governed by the subgrade itself, and that in these cases the deformations or deflections will be very much less than the permissible deflections for either the base material or the surfacing material.

The suggested test procedure and analysis of data contains additional comments on settlement, compaction, deflections, etc., that might be discussed in some detail. However, most of them tie back to a determination of critical deflections. Test data obtained on field installations and published by Col. James H. Stratton, Middlebrooks, Porter and others [12] point up rather strongly that critical deflections may be of the order of less than 0.1 in. rather than 0.2 in., or the maximum 0.5 in. contained in this report. Also, that plate loading tests may be entirely indeterminate and without basis for interpretation for design purposes.

While the testing procedure contained in the committee report may be used to determine deflection data, it is believed that until such time that considerable data have been obtained for study and field performance records established, it is quite essential to be most conservative in establishing permissible deflections in general terms.

[12] "Military Airfields, A Symposium. Construction and Design Problems" by James H. Stratton, M. Am. Soc. C. E., *Proceedings*, Am. Soc. C. E., January, 1944. "Accelerated Traffic Tests on Flexible Type Pavements" by T. A. Middlebrooks and R. M. Haines, Highway Research Board *Proceedings*, Vol. 23, 1943. "Foundations for Flexible Pavements" by O. J. Porter, and "Soil Tests for Design of Runway Pavements" by T. A. Middlebrooks and G. E. Bertram, Highway Research Board *Proceedings*, Vol. 22, 1942. "Field Investigation for Flexible Pavement Design" by T. A. Middlebrooks and G. E. Bertram, Highway Research Board *Proceedings*, Vol. 21, 1941.

A P P E N D I X 3

DEPARTMENT OF COMMERCE
Civil Aeronautics Administration
Airport Division
Washington, D.C.
August 1, 1943

CLEARING AND GRUBBING FOR AIRPORTS

C.A.A. Specification No. P-101

DESCRIPTION

1.1 This item shall consist of clearing, and/or clearing and grubbing including the disposal of materials for all areas within the limits designated on the plans or as required by the engineer.

Clearing shall consist of the cutting and removal of all trees, brush, logs and the removal of fences and other loose or projecting material from the designated areas. The trees and brush shall be cut to a height of not more than eighteen (18) inches above the ground. The removal of stumps and roots will not be required.

Clearing and grubbing shall consist of clearing the surface of the ground of the designated areas of all trees, down timber, logs, snags, brush, undergrowth, fences, structures, debris and rubbish of any nature, natural obstructions or such material which in the opinion of the engineer is unsuitable for the foundation of the runways or other required structures, including the grubbing of stumps, roots, matted roots, foundations, and the disposal from the project of all spoil materials resulting from clearing and grubbing by burning or otherwise, as specified or directed.

CONSTRUCTION METHODS

2.1 The areas denoted on the plans to be cleared and/or cleared and grubbed under this item shall be staked on the ground by the engineer. The clearing and grubbing shall be done at a satisfactory distance ahead of the grading operations. The contractor shall clear the staked or indicated area of all objectionable materials. Trees unavoidably falling outside the specified limits must be cut up, removed and disposed of in a satisfactory manner. In order to minimize damage to trees that are to be left standing, trees shall be felled toward the center of area being cleared. The contractor shall preserve and protect from injury all trees not required to be removed. Where embankments exceeding five (5) feet in depth are to be made, trees, stumps and brush shall be cut off within six (6) inches above the ground surface.

In areas to be cleared and grubbed, all stumps, roots, buried logs, brush and other unsatisfactory materials shall be removed. Tap roots or other projections over 1½″ in diameter shall be grubbed out to a depth of at least 18 inches below the finished subgrade elevation, unless otherwise directed.

All holes remaining after the grubbing operation shall have the sides broken down or leveled if necessary to flatten out the slopes, refilled with acceptable material and properly compacted by tampers and rollers. The material shall be placed, moistened and compacted in layers when directed.

All spoil materials removed by clearing or by clearing and grubbing shall be disposed of by burning or by removal to approved disposal areas. Piles for burning shall be placed either in cleared area near the center or in adjacent open spaces where no damage to trees or other vegetation will occur. The contractor will be responsible for controlling fires and for compliance with all Federal and State laws and regulations relative to building fires at the site.

In the event that a city or county requests the saving of merchantable timber, the contractor shall trim the limbs and tops from such designated trees, saw the same into suitable log lengths and make the material available for removal by other agencies.

Any blasting necessary shall be done at the contractor's responsibility and the utmost care shall be taken not to endanger life or property.

The removal of existing structures and utilities required to permit the orderly prosecution of the work will be accomplished by local agencies unless otherwise shown on the drawings. Whenever a telephone or telegraph pole, pipe line, conduit, sewer, roadway or other utility is encountered and must be removed or relocated to permit the completion of the project, the contractor will so advise the engineer who will notify the proper local authority or owner and attempt to secure prompt action.

Fences shall be removed and disposed of when directed by the engineer. Fence wire shall be neatly wound on suitable reels and the wire and posts stored on the airport if same is to be used again or stored at a designated location if the fence is to remain the property of a local owner or of a civic authority.

METHOD OF MEASUREMENT

3.1 The quantity to be paid for under this item shall be the entire area measured in acres or as specified in the bid schedule.

BASIS OF PAYMENT

4.1 Clearing shall be paid for at the contract unit price bid or lump sum as specified in the bid schedule, which payment shall include full compensation for all equipment, tools, materials, labor and incidentals necessary to complete the work.

4.2 Clearing and grubbing shall be paid for at the contract unit price bid or lump sum as specified in the bid schedule, which payment shall include full compensation for all equipment, tools, materials, labor, and incidentals necessary to complete the work.

DEPARTMENT OF COMMERCE
Civil Aeronautics Administration
Airport Division
Washington, D.C.
July 1, 1943

GRADING FOR AIRPORTS

C.A.A. Specification No. P-102

INTRODUCTION

Recognizing the fact that no structure is stronger than the foundation upon which it is constructed, the objective in this specification of careful selection and placing of grading materials is to build a foundation to support the load rather than to depend largely on the base and wearing surface.

It is essential, therefore, that efforts be made to achieve uniformity of soils in the subgrades to insure uniform subgrade conditions. For this reason soil investigations are essential to permit the selection of desirable soil in the subgrade. The use of C.A.A. Specification No. P-601 will assist in the soil's classification.

As the soil conditions will vary for each particular project, special provisions describing the grading procedure should be included in the specification, especially if selective grading is to be required. In some cases the types of soil as determined by the soil survey will be either uniformly good or uniformly poor and selective grading, therefore, will not be used. But should the soil survey indicate selective grading to be advantageous, the necessary grading procedure should be clearly and definitely stated in the special provisions. In like manner, if particular materials are to be removed to a minimum depth if encountered in the subgrade such materials should also be described as definitely as possible. The engineer will then be responsible for the carrying out of a carefully prepared grading plan. Leaving selective grading plans entirely to the engineer to improvise during the construction is an unsound procedure as well as being rather unfair to the contractor. However, the engineer should control the grading sufficiently to require modifications of the general grading plan dependent on the actual materials encountered in the excavation.

In determining the grade elevation, the type of soils existing beneath the subgrade is highly important. In many cases it will be found that the balancing of the earthwork quantities is undesirable owing to the elevation of the water table or the type of soil to be handled. In these cases borrow material often permits the selection of a much better material for subgrades and embankments and provides a higher grade line with less drainage costs.

When borrow pits are necessary, it is desirable that options be secured on an adequate supply of suitable material. The location of the pit or pits and, if feasible, the agreed pit cost should be stated in the proposal. This will allow the contractor to make his bid with the knowledge that he can obtain satisfactory embankment material with a known cost and haul.

In using this grading specification it will be noted that it contains compaction of embankment requirements. These requirements are in accordance with the Modified Proctor Density Tests, A.A.S.H.O. Method T 99-42.

DESCRIPTION

1.1 This item shall consist of excavating and grading the landing strips, runways, taxiways, aprons and other areas for drainage, building construction, parking, or other purposes, in accordance with these specifications and in conformity with the dimensions and typical sections shown on the plans and with the lines and grades established by the engineer.

All suitable material taken from excavation shall be used as fill to the extent required to construct embankments or subgrade as indicated on the plans.

In case the volume of the excavation exceeds that required to construct the embankments to the grades indicated, the excess shall be used to grade the areas of ultimate development, or wasted as directed. In case the volume of excavation is not sufficient for constructing the fill to the grades indicated, the deficiency shall be supplied from borrow sources designated within the airport or other approved area.

CONSTRUCTION METHODS

2.1 *General.* The rough excavation shall be carried to such depth that sufficient material will be left above the designated grade to allow for compaction to this grade. Likewise, on embankments, sufficient material shall be placed above the designated grade to allow for compaction and settlement. Should the contractor through negligence or other fault excavate below the designated lines, he shall replace such excavation with approved materials, in an approved manner and condition, at his own expense. The engineer shall have complete control over the excavation, moving, placing and disposition of all material. He shall determine the suitability of material to be placed in embankments. All material not considered suitable shall be disposed of in waste areas or as directed. In general, the layer of topsoil shall not be used in fills but shall be handled and placed as directed.

All material encountered shall be classed as grading unless otherwise specified. The contractor shall inform and satisfy himself as to the character, quantity and distribution of all material to be excavated. No payment will be made for any excavated material which is used for purposes other than those designated. All spoil areas shall be leveled to a uniform line and section and shall present a neat appearance before project acceptance.

If it is necessary in the prosecution of the work to interrupt existing surface drainage, sewers, or underdrainage, conduits, utilities or similar underground structures, or parts thereof, the contractor shall be responsible for and shall take all necessary precautions to protect and preserve or provide temporary services for same. When such facilities are encountered, the contractor shall notify the engineer who shall arrange for their removal if necessary. The contractor shall, at his own expense, satisfactorily repair all damage to such facilities or structures which may result from any of his operations or from negligence during the period of the contract.

2.2 *Equipment.* (a) Grading—The contractor may use any type of earth-moving equipment he may desire or has at his disposal, provided equipment is in a satisfactory condition and of such capacity that the grading schedule can be maintained; which schedule being as planned and directed by the engineer in accordance with the total calendar days or working days bid for the construction of the grading or the total completed project. The contractor shall furnish, operate and maintain such equipment as is necessary to control uniform layers, section and smoothness of grade for compaction and drainage.

(b) Compacting—The compacting equipment shall be of such design, weight and quantity to obtain the required density.

(1) Tamping Roller—The tamping roller shall consist of one or more units. Each unit shall consist of a water-tight cylindrical drum not less than 48 inches in length and shall be surmounted by metal studs with tamping feet projecting not less than 7 inches from the surface of the drum and spaced not less than six (6) inches nor more than ten (10) inches measured diagonally from center to center. The area of each tamper foot shall be not less than 4 square inches nor more than 12 square inches. Each unit shall be provided with a suitable tamper foot-cleaning device. Where more than one rolling unit is used, the rolling units shall be pivoted on the main frame in a manner which will permit the rolling units to adapt themselves to uneven ground surfaces and to rotate independently. When fully loaded, the roller shall produce at least 200 pounds per square inch of area of tamping feet in contact with the ground. The roller and the operating tractor shall meet the approval of the engineer.

(2) Pneumatic Roller—The pneumatic roller shall consist of two axles on which are mounted not less than 9 pneumatic-tired wheels in such a manner that the rear group of tires will not follow in the tracks of the forward group, and mounted in a rigid frame provided with a loading platform or body suitable for ballast loading. The front axle shall rotate around a king pin so located that the roller may be turned within a minimum circle. The roller shall have an effective rolling width of at least sixty (60) inches and shall give a compression of at least 325 lbs. per inch of width of tread when fully loaded. The tires shall be uniformly inflated. The roller and the operating tractor shall meet the approval of the engineer.

(3) Smooth Roller—The smooth self-propelled or power roller shall weigh at least ten (10) tons and may be of the tandem or 3-wheel type. The wheels of the roller shall be equipped with adjustable scrapers. The roller shall be maintained in good condition and operated by an experienced rollerman.

(4) Other Equipment—Other equipment may be used for compacting and consolidating the fills, subgrades and other areas, upon approval of the engineer. Such equipment shall be routed over the area being compacted and shall be operated until the required density is obtained.

2.3 *Stripping.* All vegetation such as brush, heavy sods, heavy growth of grass, decayed vegetable matter, rubbish, and any other unsuitable material within the area upon which embankment is to be placed, shall be stripped or otherwise removed before the embankment is started, and in no case shall such objectionable material be allowed in or under the embankment. Top soil and sod obtained from the stripping operations shall be stockpiled in an approved location when directed or as shown on the plans.

2.4 *Scarifying Foundation.* Immediately prior to the placing of the fill materials, the entire area upon which the embankment is to be placed shall be scarified and broken by means of a disc harrow or plow to a depth of four (4) inches. Scarifying shall be done approximately parallel to the axis of the fill. All roots, debris, large stones or objectionable material that would cause interference with the compaction of the foundation or fill shall be removed from the area and disposed of as directed. A thin layer (approximately three inches) of the fill material shall be spread over the scarified foundation and the whole area compacted as required in the specifications.

2.5 *Benching.* Where embankments are to be placed on natural slope steeper than 3:1, horizontal benches shall be constructed as shown on the plans or as directed by the engineer. Excavated material will be incorporated in embankments. Payment will be made for the material excavated at the unit price for grading.

2.6 *Excavation.* Excavation shall be performed at such places as are indicated on the contract plans, to the lines, grades and elevation shown or as directed by the engineer. Excavation shall be made in such manner that the requirements for formation of embankments can be followed. No excavation shall be started until the engineer has taken cross-sectional elevations and measurements of the existing ground surface, and has staked out the proposed work. All material encountered of whatever nature within the limits indicated shall be removed and disposed of as directed. During the process of excavation, the grade shall be maintained in such condition that it will be well drained at all times. When directed temporary drains and drainage ditches shall be installed to intercept or divert surface water which may affect the safety or condition of the work.

The excavation material shall be handled in such a manner as to allow the selected material to be placed in the embankment and in the capping of pavement subgrades as determined from the soil profile and soil characteristics. This material shall be deposited within the designated areas of the airport as shown on the plans or as directed by the engineer. At least the top six (6) inches of the pavement subgrade shall be constructed of selected granular material if obtainable from the excavation.

When practicable, selected material should be hauled directly from the excavation to the final position in the subgrade. Stockpiling of selected material for later placement in the subgrade shall not be allowed unless ordered by the engineer. Material stockpiled when ordered shall be paid for at the contract unit price for grading, for removing from excavation and placing in stockpile and again at the contract unit price for grading for removing from stockpile and placing in its final position in the subgrade.

Where rock, shale, or other material unsatisfactory for subgrade is encountered, it shall be excavated to a depth of at least 12 inches below the contemplated subgrade. All material so excavated shall be paid for at the contract unit price for unclassified excavation. The portion so excavated shall be refilled with suitable material obtained from the grading operations or borrow and thoroughly compacted by rolling as hereinafter specified. The necessary refilling will constitute a part of the embankment. Where rock cuts are made and refilled with earth or where trenching out is done to provide for a course of pavement, the depths thus created shall be ditched at frequent intervals to provide a free outlet for drainage.

Minor adjustments in lines and grades will be made if found necessary as the work progresses. All breakages and slides beyond the finished work as planned, if avoidable by proper methods of excavation, shall be removed by the contractor at his own expense. Otherwise, if unavoidable, it shall be paid for as unclassified excavation.

The removal of existing structures required to permit the orderly prosecution of the work will be accomplished by local agencies unless otherwise shown on the plans. All foundations shall be excavated and the material disposed of for at least two (2) feet below the subgrade. All foundations thus excavated shall be backfilled with suitable material and compacted.

In cut areas the subgrade shall be scarified and compacted to a minimum depth of six (6) inches to at least 95% density as determined by the Proctor Density Test, A.A.S.H.O. Method T 99–42 modified as follows:

(a) *Apparatus.* Weight of the rammer or metal tamper will be 10 pounds instead of 5½ pounds.

(b) *Procedure.* The tamper will be dropped from a height of 18 inches above the sample instead of 12 inches and the samples compacted in five equal (approximately 1″) layers instead of three equal layers.

The finished grading operations conforming to the typical cross section shall be completed and maintained at least 1000 feet ahead of paving operations.

In cuts, all loose or protruding rocks on the back slopes shall be barred loose or otherwise removed to line or finished grade of slope. All cut and fill slopes shall be uniformly dressed.

Blasting, when necessary, will be permitted only when proper precautions are taken for the protection and safety of all persons, the work and the property. All damage done to the work or property shall be repaired at the contractor's expense. All operations of the contractor in connection with the transportation, storage and use of explosives shall be approved by the engineer. Any approval given will not relieve the contractor of his responsibility in blasting operations.

2.7 *Embankments.* All areas over which embankments are to be placed shall be cleared, grubbed, scarified, and compacted as elsewhere provided and as specified. Embankments shall be formed of satisfactory materials placed in successive horizontal layers of not more than eight (8) inches in loose depth for the full width of the cross section.

The grading operations shall be so conducted and the various soil strata shall be placed so as to produce a soil structure as shown on the typical cross section, or as directed. All materials entering into the embankment shall be reasonably free of organic matter such as leaves, grass, roots, and other objectionable material. Soil, granular material, shale, and any other material permitted for use in embankment shall be spread in successive layers as specified.

The operations on earth work shall be suspended at any time when satisfactory results cannot be obtained on account of rain, freezing weather or other unsatisfactory conditions of the field. After heavy rains, the contractor shall drag, blade or slope the fill to properly drain the material.

If the material in the layers is not in a moist condition when placed, same shall be wetted before rolling as ordered. Harrowing or mixing the spread material may be required whenever considered necessary to secure a uniform moisture content. Should the material be too wet to permit proper compaction or rolling, all work on all portions of the embankment thus affected shall be delayed until the material has dried to the required moisture content. Sprinkling shall be done with sprinkling wagons, pressure distributors or other approved equipment that will sufficiently distribute the water. Sufficient equipment to furnish the required water shall be available at all times. Samples of all embankment materials for testing, both before and after placement and compaction will be taken at frequent intervals. From these tests, corrections, adjustments, and modifications of methods, materials and moisture content will be made to construct the embankment. Rolling operations shall be continued until all embankments are compacted to at least 90% of maximum density as determined by the Modified Proctor Density Test, A.A.S.H.O. Method T 99–42 and to at least 95% of maximum density under proposed paving areas. Any areas inaccessible to a roller shall be consolidated and compacted by mechanical tampers.

All rock and boulders shall be broken to such size as to be readily incorporated in an eight (8) inch layer. Stones larger than 4″ in diameter will not be allowed in the top 6″ of the subgrade.

Rock fill shall be brought up in layers as specified or as directed and every effort shall be exerted to fill the voids with the finer material to form a dense, compact mass.

Frozen material shall not be placed in the embankment nor shall embankment be placed upon frozen material.

The contractor shall be responsible for the stability of all embankments made under the contract and shall replace any portion which, in the opinion of the engineer has become displaced due to carelessness or negligence on the part of the contractor.

There will be no separate measurement or payment for compacted fill, and all costs incidental to placing in layers, compacting, discing, mixing, sloping and other necessary operations, of the fills will be included in the contract price for excavation, borrow, or other items.

2.8 *Ditching.* Ditch excavation shall consist of excavating for drainage ditches such as intercepting, inlet, outlet, offtake, temporary, levee construction or any other type as designed or as shown on the plans. The work shall be performed in the proper sequence with the other construction. The location of all ditches or levees will be established on the ground. All satisfactory material shall be placed in fills; unsatisfactory material shall be placed in spoil areas or as directed. No waste or surplus material shall be left within four (4) feet of the edge of any ditch. Intercepting ditches shall be constructed prior to the starting of adjacent excavation operations. All handwork as is necessary shall be performed to secure a finish true to line, elevation and cross section as designated.

The ditches constructed on the project shall be maintained to the required cross section and shall be kept free from debris or obstructions until the project is accepted. Where necessary, sufficient openings shall be provided through spoil banks to permit drainage from adjacent lands. Unless otherwise specified, no separate payment will be made for ditch excavation other than for the material removed which will be paid for at the unit price for grading.

2.9 *Finishing.* All graded areas, including excavation and embankment, shall be shaped to the grades shown on the plans or as directed by the engineer. A tolerance of 0.1 foot will be permitted except on areas to be paved where the tolerance will be 0.05 foot.

METHOD OF MEASUREMENT

3.1 The yardage to be paid for shall be the yardage in the original position computed by the method of average end areas of material acceptably excavated and stripped as hereinabove described.

BASIS OF PAYMENT

4.1 The yardage measured above shall be paid for at the contract unit price per cubic yard bid for grading, which price shall constitute full compensation for the formation and compaction of embankments, the hauling of material within the airport limits, preparation and completion of subgrade and final dressing of slopes, in accordance with the lines and grades shown in the drawings and the furnishing of all labor, equipment, tools, and incidentals necessary to complete this item.

WATERING

5.1 *Description.* This item shall consist of furnishing and applying water required in the compaction of embankments, subgrades, base courses, and for other purposes in accordance with the requirements of these specifications.

5.2 *Construction Methods.* Water, when required, shall be applied at the locations, in the amounts and during the hours, including nights, as directed by the engineer. An adequate water supply shall be provided by the contractor. The equipment used for watering shall be of ample capacity and of such design as to assure uniform application of water in the amounts directed by the engineer.

5.3 *Method of Measurement.* The units of watering to be paid for (subject to 5.4 below) shall be the number of 1000-gallon units of water, measured in the vehicle at the point of delivery on the airport and used as ordered.

5.4 *Basis of Payment.* When the bid schedule contains an estimated quantity for any one of the items below, the units measured as provided above, shall be paid for at the contract unit price per 1000-gallon unit for watering of embankment, watering of subgrade, or watering of base course, as the case may be, which price and payment shall be full compensation for furnishing, hauling, and placing and for all labor, equipment, tools and incidentals necessary to complete the item, including the furnishing of water plants if necessary.

When the bid schedule does not contain an estimated quantity for any one of the above items, the performance of these items shall be considered as a subsidiary obligation of the contractor covered under pay items involved in the contract and no allowance shall be made for providing or maintaining a water plant.

DEPARTMENT OF COMMERCE
Civil Aeronautics Administration
Airport Division
Washington, D.C.
July 1, 1943

PREPARATION OF SUBGRADE FOR AIRPORT RUNWAYS, TAXIWAYS AND APRONS

C.A.A. Specification No. P-103

DESCRIPTION

1.1 This item shall consist of the preparation, conditioning and maintenance of the subgrade to the full width of the paved areas in accordance with these specifications and in conformity with the lines, grades, and cross section shown on the plans. Where the plans indicate that a base course or pavement is to be placed, the contractor shall comply with any additional requirements as to subgrade contained in such contract items.

CONSTRUCTION METHODS

2.1 *General Requirements.* All soft and unstable material and other portions of the subgrade that will not compact readily or serve the intended purpose shall be removed as directed. All boulders and ledge rock shall be removed to a depth of not less than 6 inches below the subgrade. The resulting areas and all other low sections, holes, or depressions shall be brought to profile grade with satisfactory material and the entire subgrade shaped to line, grade, and cross section. Selected material reserved under EXCAVATION shall be used insofar as deemed suitable by the Engineer, supplemented as necessary by additional material obtained under BORROW; provided, however, that no yardage made necessary by unauthorized excavation below grade shall be paid for.

2.2 *Compaction.* As the subgrade is being shaped to line, grade and cross section, it shall be thoroughly compacted by rolling with a power roller weighing at least 8 tons supplemented by a sheep-foot roller or a pneumatic roller. The rolling and moisture content shall be regulated so as to obtain not less than 95% of the maximum compaction to a depth of 6 inches as determined by the modified Proctor Density Test, A.A.S.H.O. Method T-99. Water shall be applied uniformly to the subgrade by means of tanks mounted on trucks and fitted with spray bars, or other approved method, prior to and during the rolling, when and in the amounts directed by the engineer. Any low spots that develop in the subgrade during rolling shall be brought to grade with additional material and rerolled.

2.3 *Protection of Subgrade.* At all times the subgrade shall be kept well drained. Whenever ruts or low spots are formed, the subgrade shall be brought to grade, and if necessary shall be reshaped and recompacted. In no case shall any base course or pavement be placed on a frozen or muddy subgrade. Storage or stockpiling of materials on the subgrade will not be permitted. Until the subgrade has been checked and approved, no base course or pavement shall be laid thereon.

2.4 *Tolerances.* In that area which is to be paved the subgrade shall be of such smoothness that when tested with a ten (10) foot straight edge it shall not show any deviation in excess of three-eighths ($\frac{3}{8}$) inch or shall not be more than one-half ($\frac{1}{2}$) inch from true grade as established by grade hubs, pins, or forms or to a closer limit as required under the base course or pavement specification. Any deviation in excess of this amount shall be corrected by loosening, adding or removing material, reshaping and recompacting by sprinkling and rolling.

METHOD OF MEASUREMENT

3.1 Preparation and conditioning of subgrade shall not be measured for direct payment.

BASIS OF PAYMENT

4.1 Performance of this item under the contract is not payable directly, but shall be considered as a subsidiary obligation in the paving contract.

MODIFIED A.A.S.H.O. METHOD

The modifications of the Proctor Density Test A.A.S.H.O. Method T-99 as required in this specification are as follows:

1. *Apparatus.* Weight of the rammer or metal tamper will be 10 pounds instead of 5½ pounds.
2. *Procedure.* The tamper will be dropped from a height of 18 inches above the sample instead of 12 inches and the samples compacted in five equal (approximately 1″) layers instead of three equal layers.

APPENDIX 4

DEPARTMENT OF COMMERCE
Civil Aeronautics Administration
First Region
New York (17), New York
April 20, 1943
Revised May 20, 1945

DRAINAGE

Specification No. 1–213

GENERAL

1.1 *General*: This specification covers the requirements of the Civil Aeronautics Administration for furnishing and installing pipe, furnishing all necessary materials and constructing the various drainage structures and appurtenances described herein. The Contractor will be required to complete the work to the sizes and dimensions shown on the plans and in accordance with the lines and grades established by the Engineer.

MATERIALS

2.1 *Materials*: All products or materials of construction used in the work as called for on the plans or in the proposal, shall be in accordance with the provisions of one of the following: "Material Details" sections. The A.A.S.H.O. specifications referred to herein shall be the designations given or the latest revisions thereof.

Where no definite type of pipe is specified, the Contractor may elect to furnish, in the sizes called for, any of the types listed below. The respective A.A.S.H.O., Federal and other detailed specifications shall apply for Sections M-2, M-3, M-4, and M-5 except that minimum strength requirements (pounds per linear foot, 3-edge bearing test) for pipe sizes up to and including 54″ shall be 2000 D where D is the inside diameter of the pipe in feet.

The following listed materials covered by this specification will be referred to hereinafter and in the proposal by section designation, as follows:

SEC. M-1, CORRUGATED PIPE—METAL

M-1 (a) Plain corrugated metal pipe
M-1 (b) Perforated corrugated metal pipe
M-1 (c) Bituminous coated corrugated metal pipe
M-1 (d) Paved bituminous coated corrugated metal pipe
M-1 (e) Paved invert corrugated metal pipe
M-1 (f) Perforated bituminous coated corrugated metal pipe

SEC. M-2, CONCRETE PIPE

M-2 (a) Plain concrete sewer pipe
M-2 (b) Reinforced concrete sewer pipe
M-2 (c) Standard-strength reinforced concrete culvert pipe
M-2 (d) Extra-strength reinforced concrete culvert pipe
M-2 (e) Porous concrete pipe
M-2 (f) Perforated concrete pipe

SEC. M-3, VITRIFIED CLAY PIPE

M-3 (a) Drain tile—extra quality
M-3 (b) Vitrified sewer pipe, standard-strength
M-3 (c) Vitrified sewer pipe, extra-strength
M-3 (d) Perforated vitrified pipe

SEC. M-4, CRADLE INVERT PIPE

SEC. M-5, ASBESTOS-CEMENT PIPE

M-5 (a) Class I
M-5 (b) Class II
M-5 (c) Class III
M-5 (d) Class IV

SEC. M-6, BACKFILL MATERIAL

M-6 (a) Backfill material—general
M-6 (b) Porous backfill material
M-6 (c) Bituminous coated backfill

SEC. M-7, CONCRETE

SEC. M-8, BRICK

SEC. M-9, CONCRETE BLOCK

SEC. M-10, REINFORCING STEEL

SEC. M-11, WROUGHT IRON

M-11 (a) Shapes and bars
M-11 (b) Plates

SEC. M-12, GRAY IRON CASTINGS

SEC. M-13, STRUCTURAL STEEL

SEC. M-14, PAINT

M-14 (a) Red lead
M-14 (b) Black Paint
M-14 (c) Asphalt Varnish
M-14 (d) Coal Tar Pitch paint

SEC. M-15, RIP RAP

SEC. M-1. CORRUGATED METAL PIPE—VARIOUS TYPES: Pipe shall be of first quality, straight, circular in form, and of commercially available lengths which may be accurately laid to the line and grade given. It shall be free from all imperfections and shall be of first class workmanship throughout.

M-1 (a) Plain corrugated metal pipe: Plain corrugated metal pipe shall conform to the requirements of A.A.S.H.O. Specification M-36–42, except that pipe shall not be perforated.

M-1 (b) Perforated corrugated metal pipe: Perforated corrugated metal pipe shall conform to the requirements of A.A.S.H.O. Specification M-36–42.

M-1 (c) Bituminous coated corrugated metal pipe: Bituminous coated corrugated metal pipe shall comply with all the requirements of Section M-1 (a), and in addition shall be completely coated inside and out with a bituminous material, of such characteristics and composition as to meet the Performance Requirements set forth herein.

Performance Requirements: The bituminous material shall form a coating not less than 0.05″ thick measured at the crest of the corrugations. It shall adhere to the metal tenaciously, shall not chip off in handling, shall protect the pipe from deterioration and shall meet the following analysis and requirements:

(1)		
	Water	0.0
	Homogeneous	Yes
	Sp. Gr. @ 77°F.	1.00–1.04
	Pen. @ 77°F., 100 g., 5 Sec.	25–50
	% Pen. 39.2°F/77°F.	80–90
	% Loss @ 325°F.	1.0–
	% Pen. of Res.	100+
	% Sol. in CS_2	99.5+
	Flash Point °F.	347+
	Duct. @ 77°F.	190–230

(2) *Spalling Test.* A steel ball 2¼ inches in diameter and weighing 1.67 pounds shall be dropped from a height of 7½ feet through a vertical tube of 3 inches inside diameter, on the outside crest of a coated corrugation of a representative sample. This test shall be conducted with the specimen at a temperature of 30°F. Failure of the coating on the inside of the pipe, as indicated by spalling from the metal or the formation of cracks longer than ½ inch from the point of impact, shall be considered sufficient cause for rejection.

(3) *Stability Test.* The bituminous material shall not lose its stability when subjected to the highest summer temperature, as indicated by successfully withstanding the following test:

Parallel lines shall be drawn along the valleys of the corrugations of a representative sample of coated pipe and a specimen placed on and in a constant temperature oven, with the parallel lines in a horizontal position. The temperature of the specimen shall be maintained within 2°F. of 150°F. for a period of 4 hours. At the end of this time, no part of any line shall have dropped more than ¼ inch.

(4) *Imperviousness Test.* The bituminous material shall be impervious to corrosive liquids as indicated by the following test:

A 25% solution of sulphuric acid, or a 25% solution of sodium hydroxide shall be held in the valley of a coated corrugation for a period of 48 hours, during which time no loosening or separation of the bituminous material from the galvanizing shall have taken place.

(5) *Erosion Test.* A representative sample consisting of a 2 foot length of fully coated pipe, (with ends closed by suitable bulkheads) shall be revolved end over and about its transverse axis at a speed of 3.7 revolutions per minute and in such a manner that the erosive charge shall alternately roll along the inner surface or opposite sides of the pipe, (inside top and bottom, as when installed in service). At least 75% of the sample shall be immersed as it revolves, in a bath of water maintained at a temperature of 50°–55°F. The pipe shall not show areas of bare metal more than 2 inches in length on four of the seven central corrugations after 5 hours of continuous testing (called a test period). A new erosive charge shall be used for each period of the test. The erosive charge shall be 50 pounds of Grade B building brick, conforming to the requirements of the Standard Specifications for Building Brick, A.S.T.M. Designation C 62–40, broken up into pieces 2 to 3 inches in diameter, and 3 gallons of water.

M-1 (d) Paved bituminous coated corrugated metal pipe: Paved bituminous coated corrugated metal pipe shall comply with all the requirements of Section M-1 (a) and Section M-1 (c), and in addition the inside bottom quarter shall be paved to such a thickness as to show no failure when subjected to nine additional 5-hour test periods of the Erosion Test described in Paragraph (5) of Section M-1 (c).

License Agreement: The holders of Patent No. 1,652,703 which includes a claim similar to this specification, agree to grant licenses for the nominal payment of $1.00 per annum to any company which desires to make application therefor, permitting culverts to be manufactured by the dipping process to meet the requirements of this specification. Copy of the License Agreement follows and is made a part of this specification.

LICENSE AGREEMENT

THIS AGREEMENT, made and entered into by and between The American Rolling Mill Company, a corporation of Ohio, with a principal place of business at Middletown, Ohio, Licensor, and .... a corporation of .... with a principal place of business at ....

WHEREAS, the Licensor is the owner of the United States Letters Patent No. 1,652,703, issued December 13, 1927, covering CORRUGATED METAL CULVERTS, with an interior flooring and coating, and

WHEREAS, the Licensee is desirous of obtaining a license under said letters patent.

NOW, THEREFORE, in consideration of $1.00, each to the other paid, receipt whereof is hereby acknowledged, and the mutual covenants herein contained, it is agreed as follows:

1. The Licensor hereby grants to the Licensee a non-exclusive, non-assignable license, under the said letters patent No. 1,652,703, to manufacture a particular product set forth in Article 2 hereof, and to use and sell said product.

2. The license herein granted and conveyed shall extend only to the manufacture, use and sale of a product described as follows:

A circumferentially corrugated culvert having the interior thereof at least coated with an adhesive, resilient substance, covering at least a substantial portion of the lower half of the culvert, but so applied along the base of the culvert as to be substantially thicker than as applied to the side walls. It is understood that the product to be manufactured and sold under this license will not have one or more substantially smooth and/or level floors substantially filling the valleys of the corrugations in the bottom of the invert.

3. For and in consideration of the license grant herein contained, Licensee shall pay to the Licensor a royalty of One Dollar per year.

4. The Licensee agrees to keep Licensor informed at all times of the character and specifications of culvert made under this license, and will, at all reasonable business hours, permit Licensor to inspect the culvert on hand, and in the course of manufacture and the apparatus for making the same, wherever said culvert shall be manufactured or stored by or for Licensee.

5. Licensor reserves the right to cancel this contract forthwith if at any time it ascertains that Licensee is manufacturing and/or selling coated corrugated culvert not made in accordance with Article 2 hereof.

6. This license, unless sooner terminated in accordance with the provision of Paragraph 5 hereof, shall extend for the life of United States Letters Patent 1,652,703, excepting that Licensor reserves the right to cancel this contract for non-use extending for a period of 2 years.

7. This license shall be personal to Licensee and shall not be assignable except upon the written consent of Licensor thereto first obtained.

IN WITNESS WHEREOF, the parties hereto have set their hands and seals, this .... day of.........194 ..

THE AMERICAN ROLLING MILL COMPANY

Attest

.... BY ....

Attest

.... BY ....

M-1 (e) Paved invert corrugated metal pipe: Paved invert corrugated metal pipe shall comply with all the provisions of Section M-1 (a) and Section M-1 (d), except that the lower half only of the pipe as installed need be coated with bituminous material unless otherwise specified. This coating shall be applied in such a manner that a smooth pavement shall be formed in the lowest portion of the invert, completely filling the corrugations. The pavement shall be of such width that the thickness above the crest of the corrugation measured at the middle of the pavement shall be at least $\frac{1}{8}$ of an inch.

M-1 (f) Perforated bituminous coated corrugated metal pipe: Perforated bituminous coated corrugated metal pipe shall comply with all the requirements of Section M-1 (b), and in addition shall be coated as in Section M-1 (c), Section M-1 (d) or Section M-1 (e), whichever type is specified.

SEC. M-2. CONCRETE PIPE—VARIOUS TYPES: Under this section, the concrete pipe shall conform to the requirements of the various sub-sections following, with the exception that the cement used shall comply to the Emergency Alternate Specifications for Portland Cement (A.S.T.M. Designation

EA-C 150, June 6, 1942, types I (Normal), II (Moderate Heat), and III (High Early Strength), and corresponding Federal Designation E-SS-C-191 b; E-SS-C-206 a, and E-SS-C-201 a, June 5, 1942). The sampling and testing of cement shall be in accordance with A.S.T.M. Standard Methods of Testing Cement, Serial Designation C 77–40 and subsequent revisions. Aggregates used in manufacture of concrete shall be in accordance with A.A.S.H.O. Specifications M 6–42 and M 80–42.

M-2 (a) Plain concrete pipe: Plain concrete pipe shall be bell and spigot type conforming to A.A.S.H.O. Specification M 86–42.

M-2 (b) Reinforced concrete sewer pipe: Reinforced concrete sewer pipe shall conform to the requirements of A.A.S.H.O. Specification M 87–42.

M-2 (c) Standard strength reinforced concrete culvert pipe: Standard strength reinforced concrete pipe shall conform to the requirements of A.A.S.H.O. Specification M 41–42 and the requirements of Table 1 thereof only.

M-2 (d) Extra strength reinforced concrete culvert pipe: Extra strength reinforced concrete pipe shall conform to the requirements of A.A.S.H.O. Specification M 41–42 and the requirements of Table 2 thereof.

M-2 (e) Porous concrete pipe: The aggregates entering into the composition of porous concrete pipe shall meet all the requirements of A.A.S.H.O. Specifications M 6–42 and M 80–42. The cross section of the pipe shall be circular inside. The joints of porous concrete pipe shall be formed of a non-porous concrete to assure maximum strength; such non-porous concrete shall extend into the barrel of the pipe to a depth of approximately 1″ at each end. All joints shall be bell and spigot or tongue and groove type. All porous concrete pipe shall be cured in modern steam curing rooms and be thoroughly cured before shipping. The finished product shall withstand five (5) alternations of the magnesium sulphate test for soundness, and shall be straight, free from cracks, checks or other physical defects. All pipe shall meet the following minimum requirements:

STANDARD STRENGTH				EXTRA STRENGTH
Size Nom. Inside Diam.	Weight per ft. Pounds	Wall Thickness Permissible Variation $\frac{1}{16}$″	Aver. Crush Strength 3 edge bearing—Lbs. Per Lin. Ft.	Aver. Crush Strength 3 edge bearing—Lbs. Per Lin. Ft.
4″	12	1.00	1,600	2,000
6″	20	1.00	1,600	2,000
8″	32	1.25	1,600	2,000
10″	44	1.375	1,600	2,000
12″	64	1.50	1,600	2,500
15″	87	1.75	1,750	3,125
18″	112	2.00	1,850	3,750
21″	135	2.25	2,000	4,375
24″	175	2.50	2,150	5,000

The rate of infiltration on all sizes of porous concrete pipe shall not be less than two gallons per minute per inch of internal diameter per length of pipe.

M-2 (f) Perforated concrete pipe: Perforated concrete pipe shall conform to one of the above Sections and in addition, shall be perforated for no more than half its periphery with at least four rows of holes. The holes shall be no larger than ½ inch nor smaller than ¼ inch in diameter and shall be spaced no further than 4 inches between centers of holes measured along the pipe.

SEC. M-3. VITRIFIED CLAY PIPE:

M-3 (a) Drain tile—extra-quality. Drain tile, extra-quality shall conform to the requirements of Standard Specification for Drain Tile, A.A.S.H.O. Designation M 66–42, for the class of drain tile referred to therein as extra-quality drain tile.

M-3 (b) Vitrified sewer pipe, standard-strength: Vitrified sewer pipe, standard-strength, shall conform to the requirements of A.A.S.H.O. Specification M 65–42, and Table II thereof.

M-3 (c) Vitrified sewer pipe, extra-strength: Vitrified sewer pipe, extra-strength, shall conform to the requirements of A.A.S.H.O. Specification M 65–42, and Table III thereof or to Federal Specification SS-P-361a and Table II thereof.

M-3 (d) Perforated vitrified pipe: Perforated vitrified pipe shall conform to one of the above Sections and in addition shall be perforated for no more than half its periphery with at least four rows of holes. The holes shall be no larger than ½ inch nor smaller than ¼ inch in diameter and shall be spaced no further than 4 inches between centers of holes measured along the pipe.

SEC. M-4, CRADLE INVERT PIPE: Cradle invert pipe shall conform to the following requirements.

Dimensions: The nominal sizes and other dimensions of cradle invert pipe shall be in accordance with Table I and accompanying sketch.

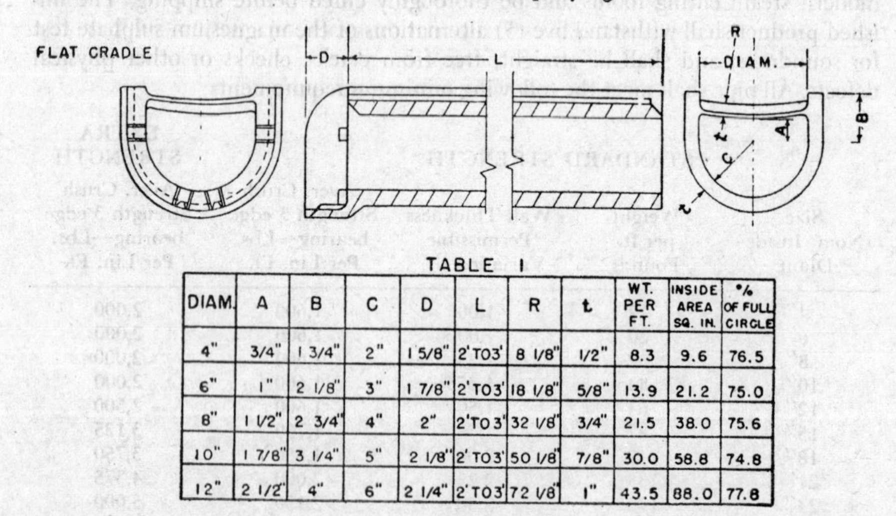

TABLE I

DIAM.	A	B	C	D	L	R	t	WT. PER FT.	INSIDE AREA SQ. IN.	% OF FULL CIRCLE
4"	3/4"	1 3/4"	2"	1 5/8"	2' TO 3'	8 1/8"	1/2"	8.3	9.6	76.5
6"	1"	2 1/8"	3"	1 7/8"	2' TO 3'	18 1/8"	5/8"	13.9	21.2	75.0
8"	1 1/2"	2 3/4"	4"	2"	2' TO 3'	32 1/8"	3/4"	21.5	38.0	75.6
10"	1 7/8"	3 1/4"	5"	2 1/8"	2' TO 3'	50 1/8"	7/8"	30.0	58.8	74.8
12"	2 1/2"	4"	6"	2 1/4"	2' TO 3'	72 1/8"	1"	43.5	88.0	77.8

Basis of Acceptance: (a) The acceptability of the pipe shall be determined (1) by the results of physical tests hereinafter specified and (2) by visual inspection, to determine whether the pipe complies with the specifications as to dimensions, shape, and freedom from visible external and internal defects.

(b) The acceptance of pipe as satisfactorily meeting one of these two general requirements shall not be construed as in any way waiving the other.

Materials: Vitrified clay cradle invert pipe shall be manufactured from an approved surface clay, fire clay or shale or a combination of these materials. Surface clay is an unconsolidated unstratified clay occurring on the surface; fire clay is a sedimentary clay of low flux content, and shale is a thinly stratified, consolidated, sedimentary clay with well-marked cleavage parallel to the bedding.

Manufacture: (a) The clay shall be thoroughly pulverized and mixed in the proper proportions before burning. The pipe shall be thoroughly burnt until the body of the pipe is vitrified through its entire thickness but not fused.

(b) The pipe shall be salt glazed on both inside and outside surfaces and the glazing shall be equal to that produced by the best salt glazing process. The glaze shall consist of a continuous layer of bright or semi-bright glass, free from all well-defined network of crazing lines or hair checks. No blisters shall exceed 2 inches in diameter and no blisters or pimples shall project more than $\frac{1}{8}$ inch above the surrounding surface of the pipe.

Physical Tests: The physical tests of the pipe shall include strength tests and absorption tests. The strength tests shall be made by the 3-edge bearing method with the top bearing of a plaster cap of full length of the pipe and with a width equal to the nominal diameter of the pipe. The individual results of the various tests for each size of pipe and for each shipment shall be tabulated separately so as to show the percentage which fails to conform to the requirements of each test. The specimens of pipe shall all be selected at the factory or at the shipping destination, or at the trench, at the option of the Contracting Officer. A standard physical test shall comprise tests of five individual pipes. Specimens of pipe may be selected by the Engineer in such number as he judges necessary to determine fairly the quality of all the pipe. The Contractor shall furnish without charge to the Government specimens of pipe necessary for tests. The specimens of pipe for the strength test shall be unbroken, full-size pipe. The specimen shall first be freed from all visible moisture. When dry, each specimen shall be measured and inspected. Each specimen shall be weighed on reliable scales just prior to testing, and the weights shall be reported. The test results shall be calculated and reported, in pounds per linear foot of pipe, in terms of the "ordinary supporting strength." The results of the strength tests shall be reported separately for each of the five individual specimens of pipe constituting a standard test, together with the average.

Physical Test Requirements: The pipe shall conform to the physical test requirements as prescribed herein.

(a) Maximum average absorption by Standard Boiling Test—not greater than eight per cent (8%) when determined by Federal Designation SS-P-361a method.

(b) The average strength shall show a minimum load supporting capacity in pounds per lineal foot as follows:

Internal Diameter Inches	Pounds Per Lineal Foot
4	1000
6	1000
8	1200
10	1500
12	2000

Limits of Fluctuation of Individual Test Specimens in Physical Tests: (a) In the strength tests, individual pipe of a standard test whose mean strength is satisfactory may fall 25 per cent below the requirement for the average without causing rejection. In the absorption test, the absorption of individual pipe of a standard sample which gives a satisfactory mean absorption percentage, may exceed the average by 25 per cent without causing rejection.

(b) In the event of the failure of a standard sample to meet the above requirements, the Contractor may thoroughly cull the material and submit a portion for retest at his own expense, and for such retest the number of pipe per sample shall be 10 for the strength and absorption tests. In the event of the failure of the material to pass the requirements after culling, it shall be rejected without further test.

Visual Inspection: All pipe shall be given a thorough visual inspection at the trench by the Engineer. The purposes of visual inspection shall be: (1) to cull and reject imperfect individual pipe, and (2) to determine whether the pipe, independently of meeting the chemical and the physical test requirements, complies with the specifications of general properties, especially as stated hereinafter.

The pipe shall be of the bell and spigot type, the cross section of which is semi-circular, having superimposed thereon and slightly depressed and an integral part thereof, a cradle invert substantially parallel with the base of the semi-circular section. The cradle shall be flat or longitudinally corrugated and of the same thickness as the barrel of the pipe. The socket or bell end shall have four lugs properly located, two near the bottom or flow line to produce a positive standard annular space and a fixed transverse slot of ⅜ inch between two adjacent sections of pipe.

The pipe shall be furnished in laying lengths as shown in Table 1. The length of pipe shall not be less than the nominal or specified length by more than ¼ inch per foot of length. Pipe shall be substantially uniform in structure throughout, and the Engineer shall investigate this property by examining fractured surfaces. When sounded with a steel hammer, the pipe shall yield a clear metallic sound. Pipe shall be reasonably smooth on the inside, shall be free from cracks and checks extending into the body of the pipe in such a manner as to decrease the strength appreciably. Pipe shall not be chipped or broken in such a manner as to decrease their strength materially.

The manufacturer or other seller of the pipe shall afford the Engineer all reasonable facilities for his work, both as to the selection of specimens for tests, and as to visual inspection.

SEC. M-5 ASBESTOS-CEMENT PIPE: Asbestos-cement pipe shall conform to the following requirements:

Sizes, Classes, and Average Crushing Strengths:

Asbestos-cement sewer pipe shall be of the following nominal sizes and classes and have the minimum crushing strengths indicated in Table II.

Note: Where 15″, 21″, 27″ or 33″ pipe is called for in the proposal, the next larger size of asbestos-cement pipe may be used at no additional compensation. Connections to other sizes listed in the bid schedule and placed under the contract shall be made by the Contractor at his own expense.

Each pipe shall be free from bulges, dents and tears on the inside surface which

TABLE I

Nominal Inside Diameter A	Wall Thickness B	Outside Diameter C	Wall Thickness of Couplings H	Inside Diameter of Coupling J	Outside Diameter of Coupling M	Length of Coupling N
			CLASS 1			
4	0.39	4.78	0.55	5.55	6.65	7.0
5	0.41	5.82	0.55	6.60	7.70	7.0
6	0.42	6.84	0.55	7.60	8.70	7.0
8	0.48	8.96	0.59	9.72	10.90	7.0
10	0.50	11.00	0.60	12.00	13.20	7.0
12	0.54	13.08	0.62	14.00	15.25	7.0
14	0.58	15.16	0.65	16.00	17.30	8.0
16	0.62	17.24	0.70	18.10	19.50	8.0
18	0.65	19.30	0.72	20.20	21.64	8.0
20	0.69	21.38	0.75	22.30	23.80	9.0
24	0.75	25.50	0.85	26.40	28.10	9.0
30	0.96	31.92	1.03	32.85	34.90	10.5
36	1.15	38.30	1.25	39.50	42.00	10.5
			CLASS 2			
10	0.56	11.12	0.67	12.00	13.34	7.0
12	0.64	13.28	0.76	14.18	15.70	7.0
14	0.73	15.46	0.85	16.36	18.06	8.0
16	0.82	17.64	0.95	18.54	20.44	8.0
18	0.90	19.80	1.03	20.76	22.82	8.0
20	0.94	21.88	1.05	22.90	25.00	9.0
24	1.06	26.12	1.17	27.10	29.44	9.0
30	1.24	32.48	1.40	33.46	36.26	10.5
36	1.41	38.82	1.57	39.80	42.94	10.5
			CLASS 3			
10	0.65	11.30	0.80	12.20	13.80	7.0
12	0.74	13.48	0.95	14.40	16.30	7.0
14	0.84	15.68	1.05	16.60	18.70	8.0
16	0.94	17.88	1.15	19.00	21.30	8.0
18	1.03	20.06	1.25	21.00	23.50	8.0
20	1.13	22.26	1.36	23.20	25.92	9.0
24	1.31	26.62	1.56	27.60	30.72	9.0
30	1.64	33.28	1.92	34.28	38.12	10.5
36	1.93	39.86	2.24	40.86	45.34	10.5
			CLASS 4			
18	1.12	20.24	1.37	21.20	23.94	8.0
20	1.25	22.50	1.52	23.46	26.50	9.0
24	1.45	26.90	1.74	27.90	31.38	9.0
30	1.85	33.70	2.19	34.70	39.08	10.5
36	2.18	40.36	2.55	41.36	46.46	10.5

result in a variation in diameter greater than 0.187 inch from that obtained on adjacent unaffected portions of the surface.

Pipe shall have a nominal length of 13 feet with an allowed tolerance of 1 inch plus or minus. No pipe less than 3 feet in length shall be used. All lengths of pipe shall be of proper size on each end to properly receive the couplings.

Each pipe shall not vary from straightness more than 0.625 inch per 13 foot length. Variations shall be measured as mid-ordinates.

The outside diameters of the coupling portions of each pipe and the inside diameter of the couplings shall be within the following tolerances of the nominal dimensions given in Table I.

Nominal Diameter in inches	Pipe Tolerance (Inch) Plus	Minus	Couplings Tolerance (Inch) Plus	Minus
4 to 10 inclusive	.12	.08	.08	.05
12 to 20 inclusive	.15	.08	.10	.05
24 to 36 inclusive	.20	.10	.12	.05

The out-of-round tolerances, applying to nominal dimensions, for the outside diameters of the coupling portions of each length of pipe shall be as follows:

Nominal Diameter in inches	Tolerance (Inch) Plus or Minus
4 to 10 inclusive	0.125
12 to 20 inclusive	0.190
24 to 36 inclusive	0.250

TABLE II

Nominal Internal Diameter Inches	Minimum Ultimate Crushing Strength, Pounds per Linear Foot Class I	Class II	Class III	Class IV
4	4125	—	—	—
6	2880	—	—	—
8	3100	—	—	—
10	2580	3690	4920	—
12	2370	3850	5100	—
14	2200	3920	5150	—
16	2120	4050	5280	—
18	2030	4140	5360	6340
20	2290	4280	5850	7100
24	2340	4550	7050	8600
30	2980	5000	8180	10450
36	3500	5400	9700	12300

MATERIAL AND WORKMANSHIP: *Material*: Pipe shall be composed of an intimate mixture of cement and graded asbestos fibre. The fibre shall be so distributed in the mixture as to serve as an aggregate and reinforcement.

The cement used in the work shall be Portland Cement of American manufacture, conforming to the Emergency Alternate Specifications for Portland Cement (A.S.T.M. Designation EA-C-150, June 6, 1942, types I (Normal), II (Moderate Heat), and III (High Early Strength), and corresponding Federal Designation E-SS-C-191 b; E-SS-C-206a, and E-SS-C-201a, June 5, 1942). The sampling and testing of cement shall be in accordance with A.S.T.M. Standard Methods of Testing Cement, Serial Designation C 77–40 and subsequent revisions.

The water used shall be practically free from dirt, oil, acid, alkali salts, organic matter, or other impurities, and shall be reasonably clear. Brackish water, sea water or water carrying sewage and manufacturing waste shall not be allowed.

Workmanship: The workmanship shall be first class and of such quality that the pipe shall conform to the requirements of this specification.

DAMAGE:

Gouges: If the pipe has been gouged to a depth of ½ its wall thickness and wider than ½″ or longer than 2″, the damaged section shall be cut out.

Bruises: When a bruise is sufficiently severe to show a broken structure on the inner surface of the pipe, the damaged section shall be cut out.

Cracks: If a section of the pipe is broken away or a definite line of separation appears, the cracked portion shall be cut out. Cuts shall be made at least 18″ from the nearest visible crack as determined by wetting the pipe and allowing the surface to dry. The crack will be apparent due to slower drying.

METHODS OF SAMPLING, INSPECTION AND TESTS:

Tests of Material. All specimens of pipe which are tested under this specification shall be stored in a building under normal atmospheric conditions for a period of one week prior to testing. Samples for testing shall be furnished by the manufacturer without charge at least two weeks prior to shipment.

Flexure. Each 13-foot length of each class and size of pipe from 4 to 8 inches, inclusive, shall be tested in flexure. Equal loads shall be applied at the third points in such a manner that the total load shall be applied at a uniform rate of 50 pounds per second. The total load shall be such as to develop a maximum fibre stress of 3,000 pounds per square inch in sizes 4 to 8 inches inclusive. The load required to develop the desired fibre stress shall be computed in accordance with the following formula:

$$P = \frac{0.589 \quad S(D^4 - d^4)}{LD}$$

S = Stress in pounds per square inch
P = Total load in pounds
d = Actual inside diameter in inches
D = Actual outside diameter in inches
L = Length of span in inches

Crushing. From each 300 lengths of pipe, or fraction thereof, of each size and class, one specimen length of pipe shall be selected by the inspector. From each specimen pipe there shall be cut one unfinished section of pipe one foot long. This section shall be tested in crushing by the three edge bearing method as provided by A.A.S.H.O. Standard Test Methods and shall develop the crushing strengths specified in Table II.

Any prime mover or hand power which will apply the load at a uniform rate of about 2000 pounds per minute, or in increments of not more than 100 pounds at the same rate, shall be used.

The testing machine shall be substantial and rigid throughout, so that the distribution of the load shall not be affected appreciably by the deformation or yielding of any part of the machine.

In the crushing test using 3 edge bearings, the two lower bearings shall consist of two straight wooden strips with vertical sides, each strip having its interior top corner rounded to a radius of approximately ½ inch. The strips shall be securely fastened to a rigid block with their interior vertical sides parallel and a distance apart not less than ½ inch nor more than 1 inch per foot of diameter of pipe. The upper bearing shall be a rigid wooden block, at least 6 by 6 inches in cross section, straight and true from end to end. The upper and lower bearing shall extend the full length of pipe. The test load shall be applied through the upper bearing block in such a way as to leave the bearing free to move in a vertical plane passing midway between the lower bearings. In testing a pipe which is "cut of straight," the lines of the bearings chosen shall be those which appear to give most favorable conditions for fair bearings.

The alkalinity test shall be made from a representative sample of pipe or sleeve so ground as to completely pass a 20 mesh sieve and then dried at 105° C for 2 hours in the absence of CO_2 and cooled in a desiccator. A one gram sample shall then be placed in a 4 oz. oil sample bottle with 100 cc. of cold distilled water. The bottle shall then be shaken vigorously for five seconds at hourly intervals during an eight hour working day and allowed to stand the remainder of 24 hours. The residue shall then be filtered and washed with 3–25 cc. portions of cold distilled water. The filtrate and washings shall then be combined. Titrate with N/10 HCl, using methyl orange indicator. Run a titration "blank" and make allowance for same. The maximum alkalinity shall not exceed 60 milligrams. Calculate net alkalinity as milligrams of KOH per gram sample.

Pipe shall be acceptable under the strength tests when all test specimens conform to the test requirements. Should any of the preliminary test specimens fail to meet the test requirements, then the manufacturer will be allowed a retest on two additional specimens for each specimen that failed, and the pipe shall be acceptable only when all of these retest specimens meet the strength requirements.

MARKING: The trade name, nominal size, and class of each length of pipe shall be stamped on its outside surface.

All component parts of the coupling shall be marked with the make, size, and class of pipe for which they are intended.

SEC. M-6 BACKFILL MATERIAL.

M-6 (a) Backfill Material—General. Backfill for pipe and other miscellaneous structures shall, in general, be made with the excavated material removed from the trench. However, when such excavated material is composed of rock, boulders, hard shale, muck, highly plastic clay or other unsuitable material, it shall be disposed of as ordered by the Engineer and suitable material from within the limits of the airport property used in its place.

M-6 (b) Porous Backfill Material. Granular material used for porous backfill may be crushed stone, gravel, crushed slag, or any other hard durable material approved by the Engineer, which will provide the percentage of voids necessary. Permissible variations as to the size of aggregate will be given in the proposal or shown on the plans. The sieves, designated, are of the U.S. Standard Sieve Series.

M-6 (c) Bituminous Coated Backfill. Bituminous coated backfill shall consist of porous backfill material meeting the requirements of Sec. M-6 (b), which material shall be pre-coated with 2.5% by weight of RC-4 asphalt complying with A.A.S.H.O. Specification M 81–42 by mixing in a central mixing plant, or by penetration with bituminous material meeting requirements of Spec. P-604 whichever is called for in the proposal or shown on the plans.

SEC. M-7 CONCRETE. Concrete used in the work shall be in accordance with the requirements of Spec. No. 1–265.

SEC. M-8 BRICK. Brick shall be new or salvaged brick conforming to the requirements of A.A.S.H.O. Specification M 114–41. Only new brick shall be used on exposed faces of structures. Brick for drainage structures shall be of S.W. grade as modified below:

(a) Minimum Compressive Strength, average of 5 brick 3500 lbs.
(b) Maximum Water Absorption, 5 hr. boiling
Average of 5 brick 10%
Individual 12%

No brick shall be used that contains chips or broken areas of more than 15% of the lower bearing surface or more than 6% of the upper bearing surface, that has more than 2 cracks either of which exceeds more than $\frac{1}{8}''$ in width or penetrates to a depth greater than $\frac{3}{4}''$ or contains kiln marks, bonds or twists which distorts the brick more than $\frac{3}{8}''$ on the sides or more than $\frac{3}{16}''$ on the bearing surface.

Salvaged brick shall be clean, whole brick, free from an excessive number of chips and adhering mortar.

SEC. M-9 CONCRETE BLOCK.

Concrete units may be used in the construction of manholes, catchbasins or inlets. They shall have a maximum dimension in length of not over eighteen inches (18″), in width not less than six inches (6″) and in height not over eight inches (8″). They must be solid and machine made. Joints must not exceed $\frac{1}{4}$ inch.

Composition. The concrete used in the manufacture of the blocks shall be in accordance with Spec. 1–265 except that the proportion of cement, fine and coarse aggregate and the water cement ratio shall be such as to give concrete of the required strength. The gradation of the aggregates shall be uniform and such as to produce a dense concrete of low water absorption.

Curing. Concrete units must be steam cured. This shall be done in a sealed chamber especially constructed for this purpose, the atmospheric temperature of which is not less than 75° nor over 115° Fahrenheit. Sufficient steam shall be used to saturate the air with moisture. The concrete units shall be kept in this chamber for not less than 24 hours.

Strength. The compressive strength of concrete units as determined upon the units themselves when 28 days old, shall not be less than 3,500 lbs. per square inch of cross-sectional area of the unit as laid in the wall.

Absorption Requirements. Concrete manhole and catchbasin block shall not absorb more than 8 per cent of the dry weight of the unit when tested as hereinafter specified. No individual unit shall absorb more than 10 per cent of the dry weight of the unit.

Sampling. Specimens for tests shall be representative of the commercial product of the plant.

Specimens used in the absorption test may be used for the strength test.

Testing. The specimens as received shall be immersed in clean water at approximately 70 deg. F. for a period of 24 hours. They shall then be removed, the surface water wiped off, and the specimens weighed. Specimens shall be dried to a constant weight at a temperature of from 212 deg. to 250 deg. F. and reweighed. Absorption is the difference in weight divided by the weight of the dry specimens and multiplied by 100. The average of the tests of not less than three specimens shall be taken as the absorption.

Specimens for the strength test shall be dried to constant weight at a temperature of from 212 deg. to 250 deg. F.

The specimens to be tested shall be carefully measured for overall dimensions of length, width and height.

Bearing surfaces shall be made plane by capping with plaster of paris or a mixture of portland cement and plaster which shall be allowed thoroughly to harden (from 3 to 6 hours) before the test. No point on the surface shall deviate from the plane more than 0.003 in. The cap shall not be thicker than ⅛ in. and shall be formed by means of a cast-iron or steel plate or plate glass which has a true surface.

Specimens shall be accurately centered in the testing machine.

The load shall be applied through a spherical bearing block placed on top of the specimen. The rate of loading after 50 per cent of the ultimate load has been applied shall be not greater than that which will produce a shortening of the specimen of 0.02 in. per minute.

When testing other than rectangular block or tile care must be taken to see that the load is applied through the center of gravity of the specimen.

Machined steel or cast-iron plates of sufficient thickness to prevent appreciable bending shall be placed between the spherical bearing block and the specimen. In no case shall the distance between the edge of the spherical bearing block and the end of the bearing plate be greater than twice the thickness of the plate. Where a number of thin plates are used, in no case shall the plates be less than one inch thick nor shall any plate extend beyond the one immediately above it a greater distance than twice the thickness of the plate.

The specimen shall be loaded to failure.

The compressive strength in pounds per square inch of gross cross-sectional area is the total applied load in pounds divided by the cross-sectional area in square inches. The average of the tests of not less than three specimens shall be taken as the compressive strength.

SEC. M-10 REINFORCING STEEL. Reinforcement shall be in accordance with the requirements of Spec. No. 1–265.

SEC. M-11 WROUGHT IRON.

M-11 (a). Wrought iron for shapes and bars shall conform to the requirements of A.A.S.H.O. Specification M 100–39.

M-11 (b). Wrought iron plates shall conform to the requirements of A.A.S.H.O. Specification M 99–39.

SEC. M-12 GRAY IRON CASTINGS. Iron castings shall conform to the requirements of A.A.S.H.O. Specification M 105–41. Unless otherwise specified, all iron castings shall be 25 Class. Castings shall be bodily filleted at angles and the arrises shall be sharp and perfect. If specified, the bearing surfaces between frame and cover or grate shall be machined.

SEC. M-13 STRUCTURAL STEEL. Structural steel shall conform to the requirements of A.A.S.H.O. Specification M 94–39.

SEC. M-14 PAINT. Paint for coating frames, covers, grates, and other metal surfaces shall conform to the following requirements:

(a) Red Lead, A.A.S.H.O. Specification M 72–42.

(b) Black Paint, A.A.S.H.O. Specification M 68–42

(c) Asphalt Varnish.

Composition: The varnish shall be composed of a good grade of asphalt fluxed and blended with properly treated drying oils and thinned to proper consistency with a volatile solvent.

Finished Varnish: The varnish shall be jet black in color. The consistency shall be such that it will give good brushing, flowing, covering and leveling properties. When brushed on a smooth vertical tin panel it shall dry within 24 hours without running, streaking or sagging. Furthermore, it shall meet the following requirements:

	Maximum	Minimum
Carbon bisulphide insoluble	1%	....
Flash point (tag closed cup)	......	30°C.
Non-volatile	......	40%
Fatty matter (based on non-volatile)	......	20%
Lieberman Starch Reaction	No violet color	....
Set to touch	5 hours	....
Dry hard	24 hours	....

Bend Test: The varnish shall be brushed on a smooth vertical tin panel (thickness 0.011 inches) and after air-drying for 72 hours at room temperature, shall be rapidly bent through 180 degree over a ⅛ inch rod at 25° C. No cracking, checking or flaking shall be noticeable.

Water Resistance: The varnish shall be brushed on a smooth vertical tin panel and allowed to air-dry for 72 hours at room temperature. The panel shall then be placed for 18 hours in a beaker containing 2½ inches of distilled water at room temperature (immerse the end of the panel which was uppermost during the drying period). Upon removal from water, no whitening, dulling or softening shall be noticeable.

Oil Resistance: The varnish shall be brushed on a smooth vertical tin panel and allowed to air-dry for 72 hours at room temperature. It shall then withstand lubricating oil for 6 hours without showing any softening or deterioration of the film.

(d) *Coal Tar Pitch Paint.*

Composition: The paint shall be derived from tar. It shall be so manufactured, proportioned and treated as to produce a good quality paint.

Finished Paint: The finished paint shall be homogeneous and free from extraneous matter. The consistency shall be such that it will give good brushing, flowing, covering and leveling qualities. When brushed on a smooth vertical tin panel it shall dry within 8 hours without running, streaking, or sagging to a glossy black. It shall also meet the following requirements:

	Maximum	Minimum
Specific gravity 25° C./25° C.	1.12	1.07
Specific viscosity 25° C. (Engler)	15	10
Carbon bisulphide insoluble (Bitumen)	96%	88%
Distillate * below 200° C.	....	20%
Distillate * below 235° C.	....	25%
Distillate * below 300° C.	45%	....
Softening point on Distillation Residue (Ring and Ball)	75° C.	55° C.
Water	0.5%	....

* By weight.

Water Resistance: The paint shall be brushed on a smooth vertical tin panel and allowed to air-dry for 72 hours at room temperature. The panel shall then be placed for 18 hours in a beaker containing 2½ inches of distilled water at room temperature (immerse the end of the panel which was uppermost during the drying period). Upon removal from the water no whitening, dulling, softening or other defects shall be noticeable.

Oil Resistance: The paint shall be brushed on a smooth vertical tin panel and allowed to air-dry for 72 hours at room temperature. It shall then withstand lubricating oil for 6 hours without showing any softening or deterioration of the film.

SEC. M-15 RIP RAP: Rip rap shall be dense, run of quarry, durable stone, maximum size 25 pounds, at least 50% of which shall weigh between 10 and 15 pounds. Material used shall be free from dirt and an excessive percentage of dust and fragments resulting from blasting.

CONSTRUCTION METHODS

3.1 *Trench and Culvert Excavation.* Trench and culvert excavation shall consist of unclassified excavation for runway, field, outfall and subsurface drainage where shown on the plans, called for in the proposal, or ordered by the Contracting Officer. Where pipe is laid in fill, the fill shall be brought up to finished subgrade or to an elevation 3 feet above the top of the pipe before trench excavation for drainage is made.

Trenches shall be excavated carefully to the required depth so as to allow the pipe to be laid on undisturbed subgrade throughout its entire length. Transverse sub-trenches shall be formed to receive the bell. Where soft spots or unsuitable materials are encountered on excavating the bottom of the trench, the Contractor shall remove such materials for an additional depth of 6 inches below the grade called for and replace with granular material similar to the stone specified for porous backfill in Material, Section M-6(b), or with impervious compacted earth, as ordered by the Engineer. Care should be taken during the excavation of the trenches so as not to remove material beyond the pay lines as shown on the plans. All loose material occurring as a result of careless excavation shall be removed from the trench, replaced and compacted in accordance with Paragraph 3.3(a) for which no extra payment will be made.

3.2 *Laying Pipe.* Pipe shall be bedded firmly on the undisturbed subgrade or granular backfill for its entire length and, if shown on the plans or called for in the proposal, partly encased in impervious compacted backfill. Pipe shall be placed with the hub end upgrade and the spigot entered into the hub of the adjoining pipe. The Contractor shall provide proper facilities for lowering the pipe into the trench in a manner so as not to disturb the material in the bottom of the trench. The pipe shall be laid true to line and grade as given. Lateral connections shall be made with all drains encountered, and the cost of same shall be included in the unit price bid per lineal foot of pipe. Where the upper end of any pipe is not connected into another pipe or a structure and is not intended to serve as an inlet, it shall be effectively blocked with concrete, flat stones or brick laid in mortar, or a precast clay stopper, payment for which shall be included in the price bid per lineal foot of pipe. Any pipe which is not in true alignment, which shows any undue settlement after laying, or is damaged, shall be taken up and re-laid without extra compensation. Laying of pipe shall begin at the outlet ends and progress toward the inlet ends unless otherwise approved by the Engineer. No pipe shall be laid until the excavated trench has been checked for grade by the Government Representative. Where bell and spigot pipe is used, the Contractor shall make the necessary provision, either by the proper casting of the pipe or other approved method, to hold the spigot end of all such pipe in position so that flow lines of adjacent pipe will be continuous. Sealed joints, where called for, shall be formed by caulking a gasket of jute or oakum into the hub and then filling with mortar specified below, or by the use of precast or manufactured joint fillers as shown on the plans or approved by the Contracting Officer.

Required connections shall be made to existing pipes of different types or sizes and to existing drainage structures in a manner satisfactory to the Engineer. This work shall be considered a subsidiary obligation of the Contractor and no direct payment will be made therefor.

Mortar shall be composed of materials meeting the requirements of Specification 1–265 mixed in the proportion of 1:2. Batching may be done by volume in approved boxes and the mortar mixed by hand. No retempering will be allowed.

3.3 *Backfilling.* (a) The backfill, where porous backfill is not called for on the plans or in the proposal, shall consist of suitable earth in accordance with Sec. M-6(a) which shall be tamped solidly around and above the pipe with pneumatic or other approved tampers, in such a manner as not to disturb the pipe. The backfill shall be carefully placed and not dumped directly into the trench from trucks, and the use of bulldozers in backfilling will not be allowed. Earth backfill shall not contain frozen material or stones larger than four (4) inches in diameter. If the pipe being so backfilled has been laid with open joints, joints of such pipe shall be wrapped with strips of 3-ply bituminous-treated roofing paper or burlap, not less than eight (8) inches in width, so installed as to prevent its displacement. The cost of wrapping such joints shall be included in the unit price bid per lineal foot of pipe. The backfill, shall be installed in layers having a loose depth not to exceed eight (8) inches, and shall be compacted until the density of each layer becomes not less than ninety-five (95) percent of the maximum density, as determined by the compaction test, A.A.S.H.O. Method T-99–38 (Proctor). Puddling shall not be allowed except by special written permission of the Contracting Officer.

(b) Where porous backfill is called for on the plans or in the proposal, granular material meeting the requirements of Materials, Section M-6(b), shall be placed to the depth shown on the plans or called for in the proposal. As soon as the pipe is installed in the trench, and approved by the Government Representative, sufficient material of the type called for shall be placed by hand or careful dumping to fill the trench up to approximately one (1) inch above the center of the pipe when compacted. This initial backfill shall be hand tamped and rodded in order to work the material around and under the pipe. Particular care shall be taken in rodding and tamping so that alignment and grade are not disturbed. After the initial backfill has been placed and compacted, the trench shall be filled with porous backfill material to the depth as indicated. All backfill shall be placed in such a manner that the pipe will not be displaced or injured and shall be compacted by tamping in one foot layers. When the trench is completely filled with porous material, a car or light truck shall be operated over the trench, parallel to the drainage line, for final compaction, as directed by the Engineer. Where porous backfill is to be used to partially fill the trench, the remaining backfill to the depth indicated shall be in accordance with Article 3.3(a).

(c) Where shown on the plans, called for in the proposal, or directed by the Contracting Officer, the Contractor will be required to furnish and install a uniform layer of bituminous coated porous backfill material meeting the requirements of Materials, Section M-6(c) of the thickness indicated over the completed trench backfill. Where penetration is allowed, the porous material shall be brought to finished grade and the bituminous material spread at the rate of 0.5 gal. per sq. yd. unless otherwise specified.

(d) Where shown on the plans, called for in the proposal or directed by the Contracting Officer, the Contractor shall raise existing porous backfill to finished grade, when necessary, and penetrate the surface with bituminous material meeting the requirements of Spec. No. P-604. The backfill material shall meet the requirements of Sec. M-6(b) and be of a gradation approximately the same as that contained in the existing drain.

(e) Where shown on the plans, called for in the proposal or directed by the Contracting Officer, the Contractor will be required to furnish and install a layer of impervious compacted earth backfill, under and around the lower half of the pipe. The work shall be done in accordance with the requirements of Paragraph 3.3(a). Compacted earth placed over porous backfill to a depth not exceeding 8 inches below finished grade shall be placed under Item 1.21 and no payment will be made under the trench backfill item.

3.4 *Drainage Structures.* The Contractor shall build drainage structures and appurtenances of the dimensions and at the locations shown on the plans or called for in the proposal and to the lines and grades established by the Engineer. All structures shall be composed of materials meeting the requirements of the Materials Section of this specification.

(a) *Excavation and Backfill.* The excavation shall be of such dimensions in all cases as will give ample room for construction. The removal of any obstruction, which is necessary in the construction of the work, shall be done by the Contractor at his own expense.

Should it be necessary to resort to blasting, the Contractor will be required to protect work already completed and all adjacent property and will be responsible for all damage to this work or adjacent property.

If the material found at grade is not suitable for foundation, a further depth shall be excavated and filled with suitable material.

The backfill shall consist of suitable material in accordance with Sec. M-6(a) and shall be placed around the work in layers not exceeding 8 inches in thickness (loose measurement) and thoroughly tamped in place with pneumatic tampers. The backfill shall not be dumped into the excavation directly from trucks and the use of bulldozers in backfilling will not be allowed. The backfill material shall not contain frozen material or stones larger than 8″ in diameter. All stones shall be completely surrounded by fine material so as to form a dense and compact mass. Clusters of stones shall be separated so that no voids will occur. The backfill shall be compacted until the density of each layer becomes not less than 95% of the maximum density as determined by the compaction test A.A.S.H.O. Method T-99–38 (Proctor). Puddling shall not be allowed except by special permission of the Contracting Officer.

The backfilling shall follow the completion of the work as closely as the type of construction will permit.

(b) *Concrete.* Concrete construction shall conform to the requirements of Specification No. 1–265.

(c) *Masonry.* Masonry shall consist of brick or solid concrete block and shall be laid up by experienced personnel. All mortar joints shall be full. At least every sixth course of brickwork shall be a full header course. The masonry shall be well soaked before being placed. Where fresh masonry joins masonry that is partly or totally set up, the exposed surface of the set masonry shall be cleaned, roughened and lightly wetted. All loose masonry and mortar shall be removed. The outside surfaces shall be plastered with mortar approximately ¼ inch in thickness. The mortar shall be in accordance with Paragraph 3.2 to which lime may be added not to exceed 10 percent of the cement by weight.

The outside surfaces of all brick masonry shall be cured with wet burlap, cotton mats or hay for a period of 48 hours, or sprayed with an approved curing compound.

3.5 *Miscellaneous Iron & Steel.*

(a) Wrought iron steps shall be securely embedded or built into the side walls of all manholes at vertical intervals not greater than 16 inches.

(b) Cast iron frames and covers or grates shall be set on a full mortar bed and a collar of mortar placed around the frame. All frames, covers, and grates shall be given one coat of paint meeting the requirements of Sec. M-14 (b), (c), or (d), after delivery to the site of the work.

(c) Steel grating (subway type) shall be fabricated by welding in accordance with standard practice of experienced manufacturers. Riveting or mechanical locking will not be acceptable. Gratings shall be placed in frames composed of angles of suitable size welded together at the corners with the legs set inward in order to form a seat for the gratings.

The frames shall be set in a full mortar bed and bolted to the structure with 4 screws placed one at each corner. Threaded inserts may be set during construction and machine screws used or the structure may be drilled and lag screw shields and lag screws used. All frames and grates shall be galvanized before leaving the shop. In concrete pavement, the frames shall be set to grade and held accurately in place while the pavement is poured.

3.6 *Changing Elevation of Existing Structures.* The Contractor shall be required to change the elevation of existing structures where shown on the plans, called for in the proposal or directed by the Contracting Officer. Where structures are to be lowered, the cutting and removal of the material shall be done in a manner satisfactory to the Engineer. Where structures are to be extended or reconstructed, the work shall be done in accordance with applicable portions of Paragraph 3.4.

The existing frames and covers or grates shall be removed, carefully stored and replaced to the grade established by the Engineer. The frame shall be set on a full mortar bed and a collar of mortar placed around the entire frame.

3.7 *Setting Government Furnished Frames and Covers or Grates.* When shown on the plans, called for in the proposal, or ordered by the Contracting Officer, the Contractor shall haul Government furnished frames and covers or grates from storage on the airport property and set them on existing basins to the grades established by the Engineer. The frames shall be set on a full mortar bed and a collar of mortar placed around the entire frame.

3.8 *Ditch Excavation.* Ditch excavation shall consist of excavation for drainage and interception ditches within the pay lines indicated, when not included in the item "Unclassified Excavation" and only when specifically shown on the plans, called for in the proposal or ordered by the Contracting Officer. Excavation shall be performed at such places as indicated on the plans, to the lines, grades, and elevations shown, or as directed by the Engineer, and all necessary excavation in fill areas shall be performed before placing the fill and no ditch excavation shall be included above the finished grade of the airport area. No excavation shall be started until the Engineer has taken the necessary cross sections and measurements. The work shall be performed in the proper sequence with the other construction. All satisfactory material shall be placed in fills; unsatisfactory materials shall be disposed of as directed by the Engineer. No waste or surplus material shall be left within four (4) feet of the edge of any ditch. All hand work as is necessary, shall be performed to secure a finish, true to line, elevation and cross section as designated.

The ditches constructed on the project shall be maintained to the required cross section and shall be kept free from debris or obstructions until the project is accepted.

3.9 *Sod for Berm Protection.* The Contractor shall furnish and place sod for berm or slope protection as shown on the plans or as directed by the Engineer.

After inspection and approval of the source of sod by the Engineer, the sod shall be cut into squares or into rectangular sections which may vary in length but shall be of equal width and of a size that will permit them to be lifted without breaking.

Mechanical devices may be used for cutting the sod. The sod shall be cut with at least 2 inches of soil adhering firmly to the roots. Care shall be exercised at all times to retain the native soil on the roots of the sod during the process of stripping, transporting, and planting. Dumping from vehicles will not be permitted.

The sod shall be transplanted within 24 hours from the time it is harvested, unless it is stored roots-to-roots or grass-to-grass at its destination in a manner satisfactory to the Engineer. All sod in stacks shall be kept moist and shall be protected from exposure to the air and sun and from freezing. Sod shall be cut and moved only when the seasonal and soil moisture conditions are such that favorable results can be expected. Where the soil is too dry, permission to cut sod may be granted only after it has been watered sufficiently to moisten the soil to the depth the sod is to be cut.

The sod shall be laid smoothly, edge-to-edge, and with staggered joints on the prepared sodbed. Screened soil of good quality shall be used to fill all cracks between sods. The quantity of fill soil shall be such as to cause no smothering of the grass. The sod shall immediately be pressed firmly into contact with the sodbed by tamping and rolling with approved equipment, so as to eliminate all airpockets, provide a true and even surface and insure knitting without displacement of the sod or deformation of the surfaces of the sodded areas.

The sod shall be given one watering as soon as there is evidence of excessive drying. Sufficient water shall be applied to wet the sod through completely and at least 2 inches of the sodbed as well. Additional applications shall be made as directed by the Engineer.

3.10 *Rip Rap.* (a) *Stone Rip Rap.* Rip rap shall be carefully placed in the best workmanlike manner upon all surfaces indicated and so laid that the weight of the large stones is carried by the soil and not by the adjacent stones. Stones shall be placed in such a manner as to reduce the voids to a minimum, and all spaces throughout the rip rap shall be packed with smaller stones and spalls of suitable size to form a dense, compact mass. Rip rap shall be a minimum of 8 inches thick.

(b) *Grouted Rip Rap.* The stones used shall be carefully placed in the best workmanlike manner upon all surfaces indicated and so laid that the weight of the larger stones is carried by the soil and not by the adjacent stones. Grouted rip rap shall have a minimum thickness of 8″. Stones shall be placed in such a manner as to reduce the voids to a minimum and all spaces between the stones shall be completely filled with grout from bottom to top and the surfaces swept off with a stiff broom. No rip rap shall be grouted in freezing weather. In hot, dry weather, the work shall be protected from the sun and kept moist for at least 3 days.

Grout shall be composed of materials meeting the requirements of Spec. No. 1–265 mixed in the proportion of 1:3 to a thick, creamy consistency. Batching may be done by volume in approved boxes and the grout mixed by hand. No grout shall be used that shows evidence of setting-up and no retempering shall be allowed.

3.11 *Berm Protection.* Berm protection shall consist of the construction of gutters, earth banks, spillways, catchbasins, pipelines and/or other structures necessary to divert surface water from earth slopes as shown on the plans, called for in the proposal or directed by the Contracting Officer. The materials forming component parts of berm protection shall be in accordance with the applicable sections and paragraphs of this specification. Earthwork required shall be placed in accordance with the item for "Unclassified Excavation."

METHOD OF MEASUREMENT

4.0 *Method of Measurement.* The following methods of measurement shall govern whenever the proposal contains an applicable item.

4.1 The quantity of trench and culvert excavation to be paid for shall be the actual number of cubic yards of material measured in position within the pay lines shown on the plans or specifically ordered by the Engineer actually excavated and disposed of. No excavation shall be included that is above the final elevation of the airport subgrade. Unsuitable material encountered at the elevation of the bottom of the pipe and removed as provided in Paragraph 3.1 shall be included in the quantity for payment.

4.2 The footage of pipe for runway, field, outfall and sub-surface drainage, and other purposes specifically designated to be paid for, shall be the actual number of lineal feet or fraction thereof, measured complete and accepted in place, from inside face of structure to inside face of structure or to existing pipe, exclusive of special features shown on the plans or called for in the proposal, but including "Y's," "T's," other shapes as required and connections to existing pipes and structures as necessary.

4.3 (a) Earth backfill shall not be paid for and the cost of this work shall be included in the price bid for trench excavation except when a specific item for earth backfill is included in the bid schedule. Where earth backfill is specified, the material shall be measured as the actual number of cubic yards of such material conforming with all requirements and placed in accordance with the specifications in the completed and accepted work. In computing the cubic yards for payment, the dimensions used shall be the actual dimensions within the pay lines shown on the plans or ordered by the Contracting Officer; no backfill shall be included that is above the original ground surface. The volume of the pipe will not be included.

(b) Porous backfill material shall be measured as the number of cubic yards of such material conforming with all requirements and placed in accordance with the specifications within the pay lines in the completed and accepted work. In computing the cubic yards for payment, the dimensions used shall be the pay lines shown on the plans or ordered by the Contracting Officer, and no payment will be made for material placed outside the pay lines as made necessary by excessive excavation. The volume of the pipe will not be included.

(c) The quantity of bituminous coated aggregate to be paid for shall be measured as the actual number of tons of such material conforming with all requirements and placed in accordance with the specifications within the pay lines in the completed and accepted work.

Where penetration is allowed, the bituminous material shall be measured as the actual number of gallons placed in accordance with the specifications in the completed and accepted work.

4.4 The quantity of concrete, brick and concrete block, including mortar shall be measured as the number of cubic yards of material conforming with all requirements and placed in accordance with the specifications in the completed and accepted work. In computing the yardage for payment, the dimensions used shall be the neat lines shown on the plans or ordered by the Contracting Officer.

No deductions will be made for the volume of embedded material or pipe with an area of less than one (1) square foot.

4.5 The quantity of miscellaneous iron and/or steel to be paid for shall be measured as the number of pounds of frames, covers, grates, steps, reinforcing, etc., actually used in the completed and accepted work. The weight, except reinforcing, shall be computed from certified shipping or weigh bills or, when suitable and accurate scales are available at the site of the work, by direct measurement in the presence of the Engineer. The weight of bar reinforcing shall be computed from table given in Sec. M-10. If indicated in the bid schedule, the weights of cast iron and steel shall be measured separately.

4.6 The quantity of changing elevations of existing structures to be paid for shall be measured as the number of cubic yards of material removed or added as shown on the plans or directed by the Engineer, or the number of structures raised or lowered measured per each whichever is specified in the bid schedule.

4.7 The quantity of setting Government furnished frames and covers or grates to be paid for shall be the actual number of such frames, etc. set in accordance with this specification in the completed and accepted work measured per each.

4.8 The quantity of ditch excavation to be paid for shall be the number of cubic yards of material measured in its original position, excavated and disposed of as directed by the Engineer, and the limits shall not exceed the pay lines shown on the plans or as ordered by the Contracting Officer. No measurement and payment will be made for ditch excavation, which shall be included in the price bid for unclassified excavation, unless a specific item for this work is included in the bid schedule.

4.9 The quantity of sod to be paid for shall be measured as the actual square yards of area sodded and accepted by the Engineer.

4.10 The rip rap to be paid for shall be measured as the actual number of square yards, a minimum of 8″ thick, measured on the surface, or the actual number of cubic yards, whichever is specified in the bid schedule, within the lines shown on the plans or ordered by the Contracting Officer, complete and accepted.

BASIS OF PAYMENT

5.0 *Basis of Payment.* The following methods of payment shall govern whenever the proposal contains an applicable item.

5.1 The cubic yardage of trench and culvert excavation, measured as provided in Paragraph 4.1 above, shall be paid for at the contract unit price per cubic yard bid for the appropriate item, when included in the schedule, which price and payment shall constitute full compensation for performing all excavation, disposal of all surplus excavated material, as well as furnishing all labor, transportation, equipment, tools, sheathing, shoring and pumping if required, and incidentals necessary to complete the item. The price and payment shall also include earth backfill in accordance with Paragraph 5.3(a) unless a specific item for separate payment is included in the bid schedule.

5.2 The footage of pipe for runway drainage, field drainage and other purposes, measured as provided in Paragraph 4.2, above, shall be paid for at the contract unit price per lineal foot bid for the appropriate item, when included in the schedule, which price and payment shall constitute full compensation for furnishing, delivering, handling and placing all pipe and making required joints and connections, as well as furnishing all pumping, labor, transportation, equipment, tools, and incidentals necessary to complete the item.

5.3 (a) The cubic yardage of earth backfill material, measured as provided in Paragraph 4.3(a) above, shall be paid for, when included in the schedule, at the contract unit price bid per cubic yard, which price and payment shall constitute full compensation for loading all material, hauling, placing, compacting and for all labor, transportation, equipment, tools, and incidentals necessary to complete the item.

(b) The cubic yardage of porous backfill material, measured as provided in Paragraph 4.3(b) above, shall be paid for when included in the schedule, at the contract unit price bid per cubic yard, which price and payment shall constitute full compensation for furnishing, hauling, placing, compacting, and for all labor, transportation, equipment, tools and incidentals necessary to complete the item.

(c) The tonnage of bituminous coated aggregate, measured as provided in Paragraph 4.3(c) above, shall be paid for when included in the schedule, at the contract unit price bid per ton which price and payment shall constitute full compensation for furnishing, hauling, and placing of all such material, as well as furnishing all labor, transportation, equipment, tools, and incidentals necessary to complete the item. The gallons of bituminous material measured as provided in Paragraph 4.3(c) above, shall be paid for when included in the schedule, at the contract price bid per gallon which price and payment shall constitute full compensation for furnishing, hauling, and placing of all such material as well as furnishing all labor, transportation, equipment, tools, and incidentals necessary to complete the item.

5.4 The cubic yardage of concrete, etc., measured as provided in Paragraph 4.4 above, and not included in any other items, shall be paid for at the contract unit price per cubic yard bid for the appropriate item, when included in the schedule, which price and payment shall constitute full compensation for excavation, for furnishing, hauling, mixing and placing the concrete and backfilling as well as furnishing all cement, labor, transportation, equipment, tools, forms, bracing, finishing and incidentals necessary to complete the item.

5.5 The pounds of miscellaneous iron and/or steel measured as provided in Paragraph 4.5 above, and not included in any other item, shall be paid for, when included in the schedule, at the contract unit price bid per pound, which price and payment shall constitute full compensation for furnishing, hauling, painting, setting and fastening as well as furnishing all labor, transportation, equipment, tools, materials (including cement and paint) and incidentals necessary to complete the work.

5.6 The cubic yards of material used in changing elevation of existing structures or the number per each, whichever is specified in the bid schedule and measured as provided in Paragraph 4.6 above shall be paid for at the contract unit price for the appropriate item when included in the schedule, which price and payment shall constitute full compensation for excavation and backfill if necessary, for removing and resetting existing heads, for cutting and removing excess material, as well as for all tools, labor, transportation, materials including cement, equipment and incidentals necessary to complete the work.

5.7 The number of setting Government furnished frames, etc. measured as provided in Paragraph 4.7 above shall be paid for when included in the schedule at the contract price bid per each, which price and payment shall constitute full compensation for hauling, handling and setting as well as furnishing all labor, transportation, equipment, tools, materials including cement and incidentals necessary to complete the item.

5.8 The cubic yardage of ditch excavation measured as provided in Paragraph 4.8 above, shall be paid for at the contract unit price per cubic yard bid for the appropriate item when included in the schedule, which price and payment shall constitute full compensation for performing all excavation, disposal of all surplus excavated material and trimming, as well as furnishing all labor, transportation, equipment, tools, and incidentals necessary to complete the item.

5.9 The square yards of sod for berm protection, measured as provided in Paragraph 4.9 above shall be paid for when included in the schedule at the contract price bid per square yard which price and payment shall constitute full compensation for any necessary grading, furnishing and placing sod, finishing, repairing, maintenance and for all labor, equipment, tools, and incidentals necessary to complete the item.

5.10 (a) The square yards or cubic yards of rip rap, measured as provided in Paragraph 4.10(a) above, shall be paid for, when included in the schedule, at the contract unit price bid per yard, which price and payment shall constitute full compensation for excavation and backfill, for furnishing, hauling, placing, compacting of all material and for labor, equipment, tools and work necessary to complete the item.

(b) The square yards or cubic yards of grouted rip rap, measured as provided in Paragraph 4.10(b) above, shall be paid for, when included in the schedule, at the contract unit price bid per yard, which price and payment shall constitute full compensation for excavation and backfill, for furnishing, hauling, placing, including cement and aggregate, of all material and for labor, equipment, tools, and work necessary to complete the item.

5.11 Berm protection does not constitute an item for which payment is to be made, all component parts will be included with and paid for under the respective applicable items.

APPENDIX 5

DEPARTMENT OF COMMERCE
Civil Aeronautics Administration
First Region
May 15, 1945

STRUCTURAL PORTLAND CEMENT CONCRETE (PLAIN AND REINFORCED)

Specification No. 1–265

DESCRIPTION

1.1 This item shall consist of either plain or reinforced structural Portland cement concrete prepared and constructed in accordance with these specifications at the locations and of the form and dimensions shown on the plans. The concrete shall be composed of coarse aggregate, fine aggregate, Portland cement and water.

MATERIALS

2.1 *General.* Only approved materials conforming to the requirements of these specifications shall be used in the work and certification or affidavits as to their conformity shall be submitted by the Contractor to the Engineer before the materials are used. The source of supply of each of the materials shall be approved before delivery or use. Representative preliminary samples of all materials shall be submitted by the Contractor, when required, for examination and test. The materials may be subjected to inspection and tests at any time during the progress of construction and failure to meet the required tests shall be sufficient grounds for rejection.

Materials shall be stored and handled so as to insure the preservation of their quality and fitness for use and shall be so located so as to facilitate prompt inspection. All equipment for handling and transporting materials and concrete must be clean before any material or concrete are placed therein. All testing and sampling shall be done in accordance with current specifications of the A.A.S.H.O., except when otherwise provided.

In no case will the use of pit run or naturally mixed aggregates be permitted. Naturally mixed aggregate must in every case be screened and washed and all fine and coarse aggregates must be stored separately and shall be kept clean. The mixing of different kinds of aggregates from different sources in one storage pile or alternating batches of different aggregates will not be permitted. Aggregates containing lumps of frozen or partially cemented material shall not be used.

2.2 *Coarse Aggregate.* The coarse aggregate for concrete shall consist of crushed gravel, crushed stone, crushed slag, gravel, or other approved materials, conforming to the following requirements.

The coarse aggregate shall have a percentage of wear not more than 50 at

500 revolutions as determined by A.A.S.H.O. Method T 96–42 (Los Angeles Rattler Test).

Crushed stone and gravel shall consist of clean, hard, tough, durable, uncoated fragments reasonably free from thin or flat pieces. The aggregate shall not show evidence of disintegration nor show a total loss greater than 12 per cent when subjected to five cycles of the sodium sulphate accelerated soundness test using A.A.S.H.O. Method T 104–42.

Slag shall be air-cooled, blast furnace slag, and shall consist of angular fragments reasonably uniform in density and quality and reasonably free from thin, elongated or soft pieces, dirt or other objectionable matter. The slag shall have compact weight per cubic foot of not less than 70 pounds, using A.A.S.H.O. Method T 19–42.

The coarse aggregate shall not have more than 1 percent of material removable by the decantation test, using A.A.S.H.O. Method T 11–42, nor more than 1 percent of shale using A.A.S.H.O. Method T 10–35, nor more than 5 percent of soft fragments, nor more than one-fourth of 1 percent of clay lumps, using the method given under section 2.3 for fine aggregate. The total of shale, coal, clay lumps and soft fragments shall not be more than 5 percent.

TABLE 1

REQUIREMENTS FOR GRADING OF COARSE AGGREGATE

Sieve Designation	Percentage by weight passing square mesh sieves (A.A.S.H.O. T-27)							
	$2\frac{1}{2}''$	$2''$	$1\frac{1}{2}''$	$1''$	$\frac{3}{4}''$	$\frac{1}{2}''$	$\frac{3}{8}''$	No. 4
$\frac{3}{4}$ to 1 inch			100	30–65	0–20			
No. 4 to $\frac{3}{4}''$				100	90–100		20–55	0–10

The sizes of coarse aggregate to be used shall conform to the grading requirements of Table 1 or to the sizes specified by the local Highway Departments most nearly meeting these requirements. The ratio of either separated size of coarse aggregate to total coarse aggregate may be varied within the range of 40 to 60 percent by weight to secure the most desirable and uniform gradation of the combined mix.

Coarse aggregate shall be well graded from coarse to fine so that concrete of the required workability, density and strength can be made without the use of excessive amount of sand, water or cement.

Different types of coarse aggregate shall not be mixed or used alternately in any one structure.

2.3 *Fine Aggregate.* The fine aggregate for concrete and mortar shall consist either of sand, or of approved inert materials having similar characteristics or of a combination thereof. The material used shall consist of hard, strong, durable particles.

When subjected to five cycles of the sodium sulphate soundness test, using A.A.S.H.O. Method T 104–42 the fine aggregate shall have a total loss not greater than 10 percent by weight. Instead of the soundness test mentioned above, the Contractor may provide evidence, satisfactory to the Engineer, that the fine aggregate has been exposed to natural weathering, either directly or in concrete, for a period of at least 5 years without appreciable disintegration.

Fine aggregate shall contain not more than 3 percent of material removable by a decantation test using A.A.S.H.O. Method T 11–42, nor more than 1 percent of clay lumps, or 1 percent of shale as determined by A.A.S.H.O. Method T 10–35. The total of coal, clay lumps, shale, soft fragments and other local deleterious substances shall not be more than 5 percent.

The percentage of clay lumps shall be determined by examining the various fractions that remain after the material has been tested for grading. Any particles that can be broken up with the fingers shall be classified as clay lumps and the total percentage by weight of all clay lumps shall be determined on the basis of the total original weight of the sample.

All fine aggregate shall be free from injurious amounts of organic impurities. Aggregates subjected to the colorimetric test for organic impurities, A.A.S.H.O. Method T 21–42, and producing a color darker than the standard shall be rejected unless they pass the mortar strength test herein required.

The fine aggregate shall be well graded from fine to coarse and shall meet the following grading requirements, using A.A.S.H.O. Method T 27–42.

TABLE 2

REQUIREMENTS FOR GRADING OF FINE AGGREGATE *

Sieve Designation	Percentage by Weight Passing Square Mesh Sieves (A.A.S.H.O. T 27–42)
3/8″	100
No. 4	95–100
No. 16	45–80
No. 30	25–55
No. 50	10–30
No. 100	2–10

* The gradation of the local Highway Department most nearly meeting the specified gradation will be allowed.

Mortar specimens made with the fine aggregate shall have a compressive strength using A.A.S.H.O. Method T 71–42, at 7 and 28 days of at least 90 percent of the strength of similar specimens made with Ottawa sand having a fineness modulus of 2.40 ± 0.10.

Blending will be permitted if necessary in order to meet the gradation requirements for fine aggregate. Fine aggregate deficient in the percentage of material passing the No. 50 sieve may be accepted provided that such deficiency does not exceed five (5) percent and is remedied by the addition of puzzolanic or cementitious materials other than Portland cement, as specified in paragraph on admixtures, in sufficient quantity to produce the required workability as approved by the Engineer.

For the purpose of controlling the grading of fine aggregate from any one source, the Contractor shall submit, prior to actual deliveries, a preliminary sample which shall be representative of the material which he proposes to furnish. Any shipment of fine aggregate made during the progress of the work that varies in fineness modulus more than 0.20 from the fineness modulus of the preliminary sample shall be rejected or, at the discretion of the Engineer, may be accepted subject to such changes in the proportions used as he may direct.

The fineness modulus of fine aggregate shall be determined by adding the total percentages by weight retained on U.S. standard sieves Nos. 4, 8, 16, 30, 50, 100 and dividing by 100.

2.4 *Cement.* The cement used in the work shall be Portland cement of American manufacture, conforming to the Emergency Alternate Specifications for Portland Cement (A.S.T.M. Designation EA-C 150, June 6, 1942, types I (normal), II (Moderate Heat), and III (High Early Strength), and corresponding Federal Designation E-SS-C-191 b; E-SS-C-206 a, and E-SS-C-201 a, June 5, 1942). The type of cement shall be as shown on the plans or as designated by the Contracting Officer. The sampling and testing of cement shall be in accordance with A.S.T.M. Standard Methods of Testing Cement, Serial Designation C 77–40 and subsequent revisions. Only one brand of each shall be used on any one job, except by specific written permission from the Engineer.

The Contractor shall provide suitable means for storing cement and protecting it from dampness. Different grades of cement shall be stored separately, and shall not be mixed.

The cement shall be delivered in canvas bags or other strong, well-made packages. Bags of cement in which for any reason the cement has become partially set or which contain lumps of caked cement, shall be rejected. Use of cement salvaged from discarded or used bags will not be permitted.

Where so indicated on the plans, high-early-strength Portland cement shall be used instead of Portland cement. When high-early-strength cement is used, concreting operations shall not be carried on if the atmospheric temperature is below or may be expected to drop below 50° F., except upon written authorization from the Engineer. All provisions of these specifications, except the cement, shall be applicable to such concrete. If the Contractor, in order to facilitate his own operations, chooses to use high-early-strength cement in portions of the work other than those where its use is required, written permission must be obtained from the Contracting Officer.

The cement shall be emptied from the shipping package directly into the skip of the mixer.

Where bulk cement is allowed, the batching equipment shall include a screen of such size and construction in the loading chute as will insure against the presence of burlap, paper and other foreign materials in the concrete, and a canvas "boot" or a similar device which will prevent wastage or loss from air currents. This screen shall be cleaned at least once daily; more frequently if conditions justify. Measurement of bulk cement shall be by weight. Whenever bulk cement is hauled, it shall be transported in suitable weather-tight trucks.

The Contractor shall furnish vendor's certified test report for each car load or equivalent of cement shipped to the project. The report shall be delivered to the Engineer before permission is granted for use of the cement.

2.5 *Water.* Water used in concrete shall be free from sewage, oil, acid, strong alkalies or vegetable matter, and also shall be free from clay and loam.

2.6 *Material Added for Workability.* The use of any material added to the mix to improve workability, which, in the opinion of the Engineer, may have an injurious effect on the strength, density, and durability of the concrete, will not be permitted. Before approval of any material, the Contractor will be required to submit the results of complete chemical and sieve analyses made by an acceptable testing laboratory. Subsequent tests will be made of samples taken by the Engineer from the supply of the material being used on the work to determine whether it is uniform in quality with that approved.

The material added shall be pozzuolanic, cementitious or silicious. It shall not contain effective early-heat-producing elements nor compounds, such as those contained in Portland cement, nor shall its use result in a material increase in the free-line content of the concrete. It shall also be in conformity with the following requirements:

Free moisture—a total of not more than 3 percent by weight.
Passing #30 sieve—not less than 100 percent by weight.
Passing #200 sieve—not less than 85 percent by weight.

2.7 *Premoulded Joint Material.* Premoulded joint material for expansion joints shall meet the requirements of one of the following A.A.S.H.O. specifications: M 33–42 or M 59–42.

2.8 *Joint Filler.* The filler for joints shall meet the requirements of A.A.S.H.O. specification M 18–42 grade A or B unless otherwise specified in the proposal.

2.9 *Steel Reinforcement.* Concrete reinforcement shall consist of deformed bars meeting the requirements for billet steel, intermediate grade, A.A.S.H.O. Designation M 31–42 except that any specimen shall not be more than 5 percent by weight under that required for any size as shown in the following table and except that the average of all specimen tested shall not be more than 3 percent by weight under that required for any specified size.

TABLE 3

Size Specified	Std. Weight Lbs. per Foot	Size Specified	Std. Weight Lbs. per Foot
$\frac{1}{4}''$ round	0.167	$\frac{5}{8}''$ round	1.043
$\frac{3}{8}''$ "	0.376	$\frac{3}{4}''$ "	1.502
$\frac{1}{2}''$ "	0.668	$\frac{7}{8}''$ "	2.044
$\frac{1}{2}''$ square	0.850	1″ "	2.670

Where wire is allowed for reinforcement, it shall meet the requirements of A.A.S.H.O. Designation M 32–42.

CONSTRUCTION METHODS

3.1 *General.* The Contractor shall furnish all labor, materials, and services necessary for, and incidental to, the completion of all work as shown on the drawings and herein specified. All machinery and equipment owned or controlled by the Contractor which is proposed to be employed by him on the work, shall be of sufficient size to meet the requirements of the work, and shall be such as to produce a satisfactory quality of work; all to be subject to the inspection and approval of the Engineer. The Contractor shall employ at all times a sufficient force of workmen, of such experience and ability that the work can be prosecuted in a satisfactory and workmanlike manner.

3.2 *Concrete Proportions.* The concrete shall consist of a mixture of coarse aggregate, fine aggregate, Portland cement and water. All aggregates and bulk cement shall be measured by weight except as hereafter specified. In proportioning aggregates and mixing water, compensation shall be made for the weight of moisture in the aggregates which shall be determined periodically.

When package cement is used the calculated quantities for each batch shall be exactly equal to one or more whole sack of cement. Each bag shall contain ninety-four (94) pounds net and shall be considered equal to one (1) cubic foot.

TABLE 4
GLASS A CONCRETE
Materials for One Cubic Yard of Concrete
(except as specified below)

Type of Coarse Aggregate	Minimum Cement Content	Maximum Net Water Content Gallons	Weights in Pounds Dry Aggregate		Slump Range Inches
			Fine Aggregate	Total Aggregate	
Gravel	6 bags	35	1070–1190	3210	2–5
Crushed Stone	6 bags	38	1220–1360	3200	2–5
Slag	6 bags	38	1330–1470	2930	2–5

The weights specified in the above table were calculated for aggregates of the following bulk specific gravities: natural sand and gravel −2.65, crushed stone −2.70, slag −2.30. For aggregates of specific gravities differing more than ±0.02 from those given above, the weights given in the tables shall be corrected. If the specific gravity of one or both of the aggregates changes, the batch weight shall be adjusted to conform to the new specific gravity by multiplying the weight given in the table by the specific gravity of the aggregate used and dividing by the corresponding specific gravity used in calculating the weight given in the table.

At any time during the construction period, the relative weights of fine and coarse aggregates as determined from the above table may be varied slightly in order to insure the use of the least amount of fine aggregate which will produce workable concrete within the specified slump range. Unless otherwise shown on the plans or in the Proposal, the ratio of either size of coarse aggregate may be varied within the range of 40 to 60 percent by weight, to secure the most desirable and uniform gradation of the combined material. However, the total weight of aggregate per bag of cement shall not be changed except as provided in the preceding paragraph or for the following conditions or both.

(a) For batch weight, the weights arrived at as described above shall be corrected to compensate for moisture contained in the aggregates at the time of use.

(b) If it is found impossible to prepare concrete of the proper consistency without exceeding the maximum net water content specified, the total weight of aggregate shall be reduced by the Engineer until concrete of the proper consistency is obtained without exceeding the maximum net water content specified. However, the Contractor shall not be compensated for any additional cement which may be required by reason of such adjustment.

For individual pours of 5 cu. yds. or less proportioning may be done by volume with approved batch boxes. Wheelbarrows will not be permitted for measuring aggregates. The proportion of cement, fine and coarse aggregates when measured dry, shall be 1:2:4 unless otherwise definitely shown on the plans or called for in the Proposal, and the slump shall be held to the limits shown in Table 4.

3.3 *Control Tests.* When directed by the Engineer, the Contractor shall make test cylinders and/or beams from the concrete as mixed for the work as herein specified.

Concrete test specimen shall be made in accordance with the standard method of "Making and Storing Compression Test Specimens of Concrete in the Field," of A.A.S.H.O. Method T 23–42; also with the standard method of "Flexural Strength of Concrete" of A.A.S.H.O. Method T 97–42 with respect to moulding specimen only. The Contractor shall cure and store the test specimens under such conditions as directed. The Engineer will make the actual tests on the test specimen at no expense to the Contractor.

When directed, the Contractor shall make yield test of the concrete mix. This test shall be made in accordance with A.A.S.H.O. Method T 121–42.

3.4 *Proportioning and Measuring Devices.* When package cement is used the quantity for each batch shall be exactly equal to one or more whole sacks of cement. If aggregates are delivered to the mixer in batch trucks, the exact amount for each mixer charge shall be contained in each batch compartment. Weighing boxes or hoppers shall be approved by the Engineer and shall provide positive means of regulating the flow of aggregates into the batch box so that the required and exact weight of aggregates can be readily obtained. An approved method of accurate weighing shall be used to insure positive control of the required amounts of aggregates.

3.5 *Consistency.* The consistency of the concrete shall be checked by the slump test, as described in "Slump Test for Consistency of Portland Cement Concrete," A.A.S.H.O. Method T 119–42. Each concrete mixer shall be equipped with a standard slump cone which shall be used to check the consistency. The maximum slump shall not exceed five (5) inches.

3.6 *Mixing.* All equipment necessary for the mixing and placing of the concrete shall be on the site of construction and approved before concreting operations are begun.

All concrete shall be thoroughly mixed in a batch mixer of an approved size and type so designed as to insure uniform and thorough distribution of the materials throughout the mix. All concrete shall be mixed for a period of not less than 1¼ minutes after all materials including the mixing water have been placed in the mixer. The entire contents of the mixer shall be removed from the drum before the materials for the succeeding batch are placed therein. The volume of materials mixed per batch shall not exceed the manufacturer's stated capacity of the drum.

Mortar may be mixed by hand.

3.7 *Ready Mix.* When ready mixed concrete is used, the materials, proportioning, mixing and consistency shall meet these specifications. There shall be sufficient plant capacity and transportation facilities available to insure delivery of concrete at the rate required. The concrete shall be delivered and placed within one (1) hour after the cement is placed in contact with damp aggregate or water.

a. *Central Mix.* The central mixer shall be approved and shall produce satisfactory concrete. The concrete shall be delivered in a watertight agitator truck or truck mixer that will protect the concrete from rain, freezing, drying out, segregating, or from becoming affected in any manner.

b. *Truck Mixer.* The truck mixer shall consist of suitable equipment for combining aggregates, cement and water into a thoroughly mixed and uniform concrete of a quality meeting all the requirements herein. The mixer shall have a revolution counter for timing the mixing and a water measuring device. Wash water, shall not be used in any concrete mix. This type of mixing equipment shall produce concrete of the proper consistency or its use shall be prohibited.

3.8 *Mixing Conditions.* The concrete shall be mixed only in such quantities as are required for immediate use. No concrete shall be mixed while the air temperature is below 40 degrees Fahrenheit without permission of the Engineer. If permission is granted for mixing under such conditions, aggregates or water, or both shall be heated and the concrete shall be placed at a temperature of not less than 50 degrees Fahrenheit nor more than 100 degrees Fahrenheit. The Contractor shall be held responsible for any defective work resulting from freezing or injury in any manner during placing and curing and shall replace such work at his expense.

Retempering of concrete by adding water or any other material shall not be permitted.

The delivery of concrete to the job shall be in such a manner that batches of concrete will be deposited at uninterrupted intervals.

3.9 *Forms.* Concrete shall not be placed until all the forms and reinforcement have been inspected and approved by the Engineer. Forms shall be of suitable material and shall be of the type, size, shape, quality and strength to build the structure as designed on the plans. The forms shall be true to line and grade, shall be mortar tight and sufficiently rigid to prevent displacement and sagging between supports. The responsibility for their adequacy shall rest with the Contractor. The surfaces of forms shall be smooth and free from irregularities, dents, sags and holes. The internal ties shall be so arranged that when the forms are removed, no metal will show in the concrete surface, or discolor the surface when exposed to weathering. All forms shall be wetted with water or with a non-staining mineral oil as directed by the Engineer, which shall be applied shortly before the concrete is placed. Forms shall be constructed so that they can be removed without injuring the concrete or concrete surface. Exposed edges of the concrete shall be chamfered 1 inch unless otherwise shown on the plans or called for in the Proposal.

3.10 *Placing Reinforcement.*

(a) *Care of Material.* All reinforcing steel when received on the work, prior to its use shall be stacked off the ground and shall be kept free from dirt, oil, grease, or avoidable rust. When placed in the concrete, it shall be clean and free from all scale and injurious rust.

(b) *Method of Placing Material.* All reinforcing steel shall be placed in the position shown on the plans fastened together at intersections, and kept in this position while the concrete is being placed. Reinforcement shall be placed in position before concrete is deposited. In no case shall reinforcing steel be driven or forced into the concrete after it has taken its initial set.

(c) *Bending.* Reinforcement shall be carefully shaped to the dimensions indicated on the plans. The radius of bends shall be as shown on the plans. Dimensions shown on plans shall be construed as center to center of bars, unless otherwise indicated. Radii of bends specified shall be to the inside of the bar.

(d) *Splicing Reinforcement.* Whenever it is necessary to splice reinforcement, the bars shall be connected by a direct splice of strength equal to that of the bar or by overlapping their ends not less than forty-eight diameters.

(e) *Supports.* Pre-cast mortar blocks or metal supports, of adequate strength, of the proper depth shall be used for supporting the bars where necessary. If metal supports are used, they shall be of such shape that they will be easily enveloped by the concrete. Shop drawings, lists and bending details shall be supplied by the Contractor when required.

3.11 *Embedded Items.* Before placing concrete, any items that are to be embedded shall be firmly and securely fastened in place as indicated. All such items shall be thoroughly clean and free from coating, rust, scale, oil or any foreign matter. The embedding of wood shall be avoided. Around and against embedded items the concrete shall be spaded and consolidated.

3.12 *Placing Concrete.* All concrete shall be placed during the daylight unless otherwise approved. The concrete shall not be placed until the depth and character of foundation, the adequacy of forms and falsework and the placing of the steel reinforcing have been approved. Concrete shall be placed as soon as practical after mixing and in no case shall concrete be used which cannot be placed within one hour after water is added to the mix. The method and manner of placing shall be such as to avoid segregation and displacement of the reinforcement. Troughs, pipes and chutes shall be used as aid in placing concrete when necessary. Dropping the concrete a distance of more than five (5) feet or depositing a large quantity at one point will not be permitted. All concrete shall be placed carefully upon clean, damp surfaces, free from running water, or upon properly consolidated soil but never upon soft mud or dry porous earth. Care shall be exercised in dropping concrete through reinforcement so that no segregation of the coarse aggregate, nor displacement of the reinforcement occurs. Concrete shall be deposited in approximately horizontal layers of not more than two (2) feet. Concrete shall be deposited as near final position as possible. Concrete shall be compacted by the use of vibrators, spaded by suitable hand tools to work the coarse aggregate back from the face of the forms and to force the concrete under and around the reinforcement and on exposed faces to secure smooth, dense, and even surfaces. When concrete is placed in water, a satisfactory tremie method shall be used.

3.13 *Construction Joints.* When the placing of concrete is suspended, necessary provisions shall be made for joining future work before the placed concrete takes its initial set. For the proper bonding of old and new concrete such provisions shall be made for grooves, steps, keys, dovetails, reinforcing bars or other devices as may be prescribed. The work shall be arranged that a section begun on any day shall be finished by daylight on the same day. Before depositing new concrete on or against concrete which has hardened, the surface of the hardened concrete shall be cleaned by a heavy steel broom, roughened slightly, wetted and covered with a coating of neat cement paste or grout.

3.14 *Expansion Joints.* Expansion joints shall be constructed at such points and of such dimensions as may be indicated on the drawings. The premoulded filler shall be cut to the same shape as that of the surfaces being joined. Along all edges that will be exposed in the finished work, the filler shall be cut one-fourth inch smaller. The filler shall be fixed firmly against the surface of the concrete already in place in such a manner that it will not be displaced when concrete is deposited against it.

3.15 *Cleaning Forms and Equipment.* Before placing concrete all equipment for mixing, transporting and placing the concrete shall be cleaned and debris, dirt or other objectional substances shall be removed from the places to be occupied by the concrete. The inside of the forms shall be thoroughly cleaned and oiled or wetted, except in freezing weather. Reinforcement shall be cleaned of rust or other coatings. If concreting is permitted in cold weather, the forms shall be coated with non-staining mineral oil.

3.16 *Defective Work.* Any defective work disclosed after the forms have been removed shall be immediately removed and replaced. If any dimensions are deficient or if the surface of the concrete is bulged, uneven, or shows honey comb, which in the opinion of the Engineer cannot be repaired satisfactorily, the entire section shall be removed and replaced at the expense of the Contractor.

3.17 *Surface Finish.* Immediately after the forms are removed, any concrete that is unsatisfactory in appearance or density shall be replaced or repaired in a manner satisfactory to the Engineer and any small cavities or openings in the surface shall be neatly pointed with cement mortar of the same proportions as used in the original mixture. All holes caused by the removal of tie rods shall be completely filled with mortar of the same proportions as used in the original mixture.

Unless otherwise specified, the surface finish of exposed concrete shall be a rubbed finish. If forms can be removed while the concrete is still green, the surface shall be pointed and wetted and then rubbed with a wooden float until all irregularities are removed. If the concrete has hardened before being rubbed, a carborundum stone shall be used to finish the surface. When approved the finishing can be done with a rubbing machine.

Concrete for contact light pads shall have a steel trowel finish.

3.18 *Curing and Protection.* All concrete and cement work shall be properly cured and protected by the Contractor. The work shall be protected from the elements, flowing water, and from defacement of any nature during the building operations.

The concrete or cement work shall be protected and cured as soon as it hardens sufficiently by spraying with curing compound, by covering with burlap, cotton or jute felt mats, non-staining sawdust, paper blankets or similar approved material. The water absorptive covering shall be thoroughly saturated when placed and kept saturated for a period of at least three days. All curing mats or blankets shall be sufficiently weighted or tied down to keep the concrete surface covered and prevent the surface from being exposed to currents of air. Where wooden forms are used they shall be kept wet at all times until removed to prevent the opening of joints and drying out of the concrete.

3.19 *Removal of Forms.* The forms on vertical faces, which will be exposed to view, shall be removed as soon as the concrete has hardened sufficiently that it will not be injured, in order to facilitate surface finishing. Forms supporting slabs such as manhole tops, etc. shall not be removed within seven days of placing concrete.

During the setting of the concrete and before the removal of forms no loading shall be placed upon the concrete.

3.20 *Drains or Ducts.* Drainage pipes, conduits and ducts that are to be encased in concrete shall be installed by the Contractor before the concrete is placed. The pipe shall be held rigidly so that it will not be displaced or moved during the placing of the concrete.

3.21 *Cold Weather Protection.* When concrete is placed at temperatures below 40° F. the Contractor shall provide satisfactory methods and means to protect the mix from injury by freezing. The aggregates, or water or both shall be heated in order to place the concrete at temperatures between 50° F. and 100° F. Placing of concrete may be started in the morning if the Contractor desires but shall be discontinued at 3 P.M. of the same day if freezing weather threatens. The concrete or aggregates shall be protected during transit, mixing, and before and after placing as directed by the Engineer to retain all heat possible in the concrete mix. After the concrete has been placed the Contractor shall provide sufficient protection such as cover, canvas, framework, heating apparatus, etc., to enclose and protect the structure and maintain the temperature of the mix at not less than 50 degrees Fahrenheit until at least sixty (60) percent of the designed strength has been attained. Salt or chemical admixtures shall not be added to the concrete.

3.22 *Filling Joints.* All joints which require filling shall be thoroughly cleaned and any excess mortar or concrete cut out with proper tools. Joint filling shall not be started until after final curing and shall be done only when the concrete is completely dry. The cleaning and filling shall be carefully done with proper equipment and in a manner to obtain a neat looking joint free from excess and unsightly filler.

METHOD OF MEASUREMENT

4.1 The yardage to be paid for shall be the number of cubic yards of concrete complete in place and accepted. In computing the yardage of concrete for payment, the dimensions used shall be those shown on the plans or ordered by the

Engineer. No measurements or other allowances will be made for forms, false work, cofferdams, pumping, bracing, expansion joints, or finishing of the concrete. No deductions in yardage will be made for the volumes of reinforcing steel or embedded items less than 1 square foot in area.

4.2 The poundage of reinforcing steel to be paid for shall be the calculated theoretical number of pounds placed as shown on the plans, complete in place and accepted. The unit weight used for deformed bars shall be the weight of square or round bars, as the case may be, given in Table 3.

BASIS OF PAYMENT

5.1 The yardage and poundage determined as provided in 4.1 and 4.2 above shall be paid for at the contract unit price per cubic yard for concrete and per pound for reinforcing steel as called for in the bid schedules, which prices and payment shall constitute full compensation for the concrete; for the reinforcing steel; for furnishing all materials; for placing and finishing; for furnishing and installing all joints, joint fillers, drains, ducts, etc.; for forms and false work; for curing and protection; and for all labor, equipment, tools, and incidentals necessary to complete the item.

APPENDIX 6

TERMS IDENTIFYING SOILS IN THE PROFILE[1]

The following terms[2] are among those used in describing the various layers of the soil profile. They definitely identify the field characteristics of the soil material as found in its natural state. In the compilation of these terms the report of the committee on terminology of the American Soil Survey Association was largely used.

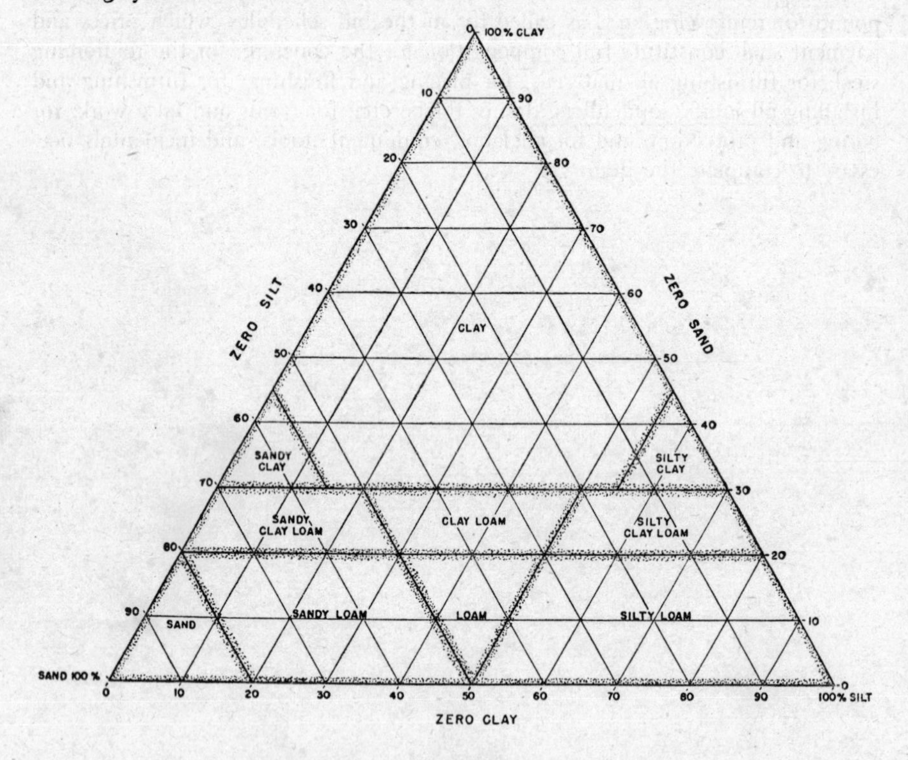

Chart for textural classification of subgrade soils.

TEXTURE

Texture is a term indicating the size of the individual soil grains or particles and the proportions of material of each size present in any given case.

[1] From U.S. Dept. of Agriculture, *Public Roads,* Vol. 12, pp. 188–190.

[2] The terms describing structure, consistency, compactness, cementation, and chemical composition have not yet been standardized, nor have they been adopted by the division of soil survey, Bureau of Chemistry and Soils. They may be considered tentative and approximate. More accurate definitions are not yet available.

As the soil is usually made up of particles of widely varying size, the textural terms express the average effect or the combined effect of all these grain sizes. They may indicate the predominance (in quantity or in textural effect) of a certain group of grains.

Texture is determined by mechanical analysis, a laboratory process of separating the soil into groups of grain sizes. The system of mechanical analysis used by the Bureau of Chemistry and Soils separates the soil material into seven grain sizes or "separates" having the following sizes and names:

2 to 1 millimeter, fine gravel.
1 to 0.5 millimeter, coarse sand.
0.5 to 0.25 millimeter, sand.
0.25 to 0.10 millimeter, fine sand.
0.10 to 0.05 millimeter, very fine sand.
0.05 to 0.005 millimeter, silt.
Below 0.005 millimeter, clay.

In the following paragraphs are given the proportions of certain of the grain sizes found in the major soil textures:

Sands contain less than 20 per cent of silt and clay. (Include coarse, fine, and very fine sands.)

Sandy loams contain from 20 per cent to 50 per cent of silt and clay but do not have over 15 per cent of clay. (Include coarse, fine, and very fine sandy loams.)

Loams have more than 50 per cent of silt and clay combined but have less than 50 per cent of silt and less than 20 per cent of clay.

Silt loams have more than 50 per cent of silt and less than 20 per cent of clay.

Clay loams have more than 50 per cent of silt and clay combined but less than 50 per cent of silt and between 20 per cent and 30 per cent of clay. (Include sandy clay loams, clay loams, and silty clay loams.)

Clays have more than 50 per cent of silt and clay combined and more than 30 per cent of clay. (Include sandy clays and silty clays.)

In the field texture is determined by the feel of the soil mass when rubbed between the fingers. The following statements give the obvious physical characteristics of the basic textural groups:

Sand.—Sand is loose and granular. The individual grains can readily be seen or felt. Squeezed in the hand when dry it will fall apart when the pressure is released. Squeezed when moist, it will form a cast, but will crumble when touched.

Sandy loam.—A sandy loam is a soil containing much sand but having enough silt and clay to make it somewhat coherent. The individual sand grains can readily be seen and felt. Squeezed when dry, it will form a cast which will readily fall apart, but if squeezed when moist a cast can be formed that will bear careful handling without breaking.

Sands and sandy loams are classed as coarse, medium, fine, or very fine, depending on the proportion of the different sized particles that are present.

Loam.—A loam is a soil having a relatively even mixture of the different grades of sand and of silt and clay. It is mellow with a somewhat gritty feel, yet fairly smooth and slightly plastic. Squeezed when dry, it will form a cast that will bear careful handling, while the cast formed by squeezing the moist soil can be handled freely without breaking.

Silt loam.—A silt loam is a soil having a moderate amount of the fine grades of sand and only a small amount of clay, over half of the particles being of the size called "silt." When dry it may appear quite cloddy, but the lumps can be readily broken, and when pulverized it feels soft and floury. When wet the soil readily runs together and puddles. Either dry or moist it will form casts that can be freely handled without breaking. If squeezed between thumb and finger it will not "ribbon" but will give a broken appearance.

Clay loam.—A clay loam is a fine-textured soil which breaks into clods or lumps that are hard when dry. When the moist soil is pinched between the thumb and finger it will form a thin ribbon which will break readily, barely sustaining its own weight. The moist soil is plastic and will form a cast that will bear much handling. When kneaded in the hand it does not crumble readily but tends to work into a heavy compact mass.

Clay.—A clay is a fine-textured soil that forms very hard lumps or clods when dry. When the moist soil is pinched out between the thumb and fingers it will form a long, flexible ribbon.

Gravelly or stony soils.—All of the above classes of soils, if mixed with a considerable amount of gravel or stone, may be classed as gravelly sandy loams, gravelly clays, etc., as stony sandy loams, stony loams, etc., or as sandy clay loams, sandy clays, etc.

Floury.—Fine-textured soil consisting predominantly of silt (or flocculated clay with aggregates of silt size) which when dry is incoherent, smooth, and dust-like.

Gritty.—Containing a sufficient amount of angular grains of coarse sand or fine gravel, so that these dominate the "feel." Usually applied to medium-textured soils (loams) where the actual quantity of these coarse grains is rather small.

Heavy (textured).—Applied to soils of fine texture in which clay predominates, with dense structure and firm to compact consistency. The term is also applied to soils containing a somewhat higher proportion of the finer separates than is typical of that textural class (as a "heavy sandy loam").

Light (textured).—Applied to soils of coarse to medium texture with very low silt and clay content, incoherent, single-grained structure, and loose consistency. The term is also applied to soils containing somewhat higher proportions of the coarser separates than is typical of that textural class (as a "light loam").

Sharp.—Containing angular particles in sufficient amount to dominate the "feel." Abrasive.

Smooth.—Containing well-rounded coarser particles and a predominance of the finer separates. Not abrasive.

COLOR

In order to recognize the same soil in some other locality, the color should be clearly stated. This statement should give the range of color included, for classification purposes. By range of color is meant such terms as black or dark brown, brown to reddish brown, etc. The color may indicate the drainage conditions under which the soil was formed and the chemical composition of the soil.

In using such terms as grayish brown, brownish gray, etc., the adjective is recognized as a modifying term. The grayish brown soil is a brown soil with a grayish cast sufficiently noticeable to require recognition; the brownish gray soil is a gray soil with a brown cast.

Other color terms are as follows:

Mottled.—The presence of spots, streaks, or splotches of one or more colors in a soil mass of another predominant color. In mottled soils the colors are not mixed and blended, but each is more or less distinct in the general ground color. In color descriptions the ground color and the color of the included spots should be designated. Mottling is usually but not necessarily associated with poor drainage. The use of the term should not be confined to poorly drained soils but should be applied wherever the term fits.

Marbled.—The presence of two or more distinct colors in approximately equal amounts not blended but more or less mixed in occurrence in the soil mass. In a marbled soil there is no general or predominant color, as in the case of a mottled soil.

Spotted, speckled, streaked, variegated.—Such terms can be used when their generally accepted meaning describes the color distributions that occur in the soils.

STRUCTURE

The term "soil structure" expresses the arrangement of the individual grains and aggregates that make up the soil mass. The structure may refer to the natural arrangement of the soil when in place and undisturbed (as structural profile) or to the soil at any degree of disturbance. The terms used indicate the character of the arrangement, the general shape and the size of the aggregates, and in some cases may indicate the consistency of those aggregates.

Adobe structure.—This term describes a soil which on drying cracks and breaks into irregular but roughly cubical blocks. The cracks are usually wide and deep and the blocks are from 20 to 50 or more centimeters across. (Adobe soils are usually heavy-textured and high in content of colloidal clay.)

Amorphous structure.—A soil of fine texture having a massive or uniform arrangement of particles throughout the horizon. Structureless. Found only in soils of finest texture, where individual grains can not be recognized.

Clod (or cloddy) structure.—Aggregates of irregular, angular shape, usually 4 centimeters or more in diameter and of a hard consistency.

Fine cloddy structure.—When most of the clods are close to the minimum size.

Coarse cloddy structure.—When most of the clods are 10 centimeters or more in diameter.

Columnar structure.—A natural arrangement of the soil mass in more or less regular columns separated by vertical cleavage lines, and usually broken by horizontal cracks into sections with longer vertical than horizontal axes, the tops of the columns being rounded.

Prismatic columnar structure.—Term used when the sections are very regular in size, straight-sided, with the vertical axes much longer than the horizontal axes and the tops of the columns flat.

Crumb structure.—Porous aggregates of irregular shape, rarely over 2 centimeters in diameter and of a medium to soft consistency.

Fine crumb structure.—Crumbs 5 millimeters or less in diameter.

Coarse crumb structure.—Crumbs 2 centimeters or more in diameter.

Crust (or crusted) structure.—This term is used where the upper or surface horizon coheres into plate or crust distinct from the horizon immediately below it.

Crust-mulch structure.—An arrangement where a surface crust is underlain by a horizon of loose, incoherent particles of mealy, crumb, or granular structure.

Fluffy structure.—A surface condition where the aggregates are loose, of light weight and fine texture, with no cohesion or evidence of arrangement; floury.

Dense structure.—Having a minimum of pore space and an absence of any large pores or cracks. Approaching amorphous.

Granular structure.—Aggregates varying in size to 2 centimeters in diameter, of medium consistency, and more or less subangular or rounded in shape.

Fine granular structure.—Aggregates under 5 millimeters diameter.

Coarse granular structure.—Aggregates close to maximum size.

Honeycomb structure.—A natural arrangement of the soil mass in more or less regular five or six sided sections separated by narrow or hairline cracks. Usually found as a surface structure or arrangement.

Hardpan.—An horizon of accumulation that has been thoroughly cemented to an indurated, rock-like layer that will not soften when wet. The term hardpan is not properly applied to hard clay layers that are not cemented, nor to those layers that may seem indurated when dry but which soften and lose their rock-like character when soaked in water. The true hardpan is cemented by materials that are not readily soluble, and is a hard layer that definitely and permanently (in nature) limits downward movement of roots and water.

Clay pan.—An horizon of accumulation or a stratum of stiff, compact, and relatively impervious clay. The clay pan is not cemented, and if immersed in water can be worked to a soft mass. Its presence may interfere with water movement or root development the same as a true hardpan. It is more difficult to overcome, for, whereas a hardpan can be shattered by explosives, the clay pan, after breaking by any means, will run together and re-form as soon as thoroughly wetted. The distinction between hardpan and clay pan is an important one in the soil classification.

Laminated structure.—An arrangement of the soil mass in very thin plates or layers, less than 1 millimeter in thickness, lying horizontal or parallel to the soil surface. Usually medium to soft consistency.

Massive structure.—A soil mass showing no evidence of any distinct arrangement of the soil particles. Structureless. May be found in soils of any structure.

Mealy structure.—A crumb-like structure in which the aggregates are of soft to very soft consistency and usually less than 5 millimeters in diameter.

Nut structure.—Compact aggregates, more or less rounded in shape, of hard to medium consistency, and from one-half to 4 centimeters in diameter.

Fine nut structure.—Aggregates below 1 centimeter in diameter.

Coarse nut structure.—Aggregates over 3 centimeters in diameter.

Plate (or platy) structure.—An arrangement of the soil mass in plates or layers 1 to 5 millimeters or more in thickness, lying horizontal or parallel to the soil surface. Usually medium to hard consistency.

Single-grained structure.—An incoherent condition of the soil mass with no arrangement of the individual particles into aggregates. Structureless. Usually found in soils of coarse texture.

Structureless.—Without any discernible structure or arrangement of the soil particles into aggregates. This condition is better expressed by the terms single-grained, massive, amorphous, etc.

Vesicular structure.—A soil horizon or soil aggregate containing many small rounded cavities smooth on the inside as though formed by gas bubbles.

CONSISTENCY

"Soil consistency" is a term expressing the degree of cohesion of the soil particles and the resistance offered to forces tending to deform or rupture the aggregates. Consistency and structure are closely related and frequently interdependent. The terms expressing consistency and structure are distinct, however, and need not be confused or used with double meaning. A study of published reports shows a general use of terms expressing both the consistency and the structure in nearly all soil descriptions.

Brittle.—A soil which when dry will break with a sharp, clean fracture. If struck a sharp blow, it will shatter into cleanly broken hard fragments.

Mellow.—Soil particles or aggregates are weakly adhered in a rather porous mass, readily yielding to forces causing rupture. A consistency softer than friable. Without tendency to pack.

Plastic.—Readily deformed without rupture. Pliable but cohesive. Can be readily molded. Puttylike. This term applies to those soils in which at certain stages of moisture the grains will readily slip over each other without the mass cracking or breaking apart.

Soft.—Yielding readily to any force causing rupture or deformation. Aggregates readily crushed between fingers.

Sticky.—Applied to soils showing a decided tendency when wet to adhere to other materials and foreign objects.

Firm.—Resistant to forces tending to produce rupture or deformation. Moderately hard. Aggregates can be broken between fingers.

Friable.—Aggregates readily ruptured and crushed with application of moderate force. Easily pulverized or reduced to crumb or granular structure.

Hard.—Resistant to forces tending to cause rupture or deformation. Difficult or impossible to crush aggregates with fingers only.

Tenacious.—Soils showing a decided resistance to rupture. Soil mass adheres firmly.

The terms "sticky" and "tenacious" are often used as synonyms, but in soil usage the former is taken to refer to adhesion, the latter to cohesion. Both terms may be applicable to a soil at the same time.

Stiff.—Resistant to rupture or deformation. A soil stratum or horizon that is firm and tenacious, and tending toward imperviousness. Usually applied to condition of the soil in place and when moderately wet.

Tight.—A stratum or horizon that is compact, impervious and tenacious, and usually plastic.

Tough.—Resistant to rupture. Tenacious. A stratum or horizon that can be readily bored into with the auger but which requires much force in breaking loose and pulling out the core of soil.

COMPACTNESS

Compactness is the degree of resistance offered by a soil to the penetration of a pointed instrument.

Impervious.—Highly resistant to penetration by water and usually resistant to penetration by air and plant roots. Impenetrable. In field practice the term is applied to strata or horizons that are very slowly penetrated by water and that retard or restrict root penetration.

Indurated.—(See under cementation).

Loose.—Soil particles or small aggregates are independent of each other or cohere very weakly with a maximum of pore space and a minimum resistance to forces tending to cause rupture.

Cheesy.—Having a more or less elastic character, deforming considerably without rupture, yet broken without difficulty or the application of much force. (Characteristic of certain highly colloidal soils when thoroughly wet.)

Compact.—The soil packed together in a dense, firm mass, but without any cementation. Noticeably resistant to forces tending to cause rupture or deformation. Coherent. Hard.

Relative degree of compactness may be expressed by terms as slightly compact, very compact, etc.

CEMENTATION

Cementation.—A condition occurring when the soil grains or aggregates are caused to adhere firmly and are bound together by some material that acts as a cementing agent (as colloidal clay, iron or aluminum hydrates, lime carbonate, etc.).

The degree of cementation or the persistence of the cementation when the soil is wetted should be stated. Some terms indicate the permanence, as "indurated," "hardpan," etc.

Firmly cemented.—Cementing material of considerable strength requiring considerable force to rupture the mass. Usually breaks, with clean though irregular fractures, into hard fragments.

Indurated.—Cemented into a very hard mass which will not soften or lose its firmness when wet, and which requires much force to cause breakage. Rock-like.

Weakly cemented.—Term applied when cementing material is not strong, and the aggregates can be readily broken into fragments with a more or less clean fracture.

Softly cemented.—Term applied when cementing material is not strong nor evenly diffused throughout the mass. Aggregates are readily crushed, but do not break with a clean fracture.

CHEMICAL COMPOSITION

Peat soil.—Composed predominantly of organic material, highly fibrous, with easily recognized plant remains.

Muck soil.—Composed of thoroughly decomposed black organic material, with a considerable amount of mineral soil material, finely divided and with a few fibrous remains.

Leaf mold.—The accumulation on the soil surface of more or less decomposed organic remains, usually the leaves of trees and remains of herbaceous plants. The A horizon.

Alkaline soil.—A soil containing an excessive amount of the alkaline (in true chemical sense) salts.

Saline soil.—A soil containing excessive amounts of the neutral or non-alkaline salts.

Calcareous soil.—A soil containing sufficient calcium carbonate to effervesce when tested with weak (N/10) hydrochloric acid. Depending on the amounts present, these soils may be designated as slightly calcareous, strongly calcareous, etc.

Acid soil.—A soil which is deficient in available bases, particularly calcium, and which gives an acid reaction when tested by standard methods. Field tests are made by the use of litmus, of Soiltex, and of other indicators. There is no full agreement on the most satisfactory test for acidity or as to the actual character of an acid soil. The intensity or degree of acidity may be expressed by qualifying words, "strongly," "moderately," etc.

A P P E N D I X 7

DEPARTMENT OF COMMERCE
Civil Aeronautics Administration
Washington
February 20, 1944

CONSTRUCTION OF CLASS I, CLASS II, AND CLASS III SUB-BASES FOR AIRPORT AND INTERMEDIATE FIELD RUNWAYS, TAXIWAYS, AND APRONS

Specification C.A.A.-689

DESCRIPTION

1.1 This item shall consist of the construction and maintenance of a Class I, Class II, or Class III sub-base, or a combination thereof, on the pavement subgrade. The subgrade shall have been prepared under another specification and the sub-base shall be constructed and maintained thereon in accordance with these specifications and in conformity with the lines, grades, and cross-sections shown on the plans.

MATERIALS

2.1 Class I, Class II, and Class III sub-base shall consist of granular material and shall meet the following minimum requirements:

		Class I	Class II	Class III	A.A.S.H.O. Test Designation
Maximum Sieve Size		2″	2″	2″	T27–42
Liquid Limit	Not greater than	25	35	35	T89–42
Plasticity Index	Not greater than	6	8	10	T91–42
% Passing No. 40 Sieve		10–80			T27–42
% Passing No. 80 Sieve		5–55	5–65	5–75	T27–42
% Passing No. 200 Sieve		3–25	3–35	3–50	T11–42
Volumetric Change at Field Moisture Equivalent	Not greater than	6	8	10	T92–42, T93–42
Ratio of Material passing No. 200 Sieve to Material passing No. 40 Sieve	Not greater than	50%	60%	60%	

SOURCE OF MATERIALS

3.1 (a) The materials for sub-base may be obtained either from the airport site or by importation from outside sources as called for in the proposal. If materials are to be obtained from the site, provisions shall be made for stripping and storing, and subsequent placement; or for excavating, hauling, and placing direct from the excavation areas as directed by the Engineer or as called for in the proposal. Instead of using material from the site, the contractor may furnish, at his option, material from an outside source provided the material meets the minimum requirements for the class sub-base called for in the schedule.

(b) When materials are imported to the site for the sub-base, the contractor shall make all arrangements for a satisfactory material without cost to the Government, other than the contract unit price for "Furnishing and Placing Sub-base."

(c) The Government will accept no responsibility for cost or loss of anticipated profits due to the rejection of materials from sources the contractor proposed to use. It is intended that the contractor will have had tests performed to ascertain the quality of the materials he proposes to use before placing his bid. Borings and test data of samples as given on the drawings are furnished for the contractor's information. However, the Government will assume no responsibility if conditions other than those indicated are actually found to exist.

(d) Blending of materials from different sources will be permitted if the blend passes the specification and if equipment is used which will provide satisfactory mixing and an adequate rate of production.

CONSTRUCTION METHODS

4.1 (a) *Operations in Pits*: The materials suitable for the class of sub-base called for shall first be stripped of overburden to the depth directed by the Engineer. Unsuitable material containing organic matter, topsoil, roots, debris, and other deleterious materials shall be removed from the sub-base material and disposed of as directed by the Engineer. The excavation of sub-base shall be carried on in such manner as to provide a uniform blend of the materials encountered.

(b) *Blending*: When the contractor elects to blend materials from two or more sources for the purpose of providing a sub-base material meeting these specifications the mixing shall be done by stationary plant, travel plant or road-mix methods, provided that a uniform mix is produced. A sufficient quantity of material shall be processed to permit normal progress of the paving operations.

4.2 *Placing of Materials*: The placing of sub-base materials shall be done in such manner that will result in the cross section, profile and grade as shown on the plans. The material shall be placed on a subgrade that has already been compacted and shaped to the section shown and shall be placed and constructed to the depth shown on the plans.

No material shall be placed on a wavy, muddy, soft or yielding subgrade. Grade and cross-section control shall be by means of grade stakes or steel pins placed at intervals and distances necessary to insure a true section and grade. Materials shall be placed in layers 3″–6″ in depth, loose measurement, as instructed by the Engineer, and successive lifts shall be placed to obtain the compacted depth shown on the plans.

4.3 *Compacting and Shaping*: Immediately after spreading, the sub-base material shall be compacted to the full width by rolling with a sheepsfoot roller, smooth wheel roller, rubber tired roller, or other equipment to at least 95% of maximum density as determined by the A.A.S.H.O. Method T99–38 modified as follows:

The weight of the tamper shall be 10 lbs. instead of 5½ lbs.

The tamper shall be dropped from a height of 18″ above the sample instead of 12″.

The sample shall be compacted in five equal layers (approximately 1″ in thickness) instead of three equal layers.

Rolling shall continue until the material has reached the required density. Watering to facilitate compaction shall be required. Any irregularities or depressions that develop under rolling shall be corrected by loosening the material and adding or removing materials until the surface is smooth and uniform. Blading and rolling shall be done alternately as required to maintain a smooth, even, uniformly compacted sub-base.

Successive lifts of the sub-base materials shall be constructed in a similar manner. The surface of Class II sub-base, when Class I sub-base is to be placed thereon, shall be finished to the grade shown with a deviation not in excess of ½″. Deviation between high and low spots shall not be in excess of 1″ when tested with a 10′ straightedge.

The surface of the sub-base on which the base course or rigid pavement is to be placed shall be finished within ½″ of the grade shown and shall be of such smoothness that when tested with a 10′ straightedge it shall show no deviation in excess of ⅜″. Any deviation in excess of either of the above requirements shall be corrected by loosening, adding or removing materials, reshaping and recompacting by watering and rolling.

4.4 *Maintenance*: (a) The contractor for placing sub-base, shall be responsible for maintenance of the subgrade from the time the runway or taxiway, etc. is released for construction of sub-base. No direct payment shall be made for such maintenance.

(b) Following the final shaping of the material, the sub-base shall be maintained by the use of a standard road machine or motor grader and rollers if required to retain specified density and surface smoothness. The sub-base and subgrade shall be properly drained at all times. Any deficiencies in grade, smoothness, density, etc. of the sub-base which may develop prior to the construction of the base course shall be corrected.

METHOD OF MEASUREMENT

5.1 The method of measurement for sub-base shall be the number of square yards included within the neat lines as shown on the plans for the class or classes of sub-base called for.

BASIS OF PAYMENT

The yardage measured as provided above shall be paid for at the contract unit price per square yard for the class, or classes, of sub-base called for, which price and payment shall constitute full compensation for furnishing material and placing the same; for mixing, blading, watering, compacting and maintaining; for reconditioning of subgrade, shoulders, and gutters; for clean-up of pits; for clearing, cleaning, and leveling stockpile sites; and for all labor, equipment, tools, and incidentals necessary to complete the item.

APPENDIX 8

DEPARTMENT OF COMMERCE
Civil Aeronautics Administration
Airport Division
Washington, D.C.
October 1, 1943

BITUMINOUS SURFACE COURSE (CENTRAL PLANT HOT MIX) FOR AIRPORT PARKING APRONS AND TURNAROUND AREAS

C.A.A. Specification No. P-409

INTRODUCTION

This specification provides a highly stable mixture for surfacing parking areas and ends of runways and taxiways to withstand parking and locked wheel turns. The composition of the mix shall consist entirely of crushed aggregates which will produce a surfacing resistant to severe stresses. Instructions on the use of this specification were issued in field memorandum F 541 (Revised), dated October 6, 1943 to which was attached Drawing No. 518.

It is the responsibility of the engineer to set up the job mix formula. After the contractor has submitted samples of the materials intended for the project, the samples shall be tested to determine the proper combinations of the aggregates and the bituminous material to produce a satisfactory mixture. All available laboratory test methods should be used to obtain the data necessary for study and guidance. A uniform gradation should be selected, that is, one that will produce a relatively smooth curve. A gradation producing a smooth curve will usually have the least voids and the highest stability, while an irregular curve will contain a skip gradation with large voids and low stability. If Hubbard-Field or other stability equipment is not available, a Proctor mould should be used to obtain results.

The field laboratory established for each job should have sufficient equipment and personnel for performing frequent tests on the gradation and quality of aggregates, the density, stability and bitumen content of samples cut from the pavement and other control tests. It is emphasized that only by the means of check testing the materials and the pavement mixture can a satisfactory job be accomplished. This checking will suggest, in some cases, the necessity for slight modifications of the formula and the need of control of other variables that are encountered during the course of the work.

If the aggregate is found to be hydrophilic as determined by the test given in the specification, the addition of 0.5 to 1.5 per cent of hydrated lime or Portland cement to the aggregate prior to mixing with the bituminous material may be sufficient to change the inherent characteristics to a hydrophobic material. If the material is of such hydrophilic characteristics that the lime or cement alone will not accomplish the desired results the addition of a proven and approved admixture to the bituminous material will be necessary.

DESCRIPTION

1.1 This item shall consist of a wearing course composed of mineral aggregate and bituminous material, mixed in a central mixing plant and placed on the prepared base course in accordance with these specifications and in conformity with the dimensions and typical cross sections shown on the plans and with lines and grades established by the engineer.

1.2 *Determination of Percentage of Bituminous Material.* The percentage of bituminous material, by weight, to be added to the aggregate shall be fixed by the engineer on the basis of preliminary laboratory tests and field sieve analysis on the aggregate furnished, and shall be within the range as shown in the table.

1.3 *Job Mix Formula.* No work shall be started on the project nor any mixture accepted therefor until the contractor has submitted samples of the materials intended for use and the engineer has established a satisfactory job mix formula based upon tests of the materials furnished. The formula shall be submitted in writing by the engineer to the contractor, indicating the definite percentage for each sieve fraction of aggregate and for bituminous cement; also the intended temperature of completed mixture at the time it is discharged from the mixer. The material furnished shall conform to the approved job mix formula within the tolerances specified herein.

Job Mix Tolerances

Aggregate passing sieves No. 4 and larger	±5%
Aggregate passing No. 10, No. 40, and No. 80 sieve	±4%
Aggregate passing No. 200 sieve	±2%
Asphaltic cement	±0.5%
Temperature of mixing and placing	±25° F.

MATERIALS

2.1 *Aggregate.* The aggregate shall consist of one hundred percent crushed stone, or crushed slag, and screenings of these materials. The crushed aggregate shall consist of particles with all faces crushed, including the combined material from the finest particles to the maximum sizes. Sand will not be permitted in this mixture as fine aggregate.

The aggregate shall be tough, durable and sound. The coarse aggregate when tested in accordance with the Los Angeles Rattler Test, after five hundred revolutions shall have a percent of wear of not more than fifty (50) according to the A.A.S.H.O., Method T 96–42.

Slag shall be air cooled, blast furnace slag and shall have a compact weight of not less than seventy (70) pounds per cubic foot. The aggregate shall consist of angular fragments reasonably uniform in density and quality and reasonably free from thin, elongated or soft pieces,. dirt or other objectionable matter.

The portion of the material retained on a No. 4 sieve shall be known as coarse aggregate; that portion passing a No. 4 sieve shall be known as fine aggregate, and the material passing the No. 200 sieve shall be known as filler. The composite material shall meet the requirements for one of the gradings given in Table 2, using A.A.S.H.O. Methods T-11 and T 27–42.

That portion of the fine aggregate, including any blended filler, passing a No. 40 sieve shall have a plasticity index of not more than 4 as determined by A.A.S.H.O. Method T 91–42, and a liquid limit of not more than 25 as determined by A.A.S.H.O. Method T 89–42.

The composite aggregate shall be free from vegetable matter, lumps or balls of clay, adherent films of clay, or other matter that will prevent thorough coating with bituminous material. The bituminized aggregate shall have a swell of not more than 1.5 percent as determined by A.A.S.H.O. Method T 101–42.

Prior to final acceptance of the proposed aggregate to be used, the inherent characteristics of said aggregate relative to stripping shall be determined. This shall be done by preparing a test sample of the paving mixture in conformity with the specifications contained herewith. After the mixture has been made it shall be spread out in a loose thin layer and allowed to air season for 24 hours before testing. A suitable size sample (approximately one-half contents of container) shall be tested by placing it in a glass jar fitted with a tight screw cap and completely covering with distilled water. The jar and contents shall be allowed to stand for a period of 24 hours. Then the sample shall be vigorously shaken for a period of 15 minutes. The sample of mixture shall be examined for stripping. If stripping or sloughing off of the bituminous coating occurs it will be necessary to treat said aggregate by a method which has proven successful in changing the material from a hydrophilic to a hydrophobic state.

2.2 *Filler.* If filler in addition to that naturally present in the aggregate is necessary, it shall consist of stone dust, loess, Portland cement or other standard approved types. The material for such purpose shall be obtained from sources approved by the engineer.

2.3 *Bituminous Material.* The bituminous material to be mixed with the mineral aggregate at the central plant shall conform to the grade, requirements and specifications as follows:

TABLE 1

Asphalt Cement

The asphalt cement shall be homogeneous, free from water, and shall not foam when heated to a temperature of 347° F.

Test Requirements	Petroleum Asphalts	Native Asphalts
Penetration at 77° F., 100 g, 5 sec.	120–150	120–150
Total Bitumen (soluble in carbon disulphide), not less than	99.5%	
Total Bitumen (soluble in carbon disulphide) (Bermudes Asphaltic cement) not less than		95.0%
Proportion of bitumen soluble in carbon tetrachloride, not less than	99.0%	99.0%
Ductility at 77° F., not less than	100 cms.	60 cms.
Flash point, ° F., not less than	347	347
Loss at 325° F., 5 hrs., not more than	1.0%	3.0%
Penetration of residue at 77° F., 100 g, 5 sec., as compared to penetration before heating, not less than	60.0%	50.0%
Temperature range ° F.	225–300	225–300
Oliensis Spot Test	Negative	

Sampling and testing of asphalt cement shall be in accordance with the following standard methods of the American Association of State Highway Officials:

(a) Sampling.. T 40–42
(b) Penetration.. T 49–42
(c) Total bitumen.. T 44–42
(d) Bitumen soluble in carbon tetrachloride.......... T 45–42
(e) Ductility.. T 51–42
(f) Flash Point.. T 48–42
(g) Loss at 325° F.. T 47–42
(h) Oliensis Spot Test.. T 102–42

Note: The Oliensis Spot Test may be used to identify products manufactured by the cracking process, which show a positive spot when present in sufficient proportions. The Test should be modified to differentiate between cracked asphalts and those asphalts from some crude sources that have never been cracked but show a positive spot.

2.4 *Hydrated Lime.* The hydrated lime shall meet the requirements of the A.S.T.M. Designation C 6–31.

GRADATION

3.1 *Composition of Mixture.* The mineral aggregate for the surface courses shall be of such size that the percentage composition by weight, as determined by laboratory sieves will conform to one of the following gradations:

TABLE 2

Surface Course

Sieve Size	Percentage Passing Sieves (Square Openings)	
	1″ Maximum	¾″ Maximum
1″	100	
¾″	82–100	100
½″	70–90	82–100
⅜″	60–82	70–90
No. 4	47–70	55–79
No. 10	35–60	40–67
No. 40	15–40	17–44
No. 80	8–26	9–29
No. 200	3–8	3–8
% Asph. Cement	4.5–7.0	5.0–7.5

In table 2 the percentages of asphalt cement are for stone aggregates. If the total aggregate is composed of slag, the percentages of bituminous material shown shall be increased by thirty (30) per cent. Where only a part of the aggregates is slag, this increase shall be made in a corresponding proportion.

The gradations in this table represent the limits which shall determine suitability of aggregate for use from the sources of supply. The final gradations decided on within the limits designated in the table shall be uniformly graded from coarse to fine, and shall not vary from the low limit on one screen to the high limit on the adjacent screens or vice versa.

The selection of any of the gradings shown in the table shall be such that the maximum size aggregate used in any course shall not be more than $\frac{2}{3}$ the thickness of the layer of the course being constructed.

The composition limits tabulated shall govern but a closer control appropriate to the job materials will be required for the specific project in accordance with a job mix formula.

The total amount of material passing the No. 200 sieve shall be determined by washing the material through the sieve with water and not less than one-half ($\frac{1}{2}$) of the material passing the No. 200 sieve by washing shall pass the No. 200 sieve by dry sieving without washing.

CONSTRUCTION METHODS

4.1 *Weather and Seasonal Limitations.* Surface course shall be constructed only when the surface is dry, when the atmospheric temperature is above 40° F., and when the weather is not foggy or rainy. The temperature requirement may be waived, but only when so directed by the engineer.

4.2 *Equipment and Organization.* (a) General. All methods employed in performing the work and all equipment, tools and other plant and machinery used for handling materials and executing any part of the work shall be subject to the approval of the engineer before the work is started and whenever found unsatisfactory shall be changed and improved as required. All equipment, tools, machinery and plant used must be maintained in a satisfactory working condition.

(b) Mixing Plant. The paving plant used by the contractor in the preparation of the bituminous concrete shall comply with the following requirements:

The drier shall be suitably designed to heat and dry the aggregate to specification requirements and to continuously agitate the aggregate during heating. The drier shall be capable of preparing aggregate to the full rated capacity of the paving plant to meet the specification requirement. A dial thermometer or other thermometric instrument shall be so placed in the bin over the mixer as to automatically register the temperature of the heated aggregate before it enters the mixer. The dial or other indicator shall be plainly visible from the mixing platform.

The plant screens shall be designed, constructed, and operated so as to screen all aggregates to appropriate fractions as established by the engineer and as necessary to meet the job mix tolerances.

The plant shall have storage bins, protected from the weather, of sufficient capacity to furnish the necessary amounts of all aggregates when operating at the maximum rated capacity of the plant. The bins shall provide two or more compartments for hot aggregates, so proportioned as to insure adequate storage of appropriate fractions of the aggregate and mineral filler. Each compartment shall be provided with an overflow pipe or other device which meets the approval of the engineer, of such size and at such locations as to prevent backing up of material into other compartments.

The plant may have either batch weighing or volumetric proportioning of mineral aggregates and bituminous cement. This equipment shall be constructed with devices that will permit easy readjustment of any working part such that it will function properly and accurately. The aggregate weighing or measuring device shall be so constructed and operated that the correct amount of each size aggregate is introduced into the mixer with an accuracy that will meet the job tolerances specified. The plant mixer shall have a capacity of at least 1200 pounds and the plant shall have a capacity of at least 40 tons per hour.

The asphalt weighing or measuring device shall be so constructed and operated that the correct amount of asphalt is introduced into the mixer with an accuracy that will meet the job tolerance specified. If weight control is used the dial scales or other weighing device shall be of an approved type.

The mixer may be either a batch drum type mixer, a twin pugmill or a continuous type twin pugmill mixer of sufficient size to maintain thorough uniform mixing at the rated plant capacity. The mixer shall be steam jacketed.

The plant shall be equipped with positive means to govern the time of mixing and to maintain it constant unless changed by order of the engineer. The time of mixing shall be considered as the interval between the time the bituminous material is spread on the aggregate and the time the same aggregate leaves the mixing unit.

Equipment for heating bituminous material shall consist of a retort or steam coils so designed that steam will not be introduced into the material. A recording thermometer shall be provided, which will record the temperature of the bituminous material at the draw off valve.

Asphalt storage and supply lines shall be insulated or steam jacketed in such a manner that there will be no appreciable drop in temperature of the asphalt between the heating unit and the mixing unit.

(c) Placing Equipment. Equipment for spreading, shaping, and finishing shall consist of an approved self-contained power machine operating in such a manner that no supplemental spreading, shaping, or finishing will be required to provide a surface which will comply with the requirements for smoothness contained herein.

(d) Rolling Equipment. Rollers shall be suitably designed for the construction of bituminous surfaces. The rolling shall be done with self-propelled tandem and three wheel type rollers weighing not less than eight (8) tons. The wheels on the rollers shall be equipped with adjustable scrapers which shall be used when necessary to clean the wheel surface. Rollers shall also be equipped with water tanks and sprinkling apparatus which shall be used to keep the wheels wet and prevent the surfacing material from sticking.

4.3 *Preparation of Mineral Aggregate.* The aggregate for the mixture shall be dried and heated at the paving plant before entering the mixer. When introduced into the mixer the combined aggregate shall not contain more than 1% moisture. Water in the aggregate shall be removed by heating to the extent that no subsequent foaming shall occur in the mixture prior to the placing of the material. The aggregate shall be heated to the temperature as designated by the Job Formula within the job tolerances specified. The maximum temperature and the rate of heating shall be such that no permanent damage occurs to the aggregates. Particular care shall be taken that aggregates high in calcium or magnesium content are not damaged by heating. The aggregates shall be screened to specified sizes and conveyed into separate bins ready for mixing with bituminous material.

Additional filler, if necessary to meet the grading requirements, shall be added to the mineral aggregate. The amount of filler shall be measured and added to the aggregate at the mixing plant by premixing it thoroughly with the other aggregates. Spreading filler over the tops of the aggregate pits or dumping it into the hoppers at crushing plants will not be permitted.

4.4 *Preparation of Bituminous Mixture.* Before being delivered to the runway, the aggregate shall be mixed with the bituminous material at a central mixing plant. The mixture shall be prepared at a temperature as directed by the engineer between 225° to 300° F. for asphalt mixtures.

The aggregate prepared as prescribed above, shall be accurately measured and conveyed into the mixer in the proportionate amounts of each aggregate required to meet the specified grading.

The bituminous material shall be melted in kettles or tanks designed to secure uniform heating of the entire contents. Asphalt shall not be heated over 325° F. Kettles for storage of bituminous cement shall have a total capacity sufficient for one day's run and shall be capable of heating the bituminous cement with an effective and positive control of the heat at all times to a temperature of between 175° F. and 350° F. Heating of the cement by steam coils is preferred. Under no circumstances will a direct flame from oil or other fuel be permitted to come in direct contact with the heating kettles. The circulating system shall be constructed of adequate size to give the proper and continuous circulation of cement throughout the operating periods. All lines and fittings shall be steam jacketed.

The quantity of bituminous material for each batch or calibrated amount for continuous mixing shall be determined by the engineer, and shall be measured by weight and introduced into the mixer at the specified temperature, holding to the lowest range possible for adequate mixing and spreading. All mineral aggregate shall be in the mixer before the bituminous material is added. The exact temperature to be used on the work within the specified range shall be fixed by the engineer. In no case shall aggregate be introduced into the mixture at a temperature more than 25° F. above the temperature of the bituminous material. The mixing shall continue for at least thirty seconds and for such longer period as may be necessary to coat all of the particles.

From zero to one percent of Portland cement or hydrated lime shall be added to the composition of the surface mixtures when provided for in the proposal.

4.5 *Transportation and Delivery of the Mixture.* The mixture shall be transported from the mixing plant to the point of use in pneumatic-tired vehicles having tight bodies previously cleaned of all foreign materials. When directed by the engineer, each load shall be covered with canvas or other suitable material of sufficient size and thickness to protect it from the weather conditions.

The mixture shall be placed at a temperature between 200° and 300° F. When the mixture is being placed during warm weather and the engineer has determined that satisfactory results can be obtained at lower temperatures, he may direct that the mixture be mixed and delivered at the lower temperatures.

No loads shall be sent out so late in the day as to interfere with spreading and compacting the mixture during daylight, unless artificial light satisfactory to the engineer is provided. The mixture shall be delivered at a temperature within the tolerance allowed in the approved Job Formula.

4.6 *Spreading and Laying.* (a) Preparation for placing. Immediately before placing the bituminous mixture, the existing surface shall be cleaned of loose or deleterious material by sweeping with a power sweeper supplemented by hand brooms if necessary, or as directed by the engineer.

The mixture shall be laid only upon an approved underlying course which is dry and only when weather conditions are suitable. No mixture shall be placed when the air temperature in the shade and away from artificial heat is 40° F. or under unless so directed by the engineer. The engineer may, however, permit work of this character to continue when overtaken by sudden rains, up to the amount which may be in transit from the plant at the time—provided the mixture is within the temperature limits specified.

Grade control between the edges of the runway shall be by means of grade stakes or steel pins placed in lanes parallel to the center line of the runway, and at intervals sufficiently close that string lines may be stretched between stakes or pins.

Placing shall commence at the point or points farthest from the mixing plant, and progress continuously toward the plant, unless otherwise ordered by the engineer. Hauling over material already placed will not be permitted until the material has been compacted thoroughly in the manner specified, and allowed to cool to atmospheric temperature.

(b) Machine Spreading. Upon arrival the mixture shall be dumped into an approved mechanical spreader and immediately spread to the full width required. It shall be struck off in uniform layer of such depth that when the work is completed, it will have the required thickness and will conform to the grade and surface contour required. The speed of the mechanical spreader shall be regulated to eliminate as far as possible the pulling and tearing of the bituminous material.

Placing and compaction of the bituminous mixture shall progress in sections. The bituminous mixture shall be spread, shaped, and finished with the power-machine specified. The mixture shall be placed in strips of a minimum width of 10 feet. To insure proper drainage, the spreading shall begin along the center line of the runway or taxiway on a crowned section or on the high side of the pavement with a one-way slope. The 6-inch strip adjacent to the area on which future material is to be laid shall not be rolled until such material has been placed, but shall not be left unrolled more than two (2) hours after being placed. After the first strip or width has been compacted, the second width shall be placed, finished and compacted as provided for the first width, except that rolling shall be extended to include the six inches of the first width not previously compacted. Whenever the adjacent or second width cannot be placed within two (2) hours, the 6-inch strip shall not be left unrolled. After the second strip has been placed and rolled, a 10-foot straight edge shall be used across the longitudinal joint to determine if the surface is to grade and contour.

In limited areas where, on account of irregularities or unavoidable obstacles, the use of mechanical spreading and finishing equipment is impractical, the mixture may be spread by hand.

When hand spreading is permitted, the mixture shall be dumped upon arrival on approved dump sheets outside of the area on which it is to be spread and be distributed into place immediately by means of hot shovels. It shall be spread with hot rakes to a uniform layer to the full width and of such depth that where the work is completed, it will have the required thickness and will conform to the grade and surface contour.

Contact surfaces shall be painted with a thin uniform coat of hot asphalt cement or cut-back asphalt just before the mixture is placed.

4.7 *Compaction of Mixture.* After spreading, and as directed by the engineer, the mixture shall be thoroughly and uniformly compressed by a power driven, three-wheel roller and tandem roller or rollers, each weighing eight (8) tons or more. Rolling of the mixture shall begin as soon after spreading as it will bear the roller without undue displacement or hair checking. On the first strip spread, rolling shall start in the center and continue toward either edge. On subsequent strips laid, rolling shall start on the edge adjacent to previously-laid material and continue toward the other edge.

Initial rolling shall be done longitudinally with three-wheel rollers overlapping on successive trips of the roller. Alternate trips of the roller shall be of slightly different lengths. The mixture shall be subjected to diagonal rolling crossing the lines of the first.

The speed of the roller shall at all times be slow enough to avoid displacement of the hot mixture. Any displacement occurring as a result of reversing the direction of the roller, or from any other cause, shall be corrected at once by the use of rakes, and of fresh mixture where required.

Sufficient rollers of the designated types shall be furnished to adequately handle the output of the plant. Rolling shall proceed at an average rate not to exceed 300 square yards per hour per roller. Rolling shall continue until all roller marks are eliminated, until the surface is of uniform texture and true to grade, and cross section, and until the density of at least 94% of the theoretical density is obtained. Field density tests shall be made at least twice daily. Final rolling shall be done with tandem rollers.

The theoretical density shall be computed as follows:

$$\text{Density} = \frac{100}{\dfrac{\%\ \text{mineral aggregate by weight}}{\text{Sp. gr. mineral aggregate}} + \dfrac{\%\ \text{bitumen by weight}}{\text{Sp. gr. of bitumen}}}$$

To prevent adhesion of the mixture to the roller, the wheels shall be kept properly moistened, but an excess of either water or oil will not be permitted. The rollers shall be kept in good condition and shall be operated by competent and experienced rollermen. The rollers shall be operated continuously as far as practicable and in such a manner that all parts of the pavement shall receive substantially equal compression.

At all places not accessible to the roller, the mixture shall be thoroughly compacted with hot hand tampers. Hand tampers shall weigh not less than 25 pounds and shall have a tamping face area of not more than 50 square inches. The surface of the mixture after compression shall be smooth and true to the established crown and grade.

Any mixture which becomes loose and broken, mixed with dirt, or in any way defective prior to the application of the finish coat shall be removed and replaced with fresh hot mixture, which shall be immediately compacted to conform with the surrounding area, all to be done at the expense of the contractor. Skin patching on an area that has been rolled shall not be allowed.

4.8 *Joints.* (a) General. The mixture at the joints shall comply with the surface requirements and present the same uniformity of texture, density, smoothness, etc., as other sections of the course. In the formation of all joints, provision shall be made for proper bond with the new surface for the full specified depth of the course. Joints shall be formed by cutting back on the previous day's run so as to expose the full depth of the course, and the exposed edge shall be given a light paint coat of asphalt, if necessary. The fresh mixture shall be raked against the joint, thoroughly tamped with tampers and rolled.

(b) Transverse. The placing of the course shall be as nearly continuous as possible. The roller shall pass over the unprotected end of the freshly laid mixture only when the laying of the course is to be discontinued.

(c) Longitudinal. The placing of the course shall be in the manner as specified and so that the joint is exposed for the shortest period possible. The joint shall be placed so that it will not coincide with that in the base or binder course and will break joints by at least one foot.

4.9 *Shaping Edges.* While the surface is being compacted and finished, the contractor shall trim the edges neatly to line.

4.10 *Surface Tests.* The finished surface shall not vary more than ¼ inch for the wearing course when measured with a sixteen (16) foot straightedge applied parallel with or at right angles to the center line. Tests for conformity with the specified crown and grade shall be made by the contractor immediately after initial compression and any variation shall be corrected by removing or adding materials and continuing the rolling. After the completion of final rolling, the smoothness of the course shall again be checked, and the humps or depressions exceeding the specified tolerances or that retain water on the surface shall be corrected by removing the defective work and replacing with new material or by adding additional material as directed by the engineer and at the expense of the contractor.

4.11 *Sampling Pavement.* For the determination of composition, compaction and density of the pavement the contractor shall remove suitable size samples of the completed pavement. Samples for each day or fraction thereof when mixtures are placed shall be taken by the engineer. The contractor shall replace the pavement where samples are removed, and these replacements shall be installed by the contractor free of charge. After the samples have been removed from the completed pavement, they will be tested by the engineer for density and composition. If the deficiency in composition, compaction and density exceeds the limits of toleration from that specified, satisfactory corrections shall be made.

4.12 *Bituminous and Aggregate Material Contractor's Responsibility.* Samples of the bituminous and aggregate materials that the contractor proposes to use, together with a statement as to their source and character must be submitted and approval obtained before use of such material begins. The contractor shall require the manufacturer or producer of the bituminous and aggregate materials to furnish material subject to this and all other pertinent requirements of the contract. Only those materials that have been demonstrated by service tests as satisfactory for the intended use will be acceptable.

For checking the adequacy of the equipment in use, inspecting the conditions and operation of the plant, for the verification of weights or proportions and character of materials and/or the determination and checking of temperatures being maintained in the preparation of the mixtures, the engineer or his authorized representative shall have access at any time to all parts of the paving plant.

The contractor shall furnish vendor's certified test report for each car load or equivalent of bitumen shipped to the project. The report shall be delivered to the engineer before permission is granted for use of the material.

4.13 *Freight and Weigh-Bills.* Before the final estimate is allowed, the contractor shall file with the engineer receipted bills where railroad shipments are made and certified weigh-bills when materials are received in any other manner, of the bituminous and paving materials actually used in the construction covered by the contract. The contractor shall not remove bituminous material from the tank car or storage tank until the initial outage and temperature measurements have been taken, nor shall he release the car or tank until the final outage has been taken by the engineer.

Copies of all freight bills and weigh-bills shall be furnished to the engineer during the progress of the work.

4.14 *Seal Coat.* As shown on the plans and called for in the bid schedule, a seal coat of the type called for shall be applied to the finished course as described under SEAL COAT.

METHOD OF MEASUREMENT

5.1 The tonnage of surface course to be paid for shall be the number of tons of bituminous mixture of the grading called for in the bid schedule and used in the accepted work. The bituminous treated material shall be weighed after mixing and no deduction shall be made for the weight of bituminous material in the mixture.

5.2 The quantities as measured in paragraph 5.1 for surface mixtures are applicable for aggregates having a bulk specific gravity between 2.55 and 2.75 as determined by A.A.S.H.O. Method T 84 and T 85–42. Proportionate corrections shall be made when the aggregate furnished on the job bulk specific gravities above 2.75 or below 2.55. In such cases the corrected quantity for payment shall be the product of the number of tons used multiplied by the ratio of 2.65 to the bulk specific gravity of the job aggregate.

5.3 The unit of measurement for the bituminous material shall be the gallon or the ton, whichever is called for in the bid schedule. The gallonage or tonnage to be paid for shall be the number of gallons or tons of bituminous material used as ordered in the accepted work. Gallonage shall be determined by measuring the material at a temperature of 60° F., or by converting the gallonage measured at other temperatures to gallonage at 60° F. in accordance with A.S.T.M. Designation D 206–36 for asphalt materials.

BASIS OF PAYMENT

6.1 The quantities of surfacing mixture and bituminous material determined as provided in 5.1, 5.2, and 5.3 above, shall be paid for at the respective contract unit prices per ton in the bid schedule for surface course and per gallon or per ton for bituminous material, which prices and payment shall constitute full compensation for preparing base; for furnishing, handling, mixing, manipulating, and placing all materials; for all shaping, compacting, and rolling; for finishing; for improving unsatisfactory areas; for reconditioning shoulders; for furnishing samples; for furnishing and sealing of scales; for furnishing the weigh house; and for all labor, equipment, tools and incidentals necessary to complete the item, except any prime coat or seal coat.

APPENDIX 9

U.S. DEPARTMENT OF COMMERCE
Civil Aeronautics Administration
Washington, D.C.
June 15, 1944

DESIGN DETAILS FOR AIRPORT PAVEMENTS

Drawing No. 549

STANDARD CONCRETE PAVEMENT DESIGN

LAYOUT OF LONGITUDINAL JOINTS

TYPE A

FOR NARROW WIDTH CONSTRUCTION

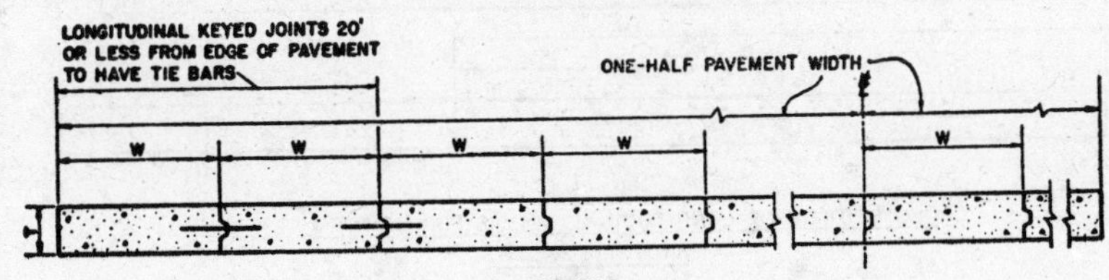

NO SCALE

CROSS SECTION OF LONGITUDINAL JOINTS FOR UNIFORM DEPTH AND NARROW WIDTHS

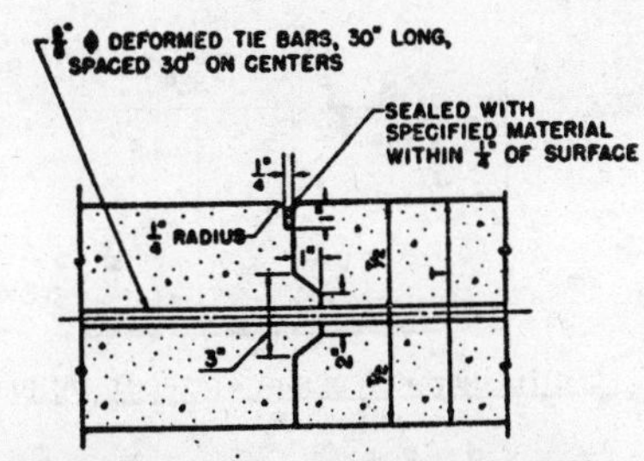

LONGITUDINAL KEYED JOINT WITH TIE BARS

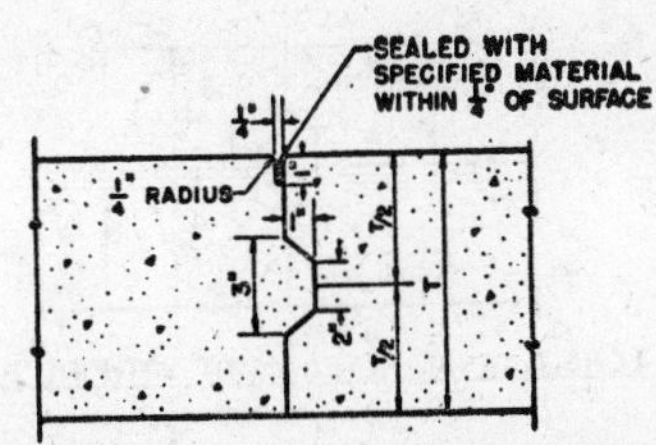

LONGITUDINAL KEYED JOINT WITHOUT TIE BARS

NOTES

1. DEFORMED TIE BARS TO BE USED AS REQUIRED.
2. T, CROSS SECTION THICKNESS, 8", 9" OR 10".
3. W, NARROW WIDTH, 10', 12½', 15', OR 16⅔'.
4. LONGITUDINAL JOINTS SHALL BE PAINTED WITH BITUMEN.
5. TIE BARS SHALL NOT BE SPACED CLOSER THAN 30 INCHES TO TRANSVERSE CONTRACTION, EXPANSION OR CONSTRUCTION JOINTS.

DEPARTMENT OF COMMERCE
CIVIL AERONAUTICS ADMINISTRATION
AIRPORTS SERVICE
ENGINEERING AND CONSTRUCTION DIVISION

DATE: 3-20-44	SHEET, 1 of EIGHT	DR. BY C.E.Z.	DR. NO. 849

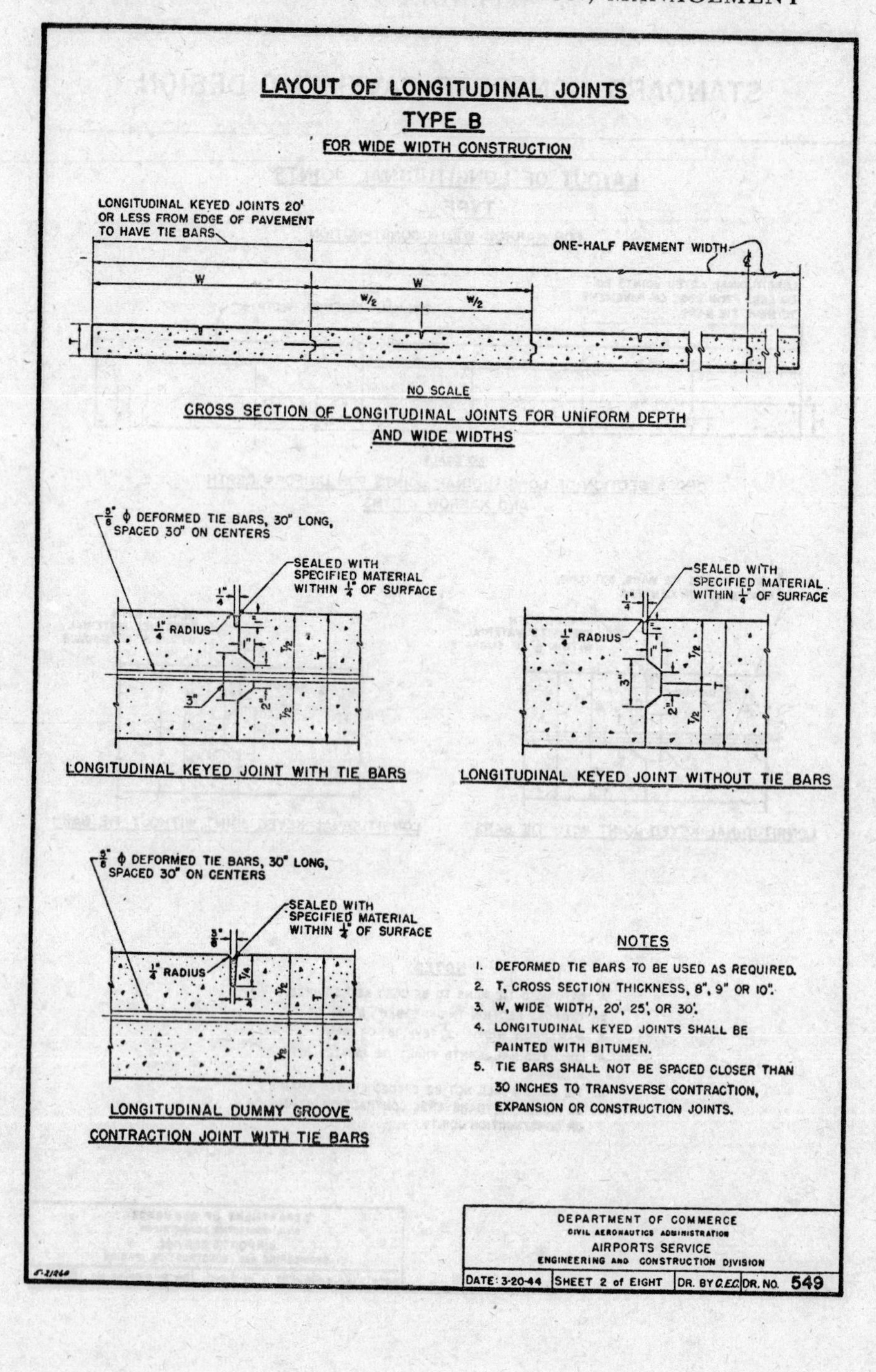
LAYOUT OF LONGITUDINAL JOINTS
TYPE B
FOR WIDE WIDTH CONSTRUCTION
LONGITUDINAL KEYED JOINTS 20' OR LESS FROM EDGE OF PAVEMENT TO HAVE TIE BARS
ONE-HALF PAVEMENT WIDTH
W
W/2
W/2
T
NO SCALE
CROSS SECTION OF LONGITUDINAL JOINTS FOR UNIFORM DEPTH AND WIDE WIDTHS
5/8" φ DEFORMED TIE BARS, 30" LONG, SPACED 30" ON CENTERS
SEALED WITH SPECIFIED MATERIAL WITHIN 1/4" OF SURFACE
1/4" RADIUS
3"
LONGITUDINAL KEYED JOINT WITH TIE BARS
LONGITUDINAL KEYED JOINT WITHOUT TIE BARS
LONGITUDINAL DUMMY GROOVE CONTRACTION JOINT WITH TIE BARS
NOTES
1. DEFORMED TIE BARS TO BE USED AS REQUIRED.
2. T, CROSS SECTION THICKNESS, 8", 9" OR 10".
3. W, WIDE WIDTH, 20', 25', OR 30'.
4. LONGITUDINAL KEYED JOINTS SHALL BE PAINTED WITH BITUMEN.
5. TIE BARS SHALL NOT BE SPACED CLOSER THAN 30 INCHES TO TRANSVERSE CONTRACTION, EXPANSION OR CONSTRUCTION JOINTS.
DEPARTMENT OF COMMERCE
CIVIL AERONAUTICS ADMINISTRATION
AIRPORTS SERVICE
ENGINEERING AND CONSTRUCTION DIVISION
DATE: 3-20-44
SHEET 2 of EIGHT
DR. BY C.E.C.
DR. NO. 549

LAYOUT OF LONGITUDINAL JOINTS TYPE C

FOR NARROW WIDTH CONSTRUCTION

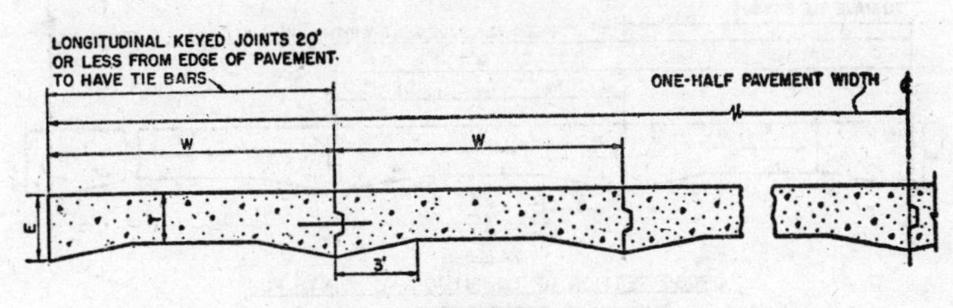

NO SCALE

CROSS SECTION OF LONGITUDINAL JOINTS FOR THICKENED EDGES AND NARROW WIDTHS

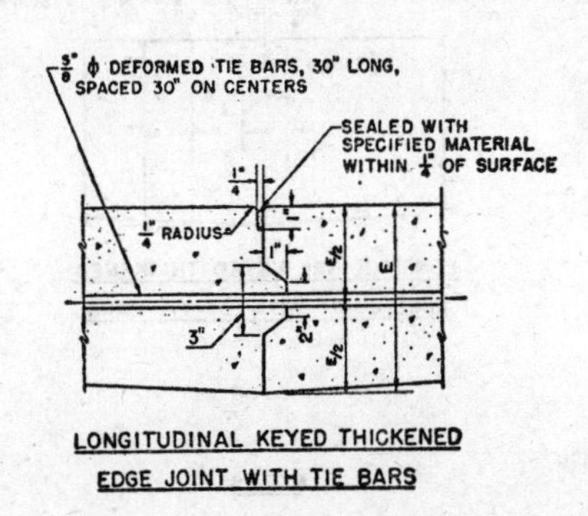

LONGITUDINAL KEYED THICKENED EDGE JOINT WITH TIE BARS

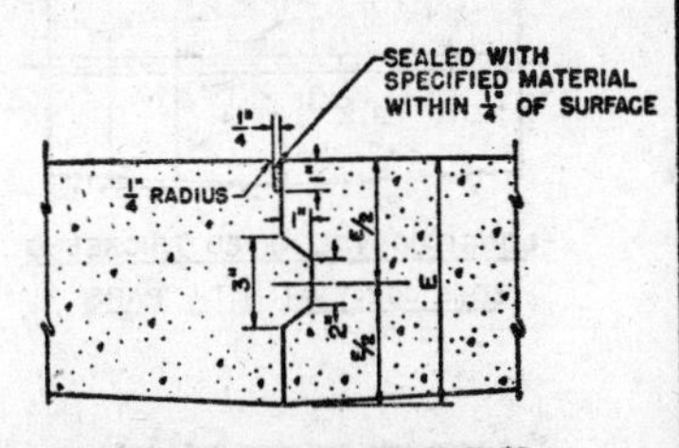

LONGITUDINAL KEYED THICKENED EDGE JOINT WITHOUT TIE BARS

NOTES

1. DEFORMED TIE BARS TO BE USED AS REQUIRED.
2. T, CROSS SECTION THICKNESS, 6"; E, THICKENED EDGE, 8".
3. T, CROSS SECTION THICKNESS, 7"; E, THICKENED EDGE, 8".
4. W, NARROW WIDTH, 10', 12½', 15', OR 16⅔'.
5. LONGITUDINAL JOINTS SHALL BE PAINTED WITH BITUMEN.
6. TIE BARS SHALL NOT BE SPACED CLOSER THAN 30 INCHES TO TRANSVERSE CONTRACTION, EXPANSION OR CONSTRUCTION JOINTS.

DEPARTMENT OF COMMERCE
CIVIL AERONAUTICS ADMINISTRATION
AIRPORTS SERVICE
ENGINEERING AND CONSTRUCTION DIVISION

DATE: 3-20-44	SHEET 3 of EIGHT	DR. BY C.E.G.	DR. NO. 549

C-11260

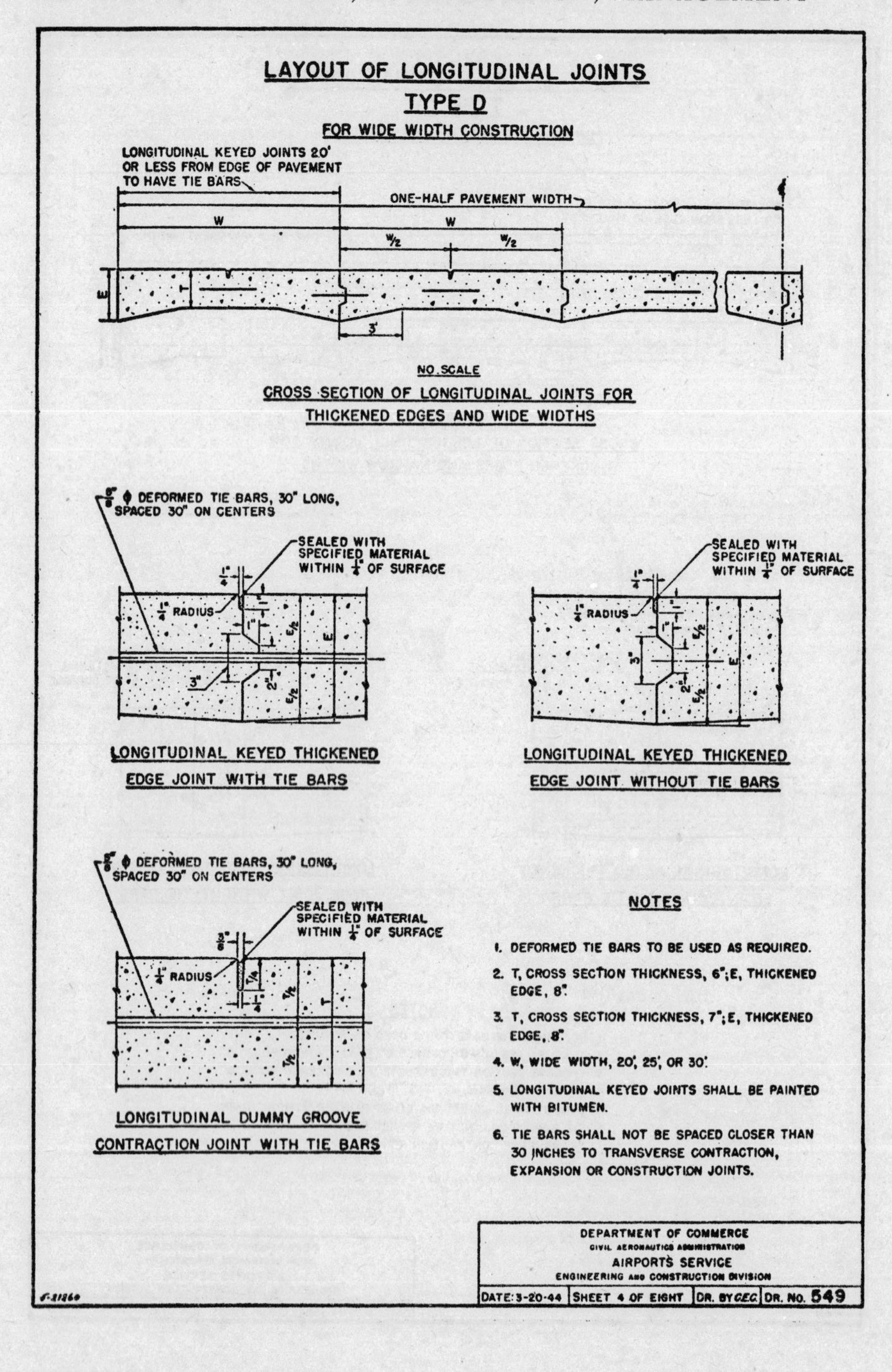
LAYOUT OF LONGITUDINAL JOINTS
TYPE D
FOR WIDE WIDTH CONSTRUCTION
LONGITUDINAL KEYED JOINTS 20' OR LESS FROM EDGE OF PAVEMENT TO HAVE TIE BARS
ONE-HALF PAVEMENT WIDTH
W
W
W/2
W/2
E
T
3'
NO SCALE
CROSS SECTION OF LONGITUDINAL JOINTS FOR THICKENED EDGES AND WIDE WIDTHS
5/8" ϕ DEFORMED TIE BARS, 30" LONG, SPACED 30" ON CENTERS
SEALED WITH SPECIFIED MATERIAL WITHIN 1/4" OF SURFACE
1/4" RADIUS
3"
2"
E/2
E
LONGITUDINAL KEYED THICKENED EDGE JOINT WITH TIE BARS
SEALED WITH SPECIFIED MATERIAL WITHIN 1/4" OF SURFACE
1/4" RADIUS
LONGITUDINAL KEYED THICKENED EDGE JOINT WITHOUT TIE BARS
5/8" ϕ DEFORMED TIE BARS, 30" LONG, SPACED 30" ON CENTERS
SEALED WITH SPECIFIED MATERIAL WITHIN 1/4" OF SURFACE
3/8"
1/4" RADIUS
T/4
T/2
T
LONGITUDINAL DUMMY GROOVE CONTRACTION JOINT WITH TIE BARS
NOTES
1. DEFORMED TIE BARS TO BE USED AS REQUIRED.
2. T, CROSS SECTION THICKNESS, 6"; E, THICKENED EDGE, 8".
3. T, CROSS SECTION THICKNESS, 7"; E, THICKENED EDGE, 8".
4. W, WIDE WIDTH, 20', 25', OR 30'.
5. LONGITUDINAL KEYED JOINTS SHALL BE PAINTED WITH BITUMEN.
6. TIE BARS SHALL NOT BE SPACED CLOSER THAN 30 INCHES TO TRANSVERSE CONTRACTION, EXPANSION OR CONSTRUCTION JOINTS.
DEPARTMENT OF COMMERCE
CIVIL AERONAUTICS ADMINISTRATION
AIRPORTS SERVICE
ENGINEERING AND CONSTRUCTION DIVISION
DATE: 3-20-44
SHEET 4 OF EIGHT
DR. BY C.E.C.
DR. NO. 549

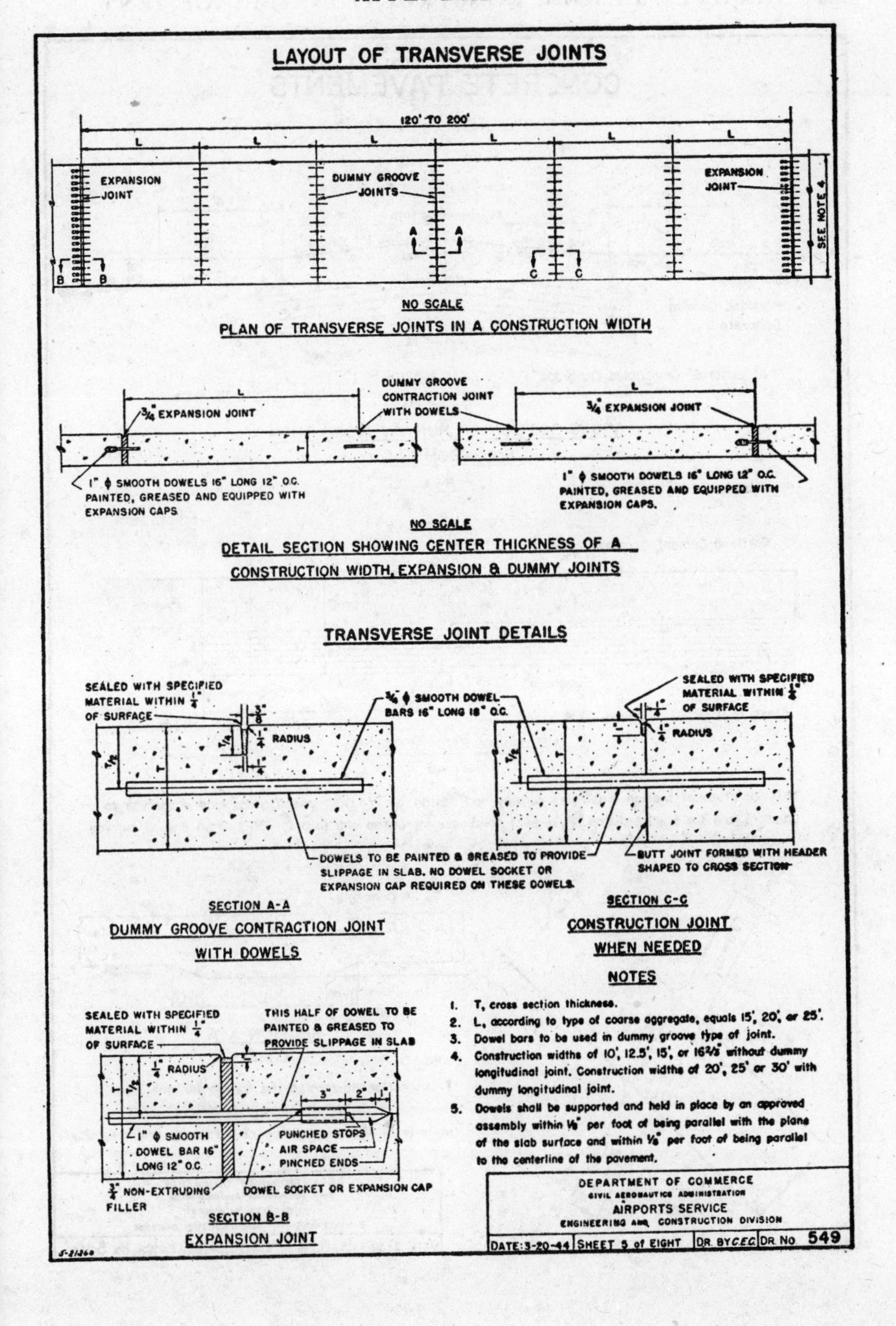
LAYOUT OF TRANSVERSE JOINTS
120' TO 200'
L
EXPANSION JOINT
DUMMY GROOVE JOINTS
SEE NOTE 4
NO SCALE
PLAN OF TRANSVERSE JOINTS IN A CONSTRUCTION WIDTH
3/4" EXPANSION JOINT
DUMMY GROOVE CONTRACTION JOINT WITH DOWELS
1" ϕ SMOOTH DOWELS 16" LONG 12" O.C. PAINTED, GREASED AND EQUIPPED WITH EXPANSION CAPS
NO SCALE
DETAIL SECTION SHOWING CENTER THICKNESS OF A CONSTRUCTION WIDTH, EXPANSION & DUMMY JOINTS
TRANSVERSE JOINT DETAILS
SEALED WITH SPECIFIED MATERIAL WITHIN 1/4" OF SURFACE
RADIUS
3/4" ϕ SMOOTH DOWEL BARS 16" LONG 18" O.C.
DOWELS TO BE PAINTED & GREASED TO PROVIDE SLIPPAGE IN SLAB. NO DOWEL SOCKET OR EXPANSION CAP REQUIRED ON THESE DOWELS.
BUTT JOINT FORMED WITH HEADER SHAPED TO CROSS SECTION
SECTION A-A
DUMMY GROOVE CONTRACTION JOINT WITH DOWELS
SECTION C-C
CONSTRUCTION JOINT WHEN NEEDED
THIS HALF OF DOWEL TO BE PAINTED & GREASED TO PROVIDE SLIPPAGE IN SLAB
1" ϕ SMOOTH DOWEL BAR 16" LONG 12" O.C.
PUNCHED STOPS
AIR SPACE
PINCHED ENDS
3/4" NON-EXTRUDING FILLER
DOWEL SOCKET OR EXPANSION CAP
SECTION B-B
EXPANSION JOINT
NOTES
1. T, cross section thickness.
2. L, according to type of coarse aggregate, equals 15', 20', or 25'.
3. Dowel bars to be used in dummy groove type of joint.
4. Construction widths of 10', 12.5', 15', or 16⅔' without dummy longitudinal joint. Construction widths of 20', 25' or 30' with dummy longitudinal joint.
5. Dowels shall be supported and held in place by an approved assembly within 1/8" per foot of being parallel with the plane of the slab surface and within 1/8" per foot of being parallel to the centerline of the pavement.
DEPARTMENT OF COMMERCE
CIVIL AERONAUTICS ADMINISTRATION
AIRPORTS SERVICE
ENGINEERING AND CONSTRUCTION DIVISION
DATE: 3-20-44
SHEET 5 of EIGHT
DR. BY C.E.C.
DR No 549

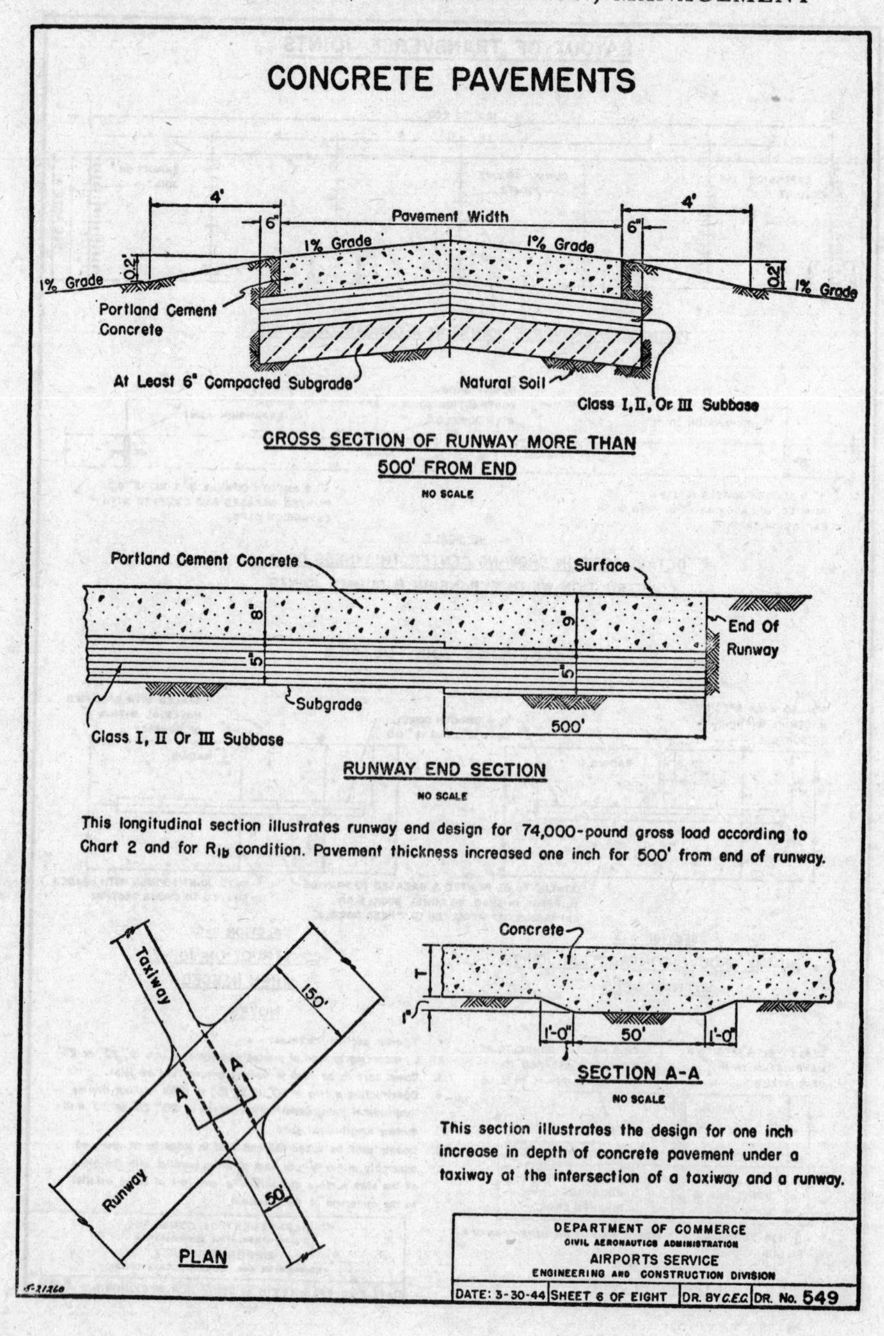
CONCRETE PAVEMENTS
4'
6"
Pavement Width
6"
4'
1% Grade
1% Grade
0.2'
1% Grade
0.2'
1% Grade
Portland Cement Concrete
At Least 6" Compacted Subgrade
Natural Soil
Class I, II, Or III Subbase
CROSS SECTION OF RUNWAY MORE THAN 500' FROM END
NO SCALE
Portland Cement Concrete
Surface
8"
9"
5"
5"
End Of Runway
Subgrade
500'
Class I, II Or III Subbase
RUNWAY END SECTION
NO SCALE
This longitudinal section illustrates runway end design for 74,000-pound gross load according to Chart 2 and for R_{1b} condition. Pavement thickness increased one inch for 500' from end of runway.
Taxiway
150'
A
A
Runway
50'
PLAN
Concrete
T
1"
1'-0"
50'
1'-0"
SECTION A-A
NO SCALE
This section illustrates the design for one inch increase in depth of concrete pavement under a taxiway at the intersection of a taxiway and a runway.
DEPARTMENT OF COMMERCE
CIVIL AERONAUTICS ADMINISTRATION
AIRPORTS SERVICE
ENGINEERING AND CONSTRUCTION DIVISION
DATE: 3-30-44
SHEET 6 OF EIGHT
DR. BY C.E.G.
DR. No. 549

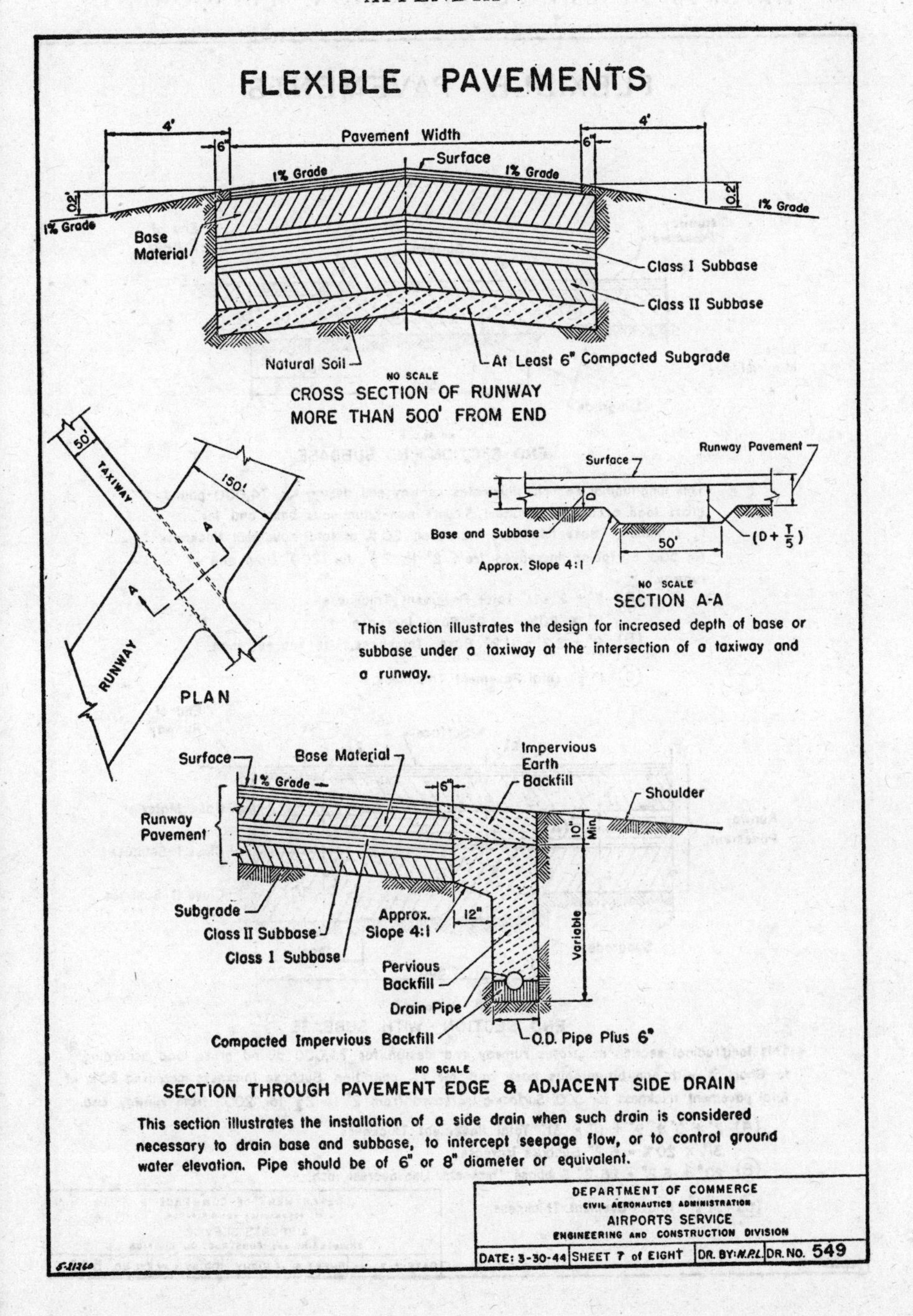
FLEXIBLE PAVEMENTS
4'
Pavement Width
6"
Surface
1% Grade
1% Grade
4'
6"
0.2'
0.2'
1% Grade
1% Grade
Base
Material
Class I Subbase
Class II Subbase
Natural Soil
At Least 6" Compacted Subgrade
NO SCALE
CROSS SECTION OF RUNWAY
MORE THAN 500' FROM END
50'
TAXIWAY
150'
A
A
RUNWAY
PLAN
Surface
Runway Pavement
D
Base and Subbase
50'
(D + T/5)
Approx. Slope 4:1
NO SCALE
SECTION A-A
This section illustrates the design for increased depth of base or subbase under a taxiway at the intersection of a taxiway and a runway.
Surface
Base Material
Impervious
Earth
Backfill
1% Grade
6"
Shoulder
Runway
Pavement
10" Min.
Subgrade
Class II Subbase
Class I Subbase
Approx.
Slope 4:1
12"
Variable
Pervious
Backfill
Drain Pipe
Compacted Impervious Backfill
O.D. Pipe Plus 6"
NO SCALE
SECTION THROUGH PAVEMENT EDGE & ADJACENT SIDE DRAIN
This section illustrates the installation of a side drain when such drain is considered necessary to drain base and subbase, to intercept seepage flow, or to control ground water elevation. Pipe should be of 6" or 8" diameter or equivalent.
DEPARTMENT OF COMMERCE
CIVIL AERONAUTICS ADMINISTRATION
AIRPORTS SERVICE
ENGINEERING AND CONSTRUCTION DIVISION
DATE: 3-30-44
SHEET 7 of EIGHT
DR. BY: N.P.L.
DR. NO. 549
5-21760

FLEXIBLE PAVEMENTS

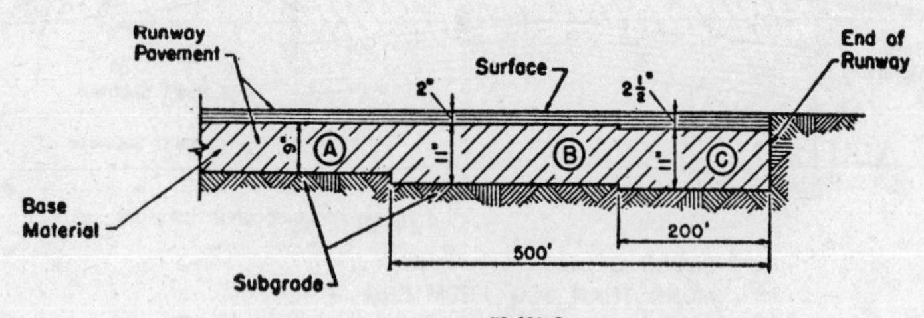

NO SCALE

END SECTION - NO SUBBASE

This longitudinal section illustrates runway end design for 74,000-pound gross load according to Chart 3 with non-bituminous base and for F_A condition. Base thickness increased 20% of total pavement thickness for 500'. Surfacing increased from 2" to $2\frac{1}{2}$" for 200' from end of runway.

Ⓐ 2" + 9" = 11" Total Pavement Thickness
11" X 20% = 2.2" Base Increase

Ⓑ 9" + 2.2" = 11.2" Base Thickness. Use nearest inch.

Ⓒ $13\frac{1}{2}$" Total Pavement Thickness.

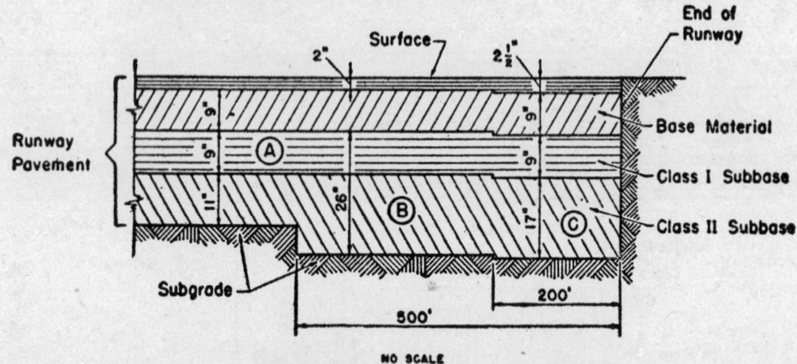

NO SCALE

END SECTION - WITH SUBBASE

This longitudinal section illustrates runway end design for 74,000-pound gross load according to Chart 3 with non-bituminous base and for F_B condition. Subbase thickness increased 20% of total pavement thickness for 500'. Surfacing increased from 2" to $2\frac{1}{2}$" for 200' from runway end.

Ⓐ 2" + 9" + 9" + 11" = 31" Total Pavement Thickness.
31" X 20% = 6.2" Subbase Increase.

Ⓑ 20" + 6.2" = 26.2" Subbase Thickness. Use nearest inch.

Ⓒ $37\frac{1}{2}$" Total Pavement Thickness.

DEPARTMENT OF COMMERCE
CIVIL AERONAUTICS ADMINISTRATION
AIRPORTS SERVICE
ENGINEERING AND CONSTRUCTION DIVISION

DATE: 3-30-44	SHEET 8 of EIGHT	DR. BY N.P.L.	DR. NO. 549

5-21260

APPENDIX 10

DEPARTMENT OF COMMERCE
Civil Aeronautics Administration
Airport Division
Washington, D.C.
January 1, 1944

DRY BOUND MACADAM BASE COURSE FOR AIRPORT RUNWAYS, TAXIWAYS AND APRONS

C.A.A. Specification No. P-205

INTRODUCTION

Dry bound macadam affords a good type of base course construction using crushed aggregates. It is essential that the subgrade or subbase be well compacted because successful macadam construction depends on ample rolling to obtain complete keying action of the stone. After the particles have been set by rolling, the voids should be filled with fine crushed materials or screenings to hold or bond the base material in place. This will prevent the shifting or creeping of the stone particles after construction. The macadam base should be built with well graded coarse aggregate with very little material passing the $\frac{3}{4}$ inch sieve. If the gradation as given in this specification is not economically available from commercial producers or local deposits, other similar gradations may be specified if they have an established satisfactory service record. The fine material should be applied only after the coarse particles have been well keyed by rolling.

This type base should be followed with a suitable prime and a dense graded wearing surface at least 2″ thick.

Note: Where the available aggregates are satisfactory for such usage consideration should be given to the use of "Water Bound Macadam Base Course. C.A.A. Specification No. P-206."

DESCRIPTION

1.1 This item shall consist of a base course composed of crushed stone or crushed slag, constructed on the prepared subgrade or a previously constructed subbase in accordance with these specifications and in conformity with the dimensions and typical cross section shown on the plans and with the lines and grades established by the engineer.

MATERIALS

2.1 *Aggregate.* The coarse aggregate and screenings shall be either crushed stone or crushed slag.

The crushed stone shall consist of hard, durable particles or fragments of stone, free from an excess of flat, elongated, soft or disintegrated pieces, dirt or other objectionable matter, and shall have a percent of wear of not more than

45 at 500 revolutions as determined by A.A.S.H.O. Method T 96–42 (Los Angeles Rattler Test).

The crushed slag shall be air-cooled blast furnace slag, and shall consist of angular fragments, reasonably uniform in density and quality, and reasonably free from thin, elongated, or soft pieces, dirt, and other objectionable matter. It shall weigh not less than 70 pounds per cubic foot, and shall have a percent of wear of not more than 45 at 500 revolutions as determined by A.A.S.H.O. Method T 96–42 (Los Angeles Rattler Test).

Crushed stone and crushed slag for coarse aggregate and screenings shall meet the requirements for grading given in Table 1, using A.A.S.H.O. Method T 27–42.

TABLE 1

REQUIREMENTS FOR GRADING OF AGGREGATE

Sieve designation	Percentage by weight passing square mesh sieves	
	Coarse Aggregate	Screenings
3 inch	100	
2½ inch	90–100	
1½ inch	25–60	
¾ inch	0–10	
⅜ inch		100
No. 4		85–100
No. 100		5–25

CONSTRUCTION METHODS

3.1 *Insulation Course.* A layer of screenings shall be spread uniformly upon the subgrade in the amount of seventy-five (75) pounds per square yard unless otherwise specified in the proposal. The screenings shall be spread by methods similar to those required for spreading coarse aggregate and if necessary shall be shaped by road machine to the required section and smoothness. The layer shall then be rolled and watered until firmly compacted. The roller shall weigh at least 10 tons, and be of a three-wheel type.

3.2 *Spreading Coarse Aggregate.* The prepared subgrade or the insulation course shall be checked and accepted by the engineer before placing and spreading operations are started.

Any ruts or soft, yielding places that appear by reason of improper drainage conditions, or hauling, or from any other cause, shall be corrected and rolled until firm before the base course is placed thereon.

The coarse aggregate shall be spread uniformly and evenly upon the prepared subgrade by the use of spreader boxes or other approved devices that shall spread the aggregate in the required amount so as to avoid or minimize the need for hand manipulation. Dumping from vehicles in piles or windrows so as to require rehandling will not be permitted. Hauling over the partly completed base course shall not be permitted.

The base course shall be constructed in layers of not less than three (3) inches nor more than four (4) inches of compacted thickness. No segregation of large or fine particles will be allowed, and the coarse aggregate as spread shall be of uniform grading with no pockets of fine materials. Coarse aggregate, unless otherwise permitted by the Engineer, shall not be spread more than 2000 square yards in advance of the rolling and application of screenings.

To protect the subgrade or insulation course and to insure proper drainage, the spreading of the coarse aggregate shall begin along the center line of the runway or taxiway on a crowned section or on the high side of the pavement with a one-way slope.

Grade control between the edges of the runways shall be by means of grade stakes, steel pins, or forms placed in lanes parallel to the center line of the runway, and at intervals sufficiently close that string lines or check boards may be placed between the stakes, pins, or forms.

3.3 *Rolling.* Immediately following the spreading of the coarse aggregate, it shall be compacted to the full width by rolling with a 3-wheel power roller weighing at least 10 tons. Rolling shall progress gradually from the sides to the center of the lane under construction or from one side toward previously placed material by lapping uniformly each preceding rear-wheel track by one-half the width of such track, and shall continue until the entire area of the course has been rolled by the rear wheels. The rolling shall continue until the stone is thoroughly keyed, the interstices of the metal reduced to a minimum and creeping of the stone ahead of the roller no longer visible.

The course shall not be rolled when the subgrade is soft or yielding or when the rolling causes a wavelike motion in the base course or subgrade. When the rolling develops irregularities that exceed three-eighths ($\frac{3}{8}$) inch when tested with a sixteen (16) foot straightedge, the irregular surface shall be loosened and then refilled with the same kind of material as that used in constructing the course and again rolled as required above.

Along places inaccessible to rollers, the base course material shall be tamped thoroughly with mechanical or hand tampers. Each hand tamper shall weigh not less than 50 lbs. and have a face area of not more than 100 square inches.

3.4 *Applying Screenings.* After the coarse aggregate has been thoroughly keyed and set by the rolling described, screenings in an amount that will completely fill the interstices shall be applied gradually and uniformly over the surface. Rolling shall be continued while the screenings are being spread, so that the jarring effect of the roller will cause them to settle into the voids of the coarse aggregate. The screenings shall not be dumped in piles on the coarse aggregate but shall be spread in thin layers.

The roller used shall meet the requirements specified above and be equipped with a broom of an approved type. The screenings shall be applied at a uniform and slow rate so as to insure filling of all voids. Hand brooms, where necessary, shall be used to sweep the screenings into unfilled voids and to distribute them. The spreading and rolling and brooming of screenings shall be performed on sections not to exceed 2000 square yards and shall continue until no more screenings can be forced into the voids of the coarse aggregate.

3.5 *Surface Test.* After the course is completely compacted, the surface shall be checked for smoothness and accuracy of grade and crown, and if any portions are found to lack the required smoothness or to fail in accuracy of grade or crown, such portions shall be scarified, reshaped, recompacted and otherwise manipulated as the engineer may direct until the required smoothness and accuracy is obtained. The finished surface shall be such that it will not vary more than three-eighths (⅜) of an inch from the sixteen (16) foot straight edge applied to the surface parallel to the center line and at right angles.

3.6 *Reconstructing Macadam.* Should the subgrade or subbase at any time become soft or churned up with the base course material or the shoulder material mixed with the base course material, the contractor shall, without additional compensation, remove the mixture from the affected portion, reshape and compact the subgrade or subbase and replace the removed section in accordance with the foregoing requirements.

3.7 *Thickness.* The thickness of the base course shall be determined by depth tests or cores taken at intervals in such manner that each test shall represent no more than 300 square yards. Where the base deficiency is more than one-half (½) inch, the contractor shall correct such areas by taking up the base material, removing and replacing with satisfactory materials properly laid, rolled, bonded and finished in accordance with these specifications. The contractor shall replace at his expense the base material where borings are taken for test purposes.

3.8 *Multiple Courses.* When it is necessary to construct the course in more than one layer to conform to the lines, grades and cross sections indicated on the plans, each layer shall be constructed as described above.

The surface of the base course shall be maintained in its finished condition until any surface course or pavement provided in the contract is placed thereon, and the contract is completed.

3.9 *Protection.* Work on the stone base shall not be prosecuted during freezing temperatures nor when the subgrade is wet. When the stone or screenings contain frozen materials or the subgrade or subbase is frozen, the construction shall be stopped.

During the placing, spreading and rolling of the insulation course, coarse aggregate and screenings, care shall be exercised to prevent the incorporation of subgrade, subbase or shoulder material into these macadam materials.

3.10 *Freight and Weigh-Bills.* Before final estimate is allowed, the contractor shall file with the Engineer receipted freight bills on all coarse aggregate and screenings as separate items where railroad shipments are made and certified weigh-bills when the material is received by any other manner showing the actual tons that have been used in this item.

Copies of all freight bills and weigh-bills shall be furnished the Engineer during the progress of the work.

METHOD OF MEASUREMENT

4.1 Yardage of base course material to be paid for shall be the cubic yards of base course material including all screenings, bonded and accepted in the completed base course. Quantities of base course material and screenings shall be measured in final position based upon depth tests or cores taken as directed by the Engineer or at the rate of one depth test for each 300 square yards of base course or by means of average end areas on the completed work computed from elevations to the nearest .01 foot.

The depth of the base shall include the insulation course. On individual depth measurements, thicknesses more than one-half (½) inch in excess of that shown on the plans shall be considered as the specified thickness plus one-half (½) inch in computing the yardage for payment.

BASIS OF PAYMENT

5.1 The yardage of base course material measured as provided above shall be paid for at the contract unit price per cubic yard for macadam base course which price and payment shall constitute full compensation for furnishing, hauling and placing the materials; for spreading and rolling; reconditioning the subgrade, subbase and shoulders; for placing, watering and rolling insulation course; for reconstruction of damaged or deficient base; for maintenance of surface; for refilling test holes and for all labor, equipment, tools, water and incidentals necessary to complete the work.

APPENDIX 11

DEPARTMENT OF COMMERCE
Civil Aeronautics Administration
Airport Division
Washington, D.C.
July 1, 1943

WATER BOUND MACADAM BASE COURSE FOR AIRPORT RUNWAYS, TAXIWAYS AND APRONS

C.A.A. Specification No. P-206

INTRODUCTION

Water bound macadam affords the best type of base course construction using crushed aggregates. It is essential that the subgrade or subbase be well compacted because successful macadam construction depends on ample rolling to obtain complete keying action of the stone. After the particles have been set by rolling, the voids should be filled with fine crushed materials or screenings to hold or bond the base material in place. This type provides the maximum of drainage and reduces capillarity to a minimum. By the use of water it is possible to work into the macadam the maximum amount of choke or screenings. This will prevent the shifting or creeping of the stone particles after construction. The macadam base should be built with well graded coarse aggregate with very little material passing the ¾ inch sieve. If the gradation as given in this specification is not economically available from commercial producers or local deposits, other similar gradations may be used if they have an established satisfactory service record. The fine material should be applied only after the coarse particles have been well keyed by rolling.

This type base should be followed with a suitable prime and a dense graded wearing surface at least 2″ thick.

DESCRIPTION

1.1 This item shall consist of a base course composed of crushed stone or crushed slag, water-bonded, constructed on a prepared subgrade or a previously constructed subbase in accordance with these specifications and in conformity with the dimensions and typical cross section shown on the plans and with lines and grades established by the Engineer.

MATERIALS

2.1 *Aggregate.* The coarse aggregate and screenings shall be either crushed stone or crushed slag.

The crushed stone shall consist of hard, durable particles or fragments of stone, free from an excess of flat, elongated, soft or disintegrated pieces, dirt or other objectionable matter, and shall have a percent of wear of not more than

50 at 500 revolutions as determined by A.A.S.H.O., Method T 96–42 (Los Angeles Rattler Test).

The crushed slag shall be air-cooled blast furnace slag, and shall consist of angular fragments, reasonably uniform in density and quality, and reasonably free from thin, elongated, or soft pieces, dirt, and other objectionable matter. It shall weigh not less than 70 pounds per cubic foot, and shall have a percent of wear of not more than 50 at 500 revolutions as determined by A.A.S.H.O., Method T 96–42 (Los Angeles Rattler Test).

Crushed stone and crushed slag for coarse aggregate and screenings shall meet the requirements for grading given in Table 1, using A.A.S.H.O., Method T 27–42.

TABLE 1

REQUIREMENTS FOR GRADING OF AGGREGATE

Sieve designation	Percentage by weight passing square mesh sieves	
	Coarse Aggregate	Screenings
3 inch	100	
2½ inch	90–100	
1½ inch	25–60	
¾ inch	0–10	
⅜ inch		100
No. 4		85–100
No. 100		5–25

CONSTRUCTION METHOD

3.1 *Insulation Course.* A layer of screenings shall be spread uniformly upon the subgrade in the amount of seventy-five (75) pounds per square yard unless otherwise specified in the proposal. The screenings shall be spread by methods similar to those required for spreading coarse aggregate and if necessary shall be shaped by road machine to the required section and smoothness. The layer shall then be rolled and watered until firmly compacted. The roller shall weigh at least 10 tons.

3.2 *Spreading Coarse Aggregate.* The prepared subgrade or the insulation course shall be checked and accepted by the engineer before placing and spreading operations are started.

Any ruts or soft, yielding places that appear by reason of improper drainage conditions, or hauling, or from any other cause, shall be corrected and rolled until firm before the base course is placed thereon.

The coarse aggregate shall be spread uniformly and evenly upon the prepared subgrade by the use of spreader boxes or other approved devices that shall spread the aggregate in the required amount so as to avoid or minimize the need for hand manipulation. Dumping from vehicles in piles or windrows so as to require rehandling will not be permitted. Hauling over the partly completed base course shall not be permitted.

The base course shall be constructed in layers of not less than three (3) inches nor more than four (4) inches of compacted thickness. Each layer shall be tested by depth blocks. No segregation of large or fine particles will be allowed, and the coarse aggregate as spread shall be of uniform grading with no pockets of fine materials. Coarse aggregate, unless otherwise permitted by the Engineer, shall not be spread more than 2000 square yards in advance of the rolling and application of screenings.

To protect the subgrade or insulation course and to insure proper drainage, the spreading of the coarse aggregate shall begin along the center line of the runway or taxiway on a crowned section or on the high side of the pavement with a one-way slope.

Grade control between the edges of the runways shall be by means of grade stakes, steel pins, or forms placed in lanes parallel to the center line of the runway, and at intervals sufficiently close that string lines or check boards may be placed between the stakes, pins, or forms.

3.3 *Rolling.* Immediately following the spreading of the coarse aggregate, it shall be compacted to the full width by rolling with a 3-wheel power roller weighing at least 10 tons. Rolling shall progress gradually from the sides to the center of the lane under construction or from one side toward previously placed material by lapping uniformly each preceding rear-wheel track by one-half the width of such track, and shall continue until the entire area of the course has been rolled by the rear wheels. The rolling shall continue until the stone is thoroughly keyed, the interstices of the metal reduced to a minimum and creeping of the stone ahead of the roller no longer visible.

The course shall not be rolled when the subgrade is soft or yielding or when the rolling causes a wavelike motion in the base course or subgrade. When the rolling develops irregularities that exceed three-eighths ($\frac{3}{8}$) inch when tested with a sixteen (16) foot straightedge, the irregular surface shall be loosened and then refilled with the same kind of material as that used in constructing the course and again rolled as required above.

Along places inaccessible to rollers, the base course material shall be tamped thoroughly with mechanical or hand tampers. Each hand tamper shall weigh not less than 50 lbs. and have a face area of not more than 100 square inches.

3.4 *Applying Screenings.* After the coarse aggregate has been thoroughly keyed and set by the rolling described, screenings in an amount that will completely fill the interstices shall be applied gradually and uniformly over the surface. Dry rolling shall be continued while the screenings are being spread, so that the jarring effect of the roller will cause them to settle into the voids of the coarse aggregate. The screening shall not be dumped in piles on the coarse aggregate but shall be spread in thin layers.

The roller used shall meet the requirements specified above and be equipped with a broom of an approved type. The screenings shall be applied at a uniform and slow rate so as to insure filling of all voids. Hand brooms, where necessary, shall be used to sweep the screenings into unfilled voids and to distribute them. The spreading and rolling and brooming of screenings shall be performed on sections not to exceed 2000 square yards and shall continue until no more screenings will go in dry.

3.5 *Sprinkling.* Immediately after the voids of a section of the course have been filled with screenings, the macadam shall be sprinkled, the sprinkler being followed by the roller. All excess screenings forming in piles or cakes on the surface shall be scattered by light sweeping. The sprinkling and rolling shall continue and additional screenings applied where necessary until all voids are completely filled and the coarse stone firmly set and bonded. The quantity of screenings and water necessary shall be determined by the engineer and shall be sufficient to completely fill and bond the entire depth of the layer of the coarse aggregate and to produce a granular surface.

Provision shall be made by the contractor for furnishing water at the site of the work by equipment of ample capacity and of such design as to assure uniform application.

After the completion of the base course as described, the surface shall be tested with a sixteen (16) foot straightedge parallel to and at right angles to the center line of the runway and all irregularities exceeding three-eighths ($\frac{3}{8}$) inch shall be corrected by removing and replacing in accordance with foregoing requirements.

3.6 *Reconstructing Macadam.* Should the subgrade at any time become soft or churned up with the base course material, the contractor shall, without additional compensation, remove the mixture from the affected portion, reshape and compact the subgrade and replace the removed section in accordance with the foregoing requirements.

The thickness of the base course shall be determined by depth tests or cores taken at intervals in such manner that each test shall represent no more than 300 square yards. Where the base deficiency is more than one-half ($\frac{1}{2}$) inch, the contractor shall correct such areas by taking up the base material, removing and replacing with satisfactory materials properly laid, rolled, sprinkled, bonded and finished in accordance with these specifications.

3.7 *Multiple Courses.* When it is necessary to construct the course in more than one layer to conform to the lines, grades and cross sections indicated on the plans, each layer shall be constructed as described above.

The surface of the base course shall be maintained in its finished condition until any surface course or pavement provided in the contract is placed thereon, and the contract is completed.

3.8 *Protection.* Work on stone base shall not be prosecuted during freezing temperature nor when the subgrade is wet. When the temperature is below 40° F., completed base course shall be protected against freezing until it dries out by a sufficient covering of straw or by any other method which the contractor may desire to use and which has been approved by the Engineer.

3.9 *Freight and Weigh-Bills.* Before final estimate is allowed, the contractor shall file with the Engineer receipted freight bills on all coarse aggregate and screenings as separate items where railroad shipments are made and certified weigh-bills when the material is received by any other manner showing the actual tons that have been used in this item.

Copies of all freight bills and weigh-bills shall be furnished the Engineer during the progress of the work.

METHOD OF MEASUREMENT

4.1 Yardage of base course material to be paid for shall be the cubic yards of base course material including all screenings, bonded and accepted in the completed base course. Quantities of base course material and screenings shall be measured in final position based upon depth tests or cores taken as directed by the Engineer or at the rate of one depth test for each 300 square yards of base course or by means of average end areas on the completed work computed from elevations to the nearest .01 foot. The depth of the base shall include the insulation course. On individual depth measurements, thicknesses more than one-half ($\frac{1}{2}$) inch in excess of that shown on the plans shall be considered as the specified thickness plus one-half ($\frac{1}{2}$) inch in computing the yardage for payment.

BASIS OF PAYMENT

5.1 The yardage of base course material measured as provided above shall be paid for at the contract unit price per cubic yard for macadam base course which price and payment shall constitute full compensation for furnishing, hauling and placing the materials; for spreading, sprinkling and rolling; reconditioning the subgrade and shoulders; for placing, watering and rolling insulation course; for reconstruction of damaged or deficient base; for maintenance of surface; for refilling test holes and for all labor, equipment, tools, water and incidentals necessary to complete the item.

APPENDIX 12

DEPARTMENT OF COMMERCE
Civil Aeronautics Administration
Airport Division
Washington, D.C.
October 1, 1943

CRUSHED AGGREGATE BASE COURSE FOR AIRPORT RUNWAYS, TAXIWAYS AND APRONS

C.A.A. Specification No. P-209

INTRODUCTION

The crushed aggregate base course as contained in these specifications is intended where this type of material is economically available, and for construction on good quality of subbases. The filler material should be stone dust made in the process of crushing the aggregate. A soil binder such as clay shall not be used. This construction should follow somewhat the operations of placing water bound macadam bases. The initial compaction and specified consolidation of the base course shall be effected by the use of three-wheel type rollers weighing not less than ten tons. Heavy rollers and thin layers should obtain maximum density. A density test should be made frequently to determine the required amount of rolling needed.

After completion of the base course, a suitable prime coat shall precede the wearing surface. Tar prime is preferable, owing to its penetrating and waterproofing characteristics. If tar is not available, a suitable grade of MC asphalt will be satisfactory.

Wearing surfaces shall be of bituminous type at least two (2) inches thick of a suitable designed dense graded plant mix.

DESCRIPTION

1.1 This item shall consist of a base course composed of crushed aggregates, constructed on a previously constructed subbase, in accordance with these specifications and in conformity with the dimensions and typical cross sections shown on the plans and with the lines and grades established by the engineer.

MATERIALS

2.1 *Aggregate.* The coarse aggregate shall be either crushed stone or crushed gravel.

The crushed stone shall consist of hard, durable particles or fragments of stone, free from an excess of flat, elongated, soft or disintegrated pieces, dirt or other objectionable matter, and shall have a percent of wear of not more than 45 at 500 revolutions as determined by A.A.S.H.O. Method T 96–42 (Los Angeles Rattler Test).

Crushed gravel shall consist of stones, rock and boulders of accepted quality crushed to specified size. The method used in the production of crushed gravel shall be such that the percentage of fractured particles occurring in the finished product shall be as nearly constant and uniform as practicable. The crushing of the gravel shall result in a product that at least sixty (60) percent of the material passing a 2″ sieve and retained on a 1″ sieve; that at least sixty (60) percent of the material passing a 1″ sieve and retained on a ¾″ sieve and that at least sixty (60) percent of the material passing a ¾″ sieve and retained on a No. 4 sieve will have at least one fractured face. If necessary to meet this requirement or to eliminate an excess of fine, uncrushed particles the gravel shall be screened before crushing. All stones, rocks and boulders of inferior quality occurring in the pit shall be separated out and wasted. The gravel shall have a percent of wear of not more than 45 at 500 revolutions as determined by A.A.S.H.O. Method T 96–42 (Los Angeles Rattler Test).

All material passing the No. 4 sieve produced in the crushing operation of either the stone or gravel shall be incorporated in the base material.

The crushed aggregate shall meet the requirements of one of the gradings given in the table on the next page, whichever is called for in the bid schedule, using A.A.S.H.O., Methods T 11–42 and T 27–42.

Gradation

Sieve Designation	Percentage by Weight Passing Square Openings		
	2″ Maximum	1½″ Maximum	1″ Maximum
2″	100		
1½″	...	100	
1″	55–85	70–95	100
¾″	50–80	55–85	70–100
No. 4	30–60	30–60	35–65
No. 40	10–25	10–25	15–25
No. 200	3–10	3–10	3–10

The gradations in the table represent the limits which shall determine suitability of aggregate for use from the sources of supply. The final gradations decided on within the limits designated in the table shall be uniformly graded from coarse to fine, and shall not vary from the low limit on one sieve to the high limit on the adjacent sieves or vice versa.

The amount of the fraction of material passing the No. 200 sieve shall not exceed one-half the fraction passing the No. 40 sieve.

That portion of the filler, including any blended material, passing the No. 40 sieve shall have a liquid limit of not more than 25 and a plasticity index of not more than 6 when tested in accordance with A.A.S.H.O., Methods T 89–42, T 90–42 and T 91–42.

The selection of any of the gradings shown in the table shall be such that the maximum size aggregate used in any course shall not be more than one-half the thickness of the layer of the course being constructed.

2.2 *Filler.* If filler, in addition to that naturally present in the base course material, is necessary for satisfactory bonding of the material, for changing the soil constants of the material passing the No. 40 mesh sieve, or for correcting the gradation to the limitations of the specified gradation, it shall be uniformly blended with the base course material at the plant. The material for such purpose shall be obtained from sources approved by the engineer and shall be of a gradation as necessary to accomplish the specified gradation in the finally processed material.

CONSTRUCTION METHODS

3.1 *Operation at Sources of Supply.* All work involved in clearing and stripping of quarries and pits and handling unsuitable material encountered shall be performed by the contractor at his own expense. The base material shall be obtained from sources that have been approved. The material shall be handled in a manner that a uniform and satisfactory product shall be secured.

3.2 *Equipment.* All equipment necessary for the proper construction of this work shall be on the project, in first-class working condition, and shall have been approved by the engineer before construction is permitted to start.

The powered roller shall be of the three-wheeled type, weighing not less than ten (10) tons. The roller shall have a rear wheel compression of not less than 330 pounds per linear inch of tire width and shall be equipped with adjustable scrapers.

Road machines shall weigh not less than 3 tons and shall have a wheel base not less than 15 feet and a blade not less than 10 feet. Road machines shall not be pulled with rollers.

Provision shall be made by the contractor for furnishing water at the plant or at the site of the work by equipment of ample capacity and of such design as to assure uniform application.

The processing plant shall be designed, constructed, operated and of such capacity so as to thoroughly mix all materials and water in the proportions as directed to produce a base course of the gradation and consistency required. The traveling plant shall be self-propelled or tractor drawn and capable of maintaining a uniform rate of travel while mixing. It shall be mounted on wheels or tread equipment of such type that when loaded to capacity it will not rut or damage the subbase course. The device for picking up the crushed aggregates from the windrow shall be such that it will take up the loose material and leave the subbase clean without damage.

3.3 *Preparing Subbase.* Before any base course material is placed, the subbase shall be prepared and conditioned as specified under subbase requirements. The subbase shall be checked and accepted by the engineer before placing and spreading operations are started. Any ruts or soft, yeilding places that appear by reason of improper drainage conditions, or hauling, or from any other cause, shall be corrected and rolled until firm before the base course is placed thereon.

Grade control between the edges of the runways shall be by means of grade stakes, steel pins, or forms placed in lanes parallel to the center line of the runway, and at intervals sufficiently close that string lines or check boards may be placed between the stakes, pins, or forms.

To protect the subbase and to insure proper drainage, the spreading of the base shall begin along the center line of the runway or taxiway on a crowned section or on the high side of the pavement with a one-way slope.

3.4 *Plant Mix.* When provided for in the proposal or when selected by the contractor and approved by the engineer, the base material shall be blended and mixed in an approved plant. The type of plant may be either a central proportioning and mixing plant or a traveling plant. The plant shall blend and mix the materials to meet these specifications and to the proper optimum moisture content for compaction.

3.5 *Placing and Spreading.* (a) Central Plant. The crushed aggregate base material that has been proportioned and processed in a central mixing plant shall be placed on the prepared subbase and compacted in layers of the thickness shown on the plans. The depositing and spreading of the material shall commence where designated and shall progress continuously without breaks. The material shall be deposited and spread in lanes in a uniform layer and without segregation of size to such loose depth that when compacted, the layer will have the required thickness. It shall be the charge of the contractor that the required amount of approved material is delivered in each 100 foot station. The base aggregate shall be spread by the use of spreader boxes or other approved devices that shall spread the aggregate in the required amount so as to avoid or minimize the need for hand manipulation. The spreader boxes or other devices shall be equipped with a strike-off gate or similar means that can be adjusted or controlled to secure the required thickness of the material. Dumping from vehicles in piles on the subbase so as to require rehandling will not be permitted. Hauling over the uncompacted base course shall not be permitted.

(b) Traveling Plant. If a traveling plant method is used for mixing, the base material shall be placed on the subgrade in windrows parallel to the center line of the runway. Sufficient quantity and proportions of materials shall be placed in the windrow to provide a base mixture conforming to the specified grading and compacted thickness. The windrow shall be shaped to a uniform section and left undisturbed until measuring and sampling are complete. After mixing and before spreading, the mixture shall be examined by the engineer who shall determine whether the mixing is complete and satisfactory and whether the optimum moisture content is maintained for spreading. No spreading shall be done except when authorized. Care shall be taken that no subbase material is mixed with the base material.

After the mixing has been completed, the base material shall be spread to the required depth and width by a self-powered or tractor-drawn blade grader, mechanical spreader or other approved method. In spreading, care shall be taken to prevent cutting into the underlying layer. The material shall be bladed, disced and dragged if necessary until smooth, uniform surface is obtained, true to line, grade and cross section and the mix is in condition for compacting.

(c)Methods of Placing. The base course shall be constructed in layers of not less than two and one-half (2½) inches nor more than four (4) inches of compacted thickness. Each layer shall be tested by depth blocks. The coarse aggregate as spread shall be of uniform grading with no pockets of fine materials. Coarse aggregate, unless otherwise permitted by the engineer, shall not be spread more than 2000 square yards in advance of the rolling and sprinkling. No material shall be placed in snow or on a soft, muddy or frozen subbase.

When more than one layer is required, the construction procedure described herein shall apply similarly to each layer.

The engineer will make tests to determine the maximum density and the optimum moisture content of the base material, and this information will be available to the contractor.

During the placing and spreading, sufficient caution shall be exercised to prevent the incorporation of subgrade, subbase or shoulder material in the base course mixture.

3.6 *Finishing and Compacting.* After spreading, the crushed aggregate shall be thoroughly compacted by sprinkling and rolling. The initial rolling of the course shall be done with suitable three-wheeled, ten ton rollers. A single roller shall perform the rolling for not more than twenty-five (25) cubic yards per hour and additional rollers shall be provided when the spreading is greater than this rate.

Rolling shall progress gradually from the sides to the center of the lane under construction or from one side toward previously placed material by lapping uniformly each preceding rear-wheel track by one-half the width of such track, and shall continue until the entire area of the course has been rolled by the rear wheels. The rolling shall continue until the stone is thoroughly set, the interstices of the metal reduced to a minimum and creeping of the stone ahead of the roller no longer visible. Rolling shall continue until the base material has been compacted to at least 100% density as determined by the modified Proctor Density Test, A.A.S.H.O. Method T 99–42. Blading and rolling shall be done alternately as required or directed to obtain a smooth, even and uniformly compacted base. For final rolling either three-wheel or eight-ton tandem rollers may be used.

In making the Proctor Density Test as required for compaction of the base course, it is advisable to use the whole sample and not only the material passing a No. 4 sieve. With some care, a Proctor mould can be used for density tests of samples with aggregate passing the 2″ sieve. By this method, the results obtained will represent more nearly the correct value.

The course shall not be rolled when the subbase is soft or yielding or when the rolling causes a wavelike motion in the base course. When the rolling develops irregularities that exceed three-eighths ($\frac{3}{8}$) of an inch when tested with a sixteen (16) foot straightedge, the irregular surface shall be loosened and then refilled with the same kind of material as that used in constructing the course and again rolled as required above.

Along places inaccessible to rollers, the base course material shall be tamped thoroughly with mechanical or hand tampers. Each hand tamper shall weigh not less than 50 lbs. and have a face area of not more than 100 square inches.

The sprinkling during rolling, if necessary, shall be in the amount and by equipment approved by the engineer.

3.7 *Surface Test.* After the course is completely compacted, the surface shall be checked for smoothness and accuracy of grade and crown, and if any portions are found to lack the required smoothness or to fail in accuracy of grade or crown, such portions shall be scarified, reshaped, recompacted and otherwise manipulated as the engineer may direct until the required smoothness and accuracy is obtained. The finished surface shall be such that it will not vary more than three-eighths (⅜) of an inch from the sixteen (16) foot straight edge applied to the surface parallel to the center line and at right angles.

3.8 *Thickness.* The thickness of the base course shall be determined by depth tests or cores taken at intervals in such manner that each test shall represent no more than 300 square yards. When the base deficiency is more than one-half (½) inch, the contractor shall correct such areas by scarifying, adding satisfactory base mixture, rolling, sprinkling, reshaping and finishing in accordance with these specifications. The contractor shall replace at his expense the base material where borings are taken for test purposes.

3.9 *Protection.* Work on base course shall not be prosecuted during freezing temperature nor when the subbase is wet. When the temperature is below 40° F., completed base course shall be protected against freezing by a sufficient covering of straw or by any other method which the contractor may desire to use and which has been approved by the engineer.

3.10 *Maintenance.* Following the construction of the course, the contractor shall do such blading, brooming, rolling, sprinkling, and other maintaining work as is necessary to prevent ravelling and rutting. These operations shall be continued as required until the course is primed and accepted.

METHOD OF MEASUREMENT

4.1 The yardage of base course to be paid for shall be the number of cubic yards of material placed, bonded and accepted in the completed base course. The quantity of base course material shall be measured in final position based upon depth tests or cores taken as directed by the engineer or at the rate of one depth test for each 300 square yards of base course or by means of average end areas on the complete work computed from elevations to the nearest .01 foot. On individual depth measurements, thicknesses more than one-half inch in excess of that shown on the plans shall be considered as specified thickness plus one-half inch in computing the yardage for payment.

BASIS OF PAYMENT

5.1 The yardage of base course as provided above shall be paid for at the contract unit price bid per cubic yard in the bid schedule for crushed aggregate base course, which price and payment shall constitute full compensation for furnishing, loading, hauling, and placing the materials; for mixing, blading, sprinkling, shaping and compacting; for reconditioning the subbase and shoulders; for reconstruction of irregular surface, or deficient thickness, and for maintenance; for refilling test holes; for any required construction, repair, and obliteration of access roads; for all pit or quarry moves; for clearing, stripping, drainage and clean-up of pits; for the handling and disposal of unsuitable materials encountered in pit or quarry operations and for all labor, equipment, tools, water and incidentals necessary to complete the work.

APPENDIX 13

DEPARTMENT OF COMMERCE
Civil Aeronautics Administration
Airport Division
Washington, D.C.
January 1, 1943

CALICHE BASE COURSE FOR AIRPORT RUNWAYS, TAXIWAYS AND APRONS

C.A.A. Specification No. P-210

DESCRIPTION

1.1 This item shall consist of a base course composed of caliche, caliche-gravel, caliche and limestone or material of similar characteristics, constructed on the prepared subgrade or previously constructed subbase course, in accordance with these specifications and in conformity with the dimensions and typical cross sections shown on the plans and with the lines and grades established by the engineer.

MATERIALS

2.1 *Materials.* The base course material shall consist of caliche, caliche-gravel, caliche-limestone or similar materials obtained from sources that have been approved by the engineer prior to use of the materials. All acceptable material shall be screened and the oversize shall be crushed and returned to the screened material in such a manner that a uniform product will be produced.

The grading of the material as finally processed and blended, shall meet the following requirements using A.A.S.H.O. Methods T-11 and T-27:

	Percent by Weight
Passing 2″ Square Opening Sieve	100
Passing a No. 40 Mesh Sieve	15 to 35
Passing a No. 200 Mesh Sieve	0 to 20

That portion of the material, including the blended filler passing a No. 40 sieve, shall be known as soil binder and shall have a liquid limit of not more than 40 and a plasticity index of not more than 12 as determined by A.A.S.H.O. Methods T-89 and T-91 respectively, and T-87 modified as outlined below.

If necessary, the contractor will be required to blend or combine materials so that the finally processed material meets all of the requirements of these specifications. The contractor will be required to make such modifications in materials and methods as are necessary to secure a material which is capable of being compacted into a dense and well-bonded base.

2.2 *Modification of Test Method T-87.* In the preparation of soil binder, the total sample shall first be dried in the air or in an oven at a temperature not to exceed 140° F. After dry screening out all material that will readily pass the 40 mesh sieve, the retained portion of the aggregate sample shall be immersed in a pan of clear water until all binder material has slaked down or disintegrated, which may require up to 72 hours, A shorter slaking time may be used provided the results are consistent with those obtained in a 72 hour slaking.

The slaked material shall then be washed over a 40 mesh sieve, care being taken that all lumps are broken down. After the sample has been wet screened, the pan containing the soil binder in the water shall be set aside and allowed to settle. The clear water shall then be siphoned or drawn off and the binder sample shall be dried at a temperature not to exceed 140° F. That portion of the soil binder secured in the slaking process, when dried, shall, if necessary, be repulverized with a rubber-covered pestle and mortar so that all particles will pass the 40 sieve and this portion of the soil binder shall then be combined and thoroughly mixed with the portion of the soil binder obtained by dry screening, and soil constants shall be run upon this composite material.

2.3 *Filler for Blending.* If filler, in addition to that naturally present in the base course material, is necessary for satisfactory bonding of the material, for changing the soil constants of the material passing the No. 40 mesh sieve, or for correcting the gradation to the limitations of the specified gradation, it shall be uniformly blended with the base course material on the runway or at the crushing plant. The material for such purpose shall be obtained from sources approved by the engineer and shall be of a gradation as necessary to accomplish the specified gradation in the finally processed material.

CONSTRUCTION METHODS

3.1 *Operations in Pits.* All work involved in clearing and stripping pits and handling unsuitable material encountered shall be performed by the contractor. The contractor shall notify the engineer sufficiently in advance of the opening of any designated pit to permit staking of boundaries of the site and taking of elevations and measurements of the ground surface before any material is disturbed. The pits as utilized shall immediately be opened up so as to expose the vertical faces of the various strata of acceptable material, and unless otherwise directed, the material shall be secured in successive vertical cuts extending through all the exposed strata, in order that a uniform material will be secured.

3.2 *Placing and Spreading.* The base course material shall be placed on the prepared subgrade and compacted in layers of the thickness shown on the plans. The depositing and spreading of the material on the prepared subgrade, or on a completed layer, shall proceed as directed and shall progress continuously without breaks. The material shall be deposited and spread in a uniform layer and without segregation of size to such loose depth that when compacted, making due allowance for any filler that is to be blended on the runway, the layer will have the required thickness. It shall be the charge of the contractor that the required amount of approved material is delivered in each 100 ft. station. When and as directed, the material shall be spread from dump boards, spreader boxes or moving vehicles equipped to distribute the material in a uniform layer. When more than one layer is required, the construction procedure described herein shall apply similarly to each layer.

Grade control between the edges of the runway shall be by means of grade stakes or steel pins placed in lanes parallel to the center line of the runway and at intervals sufficiently close that string lines may be stretched between the stakes or pins.

3.3 *Spreading Filler Material.* If the engineer directs that filler be added to the base course material on the runway, such additional filler shall be spread in a uniform layer over the loosely spread base course layer in the amounts set by the engineer.

3.4 *Blading and Blending.* When the required amount of materials have been placed on the prepared subgrade or previously placed base course, they shall be thoroughly mixed and blended by means of approved graders, supplemented by other suitable equipment if necessary. The mixing shall continue until the material is uniform throughout. Areas of segregated material shall be corrected and thoroughly remixed. Water in the amount and as directed by the engineer shall be uniformly applied prior to and during the mixing operations by means of tanks mounted on trucks and equipped with spray bars or other approved methods. When the mixing and blending has been completed, the materials shall be spread in a uniform layer which, when compacted, will meet the requirements of the typical cross section.

3.5 *Rolling.* Immediately following final spreading, the material shall be compacted to full width by rolling with an approved tamping roller, and/or a power roller weighing at least 8 tons or other approved compacting equipment. Rolling shall progress gradually from one side to the other of the lane under construction and shall continue until all the surface has been rolled and compacted. Rolling shall continue until the base material has been compacted to 95% density as determined by the modified Proctor Density Test, A.A.S.H.O. Method T-99, modified as set forth in addendum. Any irregularities or depressions that develop under rolling shall be corrected by loosening the material at these places and adding or removing materials until the surface is smooth and uniform. Prior to and during compacting, water in the amounts as directed shall be applied as specified above. Blading and rolling shall be done alternately as required or directed to maintain a smooth, even, uniformly compacted base until any surface or treatment that may be provided for in the same contract is placed thereon. The final rolling shall be done with the power roller specified. Upon completion, the caliche base course shall be allowed to dry out or partially dry for a period of at least seven days before the prime coat is applied. Along curbs, headers and walls and all places not accessible to the roller, the base course material shall be tamped thoroughly with mechanical or hand tampers. Each hand tamper shall weigh not less than 50 lbs. and have a face area of not more than 100 square inches.

3.6 *Surface Test.* In that area upon which surfacing is to be placed, the base course completed as above shall be tested with a sixteen (16) foot straightedge and any deviation in excess of three-eighths (⅜″) shall be corrected by loosening, adding or removing material, reshaping and recompacting by sprinkling and rolling.

METHOD OF MEASUREMENT

4.1 The yardage of base course material to be paid for shall be the number of cubic yards of base course material (including all filler) placed, bonded and accepted in the completed base course. The quantities of base course material and filler shall be measured in final position based upon the completed base course finished to the final lines and grades established by the engineer.

BASIS OF PAYMENT

5.1 The yardage of base course material, measured as provided above, shall be paid for at the contact unit price per cubic yard for "Caliche Base Course" which price and payment shall constitute full compensation for furnishing, hauling, and placing the materials; for mixing, blading, sprinkling and rolling; for reconditioning of subgrade, shoulders, and gutters; for any required construction, repair and obliteration of access roads; for all pit moves; for clearing, stripping, draining and clean-up of pits; for the handling and disposal of unsuitable materials encountered in pit operations; and for all labor, equipment, tools, water, and incidentals necessary to complete the work.

ADDENDUM

The modifications of the Proctor Density Test, A.A.S.H.O. Method T-99 as required in this specification are as follows:

1. *Apparatus.* Weight of the rammer or metal tamper will be 10 pounds instead of 5½ pounds.
2. *Procedure.* The tamper will be dropped from a height of 18 inches above the sample instead of 12 inches and the samples compacted in five equal (approximately 1") layers instead of three equal layers.

APPENDIX 14

DEPARTMENT OF COMMERCE
Civil Aeronautics Administration
Airport Division
Washington, D.C.
October 1, 1943

LIME ROCK BASE COURSE FOR AIRPORT RUNWAYS, TAXIWAYS AND APRONS

C.A.A. Specification No. P-211

INTRODUCTION

The use of lime rock as base course will naturally be confined to those sections where it is the most economical and practical base course material. It should be used where the subgrade elevation is 3 feet or more above the elevation of the water table. The material will furnish a semi-rigid base course with good confining effect over unstable or shifting fine sand subgrade. The stability of fine sand subgrade should be determined and where necessary raised by the addition of coarse aggregate or a binding material.

Although lower percentages than those appearing in this specification for carbonates with correspondingly higher percentages of clay have been allowed in base construction, the higher clay content might cause an increase in capillarity. Since for runway construction this type of base course will be surfaced with a dense bituminous mix, the percentage of clay should be controlled.

In using lime rock as a base course a 1½ inch dense graded plant mix bituminous wearing surface should be placed thereon with a suitable bond established between the base course and the wearing surface. A surface treatment should be used consisting of tar or asphalt prime to be followed after curing with a keystone course and at least one hundred pounds of dense bituminous surfacing.

DESCRIPTION

1.1 This item shall consist of a base course composed of lime rock constructed on the prepared subgrade or a previously-constructed subbase in accordance with these specifications and in conformity with the dimensions and typical cross sections shown on the plans and with the lines and grades established by the engineer.

MATERIALS

2.1 The lime rock base course material shall consist of fossiliferous limestone of uniform quality and shall not contain hard or flinty pieces which will prevent attainment of a smooth surface free from pits and pockets. The rocks shall show no tendency to air slack or undergo chemical change when exposed to the weather. The material when watered and rolled shall be capable of being compacted into a dense and well-bonded base.

The oolitic type of lime rock shall meet the following requirements:

Carbonates of Calcium and Magnesium, not less than	80%
Oxides of Iron and Aluminum, not more than	2%
The combined amount of carbonates, oxides and silica shall be at least	97%

All other types of lime rock shall contain not less than 97 percent of carbonates of calcium and magnesium.

The chemical analysis of lime rock shall consist of determining the silica insoluble, iron oxide and alumina by solution of the sample in hydrochloric (HCL) acid, evaporating, dehydrating, redissolving the residue and neutralizing with ammonium hydroxide, filtering, washing and igniting the residue lime rock. The difference between this insoluble matter and 100% is reported as carbonates of calcium and magnesium.

The lime rock shall not contain more than three (3) percent of roots, leaf mold, organic or foreign matter and shall be obtained from pits from which all overburden has been removed previous to blasting and quarrying.

The grading of the lime rock shall meet the following requirements:

	Percentage by Weight
Passing 3½″ sieve	100%
Passing ¾″ sieve	50–100%

All fine material shall consist entirely of dust of fracture.

CONSTRUCTION METHODS

3.1 *Sources of Supply.* All work involved in cleaning and stripping pits and handling unsuitable material encountered shall be performed by the contractor at his own expense. The lime rock shall be obtained from sources that have been approved. The pits as utilized shall be operated in such a manner that a clean and uniform material is secured.

3.2 *Equipment and Organization.* All methods employed in performing the work and all equipment, tools and other plant and machinery used for handling materials and executing any part of the work shall be subject to the approval of the engineer before the work is started and whenever found unsatisfactory shall be changed and improved as required. All equipment, tools, machinery and plant used must be maintained in a satisfactory working condition.

Powered rollers shall be of the three-wheeled type, weighing not less than ten (10) tons. Rollers shall have a rear-wheel compression of not less than 330 pounds per linear inch of tire width and shall be equipped with adjustable scrappers. Sufficient rollers shall be furnished to properly compact the base course based on seventy (70) square yards per roller per hour of continuous operation.

Pneumatic rollers shall consist of two axles mounted in a rigid frame having a loading platform or body suitable for ballast loading. On the axles shall be mounted at least nine (9) pneumatic-tired wheels in such a manner that the rear group of tires will not follow in the tracks of the forward group. Rollers shall have an effective rolling width of at least sixty(60) inches and shall have a compression of at least 325 pounds per inch of width of tread when fully loaded. The tires shall be uniformly inflated. Rollers and operating tractors shall meet the approval of the engineer.

Road machines shall weigh not less than 3 tons and shall have a wheel base not less than 15 feet and a blade not less than 10 feet. Road machines shall not be pulled with rollers.

Provision shall be made by the contractor for furnishing water at the site of the work by equipment of ample capacity and of such design as to assure uniform application.

3.3 *Preparing Subgrade.* Before any rock base course material is placed, the subgrade or subbase shall be prepared and conditioned as specified in C.A.A. Specification No. P-103. The subgrade shall be checked and accepted by the engineer before placing and spreading operations are started.

Grade control between the edges of the runways shall be by means of grade stakes, steel pins, or forms placed in lanes parallel to the center line of the runway, and at intervals sufficiently close that string lines or check boards may be placed between the stakes, pins, or forms.

To protect the subgrade and to insure proper drainage, the spreading of the lime rock shall begin along the center line of the runway or taxiway on a crowned section or on the high side of the pavement with a one-way slope.

3.4 *Placing and Spreading.* All base course material shall be placed on the prepared subgrade and compacted in layers of the thickness shown on the plans. The depositing and spreading of the material on the prepared subgrade or on a completed layer shall commence where designated and shall progress continuously without breaks. The material shall be deposited and spread in lanes in a uniform layer and without segregation of size to such loose depth that when compacted, the layer will have the required thickness. It shall be the charge of the contractor that the required amount of approved material is delivered in each 100 foot station. When more than one layer is required the construction procedure described herein shall apply similarly to each layer, excepting the scarifying and rerolling of the surface. This shall apply only to the top layer.

The rock shall be transported to the points where it is to be used, over rock previously-placed, and dumped at the end of the preceding spread. It shall then be spread uniformly with shovels or forks or with vehicles especially constructed for this purpose. In no case shall rock be dumped directly on the subgrade. Transporting over the subgrade will not be permitted except as directed, in which case the subgrade must be protected by planking if rutting occurs. During the dumping and spreading operations the rock shall be thoroughly saturated with water as required. All segregated areas of fine or coarse rock shall be removed and replaced with well-graded rock to the satisfaction of the engineer. Lime rock shall not be spread when the subgrade is in unsuitable condition.

The lime rock base course shall be constructed in layers of not less than four (4) inches nor more than six (6) inches of compacted thickness. The base course shall be constructed in lanes or strips parallel with the centerline of the paved area.

During the placing operation, sufficient caution shall be exercised to prevent the incorporation of subgrade or shoulder material in the lime rock.

3.5 *Rolling.* Immediately following final spreading, the material shall be compacted to full width by rolling with a power roller weighing at least ten (10) tons or other approved compacting equipment. Rolling shall progress gradually from the sides to the center of the lane under construction or from one side toward previously-placed material and shall continue until all the surface has been rolled and compacted. Rolling shall continue until the base material has been compacted to at least 95% density as determined by the modified Proctor Density Test, A.A.S.H.O. Method T 99–42. Large irregularities or depressions that develop under rolling shall be corrected by loosening the material at these places and adding or removing materials until the surface is smooth and uniform. Prior to and during compaction, water in the amounts as directed shall be applied as specified above. Blading and rolling shall be done alternately as required or directed to obtain a smooth, even surface and until the entire depth of base is compacted into a dense, unyielding mass. Rerolling of previous day's spread shall be done as directed. When the shoulder back-fill material has been placed, the shoulder shall be thoroughly rolled and compacted.

Along curbs, headers, and all places inaccessible to the roller, the base course material shall be tamped thoroughly with mechanical or hand tampers. Each hand tamper shall weigh not less than 50 lbs. and have a face area of not more than 100 square inches.

3.6 *Finishing Base Course.* After the watering and rolling of the base course, the entire surface shall be scarified to a depth of at least three (3) inches and shaped to the exact crown and cross section with a road machine. The scarified material shall be rewatered and thoroughly rolled. Rolling shall continue until the base is bonded and compacted into a dense, unyielding mass, true to grade and cross section. The scarifying and rolling of the surface of the base shall follow the initial rolling of the lime rock by not more than four (4) days. When the lime rock base is constructed in two layers, the scarifying of the surface shall be to a depth of two (2) inches.

If at any time the subgrade material becomes churned up and mixed with the base course material, the contractor shall, without additional compensation, dig out and remove the mixture, reshape and compact the subgrade, replace the materials removed with clean rock, which shall be watered and rolled until satisfactorily compacted.

Where cracks, checks, or failures appear in the base, either before or after priming and before the surface course is laid, the contractor shall remove such cracks, checks, or failures by rescarifying, reshaping, watering, rolling and adding lime rock where necessary.

3.7 *Surface Test.* The finished surface of the base course shall be checked with a sixteen (16) foot straight edge laid parallel to and at right angles to the center line of the runway and all irregularities greater than $\frac{3}{8}$ inch corrected by scarifying to a depth of not less than three (3) inches, removing or adding rock as may be required, after which the entire area shall be watered, rolled and brought to a satisfactory state of compaction. In testing surface of the harder lime rocks, measurement of clearances from the straight edge shall not include small holes caused by individual pieces being pulled out by the grader.

3.8 *Thickness.* The thickness of the base course shall be determined by depth tests or elevations taken at intervals in such manner that one measurement shall represent 300 square yards or as directed by the engineer.

The depth tests shall be made by test holes through the base at least three (3) inches in diameter. Where the base deficiency is more than one-half (½) inch, the contractor shall correct such areas by scarifying and adding rock. The base shall be scarified, rock added and tapered out for a distance of 100 feet in each direction from the edge of the deficient area, for each inch of rock added. The affected area shall then be watered, bladed, rolled and brought to a satisfactory state of compaction, and of required thickness and cross-section. The thickness of the base in the affected area shall be remeasured by depth tests or elevations. The operations of scarifying, adding rock and rerolling shall continue until the base thickness is within the one-half inch tolerance of base thickness. The final base thickness of the reconditioned area shall be used to determine the average job thickness.

The average job thickness shall be the average of the depth measurement as above outlined, and shall be within one-quarter (¼) inch of the thickness as shown on the typical cross-section. On individual depth measurements, thicknesses more than one-half (½) inch in excess of that shown on the plans shall be considered as specified thickness plus one-half (½) inch in computing the average job thickness. The contractor shall replace at his expense the lime rock removed from test holes.

3.9 *Maintenance.* The completed base course shall be properly cured over the entire area and further compacted by simulated and uniformly distributed traffic as directed by the engineer. Pneumatic-tired rollers or other equally suitable approved equipment shall be used for additional compacting of base course, which shall be maintained to a true and satisfactory surface until the prime coat is applied.

METHOD OF MEASUREMENT

4.1 The yardage of base course to be paid for shall be the number of cubic yards of base course material placed, bonded and accepted in the completed base course. The quantity of base course material shall be measured in final position based upon depth tests taken as directed by the engineer at the rate of one depth test for each 300 square yards of base course or by means of average end areas on the complete work computed from elevations to the nearest .01 foot. On individual depth measurements, thicknesses more than one-half inch in excess of that shown on the plans shall be considered as the specified thickness plus one-half inch in computing the yardage for payment.

BASIS OF PAYMENT

5.1 The yardage of base course measured as provided above shall be paid for at the contract unit price bid per cubic yard for lime rock base course, which price and payment shall constitute full compensation for furnishing, loading, hauling, and placing the material; for blading, sprinkling, shaping and compacting; for reconditioning the subgrade and shoulders; for reconstruction of irregular surface, or deficient thickness, for curing, and for maintenance; for scarifying and rerolling; for refilling test holes; for any required construction, repair, and obliteration of access roads; for all pit moves; for clearing, stripping, drainage and clean-up of pits; for the handling and disposal of unsuitable materials encountered in pit operations and for all labor, equipment, tools, water and incidentals necessary to complete the work.

The cost of removing cracks and checks as provided above including the labor and material for repriming, and the additional lime rock where necessary on account of such crack elimination, will not be paid for separately, but shall be included in the contract price per cubic yard for lime rock base course.

APPENDIX 15

DEPARTMENT OF COMMERCE
Civil Aeronautics Administration
Airport Division
Washington, D.C.
July 1, 1943

SHELL BASE COURSE FOR AIRPORT RUNWAYS, TAXIWAYS AND APRONS

C.A.A. Specification No. P-212

DESCRIPTION

1.1 This item shall consist of a base course composed of shell and binder constructed on a prepared subgrade or a previously constructed subbase in accordance with these specifications and in conformity with the dimensions and typical cross sections shown on the plans and with the lines and grades established by the Engineer.

MATERIALS

2.1 *Materials.* The shell shall consist of durable particles of "dead" oyster or clam shell. The base material shall consist of oyster shell together with an approved binding or filler material so blended or processed as to produce a uniform mixture complying with the requirements of these specifications as to gradation, soil constants, and capability of being compacted into a dense and well bonded base. Clam shell may be used in combination with oyster shell in the proportion up to and including fifty (50) percent.

The shell shall be reasonably clean and free from excess amount of clay or organic matter such as leaves, grass, roots and other objectionable and foreign material.

The grading of the blended or processed material shall meet the requirements of the grading given in the table below, using A.A.S.H.O., Method T 11 and T 27–42.

Gradation

	Per cent by weight
Passing a 3″ square opening	100
Passing a $\frac{3}{4}$″ square opening	60–90
Passing a $\frac{1}{4}$″ square opening	15–55
Passing a 200 mesh sieve	0–15

That portion of the material, including the blended filler passing a No. 40 sieve, shall be known as soil binder and shall have a liquid limit of not more than 25 and a plasticity index of not more than 10 as determined by A.A.S.H.O. Methods T 89–42 and T 91–42 respectively.

If necessary, the contractor will be required to blend or combine materials so that the finally processed material meets all of the requirements of these specifications. The contractor will be required to make such modifications in materials and methods as are necessary to secure a material which is capable of being compacted into a dense and well-bonded base.

2.2 *Filler for Blending.* If filler, in addition to that naturally present in the base course material, is necessary for satisfactory bonding of the material, for changing the soil constants of the material passing the No. 40 mesh sieve, or for correcting the gradation to the limitations of the specified gradation, it shall be uniformly blended with the base course material on the runway or at the plant. The material for such purpose shall be obtained from sources approved by the engineer and shall be of a gradation as necessary to accomplish the specified gradation in the finally processed material.

CONSTRUCTION METHODS

3.1 *Sources of Supply.* The contractor shall notify the engineer sufficiently in advance of the intended source of supply of shell. The shell shall be obtained from sources that have been approved. The material in the stock-pile shall be handled in a manner that a uniform and satisfactory product will be secured.

3.2 *Equipment.* All equipment necessary for the proper construction of this work shall be on the project, in first-class working condition, and shall have been approved by the engineer before construction is permitted to start.

Rollers shall be of the three-wheeled type power roller weighing not less than 10 tons, and shall have a rear wheel compression of not less than 330 pounds per lineal inch of tire width. Sufficient rollers will be required to properly compact the base course based on 200 square yards per roller per hour of continuous operation.

Road machines shall weigh not less than 3 tons and shall have a wheel base not less than 15 feet and a blade not less than 10 feet. Road machines shall not be pulled with rollers.

Provision shall be made by the contractor for furnishing water at the site of the work by equipment of ample capacity and of such design as to assure uniform application.

The processing plant shall be designed, constructed, operated and of such capacity so as to thoroughly mix the shell, binder and water in the proportions as directed to produce base material of the gradation and consistency required.

3.3 *Preparing Subgrade.* Before any shell base course material is placed, the subgrade or subbase shall be prepared and conditioned as specified in C.A.A. Specification No. P-103. The subgrade shall be checked and accepted by the engineer before placing and spreading operations are started.

Grade control between the edges of the runways shall be by means of grade stakes, steel pins, or forms placed in lanes parallel to the center line of the runway, and at intervals sufficiently close that string lines or check boards may be placed between the stakes, pins, or forms.

To protect the subgrade and to insure proper drainage, the spreading of the shell shall begin along the center line of the runway or taxiway on a crowned section or on the high side of the pavement with a one-way slope.

3.4 *Plant Mixing.* When required in the proposal the shell base material shall be processed in a central mixing plant or in a travel mixing plant. The shell together with any blended material shall be thoroughly mixed with the required amount of water. After the mixing is complete the material shall be transported to or spread on the subgrade without undue loss of the moisture content.

3.5 *Placing and Spreading.* All base course material shall be placed on the prepared subgrade and compacted in layers of the thickness shown on the plans. The depositing and spreading of the material on the prepared subgrade or on a completed layer shall commence where designated and shall progress continuously without breaks. The material shall be deposited and spread in lanes in a uniform layer and without segregation of size to such loose depth that when compacted, the layer will have the required thickness. It shall be the charge of the contractor that the required amount of approved material is delivered in each 100 foot station. When and as directed the material shall be spread from dump boards, spreader boxes or moving vehicles equipped to distribute the material in a uniform layer. When more than one layer is required the construction procedure described herein shall apply similarly to each layer.

The base shall be constructed in layers of not more than six (6) inches. The first layer on the subgrade shall not be less than four (4) inches. Hauling over material that has not been mixed and shaped will not be permitted except when necessitated by the placing of successive layers of materials. Layers of shell allowed to become partially compacted shall be scarified and disced before placing binder material or before blading and shaping for rolling.

3.6 *Mixed in Place.* (a) When the shell base material is to be mixed or blended in place on the runway, the shell shall be placed as described above except due allowance shall be made for any material that is to be blended.

(b) Spreading Binder or Filler Material—When the shell has been placed as provided above, the required amount of approved binder or filler material shall be similarly placed in a uniform layer over the shell course.

(c) Blading and Blending—When the required amount of materials have been placed as described, they shall be thoroughly mixed and blended by means of approved graders, supplemented by other suitable equipment if necessary. The mixing shall continue until the mixture is uniform throughout. Areas of segregated material shall be corrected by the addition of binder or filler material and thoroughly remixed. Water in the amount and as directed by the engineer shall be uniformly applied prior to and during the mixing operations by means of tanks mounted on trucks and equipped with spray bars or other approved methods. When the mixing and blending has been completed the material shall be spread in a uniform layer which when compacted will meet the requirements of the typical cross section.

3.7 *Rolling.* Immediately following final spreading, the material shall be compacted to full width by rolling with a power roller weighing at least 10 tons or other approved compacting equipment. Rolling shall progress gradually from the sides to the center of the lane under construction or from one side toward previously placed material and shall continue until all the surface has been rolled and compacted. Rolling shall continue until the base material has been compacted to 95% density as determined by the modified Proctor Density Test,

A.A.S.H.O. Method T 99–42. Any irregularities or depressions that develop under rolling shall be corrected by loosening the material at these places and adding or removing materials until the surface is smooth and uniform. Prior to and during compaction, water in the amounts as directed shall be applied as specified above. Blading and rolling shall be done alternately as required or directed to maintain a smooth, even, uniformly compacted base until any surface or treatment that may be provided for in the same contract is placed thereon. Upon completion, the shell base course shall be allowed to partially dry for a period of at least several days before the prime coat is applied. The drying shall not continue to the extent that the surface of the base becomes dusty with consequent loss of binder. The prime shall be applied when directed or the surface of the base kept moist by sprinkling when necessary. Along curbs, headers and walls and all places not accessible to the roller, the base course material shall be tamped thoroughly with mechanical or hand tampers. Each hand tamper shall weigh not less than 50 lbs. and have a face area of not more than 100 square inches.

3.8 *Surface Test and Thickness.* In that area upon which surfacing is to be placed the base course completed as above shall be tested with a sixteen (16) foot straightedge and any deviation in excess of three-eighths (⅜) inch shall be corrected by loosening, adding or removing material, reshaping and recompacting by sprinkling and rolling.

The thickness of the base course shall be determined by depth tests or cores taken at intervals in such manner that one core shall represent 300 square yards or as directed by the engineer. Where the base deficiency is more than one-half (½) inch, the contractor shall correct such areas by scarifying, adding base material including binder, rolling, sprinkling, reshaping and finishing in accordance with these specifications.

METHOD OF MEASUREMENT

4.1 Yardage of base course material to be paid for shall be the cubic yards of base course material including all binder placed, bonded and accepted in the completed base course. The quantities of base course material and binder shall be measured in final position based upon depth tests or cores taken as directed by the engineer or at the rate of one depth test for each 300 square yards of base course or by means of average end areas on the completed work computed from elevation to the nearest .01 foot. On individual depth measurements, thicknesses more than one-half (½) inch in excess of that shown on the plans shall be considered as specified thickness plus one-half (½) inch in computing the yardage for payment.

BASIS OF PAYMENT

5.1 The yardage of base course material measured as provided above shall be paid for at the contract unit price per cubic yard for shell base course, which price and payment shall constitute full compensation for furnishing, hauling, and placing the materials; for mixing, blading, sprinkling and rolling; for reconditioning the subgrade and shoulders; for any required construction, repair, and obliteration of access roads; for all pit moves; for clearing, stripping and cleanup of stockpiles; for the handling and disposal of unsuitable materials encountered in stockpile operations; for reconstruction of irregular surface or deficient thickness and for all labor, equipment, tools, water and incidentals necessary to complete the work.

APPENDIX 16

DEPARTMENT OF COMMERCE
Civil Aeronautics Administration
Airport Division
Washington, D.C.
June 15, 1944

BITUMINOUS BASE AND/OR SURFACE COURSE (CENTRAL PLANT HOT MIX) FOR AIRPORT RUNWAYS, TAXIWAYS AND APRONS

C.A.A. Specification No. P-201; 401

INTRODUCTION

This specification provides the most economical type of central plant bituminous mix of the highest quality. To accomplish this, a range is allowed for selection and use of local aggregates. This type of surfacing should be given preference over other types of bituminous paving.

It is the responsibility of the engineer to set up the job mix formula. After the contractor has submitted samples of the materials intended for the project, the samples shall be tested to determine the proper combinations of the aggregates and the bituminous material to produce a satisfactory mixture on basis of stability and density. All available laboratory tests methods should be used to obtain the data necessary for study and guidance. A uniform gradation should be selected, that is, one that will produce a relatively smooth curve. A gradation producing a smooth curve will usually have the least voids and the highest stability, while an irregular curve will contain a skip gradation with large voids and low stability. If Hubbard-Field or other stability equipment is not available, a Proctor mould should be used to obtain results.

The field laboratory established for each job should have sufficient equipment and personnel for performing frequent tests on the gradation and quality of aggregates, the density, stability and bitumen content of samples cut from the pavement and other control tests. It is emphasized that only by the means of check testing the materials and the pavement mixture can a satisfactory job be accomplished. This checking will suggest, in some cases, the necessity for slight modifications of the formula for unavoidable variations in the aggregate gradation (within the gradation limits) and the need of control of other variables that are encountered during the course of the work.

The use of RT-10, 11 or 12 grade of refined tar is allowed for base or binder course construction. The temperature control for tar mixes should be kept to a minimum, approximately 200° F.

If the aggregate is found to be hydrophilic as determined by the test given in the specification, the addition of 0.5 to 1.5 percent of hydrated lime or Portland cement to the aggregate prior to mixing with the bituminous material may be sufficient to change the inherent characteristics to a hydrophobic material. If the material is of such hydrophilic characteristics that the lime or cement alone will not accomplish the desired results the addition of a proven and approved admixture to the bituminous material will be necessary.

It is recommended that where grass or weed growth might cause damage to the pavement that a recognized and approved chemical treatment be applied to the subgrade or base course.

The following gradations are for use in the construction of sand asphalt pavements. These should not be included in the general specifications unless by their use a large economic saving is realized.

Sieve Size	Percentage Passing Sieves (Square Openings)	
	$\frac{3}{8}''$ Maximum	No. 4 Maximum
$\frac{1}{2}''$	100	100
$\frac{3}{8}''$	91–100	94–100
No. 4	75–100	83–100
No. 10	56–85	70–94
No. 40	24–56	30–65
No. 80	12–37	14–42
No. 200	4–10	5–10
% Bituminous Mat'l.		
Base—Asph. Cement	5.5–7.5	6.0–8.5
—Tar	5.0–6.5	5.5–7.5
Surf.—Asph. Cement	6.0–8.5	6.5–9.5

BITUMINOUS BASE AND/OR SURFACE COURSE CENTRAL PLANT HOT MIX

DESCRIPTION

1.1 This item shall consist of a base and/or wearing course composed of mineral aggregate and bituminous material, mixed in a central mixing plant and placed on the prepared base course or subgrade in accordance with these specifications and in conformity with the dimensions and typical cross sections shown on the plans and with lines and grades established by the engineer.

1.2 *Determination of Percentage of Bituminous Material.* The percentage of bituminous material, by weight, to be added to the aggregate shall be fixed by the engineer on the basis of preliminary laboratory tests and field sieve analysis on the aggregate furnished, and shall be within the range as shown in the table.

1.3 *Job Mix Formula.* No work shall be started on the project nor any mixture accepted therefor until the contractor has submitted samples of the materials intended for use and the engineer has established a satisfactory job mix formula based upon tests of the materials furnished. The formula shall be submitted in writing by the engineer to the contractor, indicating the definite percentage for each sieve fraction of aggregate and for bituminous cement; also the intended temperature of completed mixture at the time it is discharged from the mixer.

The material furnished shall conform to the approved job mix formula within the tolerances specified herein.

Job Mix Tolerances

Aggregate passing sieves No. 4 and larger	±5%
Aggregate passing No. 10, No. 40, and No. 80 sieve	±4%
Aggregate passing No. 200 sieve	±2%
Asphaltic cement	±0.5%
Tar	±0.5%
Temperature of mixing and placing	±25° F.

MATERIALS

2.1 *Aggregate.* The aggregate shall consist of crushed stone, crushed gravel, crushed slag, screenings, gravel, sand-gravel, sand or other natural, granular, approved material having essentially the same qualities and meeting all the requirements when combined within the limits for gradation.

The aggregate shall be tough, durable and sound. The coarse aggregate when tested in accordance with the Los Angeles Rattler Test, after five hundred revolutions shall have a percent of wear of not more than fifty (50) according to the A.A.S.H.O., Method T 96–42.

Slag shall be air cooled, blast furnace slag and shall have a compact weight of not less than seventy (70) pounds per cubic foot. The aggregate shall consist of angular fragments reasonably uniform in density and quality and reasonably free from thin, elongated or soft pieces, dirt or other objectionable matter.

The portion of the material retained on a No. 4 sieve shall be known as coarse aggregate; that portion passing a No. 4 sieve shall be known as fine aggregate, and the material passing the No. 200 sieve shall be known as filler. The composite material shall meet the requirements for one of the gradings given in Table 3, using A.A.S.H.O. Methods T-11 and T 27–42.

That portion of the fine aggregate, including any blended filler, passing a No. 40 sieve shall have a plasticity index of not more than 6, as determined by A.A.S.H.O. Method T 91–42, and a liquid limit of not more than 25 as determined by A.A.S.H.O. Method T 89–42.

The composite aggregate shall be free from vegetable matter, lumps or balls of clay, adherent films of clay, or other matter that will prevent thorough coating with bituminous material. The bituminized aggregate shall have a swell of not more than 1.5 percent as determined by A.A.S.H.O. Method T 101–42.

Prior to final acceptance of the proposed aggregate to be used, the inherent characteristics of said aggregate relative to stripping shall be determined. This shall be done by preparing a test sample of the paving mixture in conformity with the specifications contained herewith. After the mixture has been made it shall be spread out in a loose thin layer and allowed to air season for 24 hours before testing. A suitable size sample (approximately one-half contents of container) shall be tested by placing it in a glass jar fitted with a tight screw cap and completely covering with distilled water. The jar and contents shall be allowed to stand for a period of 24 hours. Then the sample shall be vigorously shaken for a period of 15 minutes. The sample of mixture shall be examined for stripping. If stripping or sloughing off of the bituminous coating occurs it will be necessary to treat said aggregate by a method which has proven successful in changing the material from a hydrophilic to a hydrophobic state.

2.2 *Filler.* If filler in addition to that naturally present in the aggregate is necessary, it shall consist of stone dust, loess, Portland cement or other standard approved types. The material for such purpose shall be obtained from sources approved by the engineer.

2.3 *Bituminous Material.* The bituminous material to be mixed with the mineral aggregate at the central plant shall conform to the grade, requirements and specifications as follows: Asphalt cement shall be used in the surface course and the asphalt cement or tar shall be used in the base or binder course, unless otherwise specified in the proposal.

TABLE 1

Asphalt Cement

The asphalt cement shall conform to the following requirements: The asphalt cement shall be homogeneous, free from water, and shall not foam when heated to a temperature of 347° F.

Test Requirements	Petroleum Asphalts	Native Asphalts
Penetration at 77° F., 100 g., 5 sec.	120–150	120–150
Total Bitumen (soluble in carbon disulphide), not less than	99.5%	
Total Bitumen (Soluble in carbon disulphide) (Bermudes Asphaltic cement) not less than		95.0%
Proportion of bitumen soluble in carbon Tetrachloride, not less than	99.0%	99.0%
Ductility at 77° F., not less than	100 cms.	60 cms.
Flash point, ° F., not less than	347	347
Loss at 325° F., 5 hrs., not more than	1.0%	3.0%
Penetration of residue at 77° F., 100 g, 5 sec., as compared to penetration before heating, not less than	60.0%	50.0%
Temperature range ° F.	225–300	225–300
Oliensis Spot Test	Negative	

Sampling and testing of asphalt cement shall be in accordance with the following standard methods of the American Association of State Highway Officials:

(a) Sampling	T-40–42
(b) Penetration	T-49–42
(c) Total bitumen	T-44–42
(d) Bitumen soluble in carbon tetrachloride	T-45–42
(e) Ductility	T-51–42
(f) Flash Point	T-48–42
(g) Loss at 325° F.	T-47–42
(h) Oliensis Spot Test	T-102–42

Note: The Oliensis Spot Test may be used to identify products manufactured by the cracking process, which show a positive spot when present in sufficient proportions. The Test should be modified to differentiate between cracked asphalts and those asphalts from some crude sources that have never been cracked but show a positive spot.

TABLE 2

Tar

The tar shall be homogeneous and shall be a water-gas or coal tar or a combination of these. The refined tar material to be mixed with the mineral aggregate at the central plant for use in the base or binder course shall conform to the grade, requirements and specifications as follows:

Test Requirements	A.A.S.H.O. Test Method	Grades RT–10	RT–11	RT–12
Consistency:				
Float Test at 122° F.	T-50	75–100	100–150	150–220
Sp. Gr. at 77° F./77° F.	T-43	1.15+	1.16+	1.16+
Total Bitumen, % by weight	T-44	75+	75+	75+
Water, % by volume	T-55	0	0	0
Distillation, % by weight:	T-52			
To 338° F.	....	1.0–	1.0–	1.0–
To 518° F.	....	10.0–	10.0–	10.0–
To 572° F.	....	20.0–	20.0–	20.0–
Softening Point of Distillation Residue ° F.	T-53	104–158	104–158	104–158
Temperature Range F.	....	175°–250°	175°–250°	175°–250°

2.4 *Hydrated Lime.* The hydrated lime shall meet the requirements of the A.S.T.M. Designation C 6–31.

GRADATION

3.1 *Composition of Mixture.* The mineral aggregate for the base, binder and surface courses shall be of such size that the percentage composition by weight, as determined by laboratory sieves will conform to one of the following gradations:

TABLE 3

Base, Binder and Surface Courses

Sieve Size	Percentage Passing Sieves (Square Openings) 1″ Maximum	¾″ Maximum	½″ Maximum
1″	100		
¾″	82–100	100	
½″	70–90	82–100	100
⅜″	60–82	70–90	82–100
No. 4	47–70	55–79	62–88
No. 10	35–60	40–67	45–75
No. 40	15–40	17–44	20–48
No. 80	8–26	9–29	10–32
No. 200	3–8	3–8	4–9
% Bituminous Mat'l.			
Base—Asph. Cement	4–6	4.5–6.5	5.0–7.0
—Tar	3.5–5	4–5.5	4.5–6.0
Surf.—Asph. Cement	4.5–7.0	5.0–7.5	5.5–8.0

In table 3 the percentages of asphalt cement and tar are for stone and gravel aggregates. If the total aggregate is composed of slag, the percentages of bituminous material shown shall be increased by thirty (30) per cent. Where only a part of the aggregates is slag, this increase shall be made in a corresponding proportion.

The gradations in this table represent the limits which shall determine suitability of aggregate for use from the sources of supply. The final gradations decided on within the limits designated in the table shall be uniformly graded from coarse to fine, and shall not vary from the low limit on one screen to the high limit on the adjacent screens or vice versa.

The selection of any of the gradings shown in the table shall be such that the maximum size aggregate used in any course shall not be more than one-half the thickness of the layer of the course being constructed.

The composition limits tabulated shall govern but a closer control appropriate to the job materials will be required for the specific project in accordance with a job mix formula.

The total amount of material passing the No. 200 sieve shall be determined by washing the material through the sieve with water and not less than one-half ($\frac{1}{2}$) of the material passing the No. 200 sieve by washing shall pass the No. 200 sieve by dry sieving without washing.

CONSTRUCTION METHODS

4.1 *Weather and Seasonal Limitations.* Surface course shall be constructed only when the surface is dry, when the atmospheric temperature is above 40°F., and when the weather is not foggy or rainy. The temperature requirement may be waived, but only when so directed by the engineer.

4.2 *Equipment and Organization.* (a) *General.* All methods employed in performing the work and all equipment, tools and other plant and machinery used for handling materials and executing any part of the work shall be subject to the approval of the engineer before the work is started and whenever found unsatisfactory shall be changed and improved as required. All equipment, tools, machinery and plant used must be maintained in a satisfactory working condition.

(b) *Mixing Plant.* The paving plant used by the contractor in the preparation of the bituminous concrete shall comply with the following requirements:

The drier shall be suitably designed to heat and dry the aggregate to specification requirements and to continuously agitate the aggregate during heating. The drier shall be capable of preparing aggregate to the full rated capacity of the paving plant to meet the specification requirement. A dial thermometer or other thermometric instrument shall be so placed in the bin over the mixer as to automatically register the temperature of the heated aggregate before it enters the mixer. The dial or other indicator shall be plainly visible from the mixing platform.

The plant screens shall be designed, constructed, and operated so as to screen all aggregates to appropriate fractions as established by the engineer and as necessary to meet the job mix tolerances.

The plant shall have storage bins, protected from the weather, of sufficient capacity to furnish the necessary amounts of all aggregates when operating at the maximum rated capacity of the plant. The bins shall provide two or more compartments for hot aggregates, so proportioned as to insure adequate storage of appropriate fractions of the aggregate and mineral filler. Each compartment shall be provided with an overflow pipe or other device which meets the approval of the engineer, of such size and at such locations as to prevent backing up of material into other compartments.

The plant may have either batch weighing or volumetric proportioning of mineral aggregates and bituminous cement. This equipment shall be constructed with devices that will permit easy readjustment of any working part such that it will function properly and accurately. The aggregate weighing or measuring device shall be so constructed and operated that the correct amount of each size aggregate is introduced into the mixer with an accuracy that will meet the job tolerances specified. The plant mixer shall have a capacity of at least 1200 pounds and the plant shall have a capacity of at least 40 tons per hour.

The asphalt weighing or measuring device shall be so constructed and operated that the correct amount of asphalt is introduced into the mixer with an accuracy that will meet the job tolerance specified. If weight control is used the dial scales or other weighing device shall be of an approved type.

The mixer may be either a batch drum type mixer, a twin pugmill or a continuous type twin pugmill mixer of sufficient size to maintain thorough uniform mixing at the rated plant capacity. The mixer shall be steam jacketed.

The plant shall be equipped with positive means to govern the time of mixing and to maintain it constant unless changed by order of the engineer. The time of mixing shall be considered as the interval between the time the bituminous material is spread on the aggregate and the time the same aggregate leaves the mixing unit.

Equipment for heating bituminous material shall consist of a retort or steam coils so designed that steam will not be introduced into the material. A recording thermometer shall be provided, which will record the temperature of the bituminous material at the draw off valve.

Asphalt storage and supply lines shall be insulated or steam jacketed in such a manner that there will be no appreciable drop in temperature of the asphalt between the heating unit and the mixing unit.

(c) *Placing Equipment.* Equipment for spreading, shaping, and finishing shall consist of an approved self-contained power machine operating in such a manner that no supplemental spreading, shaping, or finishing will be required to provide a surface which will comply with the requirements for smoothness contained herein.

(d) *Rolling Equipment.* Rollers shall be suitably designed for the construction of bituminous surfaces. The rolling shall be done with self-propelled tandem and three wheel type rollers weighing not less than eight (8) tons. The wheels on the rollers shall be equipped with adjustable scrapers which shall be used when necessary to clean the wheel surface. Rollers shall also be equipped with water tanks and sprinkling apparatus which shall be used to keep the wheels wet and prevent the surfacing material from sticking.

4.3 *Preparation of Mineral Aggregate.* The aggregate for the mixture shall be dried and heated at the paving plant before entering the mixer. When introduced into the mixer the combined aggregate shall not contain more than 1%

moisture if asphalt is used or more than 3% for tar mixtures. Water in the aggregate shall be removed by heating to the extent that no subsequent foaming shall occur in the mixture prior to the placing of the material. The aggregate shall be heated to the temperature as designated by the Job Formula within the job tolerances specified. The maximum temperature and the rate of heating shall be such that no permanent damage occurs to the aggregates. Particular care shall be taken that aggregates high in calcium or magnesium content are not damaged by heating. The aggregates shall be screened to specified sizes and conveyed into separate bins ready for mixing with bituminous material. Where fine aggregate gradation is used and screening is not practical, the blending of different size aggregates to obtain proper gradation may be secured by the use of a reciprocating feeder to the cold elevator. The use of two or more hot bins will be waived, provided the tolerances of the job mix formula are fully met.

Additional filler, if necessary to meet the grading requirements, shall be proportioned and added to the mineral aggregate. Filler may be added to the aggregate at the mixing plant by premixing it thoroughly with the other aggregates. Spreading filler over the tops of the aggregate pits or dumping it into the hoppers at crushing plants will not be permitted.

4.4 *Preparation of Bituminous Mixture.* Before being delivered to the runway, the aggregate shall be mixed with the bituminous material at a central mixing plant. The mixture shall be prepared at a temperature as directed by the engineer between 175° to 250° F. for tar mixtures and 225° to 300° F. for asphalt mixtures.

The aggregate prepared as prescribed above, shall be accurately measured and conveyed into the mixer in the proportionate amounts of each aggregate required to meet the specified grading.

The bituminous material shall be melted in kettles or tanks designed to secure uniform heating of the entire contents. Tar shall not be heated over 250° F. and asphalt shall not be heated over 325° F.

Kettles for storage of bituminous cement shall have a total capacity sufficient for one day's run and shall be capable of heating the bituminous cement with an effective and positive control of the heat at all times to a temperature of between 175° F. and 350° F. Heating of the cement by steam coils is preferred. Under no circumstances will a direct flame from oil or other fuel be permitted to come in direct contact with the heating kettles. The circulating system shall be constructed of adequate size to give the proper and continuous circulation of cement throughout the operating periods. All lines and fittings shall be steam jacketed.

The quantity of bituminous material for each batch or calibrated amount for continuous mixing shall be determined by the engineer, and shall be measured by weight and introduced into the mixer at the specified temperature, holding to the lowest range possible for adequate mixing and spreading. All mineral aggregate shall be in the mixer before the bituminous material is added. The exact temperature to be used on the work within the specified range shall be fixed by the engineer. In no case shall aggregate be introduced into the mixture at a temperature more than 25° F. above the temperature of the bituminous material. The mixing shall continue for at least thirty seconds and for such longer period as may be necessary to coat all of the particles.

From zero to one percent of Portland cement or hydrated lime shall be added to the composition of the surface mixtures when provided for in the proposal.

4.5 *Transportation and delivery of the mixture.* The mixture shall be transported from the mixing plant to the point of use in pneumatic-tired vehicles having tight bodies previously cleaned of all foreign materials. When directed by the engineer, each load shall be covered with canvas or other suitable material of sufficient size and thickness to protect it from the weather conditions.

The mixture shall be placed at a temperature between 150° and 225° F. when tar is used and between 200° and 300° F. when asphalt cement is used.

When the mixture is being placed during warm weather and the engineer has determined that satisfactory results can be obtained at lower temperatures, he may direct that the mixture be mixed and delivered at the lower temperatures.

No loads shall be sent out so late in the day as to interfere with spreading and compacting the mixture during daylight, unless artificial light satisfactory to the engineer is provided. The mixture shall be delivered at a temperature within the tolerance allowed in the approved Job Formula.

4.6 *Spreading and Laying.* (a) *Preparation for placing.* Immediately before placing the bituminous mixture, the existing surface shall be cleaned of loose or deleterious material by sweeping with a power sweeper supplemented by hand brooms if necessary, or as directed by the engineer.

The mixture shall be laid only upon an approved underlying course which is dry and only when weather conditions are suitable. No mixture shall be placed when the air temperature in the shade and away from artificial heat is 40° F. or under unless so directed by the engineer. The engineer may, however, permit work of this character to continue when overtaken by sudden rains, up to the amount which may be in transit from the plant at the time—provided the mixture is within the temperature limits specified.

Grade control between the edges of the runway shall be by means of grade stakes or steel pins placed in lanes parallel to the center line of the runway, and at intervals sufficiently close that string lines may be stretched between stakes or pins.

Placing shall commence at the point or points furthest from the mixing plant, and progress continuously toward the plant, unless otherwise ordered by the engineer. Hauling over material already placed will not be permitted until the material has been compacted thoroughly in the manner specified, and allowed to cool to atmospheric temperature.

(b) *Machine Spreading.* Upon arrival the mixture shall be dumped into an approved mechanical spreader and immediately spread thereby to the full width required. It shall be struck off in a uniform layer of such depth that when the work is completed, it will have the required thickness and will conform to the grade and surface contour required. The speed of the mechanical spreader shall be regulated to eliminate as far as possible the pulling and tearing of the bituminous material.

Placing and compaction of the bituminous mixture shall progress in sections. The bituminous mixture shall be spread, shaped, and finished with the power-machine specified. The mixture shall be placed in strips of a minimum width of

10 feet. To insure proper drainage, the spreading shall begin along the center line of the runway or taxiway on a crowned section or on the high side of the pavement with a one-way slope. The 6-inch strip adjacent to the area on which future material is to be laid shall not be rolled until such material has been placed, but shall not be left unrolled more than two (2) hours after being placed. After the first strip or width has been compacted, the second width shall be placed, finished and compacted as provided for the first width, except that rolling shall be extended to include the six inches of the first width not previously compacted. Whenever the adjacent or second width cannot be placed within two (2) hours, the 6-inch strip shall not be left unrolled. After the second strip has been placed and rolled, a 10-foot straight edge shall be used across the longitudinal joint to determine if the surface is to grade and contour.

In limited areas where, on account of irregularities or unavoidable obstacles, the use of mechanical spreading and finishing equipment is impractical, the mixture may be spread by hand.

When hand spreading is permitted, the mixture shall be dumped upon arrival on approved dump sheets outside of the area on which it is to be spread and be distributed into place immediately by means of hot shovels. It shall be spread with hot rakes in a uniformly loose layer to the full width required and of such depth that where the work is completed, it will have the required thickness and will conform to the grade and surface contour required.

Contact surfaces shall be painted with a thin uniform coat of hot asphalt cement, tar or cut-back asphalt just before the mixture is placed.

4.7 *Compaction of Mixture.* After spreading, and as directed by the engineer, the mixture shall be thoroughly and uniformly compressed by a power driven, three-wheel roller and tandem roller or rollers, weighing 8 tons or more. Rolling of the mixture shall begin as soon after spreading as it will bear the roller without undue displacement or hair checking. On the first strip spread, rolling shall start in the center and continue toward either edge. On subsequent strips laid, rolling shall start on the edge adjacent to previously-laid material and continue toward the other edge.

Initial rolling shall be done longitudinally with three-wheel rollers overlapping on successive trips of the roller. Alternate trips of the roller shall be of slightly different lengths. The mixture shall be subjected to diagonal rolling crossing the lines of the first.

The speed of the roller shall at all times be slow enough to avoid displacement of the hot mixture. Any displacement occurring as a result of reversing the direction of the roller, or from any other cause, shall be corrected at once by the use of rakes, and of fresh mixture where required.

Sufficient rollers of the designated types shall be furnished to adequately handle the output of the plant. Rolling shall proceed at an average rate not to exceed 350 square yards per hour per roller. Rolling shall continue until all roller marks are eliminated, until the surface is of uniform texture and true to grade, and cross section, and until the density of at least 92% of the theoretical density is obtained. Field density tests shall be made at least twice daily. Final rolling shall be done with tandem rollers.

The theoretical density shall be computed as follows:

$$\text{Density} = \frac{100}{\dfrac{\%\text{ mineral aggregate by weight}}{\text{Sp. gr. mineral aggregate}} + \dfrac{\%\text{ bitumen by weight}}{\text{Sp. gr. of bitumen}}}$$

To prevent adhesion of the mixture to the roller, the wheels shall be kept properly moistened, but an excess of either water or oil will not be permitted. The rollers shall be kept in good condition and shall be operated by competent and experienced rollermen. The rollers shall be operated continuously as far as practicable and in such a manner that all parts of the pavement shall receive substantially equal compression.

At all places not accessible to the roller, the mixture shall be thoroughly compacted with hot hand tampers. Hand tampers shall weigh not less than 25 pounds and shall have a tamping face area of not more than 50 square inches. The surface of the mixture after compression shall be smooth and true to the established crown and grade.

Any mixture which becomes loose and broken, mixed with dirt, or in any way defective prior to the application of the finish coat shall be removed and replaced with fresh hot mixture, which shall be immediately compacted to con form with the surrounding area, all to be done at the expense of the contractor. Skin patching on an area that has been rolled shall not be allowed.

4.8 *Joints.* (a) *General.* Joints shall comply with the surface requirements and present the same uniformity of texture, density, smoothness, etc., as other sections of the course.

(b) *Transverse.* The placing of the course shall be as nearly continuous as possible. The roller shall pass over the unprotected end of the freshly laid mixture only when the laying of the course is to be discontinued.

(c) *Longitudinal.* The placing of the course shall be in the manner as specified and so that the joint is exposed for the shortest period possible. The joint shall be placed so that it will not coincide with that in the base or binder course and will break joints by at least one foot.

(d) In the formation of all joints, provision shall be made for proper bond with the new surface for the full specified depth of the course. Joints shall be formed by cutting back on the previous day's run so as to expose the full depth of the course, and the exposed edge shall be given a light paint coat of asphalt, if necessary. The fresh mixture shall be raked against the joint, thoroughly tamped with tampers and rolled.

4.9 *Shaping Edges.* While the surface is being compacted and finished, the contractor shall trim the edges neatly to line.

4.10 *Surface Tests.* The finished surface shall not vary more than $\frac{1}{4}$ inch for the wearing course or $\frac{3}{8}$ inch for the binder or base course when measured with a sixteen (16) foot straightedge applied parallel with or at right angles to the center line. Tests for conformity with the specified crown and grade shall be made by the contractor immediately after initial compression and any variation shall be corrected by removing or adding materials and continuing the rolling. After the completion of final rolling, the smoothness of the course shall again be checked, and the humps or depressions exceeding the specified tolerances or that retain water on the surface shall be corrected by removing the defective work and replacing with new material or by adding additional material as directed by the engineer and at the expense of the contractor.

4.11 *Sampling Pavement.* For the determination of composition, compaction and density of the pavement the contractor shall remove suitable size samples of the completed pavement. Samples for each day or fraction thereof when mixtures are placed shall be taken by the engineer. The contractor shall replace the pavement where samples are removed, and these replacements shall be installed by the contractor free of charge. After the samples have been removed from the completed pavement, they will be tested by the engineer for density and composition. If the deficiency in composition, compaction and density exceeds the limits of toleration from that specified, satisfactory corrections shall be made.

4.12 *Bituminous and Aggregate Material Contractor's Responsibility.* Samples of the bituminous and aggregate materials that the contractor proposes to use, together with a statement as to their source and character must be submitted and approval obtained before use of such material begins. The contractor shall require the manufacturer or producer of the bituminous and aggregate materials to furnish material subject to this and all other pertinent requirements of the contract. Only those materials that have been demonstrated by service tests as satisfactory for the intended use will be acceptable.

For checking the adequacy of the equipment in use, inspecting the conditions and operation of the plant, for the verification of weights or proportions and character of materials and/or the determination and checking of temperatures being maintained in the preparation of the mixtures, the engineer or his authorized representative shall have access at any time to all parts of the paving plant.

The contractor shall furnish vendor's certified test report for each car load or equivalent of bitumen shipped to the project. The report shall be delivered to the engineer before permission is granted for use of the material.

4.13 *Freight and Weigh-Bills.* Before the final estimate is allowed, the contractor shall file with the engineer receipted bills where railroad shipments are made and certified weigh-bills when materials are received in any other manner, of the bituminous and paving materials actually used in the construction covered by the contract. The contractor shall not remove bituminous material from the tank car or storage tank until the initial outage and temperature measurements have been taken, nor shall he release the car or tank until the final outage has been taken by the engineer.

Copies of all freight bills and weigh-bills shall be furnished to the engineer during the progress of the work.

4.14 *Seal Coat.* As shown on the plans and called for in the bid schedule, a seal coat of the type called for shall be applied to the finished course as described under SEAL COAT.

METHOD OF MEASUREMENT

5.1 The tonnage of base course to be paid for shall be the number of tons of bituminous mixture of the grading called for and used in the accepted work. The bituminous treated material shall be weighed after mixing and no deduction shall be made for the weight of bituminous material in the mixture.

5.2 The tonnage of surface course to be paid for shall be the number of tons of bituminous mixture of the grading called for in the bid schedule. and used in the accepted work. The bituminous treated material shall be weighed after mixing and no deduction shall be made for the weight of bituminous material in the mixture.

5.3 The quantities as measured in paragraphs 5.1 and 5.2 for base and surface mixtures are applicable for aggregates having a bulk specific gravity between 2.55 and 2.75 as determined by A.A.S.H.O. Method T 84 and T 85–42. Proportionate corrections shall be made when the aggregate furnished on the job have bulk specific gravities above 2.75 or below 2.55. In such cases the corrected quantity for payment shall be the product of the number of tons used multiplied by the ratio of 2.65 to the bulk specific gravity of the job aggregate.

5.4 The unit of measurement for the bituminous material shall be the gallon or the ton, whichever is called for in the bid schedule. The gallonage or tonnage to be paid for shall be the number of gallons or tons of bituminous material used as ordered in the accepted work. Gallonage shall be determined by measuring the material at a temperature of 60° F., or by converting the gallonage measured at other temperatures to gallonage at 60° F. in accordance with A.S.T.M. Designation D 206–36 for asphalt materials and in accordance with A.S.T.M. Designation D 633–41 T for tar.

BASIS OF PAYMENT

6.1 The quantities of surfacing mixture and bituminous material determined as provided in 5.1, 5.2, 5.3 and 5.4 above, shall be paid for at the respective contract unit prices per ton in the bid schedule for base or surface course and per gallon or per ton for bituminous material, which prices and payment shall constitute full conmpensation for preparing base or subgrade, for furnishing, handling, mixing, manipulating, and placing all materials, for all shaping, compacting and rolling, for finishing, for improving unsatisfactory areas, for reconditioning subgrade, for furnishing samples, for furnishing and sealing of scales, for furnishing the weigh house, for all labor, equipment, tools and incidentals necessary to complete the item, except any prime coat or seal coat.

APPENDIX 17

DEPARTMENT OF COMMERCE
Civil Aeronautics Administration
Airport Division
Washington, D.C.
April 1, 1942

COLD MIX EMULSIFIED ASPHALT BASE AND/OR SURFACE COURSE FOR AIRPORT RUNWAYS, TAXIWAYS AND APRONS

C.A.A. Specification No. P-202, 402

INTRODUCTION

This specification has been prepared by the Paving Engineers of the Airport Division, Civil Aeronautics Administration in collaboration with the Paving Engineers of the Office of the Chief, U.S. Corps of Engineers.

The emulsion specified is taken from the A.S.T.M. Specifications, A.S.T.M. Designation D 631–41 T, and is considered to be the latest standard for dense graded aggregate mixes.

This type of bituminous mix requires as precise control over the mixing operations as any other central plant mix. Therefore, the type of mixing plant specified herein requires definite control of aggregate gradation, material and moisture proportioning, and mixing operations. The workability, break and final set of emulsified mixes are dependent on uniform moisture content. It is essential to accurately control the total moisture content of the mix. The absorptive characteristics of the aggregate to be used should be considered in the selection of this type of pavement.

Due to lack of control of time required for evaporation of moisture and other inherent characteristics of emulsion mixes, it is not recommended as a general practice that this specification be used for wearing surfaces in competition with standard hot or semi-hot mixtures, but to confine same to projects where the tonnage is insufficient to warrant setting up a central hot plant or in localities where these plants are not economically available.

Difficulty has been experienced with this type of mix in achieving uniform and proper curing and compaction when laid more than 2½ inches in thickness. For this reason the maximum layer thickness of 2½ inches has been specified.

If the aggregate is found to be hydrophilic as determined by the test given in the specification, the addition of aproximately 0.5% of lime to the aggregate prior to mixing with the bituminous material may be sufficient to change the inherent characteristics to a hydrophobic material. If the material is of such hydrophilic characteristics that the lime alone will not accomplish the desired results, the addition of a proven and approved admixture to the bituminous material will be necessary.

The addition of a minimum of 0.75% of Portland cement to the mix after the addition of bituminous material will hasten the set and increase stability as well as workability. For these reasons, the addition of the Portland cement should be required in all instances.

It is recommended that where grass or weed growth might cause damage to the pavement that a recognized and approved chemical treatment be applied to the subgrade in sufficient quantities or that the base course be constructed using emulsified asphalt containing an approved chemical.

DESCRIPTION

1.1 This pavement shall consist of a base and/or surface course composed of mineral aggregate and bituminous material mixed in a central mixing plant and placed on the prepared subgrade or base course, constructed in accordance with these specifications and in conformity with the dimensions and typical cross sections as shown on the plans and with the lines and grades established by the engineer.

1.2 *Determination of Percentage of Bituminous Material.* The percentage of bituminous material, by weight, to be added to the aggregate shall be between the limits as set forth in the tables. The exact percentage to be used shall be fixed by the engineer on the basis of preliminary tests and field sieve analysis of the aggregate furnished, and shall be adjusted for variations in aggregate gradings within the specified limits.

1.3 *Job Mix Formula.* No work shall be started on the project nor any mixture accepted therefor until the contractor has submitted and received approval for his intended job mix formula. The formula shall be submitted in writing indicating the definite percentage for each sieve fraction of aggregate and for emulsified asphalt which has been chosen as a fixed mean in each instance. The gradation of the aggregate and the bitumen content shall not vary from the fixed mean of the formula by more than the following tolerances:

Job Mix Tolerances

	Gradation A & C	*Gradation B*
Aggregate passing sieves No. 4 and larger	5%	6%
Aggregate passing No. 10, No. 40, and No. 80 sieve	4%	5%
Aggregate passing No. 200 sieve	2%	2%
Bitumen	0.5%	0.5%
Moisture control (See Paragraph 4.4)		

MATERIALS

2.1 *Aggregate.* The aggregate shall consist of crushed stone, crushed gravel, crushed slag, screenings, gravel, sand-gravel, sand or other natural, granular, approved material having essentially the same qualities and meeting the requirements for stability when combined within the limits for grading.

The aggregate shall be tough, durable and sound. The coarse aggregate when tested in accordance with the Los Angeles Rattler Test, after five hundred revolutions shall have a percent of wear of not more than fifty according to the A.A.S.H.O., Method T-96–38.

Slag shall be air cooled, blast furnace, and shall consist of angular fragments reasonably uniform in density and quality and reasonably free from thin, elongated or glassy pieces, dirt or other objectionable matter. The dry slag shall weigh not less than sixty-five pounds per cubic foot.

The portion of the material retained on a No. 4 sieve shall be known as coarse aggregate; that portion passing a No. 4 sieve shall be known as fine aggregate, and the material passing the No. 200 sieve shall be known as filler. The composite material shall meet the requirements for one of the gradings given in Tables 4 or 5, using A.A.S.H.O. Methods T-11 and T-27.

No intermediate sizes of aggregate shall be removed for use in the seal coat or for other purposes without the written consent of the engineer.

That portion of the fine aggregate, including any blended filler, passing a No. 40 sieve shall have a plasticity index of not more than 6, as determined by A.A.S.H.O. Method T-91; a liquid limit of not more than 25 as determined by A.A.S.H.O. Method T-89 and a maximum clay content by elutriation of 6%.

The composite aggregate shall be free from vegetable matter, lumps or balls of clay, adherent films of clay, or other matter that will prevent thorough coating with bituminous material. The bituminized aggregate shall have a swell of not more than 1.5 percent as determined by A.A.S.H.O. Method T-101.

Prior to final acceptance of the proposed aggregate to be used, the inherent characteristics of said aggregate relative to stripping shall be determined. This

TABLE 1

Emulsified Asphalt Specifications
A.S.T.M. Designation: D 631–41 T

The emulsified asphalt shall be homogeneous and shall show no separation of asphalt after thorough mixing, within 30 days after delivery, providing separation has not been caused by freezing.

It shall conform to the following requirements:

Viscosity, Saybolt Furol, 60 ml. at 77° F. sec.	20–100
Residue by Distillation, at 325° F. percent	57–62
Sieve Test, percent	0.05 minus
Modified Miscibility with Difference of Asphalt Residue Water,* percent	4.5 minus
Cement Mixing Test, percent	2.0 minus

Residue. The residue obtained from evaporation or distillation shall conform to the following requirements:

Penetration at 77° F., 100 g., 5 sec.	100 to 200
Soluble in carbon disulfide:	
Petroleum Asphalts, percent	97 plus
Native Asphalts, percent	95 plus
Ash, percent	2 minus
Ductility at 77° F., cms.	60 plus
Specific Gravity at 77° F.	1.00 plus

* If the sample of emulsified asphalt being tested fails to conform to this requirement for modified miscibility, the sample shall be tested for 5-day settlement and for miscibility, and if the numerical difference between the average percentages of asphaltic residue in the 5-day settlement test is less than 3, and if the standard miscibility test shows no appreciable coagulation in two hours, then the emulsified asphalt shall be considered as conforming to these specifications and shall be accepted.

shall be done by preparing a test sample of the paving mixture in conformity with the specifications contained herewith. After the mixture has been made it shall be spread out in a loose thin layer and allowed to air season for 24 hours before testing. A suitable size sample (approximately one-half contents of container) shall be tested by placing it in a glass jar fitted with a tight screw cap and completely covering with distilled water. The jar and contents shall be allowed to stand for a period of 24 hours. Then the sample shall be vigorously shaken for a period of 15 minutes. The sample of mixture shall be examined for stripping. If stripping or sloughing off of the bituminous coating occurs it will be necessary to treat said aggregate by a method which has proven successful in changing the material from a hydrophilic to a hydrophobic state.

2.2 *Filler.* If filler in addition to that naturally present in the aggregate is necessary, it shall consist of stone dust, loess, Portland cement or other standard approved types. The material for such purpose shall be obtained from sources approved by the engineer.

2.3 *Bituminous Material.* The bituminous material to be mixed with the mineral aggregate in the central plant shall conform to the specifications given in Table 1.

The amount of emulsion for base and surface course may be checked by the following formula, but the amount of bitumen shall conform to that shown in Table 2 or 3.

$$P = \frac{(.05A \text{ plus } .1B \text{ plus } .5C) \times K}{\text{Percent Residue by Distillation}} \text{ in which}$$

P equals total percent by weight of emulsion based on the weight of the graded mineral aggregate.

A equals the percent of the mineral aggregate retained on a No. 10 Sieve.

B equals the percent of mineral aggregate passing a No. 10 Sieve and retained on a No. 200 Sieve.

C equals the percent of the mineral aggregate passing a No. 200 Sieve.

Factor K is derived by past experience in paving and gives a definite control, both on variations of percent asphalt contained in an emulsion and the type of aggregate used. For surface course the value for K should vary between 55 and 65; 55 being used for a hard, siliceous, non-absorptive aggregate; 65 being used for soft, porous, absorptive limestones. For base course, the value of K should vary between 35 and 45, according to the absorptive properties of the aggregate; 35 being used for hard, non-absorptive aggregate, and 45 for highly absorptive aggregate.

Screen analyses shall be made as often as necessary to determine and control the grading. Material lost in the wash tests of the aggregate shall be considered a part of the fines passing the No. 200 Sieve.

Methods of Testing

The properties enumerated in these specifications shall be determined in accordance with the Standard Methods of Testing Emulsified Asphalts (A.S.T.M. Designation: D 244–40)* and the Tentative Methods of Test for Modified

Miscibility and Cement Mixing of Emulsified Asphalts (A.S.T.M. Designation: D 244–41 T)° of the American Society for Testing Materials.

2.4 *Hydrated Lime.* The hydrated lime shall meet the requirements of the A.S.T.M. Designation C 6–31.

2.5 *Portland Cement.* The Portland cement shall meet the requirements of A.A.S.H.O. Specification M-5–38.

GRADATION

3.1 *Composition of Mixture.* The mineral aggregate for the surface course shall be of such size that the percentage composition by weight, as determined by laboratory screens will conform to one of the following gradations:

TABLE 2

Surface Course

Screen Size	Percentage Passing Screens (Square Openings)					
	1″ Maximum			¾″ Maximum		
	"A"	"B"	"C"	"A"	"B"	"C"
1″	100	100	100			
¾″	85–100	90–100	94–100	100	100	100
½″	73–88	82–93	90–98	86–100	91–100	95–100
No. 4	46–60	60–75	75–89	55–67	67–80	80–91
No. 10	32–47	47–63	63–78	40–54	54–67	67–80
No. 40	16–26	26–37	37–50	22–31	31–41	41–51
No. 80	10–18	16–24	22–30	12–20	19–26	24–32
No. 200	4–8	5–9	6–10	4–8	5–9	6–10
* Bitumen %	5–6	5.5–7	6–8	5–6	5.5–7.5	6.5–8.5

Screen Size	Percentage Passing Screens (Square Openings)					
	½″ Maximum			No. 4 Maximum		
	"A"	"B"	"C"	"A"	"B"	"C"
½″	100	100	100	100	100	100
⅜″	84–100	89–100	94–100	91–100	94–100	97–100
No. 4	60–73	73–84	84–96	75–89	83–95	92–100
No. 10	43–57	57–71	71–85	57–72	70–85	85–98
No. 40	23–33	32–43	43–55	26–45	45–64	64–82
No. 80	13–20	19–27	25–34	14–29	28–43	42–60
No. 200	4–8	5–9	6–10	6–10	7–11	8–12
* Bitumen %	5–6.5	5.5–7.5	7–9	5.5–8	7–9	8–10

* Note: The range of percentage of bitumen shown in the above tables represent the maximum and minimum amounts based on the actual bituminous agencies affecting the ultimate mix after evaporation of moisture. The exact amount for the job mix shall be fixed by laboratory tests and shall be subject to change as required by actual field conditions.

* 1940 Supplement to Book of A.S.T.M. Standards, Part II, p. 94

° 1941 Supplement to Book of A.S.T.M. Standards, Part II, p. 347

TABLE 3—*Base Course*

Screen Size	Percentage Passing Screens (Square Openings)					
	1½″ Maximum			1″ Maximum		
	"A"	"B"	"C"	"A"	"B"	"C"
1½″	100	100	100			
1″	78–100	84–100	92–100	100	100	100
¾″				76–100	82–100	92–100
½″	53–70	67–82	80–93	60–79	73–89	85–97
No. 4	30–48	48–65	65–82	30–50	50–70	70–89
No. 10	20–37	37–54	54–70	20–39	39–59	59–79
No. 40	10–21	21–32	31–44	10–23	23–36	36–50
No. 80	6–15	12–21	18–27	6–15	13–22	20–30
No. 200	3–8	4–9	5–10	3–8	4–9	5–10
* Bitumen %	3.5–5.5	4–6	4.5–6.5	3.5–5.5	4–6	4.5–6.5

Screen Size	Percentage Passing Screens (Square Openings)					
	¾″ Maximum			½″ Maximum		
	"A"	"B"	"C"	"A"	"B"	"C"
¾″	100	100	100			
½″	76–100	84–100	92–100	100	100	100
⅜″				67–100	80–100	90–100
No. 4	35–54	54–73	73–91	40–61	60–80	79–96
No. 10	24–42	42–60	60–80	29–48	48–67	67–85
No. 40	10–23	23–36	36–51	15–28	28–40	40–54
No. 80	6–15	13–23	20–31	9–18	16–24	24–33
No. 200	3–8	4–9	5–10	3–8	4–9	5–10
* Bitumen %	3.5–5.5	4–6	4.5–7	4–6	4–6.5	4.5–7

Screen Size	Percentage Passing Screens (Square Openings)		
	No. 4 Maximum		
	"A"	"B"	"C"
½″	100	100	100
⅜″	70–100	80–100	90–100
No. 4	44–64	62–82	80–100
No. 10	29–51	51–75	75–98
No. 40	15–37	37–60	60–82
No. 80	9–26	25–42	40–60
No. 200	5–10	6–11	6–12
* Bitumen %	4.5–7.0	6–8	6.5–8.0

* Note: The range of percentage of bitumen shown in Table 3 represent the maximum and minimum amounts based on the actual bituminous agencies affecting the ultimate mix after evaporation of moisture. The exact amount for the job mix shall be fixed by laboratory tests and shall be subject to change as required by actual field conditions.

From 0.75 to 1.0 percent of Portland cement shall be added to the composition of the base mixtures after the addition of the emulsified asphalt.

If lime is required for correcting hydrophilic characteristics of the aggregate, it shall be added at the rate of approximately 0.5% prior to the addition of the emulsified asphalt.

From 0.75 to 1.0 percent of Portland cement shall be added to the composition of the surface mixtures after the addition of the emulsified asphalt.

If lime is required for correcting hydrophilic characteristics of the aggregate, it shall be added at the rate of approximately 0.5% prior to the addition of the emulsified asphalt.

The mineral aggregate for the base course shall be of such size that the percentage composition by weight, as determined by laboratory screens will conform to one of the gradations given in Table 3.

Referring to both Tables 2 and 3:

The gradations in these tables represent the limits which shall determine suitability of aggregate for use from the sources of supply. The final gradations decided on within the limits designated in the table shall be uniformly graded from coarse to fine, and shall not vary from the low limit on one screen to the high limit on the adjacent screens or vice versa.

The selection of any of the gradings shown in the tables shall be such that the maximum size aggregate used in any course shall not be more than one-half the thickness of the layer of the course being constructed.

The composition limits prescribed herein are ranges of tolerance to govern mixtures made from materials meeting these specifications and they are the maximum and minimum for all cases. A closer control appropriate to the job materials will be required for the specific project in accordance with a job mix formula.

The total amount of material passing the No. 200 sieve shall be determined by washing the material through the sieve with water and not less than one-half ($\frac{1}{2}$) of the material passing the No. 200 sieve by washing shall pass the No. 200 sieve by dry sieving without washing.

CONSTRUCTION METHODS

4.1 *Weather Limitations.* Base and/or surface course shall be constructed and operations shall be carried on only when the surface is dry, when the atmospheric temperature is above 50° F., and when the weather is not foggy or rainy. The temperature requirement may be waived, but only when so directed by the engineer.

4.2 *Equipment and Organization.* (1) *General.* All methods employed in performing the work and all equipment, tools and other plant and machinery used for handling materials and executing any part of the work shall be subject to the approval of the engineer before the work is started and whenever found unsatisfactory shall be changed and improved as required. All equipment, tools, machinery and plant used must be maintained in a satisfactory working condition.

(2) *Mixing Plant.* The paving plant used by the contractor in the preparation of the bituminous concrete shall comply with the following requirements:

The drier if necessary to meet moisture requirements shall be suitably designed to heat and dry the aggregate. The drier shall be capable of preparing aggregate to the full rated capacity of the paving plant and to meet the specification requirements.

The plant screens shall be designed, constructed, and operated so as to screen all aggregates to specified sizes and proportions and shall have a capacity slightly in excess of the maximum capacity of the mixer.

The plant shall have storage bins, protected from the weather, of sufficient capacity to furnish the necessary amounts of all aggregates when operating at the maximum rated capacity of the plant. The bins shall provide two or more compartments so proportioned as to insure adequate storage of appropriate fractions of the aggregate and mineral filler. Each compartment shall be provided with an overflow pipe or other device which meets the approval of the engineer, of such size and at such locations as to prevent backing up of material into other compartments.

The plant may have either batch weighing or volumetric proportioning of mineral aggregates and emulsified asphalt. This equipment shall be constructed with devices that will permit easy readjustment of any working part such that it will function properly and accurately. The aggregate weighing or measuring device shall be so constructed and operated that the correct amount of each size aggregate is introduced into the mixer with an accuracy that will meet the job tolerances specified. The plant shall have a capacity of at least 40 tons per hour. The asphalt weighing or measuring device shall be so constructed and operated that the correct amount of emulsified asphalt is introduced into the mixer with an accuracy that will meet the job tolerance specified. If weight control is used, the bucket shall be suspended on dial scales so that the tare weight of the bucket will be shown for each weighing.

The mixer may be either a batch mixer, drum type or a continuous type twin pugmill mixer of sufficient size to maintain thorough uniform mixing at the rated plant capacity.

The plant shall be equipped with positive means to govern the time of mixing and to maintain it constant unless changed by order of the engineer. The time of mixing shall be considered as the interval between the time the bituminous material is spread on the aggregate and the time the same aggregate leaves the mixing unit.

An approved method shall be provided for measuring the correct amount of Portland cement and/or hydrated lime and for their induction into the mixer.

(3) *Placing Equipment.* Equipment for spreading, shaping, and finishing shall consist of an approved self-contained power machine operating in such a manner that no supplemental spreading, shaping, or finishing will be required to provide a surface which will comply with the requirements for smoothness contained herein.

(4) *Rolling Equipment.* (a) The multiwheeled rubber-tired roller shall consist of two axles on which are mounted not less than 9 pneumatic-tired wheels in such a manner that the rear group of tires will not follow in the tracks of the forward group, and mounted in a rigid frame provided with a loading platform or body suitable for ballast loading. The front axle shall rotate around a king pin so located that the roller may be turned within a minimum circle. The roller under working conditions shall have an effective rolling width of at least sixty (60) inches and shall give a compression of at least 325 lbs. per inch of width of tread when fully loaded. The tires shall be uniformly inflated. The roller and the operating pneumatic-tired tractor shall meet the approval of the engineer. The weight of

the roller shall be increased as the rolling progresses to the maximum degree obtainable without detrimental results to the course being compacted.

(b) The steel-wheel rollers shall be of the self-propelled tandem type weighing not less than five tons and not more than eight tons. The wheels on the rollers shall be equipped with adjustable scrapers which shall be used when necessary to clean the wheel surface. Rollers shall also be equipped with water tanks and sprinkling apparatus which shall be used to keep the wheels wet and prevent the surfacing material from sticking.

4.3 *Preparation of Mineral Aggregate.* The aggregate for the mixture shall be screened to specified sizes and conveyed into separate bins ready for mixing with bituminous material, except when fine aggregate gradation is used and screening is not practical; then blending of different size aggregates to obtain proper gradation may be secured by the use of a reciprocating feeder to the elevator.

Additional filler, if necessary to meet the grading requirements, shall be proportioned and added with the mineral aggregate. Filler may be added to the aggregate at the mixing plant by premixing it thoroughly with the other aggregates. Spreading filler over the tops of the aggregate pits or dumping it into the hoppers at crushing plants will not be permitted.

4.4 *Preparation of Bituminous Mixture.* Before being delivered to the runway, the aggregate shall be mixed with the bituminous material at a central mixing plant.

The aggregate prepared as prescribed above, shall be accurately measured and conveyed into the mixer in the proportionate amounts of each size required to meet the specified grading. Lime, if necessary to correct hydrophilic characteristics, shall be added with the aggregate.

The percent of moisture is definitely stipulated in Table No. 1 for the emulsified asphalt. The free water present in the aggregates shall be determined by suitable tests, and if found variable, shall be controlled and made uniform by the use of driers. The net amount of mixing water in the plant mix shall be adjusted for the moisture contained in the aggregates and is to be fixed and controlled by that amount which governs the desired workability of the mixture for proper hauling, dumping, and mechanical spreading. This definitely established moisture content in the final mix is essential and shall be provided and accurately controlled.

The quantity of bituminous material for each batch or calibrated amount for continuous mixing shall be determined by the engineer and introduced into the mixer. The mixing shall continue for at least thirty seconds and for such longer period as may be necessary to uniformly coat all of the particles and obtain a mixture homogeneous in character. Excessive mixing shall be avoided.

The Portland cement shall be added to the mixture after the emulsified asphalt and aggregates have been mixed. The mixing shall be continued to completion.

4.5 *Transportation and delivery of the mixture.* The mixture shall be transported from the mixing plant to the point of use in pneumatic-tired vehicles having tight bodies previously cleaned of all foreign materials. When directed by the engineer, each load shall be covered with canvas or other suitable material of sufficient size and thickness to protect it from weather conditions.

No loads shall be sent out so late in the day as to interfere with spreading and other necessary manipulation during daylight unless artificial light satisfactory to the engineer is provided.

Any mixed material arriving on the project which has taken its initial set and which does not conform in every way to the specified requirements shall be wasted.

4.6 *Spreading and Laying.* (a) *General.* The base or surface course shall be placed only after the underlying course has been properly prepared, compacted, tested and approved by the engineer. In event of sudden rains, the mixture which is in transit from the plant may be used when so directed.

Grade control between the edges of the runway shall be by means of grade stakes or steel grade pins placed in lanes parallel to the centerline of the runway, and at intervals sufficiently close that string lines may be stretched between the stakes or pins.

Placing shall commence at the point or points furthest from the mixing plant, and progress continuously toward the plant, unless otherwise ordered. Hauling over material already placed will not be permitted until the final course has been laid and compacted thoroughly in the manner specified.

(b) *Machine Spreading and Finishing.* Upon arrival the mixture shall be dumped into an approved mechanical spreader and immediately spread to the full width required. It shall be struck off in a uniform layer of such depth (not to exceed 2½ inches compacted) that when the work is completed, it will have the required thickness and will conform to the grade and surface contour required. The speed of the mechanical spreader shall be regulated to eliminate as far as possible the pulling and tearing of the bituminous material.

Placing and compaction of the bituminous mixture shall progress in sections. The mixture shall be placed in strips of a minimum width of 10 feet. The 6 inch strip adjacent to the area on which future material is to be laid, shall not be rolled until such material has been placed. After the first strip or width has been compacted, the second width shall be placed, finished and compacted as provided for the first width, except that rolling shall be extended to include the six inches of the first width not previously compacted.

(c) *Hand Spreading.* In limited areas where, on account of irregularities or unavoidable obstacles, the use of mechanical spreading and finishing equipment is impractical, the mixture may be spread by hand.

When hand spreading is permitted, the mixture shall be dumped upon arrival on approved dump sheets outside of the area on which it is to be spread and be distributed into place immediately by means of shovels. It shall be spread in a uniformly loose layer to the full width required and of such depth that where the work is completed, it will have the required thickness and will conform to the grade and surface contour required.

(d) *Thickness.* In order to obtain adequate aeration, the mixture shall not be placed in layers thicker than 2½″. When directed, vertical contact surfaces shall be painted with a thin uniform coat of emulsified asphalt just before the mixture is placed.

4.7 *Compaction of Mixture.* Sufficient time shall be allowed after spreading and prior to rolling to obtain proper aeration and curing. The mixture shall then be thoroughly and uniformly compressed by rollers, as specified. Initial rolling shall be done by pneumatic-tired rollers. Rolling of the mixture shall begin as soon after spreading as is practicable.

Initial rolling shall be done longitudinally, overlapping on successive trips by at least one-half the width of the roller. Alternate trips of the roller shall be of slightly different lengths. Rolling shall continue until the surface is of uniform texture and degree of compaction and is true to grade and cross section. Final rolling shall be done with the tandem rollers.

The speed of the rollers shall at all times be slow enough to avoid displacement of the mixture. Any displacement occurring as a result of reversing the direction of the roller, or from any other cause, shall be corrected at once by the use of rakes, and of fresh mixture where required.

Sufficient rollers of the designated types shall be furnished to adequately handle the output of the plant or the rate of delivery.

Upon instructions from the engineer, the course shall be rerolled any time within two weeks after it is laid and shall be subjected to diagonal rolling crossing the lines of the first. If necessary to prevent adhesion of the mixture to the tandem roller, the wheels shall be kept properly moistened, but an excess of either water or oil will not be permitted. The rollers shall be in good condition and shall be operated by competent and experienced rollermen. The rollers shall be operated continuously as far as practicable and in such a manner that all parts of the pavement shall receive substantially equal compression.

At all places not accessible to the roller, the mixture shall be thoroughly compacted with tampers. Such tampers shall weigh not less than 25 pounds and shall have a tamping face area of not more than 50 square inches. The surface of the mixture after compression shall be smooth and true to the established crown and grade.

Any mixture which becomes loose and broken, mixed with dirt, or in any way defective prior to the application of the finish coat shall be removed and replaced, at the expense of the contractor, with fresh mixture which shall be compacted to conform with the surrounding area. Skin patching on an area that has been rolled shall not be allowed. Any mixture remaining unbonded after rolling shall be removed and replaced.

4.8 *Joints.* (a) *General.* Joints shall comply with the surface requirements and present the same uniformity of texture, density, smoothness, etc., as other sections of the course.

(b) *Transverse.* The placing of the course shall be as nearly continuous as possible, and the roller shall be permitted to pass over the unprotected end of the freshly laid mixture only when the laying of the course is discontinued. In all cases, when the work is resumed, the previously laid material shall be cut back so as to expose the full thickness of the layer, and a light paint coat of emulsified asphalt, if necessary, shall be applied along the prepared edge. The old material which has been cut away shall be removed from the work and the fresh mixture shall be raked against the joint, thoroughly tamped with tampers and rolled.

(c) *Longitudinal.* Longitudinal joints shall be placed so that the joint in the next course will not coincide with that in a lower layer and so that they break by at least one foot.

4.9 *Shaping edges.* While the surface is being compacted and finished, the contractor shall trim the edges neatly to line.

4.10 *Surface Tests.* The finished surface shall not vary more than $\frac{1}{4}$ inch for the wearing course or $\frac{3}{8}$ inch for the binder or base course when measured with a ten foot straightedge applied parallel with or at right angles to the center line. Tests for conformity with the specified crown and grade shall be made by the contractor after compaction, and any variation shall be corrected by removing or adding materials. After the completion of final rolling, the smoothness of the course shall again be checked, and any irregularities exceeding the tolerances specified or that retain water on the surface shall be corrected by removing the defective work and placing new material or by adding additional material as directed by the engineer at the contractor's expense.

4.11 *Sampling Pavement.* For the determination of composition, condition and compaction of the pavement the contractor shall remove suitable size samples of the completed pavement. Samples for each day or fraction thereof when mixtures are placed shall be taken as directed by the engineer. The contractor shall replace the pavement where samples are removed, and these replacements shall be installed by the contractor free of charge. After the samples have been removed from the completed pavement, they shall be tested for thickness, density and composition as directed. If the deficiency in composition, compaction and density exceeds the limits of toleration from that specified, no payment shall be made for the mixtures found so deficient.

4.12 *Bituminous and Aggregate Material Contractor's Responsibility.* Samples of the bituminous and aggregate materials that the contractor proposes to use, together with a statement as to their source and character must be submitted and approval obtained before use of such materials begins. The contractor shall require the manufacturer or producer of the bituminous and aggregate materials to furnish material subject to this and all other pertinent requirements of the contract. Only those materials that have been demonstrated by service tests as satisfactory for the intended use will be acceptable.

For checking the adequacy of the equipment in use, inspecting the conditions and operation of the plant, for the verification of weights or proportions and character of materials in the preparation of the mixture, the engineer or his authorized representative shall have access at any time to all parts of the paving plant.

4.13 *Freight and Weigh-Bills.* Before the final estimate is allowed, the contractor shall file with the engineer receipted bills where railroad shipments are made and certified weigh-bills when materials are received in any other manner, of the bituminous and paving materials actually used in the construction covered by the contract. The contractor shall not remove bituminous material from the tank car or storage tank until the initial outage and temperature measurements have been taken, nor shall he release the car or tank until the final outage has been taken by the engineer.

Copies of freight bills and weigh-bills shall be furnished to the engineer during the progress of the work.

4.14 *Seal Coat.* As shown on the plans and called for in the bid schedule, a seal coat of the type called for shall be applied to the finished course as described under SEAL COAT. The seal coat under no circumstances shall be placed except under the most favorable weather conditions and after sufficient lapse of time has been allowed for the wearing surface to become thoroughly cured and set.

METHOD OF MEASUREMENT

5.1 The tonnage of base course to be paid for shall be the number of tons of bituminous mixture of the grading called for in the bid schedule and used in the accepted work. The bituminous treated material shall be weighed after mixing and no deduction shall be made for the weight of bituminous material in the mixture.

5.2 The tonnage of surface course to be paid for shall be the number of tons of bituminous mixture of the grading called for in the bid schedule and used in the accepted work. The bituminous treated material shall be weighed after mixing and no deduction shall be made for the weight of bituminous material in the mixture.

5.3 The quantities of base and surface mixture required for the project are based on aggregates having a bulk specific gravity of 2.65 as determined by A.A.S.H.O. Method T-85. Proportionate corrections shall be made when the aggregate furnished on the job have bulk specific gravities above 2.75 or below 2.55. In such cases the corrected quantity shall be the product of the number of tons used multiplied by the ratio of the bulk specific gravity of the job aggregate to 2.65.

5.4 The bituminous material shall not be paid for separately but shall be included in the price bid for base and surface course above, and shall be considered incidental to the prices for these items.

BASIS OF PAYMENT

6.1 The quantities of base or wearing surfacing mixture, determined as provided in 5.1, 5.2 above, shall be paid for at the respective contract unit prices per ton in the bid schedule for base or surface course, which prices and payment shall constitute full compensation for preparing base or subgrade, for furnishing, handling, mixing, manipulating, and placing all materials, for all shaping, compacting, and rolling, for finishing, for improving unsatisfactory areas, for reconditioning subgrade, for furnishing samples, for furnishing and sealing of scales, for furnishing the weigh house, for all labor, equipment, tools and incidentals necessary to complete the item, except any prime or seal coat.

APPENDIX 18

DEPARTMENT OF COMMERCE
Civil Aeronautics Administration
Airport Division
Washington, D.C.
April 1, 1942

SOIL CEMENT BASE COURSE FOR AIRPORT RUNWAYS, TAXIWAYS AND APRONS

C.A.A. Specification No. P-301

INTRODUCTION

This specification has been prepared by the Paving Engineers of the Airport Division, Civil Aeronautics Administration in collaboration with the Paving Enineers of the Office of the Chief, U.S. Corps of Engineers, and the Soils Engineers of the U.S. Public Roads Administration.

In considering Soil Cement for base course, it is naturally expected that regular Earth type base course (A-1, Public Roads Administration classification) material is not economically available. Where the prevailing local soils are of the A-2, and A-3 classifications, the most economical type will probably be the bituminous mix. This might also apply to the A-4 group mechanically corrected to the A-2. Where the prevailing local soils are of the natural A-4 and A-6 classification, soil cement will probably be the best selection.

Before definitely deciding on any of the above mentioned types of base course, due consideration should be given to conomically available aggregate of proven service record.

In using soil cement as a base course, a minimum of 1½ inch dense graded plant mix bituminous wearing surface should be placed thereon with a suitable bond established between the base course and the wearing surface.

In lieu of the above, a surface treatment may be used consisting of tar or emulsified asphalt prime to be followed after curing with a hot asphalt application and covered with approximately 40 pounds of (¼ to ¾ inch) stone per square yard, rolled and then sealed with a minimum of 70 pounds of dense graded plant mix or natural rock asphalt. This surfacing is described in C.A.A. Specification No. P-405.

In establishing the proper quantities of cement for use in soil cement, laboratory tests using the wetting and drying, freezing and thawing cycles has proven most effective. Full investigations with variable amounts of cement should determine the economical limitations within which the work can be done.

DESCRIPTION

1.1. This work shall consist of constructing a base course by uniformly mixing together local soil, Portland Cement, and water; shaping and compacting the mixture in accordance with the requirements of these specifications and in conformity with the dimension and typical cross-section shown on the plans and to the lines and grades established by the engineer.

Runways, taxiways, or aprons shall be built in a series of alternate parallel lanes 20 to 30 feet wide. Longitudinal construction joints shall be formed by temporary 6″ × 6″ wooden side forms, or their equivalent, unless otherwise specified, set firmly to the required grade to permit thorough compaction and finishing operations to proceed along their length. The side forms shall be removed before the adjoining lanes are constructed.

MATERIALS

2.1 The materials used in this work shall meet the following requirements:

(a) *Portland Cement.* Portland cement shall be a standard brand, and shall conform to the requirements of A.A.S.H.O., Specification M-5–38. The expansion of samples tested for soundness in the Autoclave shall not exceed one-half of one per cent (0.5%).

Contractors may at their option use bulk cement, subject to approval by the engineer of the apparatus for handling and weighing the cement and subject to the work being done to the entire satisfaction of the engineer in every way.

(b) *Water.* Water for stabilized earth base course shall be free from salt, oil, acid, alkali, organic matter or other deleterious substances and shall be subject to approval by the engineer.

A comparison of the water with distilled water shall be made by making standard soundness, time-of-setting, and 1:3 mortar strength tests with standard sand, using the same cement of standard quality with each water. Any indication of unsoundness, marked change in time-of-setting, or a variation of more than ten (10) per cent in strength from results obtained with mixtures containing the water of satisfactory quality shall be sufficient cause for rejection of the water under test.

(c) *Soil.* The soil for this work shall consist of the material on the proposed paved area or selected material meeting the approval of the engineer, and shall be free of roots, sod, weeds, and stones of a greater dimension than two and one-half (2½) inches.

SOIL TESTS AND QUANTITY OF CEMENT

3.1 *Soil Tests.* Upon completion of grading and prior to base course construction, laboratory tests of soils existing in areas to be paved shall be made to determine the quantity of cement required for satisfactory results. Should these tests indicate that the quantity of cement required for satisfactory stabilization would prove uneconomical, then the contractor will be required to remove such unsuitable material and replace with material satisfactory to the engineer. Satisfactory materials for this purpose shall be obtained from an approved source as directed.

CONSTRUCTION METHODS

4.1 *Equipment.* The contractor shall provide the following minimum list of equipment which shall be used in mixing, application of water, shaping and compacting:

3 40 HP Track Type Tractors
1 30 HP Tractor Pneumatic Tired
2 9′ Offset Disc Harrows (24″ Discs)
1 Heavy Duty 3 or 4 Bottom 14″ Gang Plow
1 Heavy Duty 8′ Orchard Type Springtooth Cultivator
1 Heavy Duty 8′ Orchard Type Stiff-tooth Cultivator
1 10′ Adjustable Spike Tooth Farm Harrow
1 Subgrade Rooter
6 1½ Ton Trucks
1 Motor Patrol, 12′ Blade
1 or more Double Drum Sheepsfoot Rollers, 6 to 7 sq. in. foot, Minimum Pressure 100 lbs. per sq. in.
1 or more Double Drum Sheepsfoot Rollers, 5 to 6 sq. in. foot, Minimum Pressure 200 lbs. per sq. in.
1 5 to 8 ton Self-propelled Tandem Smooth-Wheeled Roller
1 Multiple-wheeled Pneumatic-tired Roller
1 1000 Gal. Pressure Type Water Distributor (Tank or Truck equipped with 2″ centrifugal Pump, Spray Bar and quick-acting Valve, or equal, will be satisfactory.)
2 1000 Gal. Feeder Tanks on Trucks
1 8′ Nail Drag
1 8′ Broom Drag
2 10′ metal straight edges.
Any other equipment deemed necessary by the engineer for proper execution of the work.

The contractor shall maintain the equipment specified in satisfactory working condition at all times. Any changes in items of equipment must be requested in writing and approved by the engineer before processing is begun.

4.2 *Preparation of Subgrade.* Before undertaking other construction operations, the areas to be paved, where regarded as necessary, shall be shaped to conform to the lines and grades established and the typical cross sections shown on the plans. Additional soil, if needed, shall be placed as the engineer may direct, and any unsuitable soil or materials, including materials retained on a 3-inch screen, shall be removed and replaced with materials acceptable to the engineer.

4.3 *Pulverizing.* Prior to the application of cement, the soil to be treated shall be scarified and pulverized for sufficient width and depth to give the compacted cross-section shown on the plans. Pulverizing shall continue until eighty percent (80%) of the soil, by dry weight, exclusive of gravel or stone, shall pass a No. 4 sieve, and the soil shall be manipulated until the percentage of moisture in the soil does not exceed by more than two (2) the percentage of moisture specified by the engineer for the soil-cement mixture before compaction. The length and width of area scarified and pulverized at any time shall not exceed the length and width which can be completed in accordance with this specification in two (2) working days except by special permission of the engineer. Suitable side forms for longitudinal joints for construction in lanes 20 to 30 feet in width will be set to line and grade as directed. These side forms as well as adjoining work must be kept free of earth by brooming during construction operations to permit accurate control of grade. The soil between the forms shall be carefully balanced to provide the quantity of soil required to give the cross-section shown on the plans.

4.4 *Application of Cement.* The pulverized soil shall be shaped to the approximate cross-section shown on the plans and the specified quantity of Portland Cement required for the full depth of treatment shall be uniformly spread over the surface in one operation in a manner satisfactory to the engineer. No equipment, except that used in spreading and mixing, will be allowed to pass over the freshly spread cement until it is mixed with the soil.

The work of adding cement to the material on the base or placing premixed material on the base shall not be performed unless the subsoil immediately below the material to be stabilized will support without displacement the compaction specified.

Soil samples taken from the site of the work indicate that the quantity of cement required for each square yard of completed work will vary from ______ bbls. to ______ bbls. The average quantity of ______ bbls. per sq. yd. has, therefore, been stated as the quantity required, and will be used as a basis for comparing bids.

4.5 *Mixing.* Immediately after the cement has been distributed it shall be mixed with the loose soil for the full depth of treatment. Care must be exercised that no cement is mixed below the desired depth. Mixing may be accomplished with field cultivator, gang plows, disc harrows, rotary tillers, or other implements approved by the engineer and shall be continued for as long a period of time and repeated as often as may be necessary to insure a thorough, uniform and intimate mix of the soil and cement and until the resulting mixture is homogeneous and uniform in appearance. The mixture shall then be shaped to the approximate lines and grades shown on the plans.

4.6 *Application of Water.* Immediately after mixing of soil and cement is complete, the moisture content of the soil-cement mixture shall be determined and, if required, water shall be uniformly applied in such quantities and at such a rate as directed by the engineer. A water supply and pressure-distributing equipment shall be provided which will permit the continuous application of all water required on the section of runway being processed within three (3) hours. Each application or increment of water shall be partially incorporated by field cultivators, gang plows, disc harrows, rotary tillers or other implements so as to avoid concentration of water near the surface. After the last increment of water has been added, mixing shall be continued. The equipment shall be of sufficient size and capacity to distribute the moisture uniformly throughout the full depth of the mixture in one (1) operation. Particular care shall be exercised to insure satisfactory moisture distribution along the edges of the section. When water spreading and mixing is completed, the percentage of moisture in the mixture, on a basis of dry weight, shall not vary from the specified optimum percentage of moisture of the mixture by more than one-tenth ($\frac{1}{10}$). This specified optimum moisture shall be determined in the field by a moisture-density test (A.S.T.M. Serial Designation: D558–40T) on representative samples of soil-cement mixture obtained from the proposed paved area toward the conclusion of moist mixing operations.

For the information of the contractor, the estimated moisture content of the air-dry mixture and the approximate maximum quantity of water required per sq. yd. of six (6) inch compacted base course area are shown.

Approximate Moisture Content Required in Compacted Mixture Per Cent	Estimated Moisture Content of Air-Dry Mixture Per Cent	Estimated Water Required per Sq. Yd. Gallons

4.7 *Compaction.* Prior to the beginning of compaction, and as a continuation of mixing operations, the mixture shall be thoroughly loosened for its full depth and then shall be uniformly compacted with an approved sheepsfoot roller. Compaction shall begin at the bottom and shall continue until the entire depth of soil-cement mixture is uniformly compacted to the density specified by the engineer except that the sheepsfoot roller will be removed when about one (1) inch of loose mulch remains. The specified density shall be determined in the field by a moisture-density test (A.S.T.M. Serial Designation: D558–40T) on representative samples of soil-cement mixture obtained from the proposed paved area toward the conclusion of moist mixing operations. The sheepsfoot roller shall be of the size, shape and weight specified by the Engineer as best suited to give the required densities in the soil-cement mixture being compacted. The rate of operation and number of rollers shall be sufficient to compact uniformly the section of base course being processed for the specified width and depth within two (2) hours.

After the mixture, excepting the top one (1) inch of mulch, is compacted, the surface of the base course shall be reshaped to the required lines, grades and cross-section and then shall be lightly scarified to loosen any imprints left by the compacting or shaping equipment, or until a surface mulch of about one (1) inch in thickness is obtained. The resulting surface then shall be rolled with pneumatic tired rollers and a smooth-wheel tandem roller of the type and weight approved by the engineer. The rolling shall be supplemented with the use of nail drags and broom drags. When directed by the engineer, surface finishing methods may be varied from the procedure provided a dense, uniform surface free of compaction planes is produced. The moisture content of the surface material must be maintained at its specified optimum during all finishing operations. Surface compaction and finishing shall be done in such a manner as to produce in not over two (2) hours, a smooth, closely-knit surface, free of cracks, ridges, or loose material, conforming to the crown, grade, and line shown on the plans.

4.8 *Protection and Cover.* After the base course has been finished as specified herein, it shall be protected against rapid drying for a period of seven (7) days by applying not less than four (4) pounds of straw or hay per square yard or other materials approved by the engineer which will be moistened initially and subsequently as may be necessary. Waterproof paper blankets may be used for protection of the base and shall be of a type and quality approved by the engineer.

The protective cover shall be removed immediately after this seven (7) day period. Prior to the application of the prime, sufficient time shall be allowed for the base course to dry out. The surface shall be carefully broomed and cleaned of all loose material in preparation for the application of the bituminous prime. This prime shall consist of either emulsified asphalt or tar, whichever is called for in the bid schedule.

4.9 *Alternate Method of Construction.* If approved by the engineer, in writing, a machine or combination of machines which will do the work of pulverizing the soil, spreading cement or water, mixing the materials, or compacting and finishing the mixture may be used in lieu of the method specified herein. Any machine used shall be provided with means for visibly and accurately gauging the water application in gallons per sq. yd. In case the machine does not produce a uniform homogeneous mixture of soil-cement, its use shall be discontinued unless a suitable mixture can be obtained by supplemental mixing with field cultivators, gang plows and other suitable equipment. Machines for mixing soil, cement and water should preferably be of a type which will mix the material progressively for a section at least twenty (20) feet in width. When a machine is used, precaution must be exercised to obtain the specified depth and straight longitudinal edges conforming to the crown and grade specified on the plans with all materials adjacent to the edges compacted to the same density as the remainder of the treated area. When the machine will not handle a section at least twenty (20) feet in width, it shall work forward with successive increments so a section at least twenty (20) feet in width may be compacted and finished for full width in one (1) operation. In any event, when machine mixing is used, the resulting soil-cement mixture shall be compacted at the optimum moisture content specified by the engineer before there is any appreciable moisture loss and the compaction operation shall be a continuation of the mixing operation in such a manner that the moistened soil-cement mixture after mixing does not remain undisturbed for more than thirty (30) minutes before compaction begins.

4.10 *Construction Limitations.* Cement shall be applied only to such an area that all the operations specified in Paragraphs 4.4 to 4.7, inclusive, can be continuous, and all but final surface finish completed within six (6) hours after the beginning of water application to the thoroughly mixed soil-cement. No cement shall be applied when the percentage of moisture in the soil in the subgrade immediately beneath the pulverized material exceeds the optimum moisture content specified by the engineer for that particular soil or when the percentage of moisture in the pulverized soil exceeds the optimum moisture of the soil cement mixture by more than two (2). When any of the operations after the application of cement are interrupted for more than 30 minutes for any reason, or when the uncompacted soil-cement mixture is wetted by rain so that the average moisture content exceeds the tolerance given in Paragraph 4.6, the entire section shall be reconstructed in accordance with this specification. In the event the uncompacted soil-cement mixture is wetted by rain so that the moisture content exceeds the tolerances above specified, then the contractor will be paid for the additional cement which is used in reconstructing the section. All material along longitudinal or transverse construction joints not properly compacted shall be removed and replaced with properly moistened and mixed soil-cement which will be compacted to specified density.

4.11 *Weather and Season.* During seasons of probably freezing temperatures, no cement shall be applied unless the temperature is at least forty (40) degrees Fahrenheit in the shade and rising.

4.12 *Maintenance.* The contractor shall be required to maintain, at his own expense, the entire base course within the limits of his contract in good condition satisfactory to the engineer from the time he first starts work until all the work shall have been completed. Maintenance shall include immediate repairs of any defects that may occur either before or after the cement is applied, which work shall be done by the contractor at his own expense and repeated as often as may be necessary to keep the area continuously intact. Repairs are to be made in a manner to insure restoration of a uniform surface and durability of the part repaired. Faulty work must be replaced for the full depth of treatment. Any low areas will be remedied by replacing the material for the full depth of treatment rather than adding a thin layer of soil-cement to the completed work.

4.13 *Surface Tests.* The finished surface shall not vary more than three-eighths (⅜) inch when tested with a ten (10) foot straight edge applied parallel with or at right angles to the center line. Any variations in excess of this tolerance shall be repaired by the contractor at his own expense and in a manner satisfactory to the engineer.

METHOD OF MEASUREMENT

5.1 This work will be measured by the square yard of completed and accepted base course and the number of barrels of cement actually used as authorized by the engineer. No allowance will be made for any work done outside the lines established by the engineer.

The density of the soil-cement base will be determined by the engineer after each day's construction. Any portion which has a density five (5) pounds or more below that specified by the engineer shall be removed and replaced to meet this specification.

The thickness of the soil-cement base course shall be determined from measurements of cores drilled from the finished surfacing or from thickness measurement at holes drilled in the finished surfacing of each day's work at intervals of five-hundred (500) feet or less, and at locations selected by the engineer. The average thickness of runway or landing area constructed during one (1) day shall be within one-half (½) inch thickness shown on the plans except that the thickness of any one point may be within ¾ of an inch of that shown on the plans. Where the average thickness shown by the measurements made in one (1) day's construction is not within the tolerances given the contractor will be required to reconstruct this day's work at his own expense.

BASIS OF PAYMENT

6.1 The number of square yards determined as provided above, will be paid for at the contract unit price per square yard at Soil Cement Base Course, which price will include all costs and expenses for constructing, watering, protecting, and maintaining the base course.

Cement will be paid for on the basis of the number of barrels of cement actually used in the construction as authorized by the engineer.

The removal of unsatisfactory soil and the addition of satisfactory borrow material will be paid for at the contract price of unclassified excavation.

APPENDIX 19

DEPARTMENT OF COMMERCE
Civil Aeronautics Administration
Airport Division
Washington, D.C.
September 1, 1942

LEAN MIX ROLLED CONCRETE BASE COURSE FOR AIRPORT RUNWAYS, TAXIWAYS AND APRONS

C.A.A. Specification No. P-302

INTRODUCTION

This specification has been prepared by the Paving Engineers of the Airport Division, Civil Aeronautics Administration, in collaboration with the Paving Engineers of the Office of the Chief, U.S. Corps of Engineers.

Local deposits of sand-gravel with rather wide soil constant limits can be economically used under this specification by mixing with Portland cement for construction of a serviceable base course. It is herein proposed to combine cement, aggregates and water to produce a mixture which is of such consistency that it can be spread in place and rolled. Pit run sand and gravel containing not more than 80% or less than 45% fine aggregate passing a No. 4 sieve can be used. If the source of materials has a low percentage of coarse aggregate or if the deposit runs uniform in grading, it may not be necessary to require separation on a No. 4 sieve to obtain a uniform mixture of fine and coarse aggregate.

Field experience has indicated that best results in compacting the concrete base mixture with a roller are obtained when the water content is just sufficient to flush a small amount of water to the surface in rolling. Water in excess of this amount makes the mixture rubbery and difficult to compact. Lower water content results in lower density and poor durability. Therefore, it is essential that field control should govern the basic water content to obtain this "medium consistency."

It might be pointed out that this type of construction is economical with reference to the necessary equipment. A simplified batching and mixing plant is needed together with spreading and rolling equipment. A bituminous membrane applied by a distributor will furnish a satisfactory curing medium and serve as a basis for a tack coat between the base and wearing surface.

In establishing the proper quantities of cement for use in the base, complete tests should be made on the proposed materials to determine grading, aggregate proportions, density, compression strengths at 7 and 28 days, as well as other pertinent characteristics of the base mixture. In making strength tests, it is suggested that not less than four specimens be molded for each of four cement contents, namely, 5, 7, 9 and 11 percent by weight of dry aggregate. The "Procedure for Making Specimens" as reported and described by the Portland Cement Association in "Field and Laboratory Studies of Cement-Treated Base" should be followed in molding test specimen.

It is suggested that this type of base course be topped with a minimum of 1½ inches dense graded plant mix bituminous wearing surface.

DESCRIPTION

1.1 *Description.* This work shall consist of constructing a lean mix, cement aggregate base course, consisting of Portland Cement, selected granular materials and water, proportioned and mixed in a central plant, spread on the prepared subgrade and compacted in such manner as to achieve the maximum practicable density, and cured, all as hereinafter specified. The base shall be placed in one course in conformity with the dimensions and typical cross sections shown on the plans and with lines and grades established by the engineer.

MATERIALS

2.1 *Cement.* Portland cement shall conform to the requirements of A.A.S.H.O. Specification M 5–38.

Special test requirements: Cement shall be tested by some recognized testing laboratory or agency satisfactory to the engineer. Samples to be tested shall be taken either at the mill or at the work. No cement shall be used until notice has been given by the engineer that the test results are satisfactory. Cement which has been stored other than in the bins at the mills, for more than four months after being tested shall be retested before use. Ordinarily, no cement shall be used until after it has satisfactorily passed both the 7 and 28-day tests, but in cases of emergency the engineer may waive the 28-day tests and permit the use of cement which has satisfactorily passed the soundness and 7-day tests; provided, it is the product of a quarry and mill having established a reputation of not less than three years standing, for the production of high-grade cement.

Immediately upon receipt at the site of the work, cement, unless used directly from the carrier, shall be stored in a thoroughly dry, weather-tight, and properly ventilated building with adequate provisions for the prevention of the absorption of moisture. Storage shall be such as to permit easy access for inspection and definite identification of each shipment.

When specified or permitted by the engineer, high early strength cement conforming to the requirements of A.A.S.H.O. Specifications M 39–38 shall be used. If high early strength cement is used, the operating time requirements shall be changed as directed by the engineer.

2.2 *Water.* The water used in mixing shall be clean, shall not be salty or brackish, and shall be free from acid, oil, alkali and other foreign or deleterious matter. Water shall be supplied by the contractor in sufficient quantities to comply with the requirements of these specifications.

2.3 *Aggregates.* The aggregates shall be obtained from the sources or pits designated on the plans or as approved by the Engineer. The combined aggregate may consist of material having not more than 80% or less than 45% passing a No. 4 sieve.

The aggregate shall be separated into two sizes and stored in separate stock piles or storage bins unless otherwise directed by the Engineer. One stock pile or bin shall contain the material coarser than a No. 4 sieve and the other stock pile or bin shall contain material passing a No. 4 sieve. These sizes shall be combined in the proper proportions as provided herein and as directed by the Engineer at the time of mixing. If aggregate having a low percentage of coarse aggregate is to be used or where the deposits run uniform in grading, it may not be necessary to require separation on a No. 4 sieve and recombining the aggregate to maintain a uniform mixture of fine and coarse aggregate when approved by the engineer.

The fine and coarse aggregate when separated shall conform to the following requirements.

2.31 *Fine Aggregate.* The fine aggregate shall consist of sand having durable particles and free from injurious amounts of organic impurities. Sands showing a color darker than standard in the Standard Colorimetric Test of the American Society for Testing Materials (Serial Designation C40–33) shall not be used unless it can be shown by strength tests that the darker color is caused by harmless materials.

The fine aggregate when tested by means of laboratory sieves shall conform to the following grading:

Passing a No.	4 Sieve	95 to 100%
" " No.	16 "	45 " 80%
" " No.	50 "	10 " 40%
" " No.	100 "	5 " 25%
" " No.	200 "	0 " 10%

2.32 *Coarse Aggregate.* The coarse aggregate may be that part of the material coarser than a No. 4 sieve from the same source as the fine aggregate or may be material from another source. It may consist of a mixture or wholly of either crushed or uncrushed material. Oversize material shall be removed but may be crushed to the specified size and used. The coarse aggregate shall consist of durable particles free from adherent coatings and injurious amounts of shale, clay lumps and soft fragments. The coarse aggregate shall have a percent of wear of not more than 50 at 500 revolutions as determined by A.A.S.H.O. Method T-96 (Los Angeles Rattler Test).

When tested by means of laboratory sieves, it shall conform to the following limits of grading:

Passing a 1½″	Sieve	95 to 100%
" a ¾″	"	40 " 100%
" a No. 4	"	0 " 5%

CONSTRUCTION METHODS

3.1 *Operation at Aggregate Pits.* All work involved in clearing and stripping pits and the handling of unsuitable material encountered shall be performed by the contractor. The contractor shall notify the Engineer sufficiently in advance of the opening of any designated pit to permit staking of boundaries at the site and to take elevations and measurements of the ground surface before any material is produced; also to permit the Engineer to take samples of the materials for tests to determine its quality and grading and to prepare a preliminary design of base mixture.

In order to prevent fluctuations in the grading of the aggregates, the equipment used and the methods employed shall provide for taking material from a face or slope, extending the full depth of the designated excavation and in such a manner as to provide a uniform supply of coarse and fine aggregates.

3.2 *Preparation of Subgrade.* All soft and yielding material and other portions of the subgrade which will not compact readily when rolled or tamped shall be removed, and any loose rocks or boulders found in the earth excavation shall be removed or broken off to a depth of not less than six (6) inches below the surface of the subgrade. All holes or depressions made by the removal of any unsuitable material shall be filled with an approved material and the whole subgrade brought to line and grade and compacted. The entire subgrade shall be rolled with a self-propelled 3-wheel 10-ton roller and no material shall be deposited thereon until the subgrade has been checked and approved.

After the subgrade has been prepared as specified above and immediately before the base material is placed, the subgrade shall be tested as to crown and elevation by means of a level and rod or by an approved type of subgrade templet or planer which rides on the side forms. If additional material is used to bring the subgrade up to the correct elevation, it shall be moistened and tamped or rolled until the filled material is entirely compacted and is as firm and unyielding as the surrounding subgrade surface. Any portion of the subgrade which is not accessible for compaction by a roller shall be tamped thoroughly with hand tampers. If ordered by the Engineer, water shall be applied to the subgrade prior and/or during rolling operations.

All hauling on the subgrade shall be kept to a minimum and shall be distributed over the width of the subgrade. Any ruts and deformations of the subgrade shall be corrected and compacted prior to placement of the base material.

3.3 *Forms.* When forms are required they may be of wood or of metal and shall be placed to line and grade as staked by the Engineer. Wood forms shall have a thickness of not less than that of a commercial four (4) inch timber, shall have a height equal to the compacted depth of the base and shall be not less than twelve (12) feet in length. All form lumber shall be of good quality timber, straight, well seasoned, clean and free from defects which would impair its usefulness. Forms becoming warped, split, worn or otherwise defective shall be discarded.

Steel forms shall be of a section commonly required for portland cement concrete pavement. They shall be of a depth at least equal to the edge thickness of the work prescribed. They shall be straight and free from warp. The minimum length of section of steel form shall be ten (10) feet.

All forms shall have full bearing on the compacted subgrade and shall be braced and staked in such manner as may be required to hold them rigidly in vertical position and true to established line and grade while the concrete base material is being placed and consolidated. Forms shall be placed to accommodate the spreading equipment used and shall extend at least five hundred (500) feet in advance of the placing operations. The forms shall be cleaned and oiled before each use. Forms shall be removed in such a manner as to avoid injury to the edge of the base.

When directed by the Engineer side forms will not be required. In such cases the spreading equipment and supply of base mixture shall be such as will permit the continuous and satisfactory spreading of material for one or two lane construction, compacting it to the proper thickness and contour as described under paragraph 3.6, "Placing."

3.4 *Proportioning.* It is the purpose of these specifications to so combine cement, aggregate and water as to produce a base mixture which can be satisfactorily spread, compacted and shaped as herein specified and have the desired strength and durability.

The amount of water required for satisfactory compaction and the amount of portland cement per cubic yard of compacted mixture to obtain the desired strength and durability shall be determined by the Engineer for the particular aggregates available. The amount of water used in the base mix shall be sufficient to obtain the required density (see paragraph 3.6) at the time of compaction. This amount of water shall be just short of the amount which produces a jelly-like condition of the mix or a rubbery condition of the base under the roller. Wet mixes which become rubbery under the roller cannot be satisfactorily compacted. Dry mixes will produce low density and poor durability. The net amount of water to be added at the mixer shall be adjusted for the moisture contained in the aggregate, for the moisture they will absorb and for any moisture loss between the time of mixing and compaction on the grade. The cement content shall not in any case be less than 2½ sacks per cubic yard of compacted material.

The Engineer shall determine and have available the approximate proportions of cement, aggregate and water to be used for the proposed aggregate supply. Attention is called here to the basis of payment, paragraph 5.1, which provides that the cement will be paid for separately at the contract price per barrel.

Unless authority is granted by the Engineer for the use of combined aggregates, the aggregates shall be separated into two sizes and stored in separate stock piles or bins. One bin or stock pile shall contain all material retained by a No. 4 sieve and one shall contain all material which passes the No. 4 sieve. The proportions of fine and coarse aggregate used in the combined mix shall be determined by the engineer and will be based on the most efficient and economical utilization of the local materials available. The mix design selected for the project shall produce an average compressive strength of not less than 1500 lbs. per square inch at 28 days for standard test specimens. The compressive strength shall be the average of not less than three 6″×5″ laboratory specimens converted to the equivalent strength of standard test specimens, i.e., specimens having a height twice the diameter (See A.S.T.M. C-42–39).

Aggregates and cement shall be proportioned by weight. Water may be proportioned by weight or volume. One sack of cement will be considered as weighing ninety-four (94) pounds and one gallon of water as eight and thirty-three hundredths (8.33) pounds.

3.5 *Mixing.* The aggregates, cement and water shall be mixed at a central mixing plant by means of a rotary drum, revolving spiral blade, pug mill, or other type of batch mixer approved by the Engineer. The size of each mixer unit or the number of mixer units shall be such as will produce sufficient base material to permit continuous placing and compacting operations as hereinafter specified. The mixing shall be continued until the cement and the water are evenly distributed through the mass and a uniform mixture is obtained. In no case shall the period of mixing be less than 45 seconds from the time all materials are in the mixer.

Water shall be incorporated in the mix in the amount directed by the Engineer and under such conditions as will permit accurate control of the amount of water added.

Attention is called to the necessity of a comparatively dry mix of medium consistency to permit placing and compacting as herein specified. The mixer equipment used shall be of such design and construction as will permit the satisfactory handling (charging and discharging) and insure thorough mixing of such material.

Weighing and measuring equipment shall be of approved types capable of controlling the quantity of materials for each batch to within one (1) percent by weight of the amounts fixed by the Engineer.

3.6 *Placing.* The mixed material shall be transported in suitable trucks provided with protective covers, and shall be spread on the previously prepared and approved subgrade to such depth that when thoroughly compacted it will conform to the grade and dimensions shown on the plans.

The surface of the subgrade shall be moist but not muddy at the time of placing the concrete base material.

The materials shall be spread by a spreader box, self-propelled spreading machine or other method approved by the Engineer. If spreader boxes or other spreading machines are used that do not spread the material the full width of the lane or width being placed in one construction operation, a sufficient number shall be provided and operated in staggered formation so as to obtain full width spreading. If, in the opinion of the Engineer, full width construction is found to be undesirable because of inadequate equipment, operating difficulties or climatic conditions, the base shall be constructed in partial widths. If the time elapsing between the placing of adjacent partial widths exceeds one-half hour, a vertical construction joint satisfactory to the Engineer shall be provided.

The spreading equipment and methods employed in spreading the base material shall be such as will insure satisfactory accuracy and uniformity as to depth and width. If conditions arise where such uniformity in the spreading cannot be obtained, the Engineer may require such additional equipment or modification in the spreading procedure as may be necessary to obtain satisfactory results. In special cases a self-propelled blade grader having a wheel base of not less than fifteen (15) feet may be required to spread the treated material uniformly.

Immediately upon completion of the spreading operations the base material shall be thoroughly compacted. Self-propelled rollers, of either three-wheel or three axle four-wheel type, weighing not less than ten (10) tons, vibratory equipment or other equipment which will produce the required degree of compaction throughout the full depth and width of the base to the satisfaction of the Engineer may be used. Care shall be exercised in routing construction equipment in order to avoid the formation of unnecessary ridges due to wheel tracks or tractor treads. If necessary, the base material after compaction shall be trimmed by means of self-propelled motor grader to the grade and section shown on the plans. Final rolling shall be with pneumatic-tired rollers and during this rolling the surface of the base shall be lightly fogged with water. Finishing operations shall be continued until the surface is true to the specified cross-section and will not show a variation of more than ⅜″ from a ten (10) foot straight edge laid in any location parallel to the longitudinal axis of the pavement.

It is the intent of this specification to secure the practical maximum weight of dry materials per cubic foot of compacted base material. In no case shall the weight of dry materials per cubic foot be less than ninety-six (96) percent of the weight per cubic foot determined by the Engineer as agreeing with the standard density obtainable with the equipment and materials used.

No equipment or traffic which, in the opinion of the Engineer, will damage the base course or the curing material, shall be permitted on the finished base course during the seventy-two (72)-hour curing period.

3.7 *Construction Joints.* At the end of each day's run a transverse construction joint shall be formed by a header or by cutting back into the compacted material to form a true transverse vertical face.

The protection provided for construction joints shall be such as to permit the placing, spreading, and compacting of base material without injury to the work previously laid.

When a longitudinal construction joint is required in part width construction, side forms shall be used or it shall be formed by cutting back into the compacted material to form a true vertical edge.

Care shall be exercised to insure thorough compaction of the base material immediately adjacent to all construction joints.

3.8 *Operating Time Requirements.* Not more than thirty (30) minutes shall elapse between the time the base material is mixed and the time it is deposited on the approved subgrade. The base material shall be compacted immediately after spreading and not more than one hour shall elapse between the time of spreading and the completion of final rolling.

Curing material shall be applied to each portion of the base within one hour after such portion has been compacted and finished.

3.9 *Curing.* The curing of the finished base shall be carefully and systematically accomplished in accordance with the following provisions:

As soon as possible after the surface has been finished, it shall be covered with any one of the curing materials hereinafter specified. Where, in the opinion of the Engineer, too long a period of time elapses between finishing the base and applying the curing material and attendant weather conditions cause detrimental drying of the surface, sprinkling of the base may be required before application of the curing material. In sprinkling, care shall be taken that the surface of the base is not damaged. The following materials and methods may be used for curing:

Bituminous Seal Coats. These membranes shall consist of a homogeneous emulsion made from petroleum asphalt or of a liquid asphalt, cut back with naphtha and complying with the requirements for rapid curing products RC-1 or RC-2. The asphalt emulsion shall meet the requirements of the standard specifications, A.S.T.M. Designation D 401–40 or D 631–41T. The asphalt cut back shall meet the requirements of A.A.S.H.O. Specification M-81–38.

The grade of the liquid asphalt and the quantity applied shall be determined by the Engineer but the quantity shall be approximately two tenths (0.2) gallon per square yard.

Impermeable Paper. The surface of the base shall be wetted and covered with blankets of impermeable paper. The paper for curing shall meet the requirements of the standard specifications, A.S.T.M. Designation C 171–42T. These blankets shall remain in place for a period of not less than 72 hours. The blankets shall be lapped at least eighteen (18) inches and these laps shall be weighted with a windrow of earth or by other approved methods to form a closed joint. At the edge of the base the blankets shall be weighted securely with a continuous windrow of earth to provide contact. Blankets may be reused provided they are free from perforations and tears and are kept serviceable with repairs. Any blanket which, in the opinion of the Engineer, does not comply with this requirement shall be discarded.

Wetted Straw. The surface of the base shall be covered with clean, loose straw applied at the rate of not less than five (5) pounds per square yard. Straw covering should be saturated with water as soon as placed and kept saturated for a period of not less than seventy-two (72) hours from the time applied. Care shall be taken to see that the edges of the base are protected with straw or earth. The straw may be reused when, in the opinion of the Engineer, it is in satisfactory condition. Upon completion of the curing period the straw shall be removed and disposed of as directed by the Engineer.

Wet Earth. Surface of the base shall be covered with not less than one (1) inch of earth which shall be saturated and kept wet for a period of not less than seventy-two (72) hours. The edges of the base shall be protected by banking with earth. Upon completion of the curing period the earth shall be removed and disposed of as directed by the Engineer.

Wetted Mats. Blankets made from at least two layers of burlap or from mats of cotton sandwiched between burlap, cotton fabric or other similar material shall be presaturated with water, applied to the base and kept saturated for a period of not less than seventy-two (72) hours. The mats shall be placed so that the entire surface and edges of the slab are completely covered.

3.10 *Cold Weather Protection.* The base material shall not be mixed or placed when the temperature is below freezing except under such conditions as the Engineer may direct. If at any time during the progress of the work the temperature is or will, in the opinion of the Engineer, within twenty-four (24) hours, drop to thirty-five (35) degrees Fahrenheit the water and/or the aggregates shall be heated and precautions should be taken to protect the base from freezing. During cold weather when the air temperature may be expected to drop below thirty-five (35) degrees Fahrenheit a sufficient supply of hay, straw or other material suitable for covering and protection shall be provided at the site of the work. Any base which has been damaged by freezing or otherwise shall be removed and replaced by the contractor at his own expense.

METHODS OF MEASUREMENT

4.1 *Methods of Measurement.* The quantity of one course, lean mix concrete base to be paid for will be determined by measurement of the number of square yards of base actually constructed and accepted by the Engineer as complying with the plans and specifications.

The quantity of portland cement to be paid for will be the amount actually used in the base as authorized by the engineer. One barrel of portland cement shall be considered to weigh three hundred seventy-six (376) pounds.

BASIS OF PAYMENT

5.1 *Basis of Payment.* The quantity of lean mix concrete base and portland cement as determined above shall be paid for at the contract unit price per square yard of base in place, and at the contract unit price per barrel of portland cement used therein, which contract prices shall be compensation in full for furnishing all materials; for transporting, handling, preparing, mixing and placing all materials; for clearing, stripping and cleaning up aggregate pits; for handling and disposing of unsuitable material; for such clean-up operations as are necessary to leave the site of the work in an orderly and acceptable condition; and for all labor, equipment, tools and incidentals necessary to complete the work in accordance with the plans and specifications.

APPENDIX 20

DEPARTMENT OF COMMERCE
Civil Aeronautics Administration
Airport Division
Washington, D. C.
June 15, 1944

MIXED IN PLACE BASE COURSE (TRAVEL PLANT METHOD) FOR AIRPORT RUNWAYS, TAXIWAYS AND APRONS

C.A.A. Specification No. P-204

INTRODUCTION

This specification has been prepared by the Paving Engineers of the Airport Division, Civil Aeronautics Administration in collaboration with the Paving Engineers of the Office of the Chief, U.S. Corps of Engineers.

This specification is to cover the mixing in place of naturally graded or pre-graded aggregate with bituminous material. The type of bituminous material to be used in the base course may be either cut-back asphalt, emulsion, or tar.

In view of the fact that there is no method which is satisfactory to the industries to predetermine the amount of cut-back asphalt, emulsified asphalt or tar in order to establish an accepted differential in quantities required, the materials should not be placed in competitive bidding. The type of bituminous material shall be predetermined and so specified, deleting the other types. The particular grade of cut-back asphalt or tar will depend on the season, location, and time of set required for finishing and compacting. The heavier grades will require less aeration prior to compaction. The workability, break and final set of the emulsified asphalt mixes are dependent on uniform moisture content. It is essential to control the total moisture content of the mixture.

If the aggregate is found to be hydrophilic as determined by the test given in the specification, the addition of the percentage of Portland Cement or lime as shown in the aggregate table to the aggregate prior to mixing with the bituminous material may be sufficient to change the inherent characteristics to a hydrophobic material. If the material is of such hydrophilic characteristics that the cement or lime alone will not accomplish the desired results, the addition of a proven and approved admixture to the bituminous material will be necessary.

The addition of 1% of Portland cement to the mix will hasten the set and slightly increase stability as well as to increase workability up to the time the cement takes its initial set.

It is recommended that where grass or weed growth might cause damage to the pavement that either a recognized and approved chemical treatment (C.A.A. No. P-608) be applied to the subgrade in sufficient quantities or that the base course be constructed using either tar or asphalt containing an approved chemical.

DESCRIPTION

1.1 This pavement shall consist of a base course composed of mineral aggregate and bituminous material, mixed in a travel plant, constructed on the prepared subgrade or base in accordance with these specifications and in conformity with the dimensions and typical cross sections shown on the plans and with line and grade established by the engineer.

1.2 *Determination of Percentage of Bituminous Material.* The percentage of bituminous material, by weight, to be added to the aggregate shall be between the limits as set forth in the table. The exact percentage to be used shall be fixed by the engineer on the basis of preliminary tests and field sieve analysis of the aggregate furnished.

1.3 *Job Mix Formula.* No work shall be started on the project nor any mixture accepted therefor until the contractor has submitted and received approval for his intended job mix formula. The formula shall be submitted in writing indicating the definite percentage for each sieve fraction of aggregate and for bituminous material which has been chosen as a fixed mean in each instance. The gradation of the aggregate and the bitumen content shall not vary from the fixed mean of the formula by more than the following tolerances:

Job Mix Tolerances

	Gradation A & C	*Gradation B*
Aggregate passing sieves No. 4 and larger	6%	7%
Aggregate passing No. 10, No. 40, and No. 80 sieve	4%	5%
Aggregate passing No. 200 sieve	2%	2%
Bitumen	0.5%	0.5%
Moisture content—(see paragraph 4.5)		

MATERIALS

2.1 *Aggregate.* The aggregate shall consist of crushed stone, crushed gravel, crushed slag, screenings, gravel, sand-gravel, sand or other natural, granular, approved material having essentially the same qualities and meeting the requirements for stability when combined within the limits for grading.

The aggregate shall be tough, durable and sound. The coarse aggregate when tested in accordance with the Los Angeles Rattler Test, after five hundred revolutions shall have a percent of wear of not more than fifty according to the A.A.S.H.O., Method T-96–38.

Slag shall be air cooled, blast furnace, and shall consist of angular fragments reasonably uniform in density and quality and reasonably free from thin, elongated or soft pieces, dirt or other objectionable matter. The dry slag shall weigh not less than sixty-five pounds per cubic foot.

The portion of the material retained on a No. 4 sieve shall be known as coarse aggregate; that portion passing a No. 4 sieve shall be known as fine aggregate, and the material passing the No. 200 sieve shall be known as filler. The composite material shall meet the requirements for one of the gradings given in Table 4, using A.A.S.H.O., Methods T-11 and T-27.

No intermediate sizes of aggregate shall be removed for use in the seal coat or for other purposes without the written consent of the engineer.

That portion of the fine aggregate, including any blended filler, passing a No. 40 sieve shall have a plasticity index of not more than 6, as determined by A.A.S.H.O. Method T-91; a liquid limit of not more than 25 as determined by A.A.S.H.O. Method T-89 and a maximum clay content by elutriation of 6%.

The composite aggregate shall be free from vegetable matter, lumps or balls of clay, adherent films of clay, or other matter that will prevent thorough coating with bituminous material. The bituminized aggregate shall have a swell of not more than 1.5 percent as determined by A.A.S.H.O. Method T-101.

Prior to final acceptance of the proposed aggregate to be used, the inherent characteristics of said agggregate relative to stripping shall be determined. This shall be done by preparing a test sample of the paving mixture in conformity with the specifications contained herwith. After the mixture has been made it shall be spread out in a loose thin layer and allowed to air season for 24 hours before testing. A suitable size sample (approximately one-half contents of container) shall be tested by placing it in a glass jar fitted with a tight screw cap and completely covering with distilled water. The jar and contents shall be allowed to stand for a period of 24 hours. Then the sample shall be vigorously shaken for a period of 15 minutes. The sample of mixture shall be examined for stripping. If stripping or sloughing off of the bituminous coating occurs it will be necessary

TABLE 1

CUT-BACK ASPHALT SPECIFICATIONS

The cut-back asphalt shall be homogeneous; it shall be free from water, shall show no separation upon standing and shall meet the following requirements:

		Grades		
	A.A.S.H.O. Test Method	RC-2	RC-3	RC-4
Flash Point (Open Tag) ° F.	T-79–38	80+	80+	80+
Furol Viscosity at 140° F.	T-72–35	100–200	250–500	
at 180° F.				125–250
Distillation (% of total Distillate to 680° F.)	T-78–35			
to 437° F.		40+	25+	8+
to 500° F.		65+	55+	40+
to 600° F.		87+	83+	80+
Residue from Distillation to 680° F.				
Volume percent by difference		67+	73+	78+
Tests on Residue				
Penetration at 77° F.	T-49–38	80–120	80–120	80–120
Ductility at 77° F. 5 cm./min.	T-51–38	100+	100+	100+
Percent Soluble in CCl_4 (Using CCl_4 with T-44)	T-44–35	99.5+	99.5+	99.5+
Temperature Range F.		125°–175°	150°–200°	175°–225°
Maximum amount of moisture in mineral aggregate		6%	4%	2%

to treat said aggregate by a method which has proven successful in changing the material from a hydrophilic to a hydrophobic state.

2.2 *Filler.* If filler in addition to that naturally present in the aggregate is necessary, it shall consist of stone dust, loess, Portland cement or other standard approved types. The material for such purpose shall be obtained from sources approved by the engineer.

2.3 *Bituminous Material.* The bituminous material to be mixed with the mineral aggregate in the travel plant shall conform to the grade, requirements and specifications as given in Tables 1, 2 and 3.

TABLE 2

TAR SPECIFICATIONS

The tar shall be homogeneous and shall be a water-gas or coal tar or a combination of these. It shall meet the following requirements:

		Grades				
	A.A.S.H.O. Test Method	RT-5	RT-6	RT-7	RT-8	RT-9
Consistency						
Engler Sp. Visc. at 122° F.	T-54	17–26	26–40			
Float Test at 90° F.	T-50			50–80	80–120	120–200
Sp. Gr. at 77° F.	T-43	1.10+	1.10+	1.12+	1.14+	1.14+
Total Bitumen % by wt.	T-44	83+	83+	78+	78+	78+
Water % by vol.	T-55	1.5	1.5	1.0	0	0
Distillation, % by wt.	T-52					
to 338° F.		5.0–	5.0–	3.0–	1.0–	1.0–
to 518° F.		25.0–	25.0–	20.0–	15.0–	15.0–
to 572° F.		35.0–	35.0–	30.0–	25.0–	25.0–
Softening Point of Distillation Residue ° F.	T-53	95–150	95–150	95–150	95–150	95–150
Temperature Range F		80°–150°	80°–150°	150°–225°	150°–225°	150°–225°

The allowable amount of moisture in the mineral aggregates shall be determined by laboratory tests for stability of final mix. The difference between bitumen content necessary to secure this stability and the optimum (within 2%) shall be the allowable moisture content.

During the progress of construction it may be necessary to vary the above predetermined moisture content due to field conditions as determined and approved by the engineer.

TABLE 3

Emulsified Asphalt Specifications
A.S.T.M. Designation: D 631–41 T

The emulsified asphalt shall be homogeneous and shall show no separation of asphalt after thorough mixing, within 30 days after delivery, providing separation has not been caused by freezing.

It shall conform to the following requirements:

Viscosity, Saybolt Furol, 60 ml. @ 77° F., Sec.	20–100
Residue by Distillation @ 325° F. per cent	57–62
Sieve Test, per cent	0.05 –
Modified Miscibility with Difference of Asphalt Residue Water,* per cent	4.5 –
Cement Mixing Test, per cent	2.0 –

Residue—The residue obtained from evaporation or distillation shall conform to the following requirements:

Penetration at 77° F., 100 g., 5 sec.	100–200
Soluble in carbon disulfide:	
Petroleum Asphalts, per cent	97 +
Native Asphalts, per cent	95 +
Ash, per cent	2 –
Ductility at 77° F., cms.	60 +
Specific Gravity at 77° F.	1.00 +

* If the sample of emulsified asphalt being tested fails to conform to this requirement for modified miscibility, the sample shall be tested for 5-day settlement and for miscibility, and if the numerical difference between the average percentages of asphaltic residue in the 5-day settlement test is less than 3, and if the standard miscibility test shows no appreciable coagulation in 2 hours, then the emulsified asphalt shall be considered as conforming to these specifications and shall be accepted.

The amount of emulsion for base and surface course may be checked by the following formula, but the amount of bitumen shall conform to that shown in Table 4:

$$P = \frac{(.05A \text{ plus } .1B \text{ plus } .5C) \times K}{\text{Percent Residue by Distillation}}$$ in which

P equals total per cent by weight of emulsion based on the weight of the graded mineral aggregate.

A equals the per cent of the mineral aggregate retained on a No. 10 Sieve.

B equals the per cent of mineral aggregate passing a No. 10 Sieve and retained on a No. 200 Sieve.

C equals the per cent of the mineral aggregate passing a No. 200 Sieve.

K is derived by past experience in paving and gives a definite control, both on variations of percent asphalt contained in an emulsion and the type of aggregate used. For base course, the value of K should vary between 35 and 45 according to the absorptive properties of the aggregate; 35 being used for hard, nonabsorptive aggregate, and 45 for highly absorptive aggregate.

Screen analyses shall be made as often as necessary to determine and control the grading. Material lost in the wash tests of the aggregate shall be considered a part of the fines passing the No. 200 Sieve.

Methods of Testing

The properties enumerated in these specifications shall be determined in accordance with the Standard Methods of Testing Emulsified Asphalts (A.S.T.M. Designation: D 244–40)* and the Tentative Methods of Test for Modified

* 1940 Supplement to Book of A.S.T.M. Standards, Part II, p. 94.

Miscibility and Cement Mixing of Emulsified Asphalts (A.S.T.M. Designation: D 244–41 T)° of the American Society for Testing Materials.

2.4 *Hydrated Lime.* The hydrated lime shall meet the requirements of the A.S.T.M. Designation C 6–31.

2.5 *Portland Cement.* The Portland Cement shall meet the requirements of A.A.S.H.O. Specification M-5–38.

GRADATION

3.1 *Composition of Mixture.* The mineral aggregate for the base course shall be of such size that the percentage composition by weight, as determined by laboratory screens will conform to one of the following gradations:

TABLE 4

Base Course

Screen Size	Percentage Passing Screens (Square Openings)					
	1½″ Maximum			1″ Maximum		
	"A"	"B"	"C"	"A"	"B"	"C"
1½″	100	100	100			
1″	78–100	84–100	92–100	100	100	100
¾″				76–100	82–100	92–100
½″	53–70	67–82	80–93	60–79	73–89	85–97
No. 4	30–48	48–65	65–82	30–50	50–70	70–89
No. 10	20–37	37–54	54–70	20–39	39–59	59–79
No. 40	10–21	21–32	31–44	10–23	23–36	36–50
No. 80	6–15	12–21	18–27	6–15	13–22	20–30
No. 200	3–8	4–9	5–10	3–8	4–9	5–10
* Bitumen %	3.5–5.5	4–6	4.5–6.5	3.5–5.5	4–6	4.5–6.5

Screen Size	Percentage Passing Screens (Square Openings)					
	¾″ Maximum			½″ Maximum		
	"A"	"B"	"C"	"A"	"B"	"C"
¾″	100	100	100			
½″	76–100	84–100	92–100	100	100	100
⅜″				67–100	80–100	90–100
No. 4	35–54	54–73	73–91	40–61	60–80	79–96
No. 10	24–42	42–60	60–80	29–48	48–67	67–85
No. 40	10–23	23–36	36–51	15–28	28–40	40–54
No. 80	6–15	13–23	20–31	9–18	16–24	24–33
No. 200	3–8	4–9	5–10	3–8	4–9	5–10
* Bitumen %	3.5–5.5	4–6	4.5–7	4–6	4–6.5	4.5–7

° 1941 Supplement to Book of A.S.T.M. Standards, Part II, p. 347.

TABLE 4—*Continued*

Screen Size	Percentage Passing Screens (Square Openings)		
	No. 4 Maximum		
	"A"	"B"	"C"
½"	100	100	100
⅜"	70–100	80–100	90–100
No. 4	44–64	62–82	80–100
No. 10	29–51	51–75	75–98
No. 40	15–37	37–60	60–82
No. 80	9–26	25–42	40–60
No. 200	5–10	6–11	6–12
* Bitumen	4.5–7.0	6–8	6.5–8.0

* Note: The range of Bitumen shown in Table 4 represents the maximum and minimum amounts based on the actual bituminous agencies affecting the ultimate mix after evaporation or oxidation of fluxes. The exact amount for the job mix shall be fixed by laboratory tests and shall be subject to change as required by actual field conditions.

From 0.75 to one percent of Portland Cement shall be added to the composition of the base mixture after the addition of the emulsified asphalt and prior to the addition of cut back or tar.

If lime is required for correcting hydrophilic characteristics of the aggregate in emulsion mixes, it shall be added at the rate of approximately 0.5% prior to the addition of the emulsified asphalt.

Referring to Table 4:

The gradations in this table represent the limits which shall determine suitability of aggregate for use from the sources of supply. The final gradations decided on within the limits designated in the table shall be uniformly graded from coarse to fine, and shall not vary from the low limit on one screen to the high limit on the adjacent screens or vice versa.

The selection of any of the gradings shown in the table shall be such that the maximum size aggregate used in any course shall not be more than one-half the thickness of the layer of the course being constructed.

The composition limits prescribed herein are ranges of tolerance to govern mixtures made from materials meeting these specifications and they are the maximum and minimum for all cases. A closer control appropriate to the job materials will be required for the specific project in accordance with a job mix formula.

The total amount of material passing the No. 200 sieve shall be determined by washing the material through the sieve with water and not less than one-half (½) of the material passing the No. 200 sieve by washing shall pass the No. 200 sieve by dry sieving without washing.

Sand or screenings other than that specified may be used with permission of of the engineer, provided the material has a minimum stability of 30 lbs. per square inch for the base course at 1.75% moisture content, (as determined by the C.A.A. Specification No. P-607), a maximum liquid limit of 20 with maximum plasticity index of 4 and a maximum clay content by elutriation of 6%, with a maximum of 12% passing the No. 200 sieve.

CONSTRUCTION METHODS

4.1 *Weather Limitations.* The base course shall be constructed and operations shall be carried on only when the surface is dry, when the atmospheric temperature is above 50° F., and when the weather is not foggy or rainy. The temperature requirement may be waived, but only when so directed by the engineer.

4.2 *Equipment and Organization.* (1) *General.* All methods employed in performing the work and all equipment, tools and other plant and machinery used for handling materials and executing any part of the work shall be subject to the approval of the engineer before the work is started and whenever found unsatisfactory shall be changed and improved as required. All equipment, tools, machinery and plant used must be maintained in a satisfactory working condition.

(2) *Scarifiers.* These shall be of an approved type.

(3) *Traveling Plant Mixer.* The traveling plant shall be self-propelled or tractor drawn and capable of maintaining a uniform rate of travel while mixing. It shall be mounted on wheels or tread equipment of such type that when loaded to capacity it will not rut or damage the subgrade or subbase course. The device for picking up the aggregates from the windrow shall be such that it will take up the loose material and leave the base clean without damage. Plants equipped for drying the aggregates before adding the bituminous material shall be so constructed as not to allow a loss of mineral filler or segregation of the aggregate. The equipment for proportioning the aggregate and bituminous material shall accurately measure the specified amounts of material for the mix while the machine is in operation. The plant shall be capable of thoroughly combining the aggregates and bituminous material into a mixture of uniform color with all the particles completely coated and shall also be capable of depositing the processed mixture on the subgrade or subbase.

Approved methods shall be provided for accurately controlling the correct amount of filler, Portland cement or lime and for the induction of same into the mixture at the specified time.

(4) *Spreading Equipment.* Blade graders for windrowing aggregate and for spreading processed material shall be self-powered or tractor drawn. The grader shall have a wheel base of not less than fifteen (15) feet, shall have a blade not less than ten (10) feet long, and be equipped with wheels of sufficient width to prevent excessive rutting.

If aeration is not necessary prior to compaction the mixed material may be placed and spread by a mechanical spreader and finisher.

(5) *Rolling Equipment.* (a) The multiwheeled rubber-tired roller shall consist of two axles on which are mounted not less than 9 pneumatic-tired wheels in such a manner that the rear group of tires will not follow in the tracks of the forward group, and mounted in a rigid frame provided with a loading platform or body suitable for ballast loading. The front axle shall rotate around a king pin so located that the roller may be turned within a minimum circle. The roller under working conditions shall have an effective rolling width of at least sixty (60) inches and shall give a compression of at least 325 lbs. per inch of width of tread when fully loaded. The tires shall be uniformly inflated. The roller and the

operating pneumatic-tired tractor shall meet the approval of the engineer. The weight of the roller shall be increased as the rolling progresses to the maximum degree obtainable without detrimental results to the course being compacted.

(b) The tamping roller shall consist of one or more units. Each unit shall consist of a water-tight cylindrical drum not less than 48 inches in length and shall be surmounted by metal studs with tamping feet projecting not less than 7 inches from the surface of the drum and spaced not less than 6 inches nor more than 10 inches measured diagonally from center to center. The area of the tamping feet shall be greater than that of the supporting shaft. Each unit shall be provided with a suitable tamper feet cleaning device. Where more than one rolling unit is used, the rolling units must be pivoted on the main frame in a manner which will permit the rolling units to adapt themselves to uneven surfaces and to rotate independently.

(c) The steel-wheel roller shall be of the self-propelled tandem type weighing not less than five tons and not more than eight tons. The wheels on the roller shall be equipped with adjustable scrapers which shall be used when necessary to clean the wheel surface. Rollers shall also be equipped with water tanks and sprinkling apparatus which shall be used to keep the wheels wet and prevent the surfacing material from sticking.

4.3 *Preparation of Subgrade and Base Course.* The subgrade upon which the base course is to be placed shall be properly prepared, smooth and fully compacted. It shall be cleaned of all loose material and deleterious matter and when tested with a 10 foot straightedge shall show no deviation in excess of three-eighths ($\frac{3}{8}$) inch.

4.4 *Placing Mineral Aggregate.* If borrow or foreign aggregate is used, it shall be transported to the site of paving in trucks equipped with pneumatic tires. Both speed and load shall be regulated by the engineer in order to reduce the possibility of damage to the existing surface. The aggregate existing or otherwise shall be formed in windrows in such quantity and proportions as to provide sufficient total aggregate, conforming with the specified grading, to produce a finished base course of the specified compacted thickness. The contractor may proportion the amount of coarse aggregate and mineral filler in the windrow by weighing with suitable equipment or by using any other methods or devices which will be equally as effective as weighing equipment in placing the amount of total aggregate necessary to satisfy the yardage requirements for the area to be covered. After the proportions of coarse aggregate and mineral filler have been adjusted if required to meet the gradation, the total loose aggregate shall be thoroughly mixed to the satisfaction of the engineer. It shall be bladed into windrows of uniform cross sections for the final measurement and sampling for grading adjustment.

Care shall be exercised to prevent the aggregate from becoming mixed with earth or shoulder material. The uniform windrows shall be left undisturbed until measuring and sampling are completed.

4.5 *Moisture Content of Aggregate.* Immediately prior to bituminizing, the aggregate to be treated shall be tested for moisture. If the moisture content is in excess of the maximum allowable percentage as shown in the tables for cut back asphalt and tar, the aggregate shall be turned by blades or disc harrows, or otherwise aerated, until the moisture content is reduced to the percentage designated. The prepared aggregate shall then be uniformly windrowed as before.

When using emulsified asphalt: the percent of moisture is definitely stipulated in table 3 for emulsified asphalt. The net amount of water allowed in the mixture shall be determined and controlled for workability, spreading and compaction. The net amount of water shall be adjusted for the free water present in the aggregate which shall be determined by tests and if found variable or excessive shall be controlled by aeration as described in the above paragraph.

4.6 *Mixing.* The aggregate, windrowed and prepared as specified above, shall then be mixed with the bituminous material by means of the traveling mixing plant and deposited ready for spreading.

The Portland cement and lime shall be added during the mixing procedure at the time and in the amounts as specified in Table 4.

The quantity of bituminous material as calibrated for continuous mixing shall be determined by the engineer, and introduced into the mixer. The mixing shall continue for such period as is necessary to coat all of the particles and obtain a homogeneous mixture.

Before spreading, the mixture shall be examined by the engineer who shall determine whether the mixing is complete and satisfactory. Should the mixture show an excess, deficiency, or uneven distribution of bituminous material, the unsatisfactory condition shall be corrected by the addition of the required aggregate or bituminous material, and by remixing. If necessary, the material shall be harrowed or disked and all compressed masses of material broken up. No spreading shall be done, except when authorized by the engineer.

4.7 *Spreading and Finishing.* (1) *General.* Spreading shall not be started until the subgrade or subbase has been properly prepared, compacted and approved by the engineer.

Grade control between the edges of the runway shall be by means of grade stakes or steel grade pins placed in lanes parallel to the centerline of the runway, and at intervals sufficiently close that string lines may be stretched between the stakes or pins.

(2) *Spreading and Blade Finishing.* The mixture shall be placed in lanes parallel to the centerline of the runway and ending each days run for the full width of the lane.

After the mixing has been completed, the mixed material shall be spread to the required width and depth by a self-powered or tractor drawn blade grader, mechanical spreader, or other approved method. In spreading from a windrow, care shall be taken to prevent cutting into the underlying subbase. If necessary to prevent such cutting, a layer of the mixture approximately one-half (½) inch thick shall be left at the bottom of the windrow. The mixture shall be spread and cured in thin layers. The surface shall be continually bladed, disced and dragged if necessary until a smooth uniform surface, true to line, grade and cross section has been developed. Should the mixture show an excess, deficiency or uneven distribution of bituminous material due to insufficient mixing, the conditions shall be corrected by scarifying, adding aggregate or bitumen as required, and remixing.

When emulsified asphalt is used in the paving mixture, the course shall not be placed in layers thicker than 3″. Each layer shall be spread, finished and compacted as described herewith before additional layer is placed.

If precipitation occurs during the application of bituminous material or while the material is being spread, the mixed material shall be allowed to dry before the resumption of operations, except such blading as will facilitate evaporation. In no case shall the bituminous mixture be placed while moisture content is excessive. The engineer shall authorize the resumption of work and the spreading of material when the required moisture content of the subgrade or base and bituminous mixture has been obtained.

Any oversize aggregate larger than one-half the thickness of the course being laid shall be removed from the mixture during or prior to spreading.

In limited areas where, on account of irregularities or unavoidable obstacles, the use of spreading equipment is impractical, the mixture shall be spread by hand.

When hand spreading is permitted, the mixture shall be dumped upon arrival on approved dump sheets outside of the area on which it is to be spread and be distributed into place immediately by means of shovels. It shall be spread with rakes in a uniformly loose layer to the full width required and of such depth that when the work is completed, it will have the required thickness and will conform to the grade and surface contour required.

4.8 *Compaction of Mixture.* Aeration after mixing and prior to rolling shall be continued until the mixture is in suitable condition for proper compaction. After each layer has been placed and cured, it shall be thoroughly and uniformly compressed by rollers, as specified. Blading shall continue during the rolling only if so ordered by the engineer. Initial rolling shall be done with pneumatic rollers, or tamping rollers as directed by the engineer.

Initial rolling shall be done longitudinally, overlapping on successive trips by at least twelve (12) inches. Alternate trips of the roller shall be of slightly different lengths. Rolling shall continue until the surface is of uniform texture and degree of compaction and is true to grade and cross section. Final rolling shall be done with the tandem rollers.

The speed of the rollers shall at all times be slow enough to avoid displacement of the mixture. Any displacement occurring as a result of the reversing the direction of the roller, or from any other cause shall be corrected at once by the use of rakes and of fresh mixture where required. Sufficient rollers of the designated types shall be funished to adequately handle the rate of spreading and aeration of the mixture.

Upon instructions from the engineer, the course shall be rerolled any time within two weeks after it is laid and shall be subjected to diagonal rolling, crossing the lines of the first. If necessary to prevent adhesion of the mixture to the tandem roller, the wheels shall be kept properly moistened, but an excess of either water or oil will not be permitted. The rollers shall be in good condition and shall be operated continuously as far as practicable and in such a manner that all parts of the pavement shall receive substantially equal compression.

At all places not accessible to the roller, the mixture shall be thoroughly compacted with tampers. Such tampers shall weigh not less than 25 pounds and shall have a tamping face area of not more than 50 square inches. The surface of the mixture after compression shall be smooth and true to the established crown and grade.

Any mixture which becomes loose and broken, mixed with dirt, or in any way defective prior to the application of the finish coat shall be removed and replaced, at the expense of the contractor, with fresh mixture which shall be compacted to conform with the surrounding area. Skin patching on an area that has been rolled shall not be allowed. Any mixture remaining unbonded after rolling shall be removed and replaced.

4.10 *Shaping Edges.* When forms are not used and while the surface is being compacted and finished, the contractor shall trim the edges neatly to line.

4.11 *Surface Tests.* The finished surface shall not vary more than $\frac{3}{8}$ inch for the base course when measured with a ten foot straightedge applied parallel with or at right angles to the center line. Tests for conformity with the specified crown and grade shall be made by the contractor after compaction and any variation shall be corrected by properly removing or adding materials. After the completion of final rolling, the smoothness of the course shall again be checked, and any irregularities exceeding the specified tolerances or that retain water on the surface shall be corrected by removing the defective work and placing new material or by adding additional material as directed by the engineer at the contractor's expense.

4.12 *Sampling Pavement.* For the determination of composition, condition and compaction of the base, the contractor shall remove suitable size samples of the completed base. Samples for each day or fraction thereof when mixtures are placed shall be taken as directed by the engineer. The contractor shall replace the base where samples are removed, and these replacements shall be installed by the contractor free of charge. After the samples have been removed from the completed base, they shall be tested for thickness, density and composition as directed. If the deficiency in composition, compaction and density exceeds the limits of toleration from that specified, no payment shall be made for the mixtures found so deficient.

4.13 *Bituminous and Aggregate Material Contractor's Responsibility.* Samples of the bituminous and aggregate materials that the contractor proposes to use, together with a statement as to their source and character must be submitted and approval obtained before use of such materials begins. The contractor shall require the manufacturer or producer of the bituminous and aggregate materials to furnish material subject to this and all other pertinent requirements of the contract. Only those materials that have been demonstrated by service tests as satisfactory for the intended use will be acceptable.

4.14 *Freight and Weigh-Bills.* Before the final estimate is allowed, the contractor shall file with the engineer receipted bills where railroad shipments are made and certified weigh-bills when materials are received in any other manner, of the bituminous and paving materials actually used in the construction covered by the contract. The contractor shall not remove bituminous material from the tank car or storage tank until the initial outage and temperature measurements have been taken, nor shall he release the car or tank until the final outage has been taken by the engineer.

Copies of freight and weigh-bills shall be furnished to the engineer during the progress of the work.

METHOD OF MEASUREMENT

5.1 The unit of measurement for base course laid shall be the square yard. The yardage to be paid for shall be the square yards of base course completed and accepted in accordance with the plans and specifications, or as directed by the engineer.

5.2 The unit of measurement for the bituminous material shall be the gallon or the ton, whichever is called for in the bid schedule. The gallonage or tonnage to be paid for shall be the number of gallons or tons of bituminous material used as ordered in the accepted work. Gallonage shall be determined by measuring the material at a temperature of 60° F., or by converting the gallonage measured at other temperatures to gallonage at 60° F. in accordance with A.S.T.M. Designation D-206–36 for asphalt materials and in accordance with appropriate formulae or tables for emulsified asphalt or tar.

BASIS OF PAYMENT

6.1 The quantities of base mixture and bituminous material determined as provided in 5.1 and 5.2 above, shall be paid for at the respective contract unit prices in the bid schedule, which prices and payment shall constitute full compensation for preparing base or subgrade, for furnishing, handling, mixing, manipulating, and placing all materials, for all shaping, compacting, and rolling, for finishing, for improving unsatisfactory areas, for reconditioning subgrade, for furnishing samples, for furnishing and sealing of scales, for furnishing the weigh house, for all labor, equipment, tools and incidentals necessary to complete the item, except any prime coat or tack coat.

APPENDIX 21

SPECIFICATIONS
PENETRATION MACADAM BASE COURSE
(EMULSIFIED ASPHALT TYPE)

DESCRIPTION

1.1 This item shall consist of a base course composed of crushed stone or crushed slag, asphalt-bonded, constructed on a prepared subgrade or a previously constructed subbase in accordance with these specifications and in conformity with the dimensions and typical cross-section shown on the plans and with lines and grades established by the Engineer.

1.2 *Quantities of Materials per Square Yard.* The finished thickness of the penetration macadam base shall be as specified or as shown on the plans. The quantities of aggregate and emulsified asphalt shall be as given in Table 1 opposite the particular thickness shown on the plans for the base. When the total thickness of the penetration macadam base exceeds four (4) inches, it shall be constructed in multiple courses of combinations of the thicknesses indicated. At the beginning of construction and during its progress, the individual weights of the various aggregates shall be varied and adjusted as directed by the Engineer in accordance with field requirements.

TABLE 1

Quantities of Materials per Square Yard of Emulsified Asphalt Penetration Base Course for Different Thicknesses

Compacted Thickness indicated on plans	Coarse Aggregate		Choke Aggregate		1st Appl. Emul.	Keystone		2nd Appl. Emul.	Total Aggr.	Total Emulsion
	Grad.	Lbs.	Grad.	Lbs.	Gals.	Grad.	Lbs.	Gals.	Lbs.	Gals.
2″ Course	C	140	E	20	0.6 – 0.8	D	25	0.7 – 0.9	185	1.3 – 1.7
3″ Course	B	225	E	28	0.8 – 1.0	D	35	0.9 – 1.1	288	1.7 – 2.1
4″ Course	A	315	E	38	1.0 – 1.2	D	40	1.1 – 1.3	393	2.1 – 2.5

The weights given in Table 1 are approximate and are for aggregates having a bulk specific gravity of 2.65, as determined by A.A.S.H.O. Method T-85–42. Proportionate corrections shall be made when the aggregates furnished have bulk specific gravities above 2.75 or below 2.55. In such case the corrected amount shall be the product of the number of pounds shown in Table 1 multiplied by the ratio of the bulk specific gravity of the aggregate to 2.65.

In Table 1 the amounts of emulsion given are for stone aggregates. If the total aggregate is composed of slag, the gallons of emulsion shall be increased by from 15 to 20 percent.

MATERIALS

2.1 *Aggregate.* The coarse aggregate, keystone and screenings shall be either crushed stone or crushed slag.

The crushed stone shall consist of hard, durable particles or fragments of stone, free from an excess of flat, elongated, soft or disintegrated pieces, dirt or other objectionable matter, and shall have a percent of wear of not more than 50 at 500 revolutions as determined by A.A.S.H.O., Method T 96–42 (Los Angeles Rattler Test).

The crushed slag shall be air-cooled blast furnace slag and shall consist of angular fragments, reasonably uniform in density and quality and reasonably free from thin, elongated or soft pieces, dirt and other objectionable matter. It shall have a compact weight of not less than 70 pounds per cubic foot, and shall have a percent of wear of not more than 50 at 500 revolutions as determined by A.A.S.H.O., Method T 96–42 (Los Angeles Rattler Test).

Crushed stone and crushed slag for coarse aggregate, keystone and screenings shall meet the requirements for grading given in Table 2, using A.A.S.H.O., Method T 27–42.

TABLE 2

Requirements for Grading of Aggregate

Sieve Designation	Percentage by Weight Passing Square Mesh Sieves				
	Grading A (A.A.S.H.O. No. 1)	Grading B (A.A.S.H.O. No. 2)	Grading C (A.A.S.H.O. No. 3)	Grading D (A.A.S.H.O. No. 68)	Grading E (A.A.S.H.O. No. 8)
4 inch	100				
$3\frac{1}{2}$ inch	90–100				
3 inch		100			
$2\frac{1}{2}$ inch	25–60	90–100	100		
2 inch		35–70	90–100		
$1\frac{1}{2}$ inch	0–15	0–15	35–70		
1 inch			0–15	100	
$\frac{3}{4}$ inch	0–5	0–5		90–100	
$\frac{1}{2}$ inch			0–5		100
$\frac{3}{8}$ inch				30–65	85–100
No. 4				5–25	10–30
No. 8				0–5	0–10

Prior to final acceptance of the proposed aggregate to be used, the inherent characteristics of said aggregate relative to stripping shall be determined. This shall be done by preparing a test sample by immersing at least two pounds of the aggregate in the emulsified asphalt for a period of approximately 10 minutes. After the sample has been prepared, it shall be spread out in a loose, thin layer and placed in a constant temperature oven controlled to 140° F. for a period of 48 hours before testing. A suitable size sample (approximately one-half contents of container) shall be tested by placing it in a glass jar fitted with tight screw cap and completely covering with distilled water. The jar and contents shall be allowed to stand for a period of 24 hours. Then, the sample shall be vigorously shaken for a period of 15 minutes. The sample shall be examined for stripping. If any stripping or sloughing off of the bituminous coating occurs, it will be necessary to treat said aggregate by a method which has proven successful in changing the material from a hydrophilic to a hydrophobic state, or the aggregate shall be rejected.

2.2 *Emulsified Asphalt.* The emulsified asphalt shall be a quick-setting emulsion that is homogeneous and that will show no separation after thorough mixing, within 30 days after delivery. When tested as herein specified, the emulsion shall conform to the following requirements:

TABLE 3

Requirements for Emulsified Asphalt

Tests	Method A.A.S.H.O.	Limits
Viscosity, Saybolt Furol, at 77° F., sec.	T 59–42	30–70
Specific Gravity, 77°/77° F., not less than	T 43–35	1.00
Residue from Distillation Test, %	T 59–42	55–60
Demulsibility: 35 ml. N/50 $CaCl_2$, not less than, %	T 59–42	75
Settlement, 10 days—not more than, %	T 59–42	3
Sieve Test, not more than, %	T 59–42	0.05
Sampling Material	T 40–42	
The residue from distillation shall have the following characteristics:		
Penetration at 77° F., 100 g., 5 sec.	T 49–42	100–200
Sol. in Carbon Disulphide, not less than, %	T 44–42	97
Ash, not more than, %	T 59–42	2
Ductility at 77° F., not less than, cms.	T 51–42	60

Ductility—When the ductility test is made on the residue from distillation or evaporation, the residue shall be screened through a No. 50 sieve while still hot, and shall then be kneaded until uniform and homogeneous. It shall then be tested for ductility.

CONSTRUCTION METHODS

3.1 *Weather Limitations.* The emulsified asphalt penetration base shall be constructed and operations carried on only when the surface of the underlying course and the base is dry, when the atmospheric temperature is above 45° F. and when the weather is not foggy and rainy. The temperature requirement may be waived, but only when so directed by the Engineer.

3.2 *Equipment and Organization.* (a) General. All methods employed in performing the work and all equipment, tools and other machinery used for handling materials and executing any part of the work shall be subject to the approval of the engineer before the work is started, and whenever found unsatisfactory, shall be changed and improved as required. All equipment, tools and machinery used must be maintained in a satisfactory working condition.

(b) *Drag Brooms.* The drags shall be of rectangular shape and not less than seven feet by twelve feet. They shall be so designed that when pulled at a uniform rate of speed they will distribute stone chips and keystone over the surface without leaving waves or ridges of material, and without loosening or removing the coarse aggregate. Fibre brooms are preferred to other types.

(c) *Pressure Distributor.* The distributor shall have pneumatic tires of such width and number that the load produced on the runway surface shall not exceed 650 pounds per inch of tire width, and shall be so designed, equipped, maintained and operated that bituminous material may be applied uniformly on variable widths of surface at readily determined and controlled rates of from 0.05 to 2.0 gallons per sq. yd., with a pressure range of from 25 to 75 pounds per sq. in., and with an allowable variation from any specified rate not to exceed 5%. Distributor equipment shall include a tachometer, pressure gages, volume measuring devices, and a thermometer for reading temperatures of tank contents.

(d) *Rolling Equipment.* The steel-wheel rollers shall be of the self-propelled tandem or three-wheel type weighing not less than eight tons and not more than ten tons. The wheels of the rollers shall be equipped with adjustable scrapers which shall be used when necessary to clean the wheel surface.

(e) *Spreading Equipment.* The spreading equipment shall consist of spreader boxes and/or other approved mechanical spreading devices for placing the required amounts of the crushed aggregate, the choke aggregate and the keystone. The materials shall be spread and placed in a manner to avoid or minimize the need for hand manipulation. Dumping from vehicles in piles or windrows on the paved areas so as to require rehandling will not be permitted.

3.3 *Preparing Subbase.* Before any base course material is placed, the subbase shall be prepared and conditioned as specified under subbase requirements. The subbase shall be checked and accepted by the engineer before placing and spreading operations are started. Any ruts or soft, yielding places that appear by reason of improper draining conditions, or hauling, or from any other cause, shall be corrected and rolled until firm before the base course is placed thereon.

Grade control between the edges of the runways shall be by means of grade stakes, steel pins, or forms placed in lanes parallel to the center line of the runway, and at intervals sufficiently close that string lines or check boards may be placed between the stakes, pins, or forms.

To protect the subbase and to insure proper draining, the spreading of the base shall begin along the center line of the runway or taxiway on a crowned section or on the high side of the pavement with a one-way slope.

3.4 *Placing and Spreading Coarse Aggregate.* The coarse aggregate designated in Table 1 shall be placed on the prepared subbase and compacted in layers of the thickness shown on the plans. The depositing and spreading of the aggregate shall commence where designated and shall progress continuously without breaks. The aggregate shall be deposited and spread in lanes in a uniform layer and without segregation of size to such loose depth that when compacted, the layer will have the required thickness. It shall be the charge of the contractor that the required amount of approved material is delivered in each 100-foot station. The base aggregate shall be spread by the use of approved spreading equipment that shall spread the aggregate in the required amount so as to avoid or minimize the need for hand manipulation. The spreaders shall be equipped with a strike-off gate or similar means that can be adjusted or controlled to secure the required thickness of the base. Hauling over the uncompacted base course shall not be permitted.

The surface of the aggregate shall then be carefully trued up and all high or low spots remedied by removing or adding aggregates as may be required. It shall be lightly rolled, after which the surface shall again be trued up. This operation shall be repeated until a uniform surface is secured which, when checked with a 16-foot straightedge, shall be found to be free from high or low spots.

The base course shall be constructed in layers of not less than two inches nor more than four inches of compacted thickness. The coarse aggregate as spread shall be of uniform grading with no pockets of fine materials. Coarse aggregate, unless otherwise permitted by the engineer, shall not be spread more than 2000 sq. yds. in advance of the rolling and choking. No material shall be placed in snow or on a soft, muddy or frozen subbase.

When more than one layer is required, the construction procedure described herein shall apply similarly to each layer.

During the placing and spreading or any other operation, sufficient caution shall be exercised to prevent the incorporation of subgrade, subbase or shoulder material in the coarse aggregate.

3.5 *Rolling.* Immediately following the spreading and truing up of the surface of the coarse aggregate, it shall be compacted to the full width by rolling with a 3-wheel power roller weighing at least 10 tons. Rolling shall progress gradually from the sides to the center of the lane under construction or from one side toward previously placed material by lapping uniformly each preceding rear-wheel track by one-half the width of such track, and shall continue until the entire area of the course has been rolled by the rear wheels. The rolling shall continue until the stone is thoroughly interlocked, the interstices of the metal reduced to a minimum and creeping of the stone ahead of the roller no longer visible.

The course shall not be rolled when the subbase is soft or yielding or when the rolling causes a wavelike motion in the base course, subbase, or subgrade. When the rolling develops irregularities that exceed three-eighths ($\frac{3}{8}$) inch when tested with a sixteen (16) foot straightedge, the irregular surface shall be loosened and then refilled with the same kind of material as that used in constructing the course and again rolled as required above.

Along places inaccessible to rollers, the base course material shall be tamped thoroughly with mechanical or hand tampers. Each hand tamper shall weigh not less than 50 lbs. and have a face area of not more than 100 sq. in.

3.6 *Application of Chips for Filling Voids.* The voids in the coarse aggregate placed as above described shall then be filled to within $\frac{1}{2}''$ of the surface with chips designated in Table 1 as "choke aggregate." The chips shall be evenly spread with approved devices and shall be lightly rolled and broomed until worked down. Care shall be taken to prevent chips from bunching or caking on the surface. If necessary to insure complete filling of the voids, spreading of the chips shall be made in more than one application.

3.7 *First Application Emulsified Asphalt and Keystone.* Upon the surface prepared as above described, Emulsified Asphalt shall be uniformly applied with pressure distributors at the rate per sq. yd. specified in Table 1. Immediately following this application of emulsified asphalt, keystone or gradation indicated in Table 1 shall be uniformly spread in quantity sufficient to fill the remaining voids completely. This shall be broom-dragged and thoroughly rolled. Additional keystone, if required, shall be spread and rolling and brooming shall continue until the voids in the coarse aggregate are completely filled and the keystone is thoroughly locked into the surface. No excess loose stone will be permitted.

3.8 *Second Application of Emulsified Asphalt.* The second application of emulsified asphalt shall then be made at the rate shown in Table 1. It is intended that this application shall act as a tack coat as well as penetrate and bond the base aggregate. The timing of this application shall be as directed by the engineer. The second application shall be made early enough following the previous construction to properly protect the base course and sufficiently in advance of the surfacing to allow the emulsified asphalt to set and dry. After the second application of emulsified asphalt has set and dried, the entire surface of the penetration macadam base course shall be given a final rolling. Water shall be used on the roller wheels if necessary to prevent sticking and pick-up.

3.9 *Rolling Time and Rollers.* A sufficient number of rollers shall be furnished on the work to provide one roller for each 25 tons of aggregate laid per hour. The rolling shall be so distributed following the various applications of aggregate as required by the engineer to get the maximum density in the finished base. Tandem rollers may be used at the option of the contractor on all operations except in compaction and consolidation of the coarse aggregate.

3.10 *Surface Test.* After the final application of the emulsified asphalt the surface shall be checked for smoothness and accuracy of grade and crown, and if any portions are found to lack the required smoothness or to fail in accuracy of grade or crown, such portions shall be reshaped, recompacted and otherwise manipulated as the engineer may direct until the required smoothness and accuracy is obtained. The finished surface shall be such that it will not vary more than three-eighths (⅜) of an inch from the sixteen (16) foot straightedge applied to the surface parallel to the center line and at right angles.

3.11 *Thickness.* The thickness of the base course shall be determined by depth tests or cores taken at intervals in such manner that each test shall represent no more than 300 sq. yds. When the base deficiency is more than one-half (½) inch, the contractor shall correct such areas by adding satisfactory base aggregate, rolling, penetrating with emulsified asphalt, and finishing in accordance with these specifications. The contractor shall replace at his expense the base material where borings are taken for test purposes.

3.12 *Maintenance.* Following the completion of the construction of the base course, the contractor shall maintain and protect same. All maintenance work that is necessary to keep the surface in a satisfactory condition shall be performed as directed. The surface shall be kept clean and free from foreign material. If the surface becomes dirty, it shall be cleaned and an additional tack coat applied at the expense of the contractor.

3.13 *Bituminous Material Contractor's Responsibility.* Samples of the Emulsified Asphalt that the contractor proposes to use, together with a statement as to its source and character must be submitted and approval obtained before use of such material begins.

The contractor shall furnish vendors' certified test report for each carload or equivalent of Emulsified Asphalt shipped to the project. The report shall be delivered to the engineer before permission is granted for the use of the material. The furnishing of the vendors' certified test report for the emulsified asphalt shall not be interpreted as a basis for final acceptance. All such test reports shall be subject to verification by testing of samples of materials as received for use on the project.

3.14 *Freight and Weigh-Bills.* Before the final estimate is allowed, the contractor shall file with the engineer receipted bills where railroad shipments are made and certified weigh-bills where materials are received in any other manner, of the emulsified asphalt and aggregates actually used in the construction covered by the contract. The contractor shall not remove emulsified asphalt from the tank car or storage tank until the initial outage and temperature measurements have been taken by the engineer, nor shall he release the car or tank until the final outage has been taken by the engineer.

Copies of all freight bills and weigh bills shall be furnished to the engineer during the progress of the work.

METHOD OF MEASUREMENT

4.1 The yardage of base course to be paid for shall be the number of square yards of material placed penetrated and accepted in the completed base course.

The gallons of emulsified asphalt used in the accepted work shall not be measured and paid for separately but the cost of same shall be included in the price bid in the schedule per square yard for the penetration macadam base course, and shall be considered incidental to the price for the base.

BASIS OF PAYMENT

5.1 The yardage of base course, determined as described in 4.1 above, shall be paid for at the contract unit price per sq. yd. for the penetration macadam base course, which price and payment shall constitute full compensation for furnishing, delivering, hauling and placing all materials; for spreading, brooming, penetrating and rolling; for covering excess bituminous material; for reconditioning the subbase and shoulders; for the removal of excess aggregates; for reconstruction of damaged or deficient base; for maintenance of surface, for clearing, cleaning and leveling of stockpile sites; for refilling test holes; and for all labor, equipment, tools and incidentals necessary to complete the base.

APPENDIX 22

DEPARTMENT OF COMMERCE
Civil Aeronautics Administration
Airport Division
Washington, D.C.
February 1, 1942

BITUMINOUS PRIME COAT FOR AIRPORT RUNWAYS, TAXIWAYS AND APRONS

C.A.A. Specification No. P-602

INTRODUCTION

This specification has been prepared by the Paving Engineers of the Airport Division, Civil Aeronautics Administration in collaboration with the Paving Engineers of the Office of the Chief, U.S. Corps of Engineers.

The prime coat as set forth in the specifications in general is to prepare the respective base course for the wearing course to be constructed thereon. It will be noted that several particular types and grades of bituminous material are included; the recommended usages are as follows:

The RT or tar grades given are preferable where available due to their penetrating quality and other inherent characteristics.

The MC material is selected over other asphalt cut-backs due to the kerosene flux giving a delayed set resulting in better penetration. On evaporation of the kerosene little or no surplus oils remain which would be detrimental to the wearing course placed thereon. If SC types are used, the oils remaining would have a tendency to cause excessive softening of the wearing surface. The RC cut-back would set up prior to maximum penetration.

Care should be exercised in the selection of the proper grade of bituminous material in order to obtain maximum penetration as well as binding qualities necessary dependent on the texture of the course being treated, avoiding a material that will not penetrate and cure. This is particularly essential when a plant-mix wearing surface is to be constructed on the primed course. The RT-2 or MC-0 should be used on tight or dense surfaces, while RT-3 and MC-1 should be used on more open surfaces.

Whichever material is decided upon, the table should be left in the specifications. The other should be discarded.

DESCRIPTION

1.1 This item shall consist of an application of bituminous material on the prepared base course in accordance with this specification and at the rate of application ordered by the engineer. The bituminous material shall meet one of the following requirements. The particular grade shall be selected by the engineer from the tables given herein below.

1.2 *Quantities of Bituminous Material.* The approximate amount of bituminous material per square yard for the prime coat shall be as provided in the table. The exact amount to be used shall be determined by the engineer.

TABLE 1

Quantities of Material

MATERIAL	AMOUNT
Bituminous Material	Gals. per sq. yd. 0.25 to 0.50

MATERIALS

2.1 The bituminous material to be used for the Prime Coat shall conform to the kind, grade, and specifications as follows:

TABLE 2

Requirements for ____________ (enter grade desired)

The tar shall be homogeneous and meet the following requirements:

	A.A.S.H.O. Test Methods	GRADES RT-2	RT-3
Consistency:			
Engler Sp. Visc. at 104° F	T-54	8–13	13–22
Sp. Gr. at 77° F	T-43	1.08+	1.09+
Total Bitumen, % by weight	T-44	88+	88+
Water, % by volume	T-55	2.0–	2.0–
Distillation, % by weight:			
To 338° F		7.0–	7.0–
To 518° F	T-52	35.0–	30.0–
To 572° F		45.0–	40.0–
Softening Point of Distillation Residue ° F	T-53	86–140	95–140
Temp. of application ° F		80–150	80–150
Sulfonation Factor			
Total Dist. to 572° F		7–	6–
Distillate 572°–680° F		1½–	1½–

Note: The Sulfonation factor is the milliliters of sulfonation residue from 100 grams of the distillate, (a) multiplied by the percentage of distillate based on the weight of the tar and (b) divided by 100.

The cut-back asphalt shall be homogeneous and free from water. It shall meet the following requirements:

	A.A.S.H.O. Test Methods	GRADES MC-0		MC-1	
		Min.	Max.	Min.	Max.
Water			0		0
Flash Point, Tag., ° F	T-79	100		100	
Furol Viscosity					
at 77° F	T-72	75	150		
at 122° F				75	150
Partial Distillation					
(Ratio to distillate to 680° F)	T-78				
to 437° F			25		20
to 500° F		40	70	25	65
to 600° F		75	93	70	90
Residue from Distillation to 680° F					
Vol. percent of sample by difference		50		60	
Penetration at 77° F	T-49	120	300	120	300
Ductility, cm.	T-51	100		100	
Percent soluble in CCl_4	T-44	99.5		99.5	
Temp. of application ° F		50	125	100	175
Material shall not be cracked					

CONSTRUCTION METHODS

3.1 *Weather Limitations.* The Prime Coat shall be applied only when the existing surface is dry or contains sufficient moisture to get uniform distribution of the bituminous material, when the atmospheric temperature is above 60° F, and when the weather is not foggy or rainy. The temperature requirements may be waived, but only when so directed by the engineer.

3.2 *Equipment.* The equipment used by the contractor shall include a self-powered pressure bituminous material distributor, and equipment for heating bituminous material.

The distributor shall have pneumatic tires of such width and number that the load produced on the base surface shall not exceed 650 pounds per inch of tire width and shall be so designed, equipped, maintained, and operated that bituminous material at even heat may be applied uniformly on variable widths of surface at readily determined and controlled rates of from 0.05 to 2.0 gallons per square yard, with a pressure range of from 25 to 75 pounds per square inch, and with an allowable variation from any specified rate not to exceed 5 percent. Distributor equipment shall include a tachometer, pressure gages, volume measuring devices, and a thermometer for reading temperatures of tank contents.

Equipment for heating bituminous material shall consist of a retort or steam coils so designed that steam will not be introduced into the material.

3.3 *Application of Bituminous Material.* Immediately before applying the prime coat, if the surface is sufficiently bonded, the full width of the surface to be primed shall be swept with a power broom. In any case care shall be taken to remove all loose dirt and clay or other loose and objectionable material.

After the operation of removing the dust has been completed and prior to the application of the prime coat an inspection shall be made of the base to determine its fitness to receive the bituminous priming material. That portion of the base proposed for immediate treatment if very dry shall be lightly sprinkled immediately in advance of the application, as directed.

The application of the bituminous priming material shall be by means of a pressure distributor of approved type at the temperature for application as contained in these specifications, and shall be applied at the pressure and in amounts as directed by the engineer.

Following the application, the primed surface shall be allowed to dry for a period of not less than 48 hours without being disturbed, or for such additional period of time as may be necessary to permit the drying out of the prime until it will not be picked up by traffic or equipment, which period shall be determined by the engineer. The surface shall then be maintained by the contractor until the surfacing has been placed. Suitable precautions shall be taken by the contractor to protect the prime surface against damage during this interval, including supplying and spreading any sand necessary to blot up excess bituminous material.

3.4 *Bituminous Material Contractor's Responsibility.* Samples of the bituminous matcrials that the contractor proposes to use, together with a statement as to their source and character must be submitted and approval obtained before use of such materials begins. The contractor shall require the manufacturer or producer of the bituminous materials to furnish material subject to this and all other pertinent requirements of the contract. Only those materials that have been demonstrated by service tests as satisfactory for the intended use will be acceptable.

3.5 *Freight and Weigh-Bills.* Before the final estimate is allowed, the contractor shall file with the engineer receipted bills where railroad shipments are made and certified weigh-bills when materials are received in any other manner, of the bituminous and covering materials actually used in the construction covered by the contract. The contractor shall not remove bituminous material from the tank car or storage tank until the initial outage and temperature measurements have been taken by the engineer, nor shall he release the car or tank until the final outage has been taken by the engineer.

Copies of freight bills and weigh-bills shall be furnished to the engineer during the progress of the work.

METHOD OF MEASUREMENT

4.1 The gallonage of bituminous prime coat to be paid for shall be the number of gallons of the material used as ordered for the accepted work, corrected to gallons at 60° F in accordance with A.S.T.M. Specification D 206–36 for asphalt materials and in accordance with an appropriate table for tars; provided, however, that the measurement shall be in tons (2000 pounds) in cases where the Bid Schedule calls for tons of bituminous material.

BASIS OF PAYMENT

5.1 The gallonage or tonnage determined as provided above, shall be paid for at the respective contract unit price per gallon or ton in the bid schedule for bituminous prime coat which price and payment shall be full compensation for furnishing, delivering and applying the material, for furnishing and spreading blotter material, and for all labor, equipment, tools and incidentals necessary to complete the item.

APPENDIX 23

DEPARTMENT OF COMMERCE
Civil Aeronautics Administration
Airport Division
Washington, D.C.
June 15, 1944

BITUMINOUS TACK COAT FOR AIRPORT RUNWAYS, TAXIWAYS AND APRONS

C.A.A. Specification No. P-603

INTRODUCTION

This specification has been prepared by the Paving Engineers of the Airport Division, Civil Aeronautics Administration in collaboration with the Paving Engineers of the Office of the Chief, U.S. Corps of Engineers.

The requirement of the tack coat as set forth in general in this specification is to obtain a bond between two courses constructed in different operations. It is not intended by the use of the tack coat to primarily secure penetration other than that necessary to obtain adhesion to surface of base course proper. With this in mind the following types of bituminous materials have been selected:

(a) The asphalt cement shown in the table so designated shall be applied hot. This material should be used on clean and inherently bonded bases with practically no chalk-like surfaces.

(b) The RC cut-back and emulsified asphalts are selected both for their penetrative and adhesive qualities, enabling them to penetrate the dust or chalk-like surfaces and adhere to the base, and still leave a tacky surface to secure proper bond with the wearing surface to be constructed thereon. The emulsified asphalt is generally recommended to be used on bases employing emulsified asphalt material in construction and on bases such as soil cement or lime rock where it is considered the water carrying agent will probably give better penetration. The cut-back asphalt is suggested for bases employing the cut-back asphalt in construction or for old asphalt bases that should be livened up to obtain proper adhesion.

The particular grade to be selected from the respective table will depend upon the length of time required and the viscosity to secure the amount of penetration necessary to obtain proper adhesion to base course.

The type of material decided upon should be left in the specification. The others should be deleted.

DESCRIPTION

1.1 This item shall consist of supplying and applying bituminous material to a previously prepared, bonded and/or bituminized binder, leveling, or base course or existing pavement in accordance with these specifications and to the width shown on the typical cross section on the plans.

1.2 *Quantity of Material.* The approximate amount of bituminous material per square yard for the tack coat shall be as provided in the table. The exact amount shall be as ordered by the engineer.

TABLE 1

Quantity of Material for Tack Coat

	Gallons per sq. yd.
Bituminous Material	0.10 to 0.25

MATERIALS

2.1 *Bituminous Material.* The bituminous material to be used shall conform to the kind, grade and specifications as follows:

TABLE 2

CUT-BACK ASPHALT SPECIFICATIONS

The cut-back asphalt shall be homogeneous, free from water, shall show no separation upon standing and shall meet the following requirements:

	A.A.S.H.O. Test Method	Grades RC-2	RC-3	RC-4
Flash Point (Open Tag) ° F	T-79–38	80+	80+	80+
Furol Viscosity at 140° F	T-72–35	100–200	250–500	
at 180° F				125–250
Distillation (% of total Distillate to 680° F.)	T-78–35			
to 437° F.		40+	25+	8+
to 500° F.		65+	55+	40+
to 600° F.		87+	83+	80+
Residue from Distillation to 680° F. Volume percent by difference		67+	73+	78+
Tests on Residue				
Penetration at 77° F.	T-49–38	80–120	80–120	80–120
Ductility at 77° F.	T-51–38	100+	100+	100+
Percent Soluble in CCl_4	T-44–35	99.5+	99.5+	99.5+
Temperature Range F		125°–175°	150°–200°	175°–225°

TABLE 3

ASPHALT CEMENT SPECIFICATIONS

The asphalt cement shall be homogeneous, free from water and shall not foam when heated to a temperature of 347° F.

	A.A.S.H.O.	Min.	Max.
	Test Methods		
Water, percent	T-55	. . .	0
Furol vis., at 210° F	T-72	250	500
Flash point, ° F (Cleve. Open Cup)	T-48	275	. . .
Distillation:			
Total distillate to 680° F., % by vol.	T-78	. . .	2
Float test on residue at 122° F., sec.	T-50	150	350
Asphalt residue of 100 pene., percent	T-56	90	. . .
Duct. asphalt residue at 77° F., cm.	T-51	100	. . .
Percent sol. in CCl_4 (Using CCl_4 with T-44)		99.5	. . .
Temperature of Application ° F		250	350

TABLE 4

EMULSIFIED ASPHALT SPECIFICATIONS

The emulsified asphalt shall be homogeneous, shall be mixable with pure water in all proportions and shall show no separation of asphalt after thorough mixing within thirty days after delivery, provided separation has not been caused by freezing. It shall conform to the following requirements:

	A.S.T.M.	
	D 401–40	D 631–41T
Viscosity, Furol @ 77° F., sec.	20–100	20–100
Residue by Distillation, %	55–60	57–62
Settlement, 5 days	3 –	
Demulsibility 35 c.c. N/50 $CaCl_2$	60 +	
Sieve test, Retained on 20 Mesh	0.10 –	0.05 –
Modified Miscibility, %	. . .	4.5 –
Cement Mixing Test, %		2.0 –
Tests on Residue		
Penetration @ 77° F., 100 g., 5 sec.	100–200	100–200
Soluble in CS_2, %	97.5 +	97.0 +
Ash	2.0 –	2.0 –
Ductility @ 77° F., cm.	40 +	60 +
Temperature Range ° F.	50–125	50–125

CONSTRUCTION METHODS

3.1 *Weather Limitations.* The tack coat shall be applied only when the existing surface is dry, when the atmospheric temperature is above 60° F., and when the weather is not foggy or rainy. The temperature requirements may be waived, but only when so directed by the engineer.

3.2 *Equipment.* The equipment used by the contractor shall include a self-powered pressure bituminous material distributor, and equipment for heating bituminous material.

The distributor shall have pneumatic tires of such width and number that the load produced on the road surface shall not exceed 650 pounds per inch of tire width, and shall be so designed, equipped, maintained, and operated that bituminous material at even heat may be applied uniformly on variable widths of surface at readily determined and controlled rates of from 0.05 to 2.0 gallons per square yard, with a pressure range of from 25 to 75 pounds per square inch, and with an allowable variation from any specified rate not to exceed 5 percent. Distributor equipment shall include a tachometer, pressure gages, volume measuring devices, and a thermometer for reading temperatures of tank contents.

Equipment for heating bituminous material shall consist of a retort or steam coils so designed that steam will not be introduced into the material.

3.3 *Application of Bituminous Material.* Immediately before applying the tack coat, if the surface is sufficiently bonded, the full width of surface to be treated shall be swept with a power broom, supplemented by hand brooms if necessary or otherwise as directed by the engineer. In any case care shall be taken to remove all loose dirt and clay or other loose and objectionable material.

After the operation of removing the dust has been completed and prior to the application of the tack coat an inspection shall be made of the binder, levelling or base course to determine its fitness to receive the bituminous material. That portion of the surface of the course proposed for immediate treatment must be dry and altogether in a satisfactory condition.

The application of the bituminous tack material shall be made by means of a pressure distributor of approved type at the temperature for application as contained in these specifications, and shall be applied at the pressure and in amounts as directed by the engineer.

Following the application, the surface shall be allowed to cure without being disturbed for such period of time as may be necessary to permit drying out and setting of the tack coat, which period shall be determined by the engineer. The surface shall then be maintained by the contractor until the surfacing has been placed. Suitable precautions shall be taken by the contractor to protect the surface against damage during this interval, including any sand necessary to blot up excess bituminous material.

3.4 *Bituminous Material Contractor's Responsibility.* Samples of the bituminous materials that the contractor proposes to use, together with a statement as to their source and character must be submitted and approval obtained before use of such materials begins. The contractor shall require the manufacturer or producer of the bituminous materials to furnish material subject to this and all other pertinent requirements of the contract. Only those materials that have been demonstrated by service tests as satisfactory for the intended use will be acceptable.

3.5 *Freight and Weigh-Bills.* Before the final estimate is allowed, the contractor shall file with the engineer receipted bills where railroad shipments are made and certified weigh-bills when materials are received in any other manner, of the bituminous and covering materials actually used in the construction covered by the contract. The contractor shall not remove bituminous material from the tank car or storage tank until the initial outage and temperature measurements have been taken by the engineer, nor shall he release the car or tank until the final outage has been taken by the engineer.

Copies of freight bills and weigh-bills shall be furnished to the engineer during the progress of the work.

METHOD OF MEASUREMENT

4.1 The gallonage of bituminous tack coat to be paid for shall be the number of gallons of the material used as ordered for the accepted work, corrected to gallons at 60° F. in accordance with A.S.T.M. Specification D 206–36 for asphalt materials and in accordance with an appropriate formula or table for emulsified asphalt; provided, however, that the measurement shall be in tons (2000 pounds) in cases where the Bid Schedule calls for tons of bituminous material.

BASIS OF PAYMENT

5.1 The gallonage or tonnage determined as provided above, shall be paid for at the respective contract unit price per gallon or ton in the bid schedule for bituminous tack coat, which price and payment shall be full compensation for furnishing, delivering and applying the material, and for all labor, equipment, tools, and incidentals, necessary to complete the item.

APPENDIX 24

DEPARTMENT OF COMMERCE
Civil Aeronautics Administration
Airport Division
Washington, D.C.
September 1, 1943

EMULSIFIED ASPHALT AGGREGATE BASE COURSE (CENTRAL PLANT MIX) FOR AIRPORT RUNWAYS, TAXIWAYS AND APRONS

C.A.A. Specification P-215

INTRODUCTION

Emulsified asphalt aggregate base course as contained in this specification is intended for localities where suitable local gravel, crushed stone or other aggregate mixtures are available or can be procured economically. The gradations included are flexible so that natural pit-run or crusher run materials can be utilized. The amount of clay in the aggregate should be controlled and kept to a low content.

This type of treatment of the base aggregate should produce a base course of excellent value. It is preferred over soil-bound base courses principally because of the lack of control and of non-uniform characteristics of soil binders.

The graded aggregate shall be mixed with the emulsified asphalt in a central mixing plant. The mix shall be meally and not wet. After spreading and aeration, the initial compaction should be obtained by the use of tamping or pneumatic rollers; final compaction by powered rollers weighing at least eight tons.

Trial mixes should be made using the emulsified asphalt and mineral aggregate intended for use in the base mixture, containing the maximum percent of moisture allowed in this specification. The failure of the emulsified asphalt to give a uniform coating of the mineral aggregate shall be sufficient cause for rejection of the emulsified asphalt or aggregate, depending on whether the aggregate particles will not coat properly due to inherent characteristics, to excessive moisture content, or to agents used in the manufacture of the emulsified asphalt.

This type of base should be followed by a tack coat and a dense graded wearing surface.

DESCRIPTION

1.1 This item shall consist of a base course composed of mineral aggregate and emulsified asphalt, mixed in a central mixing plant and placed on the prepared subgrade or subbase in accordance with these specifications and in conformity with the dimensions and typical cross sections shown on the plans and with lines and grades established by the engineer.

1.2 *Determination of Percentage of Bituminous Material.* The percentage of emulsified asphalt, by weight, to be added to the aggregate shall be fixed by the engineer on the basis of preliminary laboratory tests and field sieve analysis on the aggregate furnished, and shall be within the range as shown in the table.

1.3 *Job Mix Formula.* No work shall be started on the project nor any mixture accepted therefor until the contractor has submitted samples of the materials intended for use and the engineer has established a satisfactory job mix formula based upon tests of the materials furnished. The formula shall be submitted in writing by the engineer to the contractor, indicating the definite percentage for each sieve fraction of aggregate and emulsified asphalt. The mixture furnished shall conform to the approved job mix formula within the tolerances specified herein.

Job Mix Tolerances

Aggregate passing sieves No. 4 and larger	± 6%
Aggregate passing No. 40 sieve	± 4%
Aggregate passing No. 200 sieve	± 2%
Emulsified Asphalt	±0.5%

MATERIALS

2.1 *Aggregate.* The aggregate shall consist of crushed stone, crushed gravel, screenings, gravel, sand-gravel or other natural, granular, approved materials.

The aggregate shall be tough, durable and sound. The coarse aggregate when tested in accordance with the Los Angeles Rattler Test, after five hundred revolutions shall have a percent of wear of not more than fifty (50) according to the A.A.S.H.O., Method T 96–42.

The composite material shall meet the requirements for one of the gradings given in Table 2, using A.A.S.H.O. Methods T 11 and T 27–42. That portion of the fine aggregate, including any blended filler, passing a No. 40 sieve shall have a plasticity index of not more than 6, as determined by A.A.S.H.O. Method T 91–42, and a liquid limit of not more than 25 as determined by A.A.S.H.O. Method T 89–42.

The composite aggregate shall be free from vegetable matter, lumps or balls of clay, adherent films of clay, or other matter that will prevent thorough coating with bituminous material. The bituminized aggregate shall have a swell of not more than 1.5 percent as determined by A.A.S.H.O. Method T 101–42.

Prior to final acceptance of the proposed aggregate to be used, the inherent characteristics of said aggregate relative to stripping shall be determined. This shall be done by preparing a test sample of the base mixture in conformity with these specifications and using the maximum amount of moisture allowed. After the mixture has been made, it shall be spread out in a loose thin layer and allowed to air season for 24 hours before testing. A suitable size sample (approximately one-half contents of container) shall be tested by placing it in a glass jar fitted with a tight screw cap and completely covering with distilled water. The jar and contents shall be allowed to stand for a period of 24 hours. Then the sample shall be vigorously shaken for a period of 15 minutes. The sample of mixture shall be examined for stripping. If stripping or sloughing off of the bituminous coating occurs it will be necessary to treat said aggregate by a method which has proven successful in changing the material from a hydrophilic to a hydrophobic state.

2.2 *Bituminous Material.* The bituminous material to be mixed with the mineral aggregate in the central plant shall conform to the following specifications:

TABLE 1

Requirements for Emulsified Asphalt

The emulsified asphalt shall be homogeneous and of such character that it will mix with distilled water in all proportions.

Tests	A.A.S.H.O. Test Method	Grade AE–200
Viscosity, Saybolt Furol, at 77° F., sec.	T 59–42	20–120
Distillation to a temperature of 500° F., not more than, %	"	44
Oil distillate, by volume, not more than, %		3
Demulsibility: 50 ml. of 0.1 N $CaCl_2$, not less than, %	T 59–42	30
Sieve Test, not more than, %	"	0.05
Settlement 5 days not more than, %	T 59–42	5
Stone Coating Test	"	Shall Pass
Oliensis Spot Test	T 102–42	Negative
Sampling Material	T 40–42	

The residue from distillation shall have the following characteristics:

Specific Gravity at 77° F. not less than	T 43–35	1.01
Penetration at 77° F., 100 g., 5 sec.	T 49–42	180–250
Soluble in Carbon Tetrachloride, not less than, %	T 45–42	97
Ductility at 77° F., not less than, cm.	T 51–42	60

The base asphalt for the emulsified asphalt shall have a range of penetration at 77° F., 100 g., 5 sec., of 175–250. The mixture of emulsified asphalt and aggregate shall develop no indication of re-emulsifying due to its coming in contact with moisture or water. The emulsified asphalt shall be of such stability that it will remain constant and uniform while being combined and mixed with the aggregates and shall show satisfactory mixing properties when combined with the aggregates without balling up or becoming hard or tacky.

Coating test shall not show appreciable separation when emulsified asphalt is mixed with washed, dry, clean stone for 3 minutes. The emulsified asphalt shall coat the stone thoroughly.

When the ductility test is made on the residue from distillation or evaporation, the residue shall be screened through a No. 50 sieve while still hot and shall then be kneaded until uniform and homogeneous. It shall then be tested for ductility.

The Oliensis Spot Test may be used to identify products manufactured by the cracking process, which show a positive spot when present in sufficient proportions. The Test should be modified to differentiate between cracked asphalts and those asphalts from some crude sources that have never been cracked but show a positive spot.

2.3 *Filler.* If filler in addition to that naturally present in the aggregate is necessary, it shall consist of stone dust, loess, Portland cement or other standard approved types. The material for such purpose shall be obtained from sources approved by the engineer.

2.4 *Hydrated Lime.* The hydrated lime shall meet the requirements of the A.S.T.M. Designation C 6–31.

2.5 *Portland Cement.* The Portland cement shall meet the requirements of A.A.S.H.O. Specification M 85–42.

COMPOSITION OF MIXTURE

3.1 *Gradation of Aggregate.* The mineral aggregate for the base course shall be of such size that the percentage composition by weight, as determined by laboratory sieves will conform to one of the following gradations:

TABLE 2

Sieve Size	Percentage by Weight Passing (Square Openings)		
	A 2″ Maximum	B 1½″ Maximum	C 1″ Maximum
2″	100		
1½″	...	100	
1″	55–85	70–95	100
¾″	50–80	55–85	70–100
No. 4	30–60	30–60	35–65
No. 40	5–30	5–30	10–30
No. 200	0–5	0–5	0–5

The gradations in this table represent the limits which shall determine suitability of aggregate for use from the sources of supply. The gradations of the composite mix shall be within the limits designated in the table, shall be uniformly graded from coarse to fine, and shall not vary from the low limit on one screen to the high limit on the adjacent screens or vice versa.

The selection of any of the gradings shown in the table shall be such that the maximum size aggregate used in any course shall not be more than one-half the thickness of the layer of the course being constructed.

The composition limits tabulated shall govern but a closer control appropriate to the job materials will be required for the specific project in accordance with a job mix formula.

The total amount of material passing the No. 200 sieve shall be determined by washing the material through the sieve with water and not less than one-half

(½) of the material passing the No. 200 sieve by washing shall pass the No. 200 sieve by dry sieving without washing.

3.2 *Proportion of Emulsified Asphalt.* The proportion of emulsified asphalt by weight shall be one of the following:

TABLE 3

Gradation of Aggregate	Emulsified Asphalt Percentage by Weight	
	Sub-base	Base
A	4–5	4½–6
B	4½–5½	5–6½
C	5–6	5½–7

CONSTRUCTION METHODS

4.1 *Weather Limitations.* Base course shall be constructed and operations shall be carried on only when the surface is dry, when the atmospheric temperature is above 50° F., and when the weather is not foggy or rainy. The temperature requirement may be waived, but only when so directed by the engineer.

4.2 *Equipment and Organization.* (a) General. All methods employed in performing the work and all equipment, tools and other plant and machinery used for handling materials and executing any part of the work shall be subject to the approval of the engineer before the work is started and whenever found unsatisfactory shall be changed and improved as required. All equipment, tools, machinery and plant used must be maintained in a satisfactory working condition.

(b) Mixing Plant. The paving plant used by the contractor in the preparation of the base mixture shall comply with the following requirements:

The plant shall have a storage bin, protected from the weather, of sufficient capacity to furnish the necessary amount of aggregate when operating at the maximum rated capacity of the plant.

The plant may have either batch weighing or volumetric proportioning of mineral aggregates and emulsified asphalt. This equipment shall be constructed with devices that will permit easy readjustment of any working part such that it will function properly and accurately. The aggregate weighing or measuring device shall be so constructed and operated that the correct amount of aggregate is introduced into the mixer with an accuracy that will meet the job tolerances specified. The plant shall have a capacity of at least 100 tons per hour.

The asphalt weighing or measuring device shall be so constructed and operated that the correct amount of emulsified asphalt is introduced into the mixer with an accuracy that will meet the job tolerance specified. If weight control is used, the dial scales or other weighing device shall be of an approved type.

The mixer shall be of sufficient size to maintain uniform and thorough mixing and be one of the following types: (1) The mixer shall be of the batching type, twin-shaft, pug-mill mixer operated with a bin and scales for accurate weighing of batches. (2) The mixer shall be twin-shaft, continuous type, pug-mill mixer, or a primary and secondary type pug-mill mixer, equipped with an approved volumetric proportioning system for aggregate and asphalt. (3) The mixer shall be a pulverizing type mixer equipped with an approved volumetric proportioning system for aggregate and asphalt. The pulverizers shall be mounted laterally to the direction of flow of the aggregate. They shall turn at a speed of not less than two hundred (200) R.P.M. and shall be enclosed except for the inlet and outlet. The pulverizers shall be mounted on the proportioning belt so as to mix thereon in the direction of belt travel or they shall be set to receive the proportioned aggregate and emulsified asphalt and to move the mixture through the system in the process of mixing.

When aggregates of different sizes are to be mixed, they shall be combined before being introduced into the mixing plant. When it is necessary to screen the aggregate on the project auxiliary storage bins with screening equipment shall be provided. The screens shall be designed, constructed and operated so as to screen the aggregate to specified sizes and appropriate fractions as established by the engineer and as necessary to meet the job mix tolerances. The blending or mixing of different sizes of aggregates to obtain the proper gradation shall be obtained by the use of satisfactory equipment such as reciprocating feeders, volumetric feeders or special belt feeders.

The drier if necessary to meet moisture requirements shall be suitably designed to heat and dry the aggregate. The drier shall be capable of preparing aggregate to the full rated capacity of the paving plant and to meet the specification requirements.

The plant shall be equipped with positive means to govern the time of mixing and to maintain it constant unless changed by order of the engineer. The time of mixing shall be considered as the interval between the time the bituminous material is spread on the aggregate and the time the same aggregate leaves the mixing unit.

An approved method shall be provided for measuring the correct amount of Portland cement and/or hydrated lime and for their induction into the mixer.

(c) Placing Equipment. Equipment for spreading, shaping, and finishing shall consist of an approved self-contained power machine operating in such a manner that no supplemental spreading, shaping, or finishing will be required to provide a surface which will comply with the requirements for smoothness contained herein.

Spreader boxes or similar spreading equipment will not be permitted. Dumping of the material from the rear of trucks into spreader boxes drawn by tractors will not be allowed.

(d) Rolling Equipment. (1) The steel-wheel rollers shall be of the self-propelled tandem or three-wheel type weighing not less than eight (8) tons and not more than ten (10) tons. The wheels on the rollers shall be equipped with adjustable scrapers which shall be used when necessary to clean the wheel surface. Rollers shall also be equipped with water tanks and sprinkling apparatus which shall be used to keep the wheels wet and prevent the base material from sticking.

(2) The multiwheeled rubber-tired roller shall consist of two axles on which are mounted not less than 9 pneumatic-tired wheels in such a manner that the rear

group of tires will not follow in the tracks of the forward group, and mounted in a rigid frame provided with a loading platform or body suitable for ballast loading. The front axle shall rotate around a king pin so located that the roller may be turned within a minimum circle. The roller under working conditions shall have an effective rolling width of at least sixty (60) inches and shall give a compression of at least 325 lbs. per inch of width of tread when fully loaded. The tires shall be uniformly inflated. The roller and the operating pneumatic-tired tractor shall meet the approval of the engineer. The weight of the roller shall be increased as the rolling progresses to the maximum degree obtainable without detrimental results to the course being compacted.

(3) The tamping roller shall consist of one or more units. Each unit shall consist of a water-tight cylindrical drum not less than 48 inches in length and shall be surmounted by metal studs with tamping feet projecting not less than 7 inches from the surface of the drum and spaced not less than six (6) inches nor more than ten (10) inches measured diagonally from center to center. Each unit shall be provided with a suitable tamper feet-cleaning device. Where more than one rolling unit is used, the rolling units must be pivoted on the main frame in a manner which will permit the rolling units to adapt themselves to uneven ground surfaces and to rotate independently. When fully loaded, the roller shall produce at least 250 pounds per square inch of area of tamping feet in contact with the ground. The roller and the operating tractor shall meet the approval of the engineer.

4.3 *Preparation of Mineral Aggregate.* The aggregate for the mixture shall be conveyed into the main bin ready for mixing with the emulsified asphalt. The aggregate shall be at a temperature between 50° F. and 150° F. and shall not contain more than three (3) percent moisture. The moisture shall be reduced when necessary by drying or aeration before being placed in the bin. When aggregates of different sizes are to be mixed, they shall be combined before being placed in the main plant bin. The combining of the aggregate shall be in a manner to meet the grading requirements within the job mix tolerances.

Additional filler, if necessary to meet the grading requirements, shall be proportioned and added to the mineral aggregate. Filler may be added to the aggregate at the mixing plant by premixing it thoroughly with the other aggregates. Spreading filler over the tops of the aggregate pits or dumping it into the hoppers at crushing plants will not be permitted.

All work involved in clearing and stripping pits and handling unsuitable material encountered shall be performed by the contractor at his own expense. The base material shall be obtained from pits or sources that have been approved. The material in the pits shall be excavated and handled in a manner that a uniform and satisfactory product shall be secured.

4.4 *Preparation of Bituminous Mixture.* Before being delivered to the runway, the aggregate shall be mixed with the bituminous material at a central mixing plant.

The aggregate prepared as prescribed above, shall be accurately measured and conveyed into the mixer in the proportionate amount. Lime, if necessary to correct hydrophilic characteristics, shall be added with the aggregate.

The percent of moisture is definitely stipulated in Table No. 1 for the emulsified asphalt. The free water present in the aggregates shall be determined by suitable tests, and if found excessive or variable, shall be controlled and made uniform. No water shall be added before or during the mixing operation. The total moisture present shall be that contained in the emulsified asphalt and the maximum of three (3) percent allowed in the aggregates. This definitely establishes the moisture content in the final mix. Not more than two and one-half (2½) percent of moisture shall be contained in the mixed material at the time of spreading.

The quantity of bituminous material for each batch or calibrated amount for continuous mixing shall be determined by the engineer and introduced into the mixer. The mixing shall continue for at least thirty seconds and for such longer period as may be necessary to uniformly coat all of the particles and obtain a mixture homogeneous in character. Excessive mixing shall be avoided.

The Portland Cement shall be added to the mixture after the emulsified asphalt and aggregates have been mixed. The mixing shall be continued to completion. The cement and the lime shall be added to the mixture when provided for in the proposal.

4.5 *Transportation and Delivery of the Mixture.* The mixture shall be transported from the mixing plant to the point of use in pneumatic-tired vehicles having tight bodies previously cleaned of all foreign materials. When directed by the engineer, each load shall be covered with canvas or other suitable material of sufficient size and thickness to protect it from weather conditions.

No loads shall be sent out so late in the day as to interfere with spreading and other necessary manipulation during daylight unless artificial light satisfactory to the engineer is provided.

Any mixed material arriving on the project which does not conform in every way to the specified requirements shall be wasted.

4.6 *Spreading and Laying.* (a) Preparation for placing. Immediately before placing the bituminous mixture, the existing subgrade or subbase shall be cleaned of loose or deleterious material by sweeping with a power sweeper supplemented by hand brooms if necessary, or as directed by the engineer.

The mixture shall be laid only upon an approved underlying course which is dry and only when weather conditions are suitable. No mixture shall be placed when the air temperature in the shade and away from artificial heat is 50° F. or under unless so directed by the engineer. In event of sudden rains, no more mixture in transit shall be dumped into the spreading machine. All work shall stop and the mixture that has been spread but not compacted by rolling shall be allowed to dry out.

Grade control between the edges of the rnnway shall be by means of grade stakes or steel pins placed in lanes parallel to the center line of the runway, and at intervals sufficiently close that string lines may be stretched between stakes or pins. The elevations of the grade stakes or pins shall be checked immediately before placing of the mixture.

Placing shall commence at the point or points furthest from the mixing plant, and progress continuously toward the plant, unless otherwise ordered by the engineer. Hauling over material already placed will not be permitted until the material has been compacted thoroughly in the manner specified.

Contact surfaces shall be painted with a thin uniform coat of emulsified asphalt just before the mixture is placed.

(b) Machine Spreading. Upon arrival the mixture shall be dumped into an approved mechanical spreader and immediately spread thereby to the full width required. It shall be struck off in a uniform layer of such depth (not to exceed four (4) inches when compacted) that when the work is completed, it will have the required thickness and will conform to the grade and surface contour required. The speed of the mechanical spreader shall be regulated to eliminate as far as possible the pulling and tearing of the bituminous material.

Placing and compaction of the bituminous mixture shall progress in sections. The bituminous mixture shall be spread, shaped, and finished with the power-machine specified. The mixture shall be placed in strips of a minimum width of 10 feet. To insure proper drainage, the spreading shall begin along the center line of the runway or taxiway on a crowned section or on the high side of the pavement with a one-way slope. The 6-inch strip adjacent to the area on which future material is to be laid shall not be rolled until such material has been placed, but shall not be left unrolled more than twenty-four (24) hours after being placed. After the first strip or width has been compacted, the second width shall be placed, finished and compacted as provided for the first width, except that rolling shall be extended to include the six inches of the first width not previously compacted. Whenever the adjacent or second width cannot be placed within twenty-four (24) hours, the 6-inch strip shall not be left unrolled. After the second strip has been placed and rolled, a 10-foot straight edge shall be used across the longitudinal joint to determine if the surface is to grade and contour.

(c) Hand Spreading. In limited areas where, on account of irregularities of unavoidable obstacles, the use of mechanical spreading and finishing equipment is impractical, the mixture may be spread by hand.

When hand spreading is permitted, the mixture shall be dumped upon arrival on approved dump sheets outside of the area on which it is to be spread and be distributed into place immediately by means of shovels. It shall be spread in a uniformly loose layer to the full width required and of such depth that where the work is completed, it will have the required thickness and will conform to the grade and surface contour required.

(d) Layers. The base shall be constructed in layers of not more than four (4) inches in thickness. When more than one layer is required, the construction procedure described herein shall apply similarly to each layer.

4.7 *Compaction of Mixture.* After spreading, and as directed by the engineer, sufficient time shall be allowed to obtain proper aeration and curing. The mixture shall not be compacted until the moisture content is two and one-half ($2\frac{1}{2}$) percent or less. The mixture shall then be thoroughly and uniformly compacted by tamping or pneumatic-tired rollers followed by power-driven three-wheel or tandem rollers as specified. On the first strip spread, rolling shall start in the center and continue toward either edge. On subsequent strips laid, rolling shall start on the edge adjacent to previously-laid material and continue toward the other edge.

Initial rolling shall be done longitudinally, overlapping on successive trips by at least twelve (12) inches. Rolling shall continue until the mixture is of uniform texture and degree of compaction and is true to grade and cross section. The surface shall be maintained during compaction by alternate blading and rolling as required or directed. Upon instruction from the engineer, the course shall be rerolled any time within two weeks after the mixture is laid. The mixture shall be subjected to diagonal rolling crossing the lines of the first.

Alternate trips of the powered rollers shall be of slightly different lengths. The speed of these rollers shall at all times be slow enough to avoid displacement of the mixture. Any displacement occurring as a result of reversing the direction of the roller, or from any other cause, shall be corrected at once by the use of rakes and of fresh mixture where required. Final rolling shall be done with powered rollers. Sufficient rollers of the designated types shall be furnished to adequately handle the output of the plant. Rolling shall proceed at an average rate not to exceed 350 square yards per hour per roller.

Rolling shall continue until a density of at least 90 percent of the theoretical density is obtained. Field density tests shall be made at least twice daily. The theoretical density shall be computed as follows:

$$\text{Density} = \frac{100}{\dfrac{\%\text{ mineral aggregate by weight}}{\text{Sp. Gr. mineral aggregate}} + \dfrac{\%\text{ bitumen by weight}}{\text{Sp. Gr. of bitumen}}}$$

To prevent adhesion of the mixture to the powered rollers, the wheels shall be kept properly moistened, but an excess of either water or oil will not be permitted. The rollers shall be kept in good condition and shall be operated by competent and experienced rollermen. The rollers shall be operated continuously as far as practicable and in such a manner that all parts of the pavement shall receive substantially equal compression.

At all places not accessible to the roller, the mixture shall be thoroughly compacted with hand tampers. Hand tampers shall weigh not less than 25 pounds and shall have a tamping face area of not more than 50 square inches. The surface of the mixture after compression shall be smooth and true to established crown and grade.

Any mixture which becomes loose and broken, mixed with dirt, or in any way defective prior to the application of the tack coat or surfacing shall be removed and replaced with fresh mixture, which shall be immediately compacted to conform with the surrounding area, all to be done at the expense of the contractor. Skin patching on an area that has been rolled shall not be allowed.

4.8 *Joints.* (a) General. The mixture at the joints shall comply with the surface requirements and present the same uniformity of texture, density, smoothness, etc., as other sections of the course. In the formation of all joints, provision shall be made for proper bond with the new surface for the full specified depth of the course. Joints shall be formed by cutting back of the previous day's run so as to expose the full depth of the course, and the exposed edge shall be given a light paint coat of asphalt, if necessary. The fresh mixture shall be raked against the joint, thoroughly tamped with tampers and rolled.

(b) Transverse. The placing of the course shall be as nearly continuous as possible. The roller shall pass over the unprotected end of the freshly laid mixture only when the laying of the course is to be discontinued.

(c) Longitudinal. The placing of the course shall be in the manner as specified and so that the joint is exposed for the shortest period possible. The joint shall be placed so that it will not coincide with that in the subbase and will break joints by at least one foot.

4.9 *Shaping Edges.* While the base is being compacted and finished, the contractor shall trim the edges neatly to line.

4.10 *Surface Tests.* The finished surface shall not vary more than ⅜ inch for the base course when measured with a sixteen (16) foot straightedge applied parallel with or at right angles to the center line. Tests for conformity with the specified crown and grade shall be made by the contractor immediately after initial compression by powered rollers and any variation shall be corrected by removing or adding materials and continuing the rolling. After the completion of final rolling, the smoothness of the course shall again be checked, and the humps or depressions exceeding the specified tolerances or that retain water on the surface shall be corrected by removing the defective work and replacing with new material or by adding additional material as directed by the engineer and at the expense of the contractor.

4.11 *Sampling Base.* For the determination of composition, compaction and density of the base the contractor shall remove suitable size samples of the completed base. Samples for each day or fraction thereof when mixtures are placed shall be taken by the engineer. The contractor shall replace the base where samples are removed, and these replacements shall be installed by the contractor free of charge. After the samples have been removed, they will be tested by the engineer for density and composition. If the deficiency in composition, compaction and density exceeds the limits of toleration from that specified, satisfactory corrections shall be made.

4.12 *Bituminous and Aggregate Material Contractor's Responsibility.* Samples of the bituminous and aggregate materials that the contractor proposes to use, together with a statement as to their source and character must be submitted and approval obtained before use of such material begins. The contractor shall require the manufacturer or producer of the bituminous and aggregate materials to furnish material subject to this and all other pertinent requirements of the contract. Only those materials that have been demonstrated by service tests as satisfactory for the intended use will be acceptable.

For checking the adequacy of the equipment in use, inspecting the conditions and operation of the plant, for the verification of weights or proportions and character of materials and/or the determination and checking of temperatures being maintained in the preparation of the mixtures, the engineer or his authorized representative shall have access at any time to all parts of the paving plant.

The contractor shall furnish vendor's certified test report for each car load or equivalent of emulsified asphalt shipped to the project. The report shall be delivered to the engineer before permission is granted for use of the material.

4.13 *Freight and Weigh-Bills.* Before the final estimate is allowed, the contractor shall file with the engineer receipted bills where railroad shipments are made and certified weigh-bills when materials are received in any other manner, of the bituminous and paving materials actually used in the construction covered by the contract. The contractor shall not remove bituminous material from the tank car or storage tank until the initial outage and temperature measurements have been taken, nor shall he release the car or tank until the final outage has been taken by the engineer.

Copies of all freight bills and weigh-bills shall be furnished to the engineer during the progress of the work.

METHOD OF MEASUREMENT

5.1 The tonnage of base course to be paid for shall be the number of tons of bituminous mixture of the grading called for in the bid schedule and used in the accepted work. The bituminous treated material shall be weighed after mixing and no deduction shall be made for the weight of bituminous material in the mixture.

5.2 The bituminous material shall not be paid for separately but shall be included in the price bid for base course above, and shall be considered incidental to the price for this item.

BASIS OF PAYMENT

6.1 The quantities of base mixture, determined as provided in 5.1, 5.2 above, shall be paid for at the contract unit price per ton in the bid schedule for base course, which price and payment shall constitute full compensation for preparing base or subgrade; for furnishing, handling, mixing, manipulating, and placing all materials; for all shaping, compacting, and rolling; for finishing; for improving unsatisfactory areas; for reconditioning subgrade and shoulders; for furnishing samples; for furnishing and sealing of scales; for furnishing the weigh house; for all labor, equipment, tools and incidentals necessary to complete the item, except any prime or tack coat.

APPENDIX 25

DEPARTMENT OF COMMERCE
Civil Aeronautics Administration
Airport Division
Washington, D.C.
September 1, 1943

FLUXED NATURAL ROCK ASPHALT SURFACE COURSE FOR AIRPORT RUNWAYS, TAXIWAYS AND APRONS

C.A.A. Specification No. P-406

INTRODUCTION

This specification consists of fluxed natural rock asphalts and is intended for use in localities within the economic range of sandstone or limestone rock asphalt mines; also for use in localities where portable, central mixing plants are not available or where the tonnage does not justify setting up a central mixing plant.

In this specification, provision is made for the use of natural sandstone or limerock asphalt which contain insufficient asphalt to be placed as paving surfaces but by adding a small amount of fluxing material produce satisfactory paving mixtures. The type of fluxing material is dependent on the characteristics of the natural rock asphalt. The flux is added in a suitable mixing plant under controlled operations.

DESCRIPTION

1.1 This item shall consist of a surface course composed of one or more courses of fluxed natural rock asphalt constructed on the prepared base in accordance with these specifications and in conformity with the dimensions and typical cross sections shown on the plans and with the lines and grades established by the engineer.

The raw rock asphalt for this item shall be a limestone rock asphalt, or a sandstone rock asphalt, all particles of which are naturally impregnated or coated with bitumen. The rock asphalt for this item shall be processed and fluxed at a plant capable of maintaining the required uniformity of quality at the necessary rate of production.

1.2 *Job Mix Formula.* A job mix formula shall be prepared to provide proper control of the mixture for the project. No work shall be started nor any mixture accepted until the producer, through the contractor, has submitted in writing the percent of bitumen and gradation of the rock asphalt mixture proposed for use in the surface course. The material furnished shall conform to the approved job mix formula within the tolerances specified herein.

Job Mix Tolerances

Aggregate passing No. 10, No. 40, and No. 80 sieve	±5%
Aggregate passing No. 200 sieve	±2%
Asphaltic cement	±0.7%

MATERIALS

2.1 *Fluxed Rock Asphalt.* The fluxed rock asphalt furnished under this specification shall consist of rock asphalt practically free from sulphates, iron pyrites, and alumina and shall conform with one or both of the following requirements:

(a) Sandstone Rock Asphalt—Sandstone rock asphalt used in the production of fluxed rock asphalt shall consist of firm, hard grains of siliceous sand occurring in natural deposit, uniformly coated with asphalt to such an extent that the grains are bonded together into a rock-like mass, the bonding being due to the asphalt and not, to an appreciable extent, to lime or limestone or other mineral coatings on the grains. The sandstone rock asphalt shall contain asphalt so that the content of bitumen soluble in carbon disulphide shall be not less than four (4) percent by weight.

(b) Limestone Rock Asphalt—Limestone rock asphalt used in the production of fluxed rock asphalt shall consist of tough, hard, durable limestone occurring in natural deposit, impregnated with asphalt to such an extent that when the material is crushed the fractured surfaces shall be predominantly filmed with asphalt. The limestone rock asphalt shall contain sufficient asphalt so that the content of bitumen soluble in carbon disulphide shall be not less than five (5) percent by weight. The rock asphalt shall have a percent of wear not more than fifty (50) as determined by the Los Angeles Rattler Test for coarse aggregate, A.A.S.H.O. Method T 96–42.

(c) Service Record—The rock asphalt shall be obtained from deposits, which for a period of at least two (2) years have produced, when properly fluxed with additional asphaltic oil, a paving material with a satisfactory service record showing no excessive loss in penetration or ductility of the bitumen after placement as a paving surface.

2.2 *Fluxing Asphalt.* The flux for treating the rock asphalt shall meet the following requirements:

	PENETRATION @ 77° F. OF NATIVE BITUMEN IN THE ROCK ASPHALT		
	Less than 50	Over 50	
		RC-2	RC-3
Flash Point F.	150+	80+	80+
Furol Viscosity @ 122° F.	60–160		
140° F.		100–200	250–500
Distillation (Percent of total Distillate to 680° F.)			
to 437° F.		40+	25+
to 500° F.		65+	55+
to 600° F.		87+	83+
Residue from distillation to 680° F. Volume percent by difference		67+	73+
Loss—20 gms. 5 hrs. @ 325° F.	0–5		
Tests on Residue from Distillation			
Penetration 77° F. 100 g. 5 sec.		80–120	80–120
Ductility 77° F. cm.		100+	100+
Soluble in CCl_4 percent		99.5+	99.5+

2.3 *Bitumen.* The rock asphalt mixture after being fluxed shall have a bitumen content of from six (6) percent to eleven (11) percent soluble in carbon disulphide.

The bitumen extracted from the rock asphalt after the flux has been added and the mixture has been prepared in the plant shall meet the following requirements:

	A.A.S.H.O.	Min.	Max.
Penetration 77° F.	T 49–42	100	150
Ductility 77° F.	T 51–42	100 cm.	

2.4 *Gradation of Mixture.* The rock asphalt shall be crushed and then fluxed so that it will meet the following requirements as to gradation, using square mesh sieves:

	Limestone Rock Asphalt	Sandstone Rock Asphalt
Passing $\frac{5}{8}''$ sieve	100	100
Passing $\frac{1}{2}''$ sieve	90–100	96–100
Passing $\frac{1}{4}''$ sieve	40–65	82–98
Passing No. 10 sieve	20–35	58–88
Passing No. 40 sieve	8–25	32–54
Passing No. 80 sieve	6–20	18–35
Passing No. 200 sieve	4–12	4–14

CONSTRUCTION METHODS

3.1 *Weather and Seasonal Limitations.* Surface course shall be constructed only when the surface is dry, when the atmospheric temperature is above 60° F., and when the weather is not foggy or rainy. The temperature requirement may be waived, but only when so directed by the engineer.

3.2 *Equipment and Organization.* (a) General. All methods employed in performing the work and all equipment, tools, and other plant and machinery used for handling materials and executing any part of the work shall be subject to the approval of the engineer before the work is started and whenever found unsatisfactory shall be changed and improved as required. All equipment, tools, machinery and plant used must be maintained in a satisfactory working condition.

(b) Mixing Plant—The plant shall provide for weight proportioning of rock asphalt, flux and water. This equipment shall be constructed with devices that will permit easy readjustment of any working part such that it will function properly and accurately. The weighing device shall be so constructed and operated that the correct amount of each material is introduced into the mixer with an accuracy that will meet the job tolerances specified. The plant shall have a capacity of at least 40 tons per hour. Flux and water may be proportioned by volume based upon weight.

The mixer shall be a batch mixer, drum type or a twin pugmill mixer of sufficient size to maintain thorough uniform mixing at the rated plant capacity.

The plant shall be equipped with positive means to govern the time of mixing and to maintain it constant unless changed by order of the engineer. The time of mixing shall be considered as the interval between the time the flux material is spread on the rock asphalt and the time the mixture leaves the mixing unit.

Equipment for heating flux material shall consist of a retort or steam coils, so designed that steam will not be introduced into the material. If direct fire heating is used, the heating equipment shall be such that positive circulation of the flux while being heated is assured. A recording thermometer shall be provided which will record the temperature of the flux material at the draw-off valve.

(c) Placing Equipment—Equipment for spreading, shaping, and finishing shall consist of an approved self-contained power machine operating in such a manner that no supplemental spreading, shaping, or finishing will be required to provide a surface which will comply with the requirements for smoothness contained herein. A power grader of approved type shall also be provided.

(d) Rolling Equipment—Rollers shall be suitably designed for the construction of bituminous surfaces. The rolling shall be done with self-propelled tandem and three-wheel-type rollers weighing not less than eight (8) tons, and approved pneumatic rollers. The wheels on the power rollers shall be equipped with adjustable scrapers which shall be used when necessary to clean the wheel surface. Rollers shall also be equipped with water tanks and sprinkling apparatus which shall be used to keep the wheels moist and prevent the surfacing material from sticking.

3.3 *Preparation of Fluxed Rock Asphalt.* The rock asphalt prepared as prescribed above and free from clay, shale, dirt or uncoated particles shall be accurately measured and conveyed into the mixer in the proportionate amounts required to meet the specified grading.

The flux material shall be heated in retorts or tanks designed to secure uniform heating of the entire contents. Retorts or tanks shall be capable of heating the flux with an effective and positive control of the heat at all times to a temperature of not to exceed 180° F.

The quantity of flux material for each batch or calibrated amount shall be determined by the engineer, and shall be measured or weighed and introduced into the mixer at the specified temperature, holding to the lowest range possible for adequate mixing. The exact temperature to be used on the work within the specified range shall be fixed by the engineer. The mixing shall continue for at least thirty seconds and for such longer period as may be necessary to coat all of the particles.

If the rock asphalt mixture is prepared at some central point and shipped to the work, water may be added to prevent setting-up in transit. If water is added, the total water so added shall not exceed 4% by weight. If the rock asphalt mixture is prepared on or adjacent to the project, the addition of water will not be permitted unless authorized by the engineer. All water in the mixture in excess of 4% by weight at the time of weighing the mixture shall be deducted in determining the tonnage of mixture for payment. The method of determining the water content of the mixture shall be as prescribed in A.S.T.M. Designation D-95.

3.4 *Transportation and Delivery of the Mixture.* The mixture shall be transported from the mixing plant or point of delivery to the point of use in pneumatic-tired vehicles having tight bodies previously cleaned of all foreign materials. When directed by the engineer, each load shall be covered with canvas or other suitable material of sufficient size and thickness to protect it from the weather conditions.

The fluxed rock asphalt shall be kept free from dirt or vegetable matter and any rock asphalt which becomes contaminated with foreign material shall be rejected. In case the rock asphalt has set in storage or in transit to the extent that it cannot be readily handled on the runway, it shall be refluxed to conform to the specified gradation before being used. Storage or handling of the rock asphalt shall be in such manner as to prevent undue segregation.

No loads shall be sent out so late in the day as to interfere with spreading and compacting the mixture during daylight, unless artificial light satisfactory to the engineer is provided.

A sample of fluxed rock asphalt taken from each carload (or equivalent) delivered shall be tested for bitumen content and for analysis as herein outlined in this specification.

3.5 *Spreading and Laying.* (a) Preparation for Placing—Immediately before placing the bituminous mixture, the existing surface shall be cleaned of loose or deleterious material by sweeping with a power sweeper supplemented by hand brooms if necessary, or as directed by the engineer, and if called for in the proposal or shown on the plans, a uniform application of bituminous material shall be applied as described in C.A.A. Specification No. P-603.

The mixture shall be laid only upon an approved underlying course which is dry and only when weather conditions are suitable. No mixture shall be placed when the air temperature in the shade and away from artificial heat is 60° F. or under unless so directed by the engineer. In event of sudden rains, no more mixture in transit shall be dumped into the spreading machine. All work shall stop and the mixture that has been spread but not compacted by rolling shall be allowed to dry out.

Grade control between the edges of the runway shall be by means of grade stakes or steel pins placed in lanes parallel to the center line of the runway, and at intervals sufficiently close that string lines may be stretched between stakes or pins.

Placing shall commence at the point or points furthest from the point of supply, and progress continuously toward the point of supply, unless otherwise ordered by the engineer. Hauling over material already placed will not be permitted until the material has been compacted thoroughly in the manner specified.

Contact surfaces shall be painted with a thin uniform coat of cutback asphalt just before the mixture is placed.

(b) Machine Spreading—Upon arrival the fluxed rock asphalt shall be dumped into an approved mechanical spreader and immediately spread thereby to the full width required. Other types of spreading equipment will be permitted if approved by the engineer. It shall be struck off in a uniform layer of such depth that when the work is completed, it will have the required thickness, and will conform to the grade and surface contour required. The speed of the mechanical spreader shall be regulated to eliminate as far as possible the pulling and tearing of the mixture.

Placing and compaction of the mixture shall progress in sections. The mixture shall be placed in strips of a minimum width of 10 feet. To insure proper drainage, the spreading shall begin along the center line of the runway or taxiway on a crown section or on the high side of the pavement with a one-way slope. The six-inch strip adjacent to the area on which future material is to be laid shall not be rolled until such material has been placed, but shall not be left unrolled more than twenty-four (24) hours after being placed. After the first strip or width has been compacted, the second width shall be placed, finished and compacted as provided for the first width except that rolling shall be extended to include the six inches of the first width not previously compacted. Whenever the adjacent or second width cannot be placed within twenty-four (24) hours, the six-inch strip shall not be left unrolled. After the second width has been placed and rolled, a ten-foot straightedge shall be used across the longitudinal joint to determine if the surface is to grade and contour.

(c) Blading—Supplementary blading of the mixture with an approved power grader may be required by the engineer as necessary to aeration of the mixture and securing uniform surface texture and contour.

(d) Hand Spreading—In limited areas where, on account of irregularities or unavoidable obstacles, the use of mechanical spreading and finishing equipment is impractical, the mixture may be spread by hand.

When hand spreading is permitted, the mixture shall be dumped upon arrival on approved dump sheets outside of the area on which it is to be spread and be distributed into place immediately by means of shovels. It shall be spread with rakes in a uniformly loose layer to the full width required and of such depth that when the work is completed, it will have the required thickness and will conform to the grade and surface contour required.

3.6 *Compaction of Mixture.* After spreading and as directed by the engineer, sufficient time shall be allowed to obtain proper aeration and curing. The mixture shall not be compacted until the moisture content is two and one-half ($2\frac{1}{2}$) percent or less. The mixture shall then be thoroughly and uniformly compressed by a power-driven, three-wheel roller, and tandem roller or rollers, weighing eight (8) tons or more, and approved pneumatic rollers. On the fist strip spread, rolling shall start in the center and continue toward either edge. On subsequent strips laid, rolling shall start on the edge adjacent to previously-laid material and continue toward the other edge.

Initial rolling shall be done longitudinally with three-wheel rollers overlapping on successive trips of the roller. Alternate trips of the roller shall be of slightly different lengths. The mixture shall be subjected to diagonal rolling crossing the lines of the first.

The speed of the roller shall at all times be slow enough to avoid displacement of the mixture. Any displacement occurring as a result of reversing the direction of the roller, or from any other cause, shall be corrected at once by the use of rakes, and of fresh mixture where required.

Sufficient rollers of the designated types shall be furnished to adequately handle the output of the plant. Rolling shall proceed at an average rate not to exceed 350 square yards per hour per roller. Rolling shall continue until all roller marks are eliminated, until the surface is of uniform texture and true to grade, and cross section, and until the density of at least ninety (90) percent of the theoretical density is obtained. Field density tests shall be made at least once daily. Final rolling shall be done with tandem rollers and pneumatic rollers. Rolling shall be done upon direction of the engineer at any time within two weeks after the mixture is placed.

To prevent adhesion of the mixture to the powered roller, the wheels shall be kept properly moistened, but an excess of either water or oil will not be permitted.

The rollers shall be kept in good condition and shall be operated by competent and experienced rollermen. The rollers shall be operated continuously as far as practicable and in such a manner that all parts of the pavement shall receive substantially equal compression.

At all places not accessible to the roller, the mixture shall be thoroughly compacted with hand tampers. Hand tampers shall weigh not less than 25 pounds and shall have a tamping face area of not more than 50 square inches. The surface of the mixture after compression shall be smooth and true to the established crown and grade.

Any mixture which becomes loose and broken, mixed with dirt, or in any way defective prior to the application of the finish coat shall be removed and replaced with fresh mixture, which shall be immediately compacted to conform with the surrounding area, all to be done at the expense of the contractor. Skin patching on an area that has been rolled shall not be allowed, unless the underlying surface is scarified before additional material is placed.

3.7 *Joints.* (a) General—The mixture at the joints shall comply with the surface requirements and present the same uniformity of texture, density, smoothness, etc., as other sections of the course. In the formation of all joints, provision shall be made for the proper bond with the new surface for the full specified depth of the course. Joints shall be formed by cutting back on the previous day's run so as to expose the full depth of the course, and the exposed edge shall be given a light paint coat of asphalt, if necessary. The fresh mixture shall be raked against the joint, thoroughly tamped with tampers and rolled.

(b) Transverse—The placing of the course shall be as nearly continuous as possible. The roller shall pass over the unprotected end of the freshly laid mixture only when the laying of the course is to be discontinued.

(c) Longitudinal—The placing of the course shall be in the manner as specified and so that the joint is exposed for the shortest period possible. The joint shall be placed so that it will not coincide with that in the binder or base course and so they break by at least one foot.

3.8 *Shaping Edges.* While the surface is being compacted and finished, the contractor shall trim the edges neatly to line.

3.9 *Surface Tests.* The finished surface shall not vary more than ¼ inch for the wearing course or ⅜ inch for the binder course when measured with a sixteen (16) foot straightedge applied parallel with or at right angles to the center line. Tests for conformity with the specified crown and grade shall be made by the contractor immediately after initial compression and any variation shall be corrected by removing or adding materials and continuing the rolling. After the completion of final rolling, the smoothness of the course shall again be checked, and the humps or depressions exceeding the specified tolerances or that retain water on the surface shall be corrected by removing the defective work and replacing with new material or by adding additional material as directed by the engineer and at the expense of the contractor.

3.10 *Sampling Pavement.* For the determination of composition, compaction and density of the pavement the contractor shall remove suitable size samples of the completed pavement. Samples for each day or fraction thereof when mixtures are placed shall be taken by the engineer. The contractor shall replace the pavement where samples are removed, and these replacements shall be installed by the contractor free of charge. After the samples have been removed from the completed pavement, they will be tested by the engineer for density and composition. If the deficiency in composition, compaction and density exceeds the limits of toleration from that specified, satisfactory corrections shall be made.

3.11 *Rock Asphalt Material Contractor's Responsibility.* Samples of the flux and rock asphalt materials that the contractor proposes to use, together with a statement as to their source and character must be submitted and approval obtained before use of such materials begins. The contractor shall require the manufacturer or producer of the flux and rock asphalt materials to furnish material subject to this and all other pertinent requirements of the contract.

For checking the adequacy of the equipment in use, inspecting the conditions and operation of the plant, for the verification of weights or proportions and character of materials and/or the determination and checking of temperatures being maintained in the preparation of the mixtures, the engineer or his authorized representative shall have access at any time to all parts of the plant, and the contractor shall furnish the necessary calibrated weights, thermometers, and other facilities.

The contractor shall furnish or shall be responsible for the rock asphalt producer furnishing, vendor's certified test report for each car load or equivalent of fluxing asphalt used in the preparation of the rock asphalt mixture placed as surfacing on the project. The report shall be delivered to the engineer before permission is granted for the use of the rock asphalt material.

3.12 *Freight and Weigh-Bills.* Before the final estimate is allowed, the contractor shall file with the engineer receipted bills where railroad shipments are made and certified weigh-bills when materials are received in any other manner, of the paving materials actually used in the construction covered by the contract. The contractor shall not remove flux material from the tank car or storage tank until the initial outage measurements have been taken, nor shall he release the car or tank until the final outage has been taken by the engineer.

Copies of all freight bills and weigh-bills shall be furnished to the engineer during the progress of the work.

3.13 *Seal Coat.* As shown on the plans and called for in the bid schedule, a seal coat of the type called for shall be applied to the finished course as described under "Seal Coat."

METHOD OF MEASUREMENT

4.1 The tonnage of fluxed rock asphalt to be paid for shall be the number of tons of mixture of the grading called for in the bid schedule and used in the accepted work. The treated material shall be weighed after mixing and no deductions shall be made for the weight of flux material in the mixture. Moisture in excess of 4% shall, however, be deducted.

BASIS OF PAYMENT

5.1 The quantities of fluxed rock asphalt determined as provided in 4.1 above, shall be paid for at the respective contract unit prices per ton in the bid schedule for binder or surface course, which prices and payment shall constitute full compensation for preparing base or subgrade to receive the pavement; for furnishing, handling, mixing, manipulating, and placing all materials; for all shaping, compacting, rolling, and for finishing; for improving unsatisfactory areas; for reconditioning subgrade; for furnishing samples; for furnishing and sealing of scales; for furnishing the weigh house; for all labor, equipment, tools and incidentals necessary to complete the item, except any "Tack Coat" or "Seal Coat."

APPENDIX 26

DEPARTMENT OF COMMERCE
Civil Aeronautics Administration
Airport Division
Washington, D.C.
May 1, 1942

BLENDED NATURAL ROCK ASPHALT SURFACE COURSE FOR AIRPORT RUNWAYS, TAXIWAYS AND APRONS

C.A.A. Specification No. P-407

INTRODUCTION

This specification has been prepared by the paving engineers of the Airport Division, Civil Aeronautics Administration in collaboration with the paving engineers of the Office of the Chief, U.S. Corps of Engineers.

The blended rock asphalt surface course as contained in this specification is intended for use in localities within the economic range of sandstone and/or limestone rock asphalt mines, or in localities where portable central mixing plants are not economically available, or where tonnage does not justify setting up a central mixing plant.

This specification covers naturally impregnated or coated sandstone rock asphalt, limestone rock asphalt, or combinations of both, which contain sufficient quantity and quality of bituminous material so that a fluxing agent is unnecessary. In combining the two materials, the amount of limestone rock asphalt shall not be greater than 50 percent of the blended mixture.

DESCRIPTION

1.1 This item shall consist of a surface course composed of one or more courses of blended natural rock asphalt constructed on the prepared base in accordance with these specifications and in conformity with the dimensions, and typical cross sections shown on the plans and with the lines and grades established by the engineer.

The raw rock asphalt for this item shall be a sandstone rock asphalt, and/or a limestone rock asphalt, all particles of which are naturally impregnated or coated with bitumen. The rock asphalt for this item shall be processed at a plant capable of maintaining the required uniformity of quality at the necessary rate of production.

1.2 *Job Mix Formula.* The bitumen content and the gradation prescribed below in the blended natural rock asphalt fixes the limits for all cases. A closer control is required for the specific project, and no work shall be started on the project until the producer has submitted through the contractor, in writing, the definite proportions of materials, the percent of bitumen chosen as the fixed mean for the blended natural rock asphalt, and the gradation proposed for use on the project. Upon approval, the bitumen content of the blended natural rock asphalt shall not vary more than plus or minus 0.7% from the mean so fixed, and the gradation of the aggregate shall not vary in excess of the limits set forth below:

Aggregate passing the No. 10 sieve—plus or minus 5%
Aggregate passing the No. 40 sieve—plus or minus 5%
Aggregate passing the No. 80 sieve—plus or minus 3%
Aggregate passing the No. 200 sieve—plus or minus 2%

MATERIALS

2.1 *Blended Rock Asphalt.* The blended rock asphalt furnished under this specification shall consist of rock asphalt practically free from sulphates, iron pyrites, and alumina and shall conform with one or both of the following requirements:

(a) *Sandstone Rock Asphalt*: Sandstone rock asphalt used in the production of blended rock asphalt shall consist of firm hard grains of siliceous sand occurring in natural deposit, uniformly coated with asphalt to such an extent that the grains are bonded together into a rock-like mass, the bonding being due to the asphalt and not, to an appreciable extent, to lime or limestone or other mineral coatings on the grains. The sandstone rock asphalt shall contain asphalt so that the content of bitumen soluble in carbon disulphide shall be not more than twelve (12%) percent by weight.

(b) *Limestone Rock Asphalt*: Limestone rock asphalt used in the production of blended rock asphalt shall consist of tough, hard, durable limestone occurring in natural deposit, impregnated with asphalt to such an extent that when the material is crushed the fractured surfaces shall be predominantly filmed with asphalt. The limestone rock asphalt shall contain sufficient asphalt so that the content of bitumen soluble in carbon disulphide shall be not less than three (3%) percent by weight. The rock asphalt shall have a percent of wear not more than fifty (50) as determined by the Los Angeles Rattler Test for coarse aggregate, A.A.S.H.O. Method T-96.

2.2 *Composition of Blended Rock Asphalt.* The blended rock asphalt shall be crushed and then blended so that it will meet the following requirements as to composition and gradation, using square mesh sieves: (a)

Blended Rock Asphalt

Passing ¾″ sieve	100
Passing ½″ sieve	88–100
Passing ¼″ sieve	70–100
Passing No. 10 sieve	45–100
Passing No. 40 sieve	25–100
Passing No. 80 sieve	14–55
Passing No. 200 sieve	4–12

A minimum of 45 percent shall pass the No. 10 mesh sieve.
Material passing the No. 10 mesh sieve shall have a minimum stability of 35 pounds per square inch at 1.75% moisture content, as determined by C.A.A. Specification No. P-607.
If the material does not meet this stability, sufficient crushed natural rock asphalt

retained on the No. 40 mesh sieve and passing the ¼ inch sieve shall be added to bring the stability to the required 35 pounds per square inch.

(b) The prepared mixture shall have a bitumen content of from five and eight tenths (5.8) to nine (9) percent. No fluxing materials or hard asphalt shall be added to bring the bitumen content within the specified limits. The blended rock asphalt mixture shall contain not more than 50 percent of the limestone rock asphalt when used in combination with sandstone rock asphalt.

(c) The bitumen extracted from the blended rock asphalt shall meet the following requirements:

	A.A.S.H.O.	Min.
Penetration, 77° F.	T-49	100
Ductility, 77° F.	T-51	100 cm.

The blended rock asphalt shall be material obtained from deposits which for a period of at least two years have produced raw rock asphalt laid in pavement producing satisfactory service and which show no excessive loss in either penetration or ductility after placement as a pavement.

CONSTRUCTION METHODS

3.1 *Weather Limitations.* Surface course shall be constructed only when the surface is dry, when the atmospheric temperature is above 60° F., and when the weather is not foggy or rainy. The temperature requirement may be waived, but only when so directed by the engineer.

3.2 *Equipment and Organization.* (a) *General.* All methods employed in performing the work and all equipment, tools, and other plant and machinery used for handling materials and executing any part of the work shall be subject to the approval of the engineer before the work is started and whenever found unsatisfactory shall be changed and improved as required. All equipment, tools, machinery and plant used must be maintained in a satisfactory working condition.

(b) *Mixing Plant.* The plant shall provide for weight proportioning of rock asphalt. This equipment shall be constructed with devices that will permit easy readjustment of any working part such that it will function properly and accurately. The weighing device shall be so constructed and operated that the correct amount of each material is introduced into the mixer, crusher or pulverizer with an accuracy that will meet the job tolerances specified. The plant shall have a capacity of at least 40 tons per hour.

(c) *Placing Equipment.* Equipment for spreading, shaping, and finishing shall consist of an approved self-contained power machine operating in such a manner that no supplemental spreading, shaping, or finishing will be required to provide a surface which will comply with the requirements for smoothness contained herein. A power grader of approved type shall also be provided.

(d) *Rolling Equipment.* Rollers shall be suitably designed for the construction of bituminous surfaces. The rolling shall be done with self-propelled tandem and three-wheel-type rollers weighing not less than eight (8) tons, and approved pneumatic rollers. The wheels on the power rollers shall be equipped with adjustable scrapers which shall be used when necessary to clean the wheel surface. Rollers shall also be equipped with water tanks and sprinkling apparatus which shall be used to keep the wheels moist and prevent the surfacing material from sticking.

3.3 *Preparation of Blended Rock Asphalt.* The rock asphalt, free from clay, shale, dirt or uncoated particles, shall be accurately measured and conveyed into the mixer, crusher or pulverizer in the proportionate amounts required to meet the specified grading.

The raw materials from the sandstone rock asphalt and/or from the limestone rock asphalt deposit being used shall be combined in the proportions required by weighing each separately and accurately and introducing into the mixer, crusher or pulverizer. The weighing apparatus shall be accurate to within four tenths (.4) of one (1) percent, and such provisions satisfactory to the engineer as are necessary to the determination and maintenance of the accuracy of all weighing devices, at all times, shall be provided. The proportions shall be established by the engineer and changed only on his order. No additions shall be made of any material not specifically described and stipulated in this specification.

If the rock asphalt mixture is prepared at some central point and shipped to the work, water may be added to prevent setting-up in transit. If water is added, the total water so added shall not exceed 4% by weight. If the rock asphalt mixture is prepared on or adjacent to the project, the addition of water will not be permitted unless authorized by the engineer. All water in the mixture in excess of 4% by weight at the time of weighing the mixture shall be deducted in determining the tonnage of mixture for payment. The method of determining the water content of the mixture shall be as prescribed in A.S.T.M. Designation D-95.

3.4 *Transportation and Delivery of the Mixture.* The mixture shall be transported from the mixing plant or point of delivery to the point of use in pneumatic-tired vehicles having tight bodies previously cleaned of all foreign materials. When directed by the engineer, each load shall be covered with canvas or other suitable material of sufficient size and thickness to protect it from the weather conditions.

The blended rock asphalt shall be kept free from dirt or vegetable matter and any blended rock asphalt which becomes contaminated with foreign material shall be rejected. In case the blended rock asphalt has set in storage or in transit to the extent that it cannot be readily handled on the runway, it shall be reprocessed to conform to the specified gradation before being used. Storage or handling of the blended rock asphalt shall be in such manner as to prevent undue segregation.

No loads shall be sent out so late in the day as to interfere with spreading and compacting the mixture during daylight, unless artificial light satisfactory to the engineer is provided.

A sample of blended rock asphalt taken from each carload (or equivalent) delivered shall be tested for bitumen content and for analysis as herein outlined in this specification.

3.5 *Spreading and Laying.* (a) *Preparation for Placing.* Immediately before placing the bituminous mixture, the existing surface shall be cleaned of loose or deleterious material by sweeping with a power sweeper supplemented by hand brooms if necessary, or as directed by the engineer, and if called for in the proposal or shown on the plans, a uniform application of bituminous material shall be applied as described under "Tack Coat."

The mixture shall be laid only upon an approved underlying course which is dry and only when weather conditions are suitable. No mixture shall be placed when the air temperature in the shade and away from artificial heat is 60° F. or under unless so directed by the engineer. The engineer may, however, permit work of this character to continue when overtaken by sudden rains, up to the amount which may be in transit at the time.

Grade control between the edges of the runway shall be by means of grade stakes or steel pins placed in lanes parallel to the center line of the runway, and at intervals sufficiently close that string lines may be stretched between stakes or pins.

Placing shall commence at the point or points furthest from the point of supply, and progress continuously toward the point of supply, unless otherwise ordered by the engineer. Hauling over material already placed will not be permitted until the material has been compacted thoroughly in the manner specified.

(b) *Machine Spreading.* Upon arrival the blended rock asphalt shall be dumped into an approved mechanical spreader and immediately spread thereby to the full width required. Other types of spreading equipment will be permitted if approved by the engineer. It shall be struck off in a uniform layer of such depth that when the work is completed, it will have the required thickness, and will conform to the grade and surface contour required. The speed of the mechanical spreader shall be regulated to eliminate as far as possible the pulling and tearing of the mixture.

Placing and compaction of the mixture shall progress in sections. The mixture shall be placed in strips of a minimum width of 10 feet. The 6-inch strip adjacent to the area on which future material is to be laid, shall not be rolled until such material has been placed. After the first strip or width has been compacted, the second width shall be placed, finished and compacted as provided for the first width, except that rolling shall be extended to include the six inches of the first width not previously compacted.

In limited areas where, on account of irregularities or unavoidable obstacles, the use of mechanical spreading and finishing equipment is impractical, the mixture may be spread by hand.

When hand spreading is permitted, the mixture shall be dumped upon arrival on approved dump sheets outside of the area on which it is to be spread and be distributed into place immediately by means of shovels. It shall be spread with rakes in a uniformly loose layer to the full width required and of such depth that when the work is completed, it will have the required thickness and will conform to the grade and surface contour required.

Supplementary blading of the mixture with an approved power grader may be required by the engineer as necessary to aeration of the mixture and securing uniform surface texture and contour.

3.6 *Compaction of Mixture.* After spreading, the moisture content in the mixture shall be reduced to 2½% or less; and the mixture shall be thoroughly and uniformly compressed by a power driven, three-wheel roller, tandem roller or rollers, weighing eight (8) tons or more, and approved pneumatic rollers.

Initial rolling shall be done longitudinally, overlapping on successive trips by at least one-half the width of the roller. Alternate trips of the roller shall be slightly different lengths. The mixture shall be subjected to diagonal rolling crossing the lines of the first.

The speed of the roller shall at all times be slow enough to avoid displacement of the mixture. Any displacement occurring as a result of reversing the direction of the roller, or from any other cause, shall be corrected at once by the use of rakes, and of fresh mixture where required.

Sufficient rollers of the designated types shall be furnished to adequately handle the output of the plant or rate of delivery. Rolling shall continue until all roller marks are eliminated, until the surface is of uniform texture and true to grade, and cross section. Rolling shall be done upon direction of the engineer at any time within two weeks after the mixture is placed.

To prevent adhesion of the mixture to the roller, the wheels shall be kept properly moistened, but an excess of either water or oil will not be permitted.

The rollers shall be kept in good condition and shall be operated by competent and experienced rollermen. The rollers shall be operated continuously as far as practicable and in such a manner that all parts of the pavement shall receive substantially equal compression.

At all places not accessible to the roller, the mixture shall be thoroughly compacted with hand tampers. Hand tampers shall weigh not less than 25 pounds and shall have a tamping face area of not more than 50 square inches. The surface of the mixture after compression shall be smooth and true to the established crown and grade.

Any mixture which becomes loose and broken, mixed with dirt, or in any way defective, prior to the application of the finish coat shall be removed and replaced with fresh mixture, which shall be immediately compacted to conform with the surrounding area, all to be done at the expense of the contractor. Skin patching on an area that has been rolled shall not be allowed, unless the underlying surface is scarified before additional material is placed.

3.7 *Joints.* (a) *General.* Joints shall comply with the surface requirements and present the same uniformity of texture, density, smoothness, etc., as other sections of the course.

(b) *Transverse.* The placing of the course shall be as nearly continuous as possible. The roller shall pass over the unprotected end of the freshly laid mixture only when the laying of the course is to be discontinued.

In all such cases, including the formation of joints as hereinafter specified, provision shall be made for proper bond with the new surface for the full specified depth of the course. Joints shall be formed by cutting back on the previous day's run so as to expose the full depth of the course. The fresh mixture shall be raked against the joint, thoroughly tamped with tampers and rolled.

(c) *Longitudinal.* Longitudinal joints shall be placed so that the joint in the surface course will not coincide with that in the base or binder, and so that they break by at least one foot.

3.8 *Shaping Edges.* While the surface is being compacted and finished, the contractor shall trim the edges neatly to line.

3.9 *Surface Tests.* The finished surface shall not vary more than ¼ inch for the wearing course or $\frac{3}{8}$ inch for the binder course when measured with a ten-foot straightedge applied parallel with or at right angles to the center line. Tests for conformity with the specified crown and grade shall be made by the contractor immediately after initial compression and any variation shall be corrected by removing or adding materials and continuing the rolling. After the completion of final rolling, the smoothness of the course shall again be checked, and the humps or depressions exceeding the specified tolerances or that retain water on the surface shall be corrected by removing the defective work and replacing with new material or by adding additional material as directed by the engineer and at the expense of the contractor.

3.10 *Sampling Pavement.* For the determination of composition, compaction and density of the pavement the contractor shall remove suitable-size samples of the completed pavement. Samples for each day or fraction thereof when mixtures are placed shall be taken as directed by the engineer. The contractor shall replace the pavement where samples are removed, and these replacements shall be installed by the contractor free of charge.

3.11 *Rock Asphalt Material Contractor's Responsibility.* Samples of the blended rock asphalt materials that the contractor proposes to use, together with a statement as to their source and character must be submitted and approval obtained before use of such materials begins. The contractor shall require the manufacturer or producer of the blended rock asphalt materials to furnish material subject to this and all other pertinent requirements of the contract.

For checking the adequacy of the equipment in use, inspecting the conditions and operation of the plant, for the verification of weights or proportions and character of materials maintained in the preparation of the mixtures, the engineer or his authorized representative shall have access at any time to all parts of the plant, and the contractor shall furnish the necessary calibrated weights, samples and other facilities.

3.12 *Freight and Weigh-Bills.* Before the final estimate is allowed, the contractor shall file with the engineer receipted bills where railroad shipments are made and certified weigh-bills when materials are received in any other manner, of the paving materials actually used in the construction covered by the contract. The contractor shall not remove the blended rock asphalt from the car or storage until the initial samples have been taken.

Copies of freight and weigh-bills shall be furnished to the engineer during the progress of the work.

METHOD OF MEASUREMENT

4.1 The tonnage of blended rock asphalt to be paid for shall be the number of tons of mixture of the grading called for in the bid schedule and used in the accepted work. The blended material shall be weighed after mixing. Moisture in excess of 4% shall, however, be deducted.

BASIS OF PAYMENT

5.1 The quantities of blended rock asphalt determined as provided in 4.1 above, shall be paid for at the respective contract unit prices per ton in the bid schedule for binder or surface course, which prices and payment shall constitute full compensation for preparing base or subgrade to receive the pavement, for furnishing, handling, mixing, manipulating, and placing all materials, for all shaping, compacting, and rolling, for finishing, for improving unsatisfactory areas, for reconditioning the subgrade, for furnishing samples, for furnishing and sealing of scales, for furnishing the weigh house, for all labor, equipment, tools and incidentals necessary to complete the item, except any "Tack Coat" or "Seal Coat."

APPENDIX 27

DEPARTMENT OF COMMERCE
Civil Aeronautics Administration
Airport Division
Washington, D.C.
October 1, 1943

BLENDED NATURAL ROCK AND SAND ASPHALT SURFACE COURSE (CENTRAL PLANT HOT MIX) FOR AIRPORT RUNWAYS, TAXIWAYS AND APRONS

C.A.A. Specification No. P-408

INTRODUCTION

This specification provides an economical type of central plant bituminous mix of high quality by means of blending natural asphaltic limestone with local sand aggregate. The stability of sand mixtures can be improved either by the addition of coarse aggregate or by the admixture of the natural asphaltic limestone. A wide range is permitted in the selection and use of local sand aggregates. It will be noted that the procedures of the preparation of the mixture and of construction in this specification are the same as those in the central plant hot mix bituminous base and surface course specification.

If the sand is found to be hydrophilic as determined by the test given in the specification, the addition of 0.5 to 1.5 percent of hydrated lime or Portland cement to the aggregate prior to mixing with the bituminous material may be sufficient to change the inherent characteristics to a hydrophobic material. If the material is of such hydrophilic characteristics that the lime or cement alone will not accomplish the desired results, the addition of a proven and approved admixture to the bituminous material will be necessary.

It is recommended that where grass or weed growth might cause damage to the pavement that a recognized and approved chemical treatment be applied to the subgrade or base course.

DESCRIPTION

1.1 This item shall consist of a wearing course composed of sand, natural limerock asphalt and bituminous material, mixed in a central mixing plant and placed on the prepared base course in accordance with these specifications and in conformity with the dimensions and typical cross sections shown on the plans and with lines and grades established by the engineer. The blended natural rock and sand asphalt surface course mixture as specified shall be composed by weight of at least 20 per cent of natural limerock asphalt added to the sand.

1.2 *Determination of Percentage of Bituminous Material.* The percentage of bituminous material, by weight, to be added to the aggregate and the native bituminous material in the rock asphalt shall meet the requirements for bitumen as specified. The exact percentage to be used within the limits specified shall be fixed by the engineer on the basis of preliminary laboratory tests and field sieve analysis of the aggregate furnished.

1.3 *Job Mix Formula.* No work shall be started on the project nor any mixture accepted therefor until the contractor has submitted samples of the materials intended for use and the engineer has established a satisfactory job mix formula based upon tests of the materials furnished. The formula shall be submitted in writing by the engineer to the contractor, indicating the definite percentage for the sand, the rock asphalt and for asphaltic cement; also the intended temperature of completed mixture at the time it is discharged from the mixer. The mixture furnished shall conform to the approved job mix formula within the tolerances specified herein.

Job Mix Tolerances

Aggregate passing sieves No. 4 and larger	±5%
Aggregate passing No. 10, No. 40, and No. 80 sieve	±4%
Aggregate passing No. 200 sieve	±2%
Bitumen	±0.5%
Temperature of mixing and placing	±25° F.

MATERIALS

2.1 *Aggregate.* The aggregate shall consist of a mixture of sand and limerock asphalt with the minimum of 20 percent of limerock asphalt. The sand shall be sound, tough and durable and be obtained from approved sources. The sand when combined with the rock asphalt shall meet the requirements for gradation given in Table 2 using A.A.S.H.O. Method T 11 and T 27–42.

That portion of the aggregate, including any blended filler, passing a No. 40 sieve shall have a plasticity index of not more than 6, as determined by A.A.S.H.O. Method T 91–42; a liquid limit of not more than 25 as determined by A.A.S.H.O. Method T 89–42 and a maximum of 12 percent passing the No. 200 sieve.

The sand shall be free from vegetable matter, lumps or balls of clay, adherent films of clay, or other matter that will prevent thorough coating with bituminous material. The bituminized aggregate shall have a swell of not more than 1.5 percent as determined by A.A.S.H.O. Method T 101–42.

Prior to final acceptance of the sand aggregate to be used, the inherent characteristics of said aggregate relative to stripping shall be determined. This shall be done by preparing a test sample of the paving mixture in conformity with the specifications contained herewith. After the mixture has been made it shall be spread out in a loose thin layer and allowed to air season for 24 hours before testing. A suitable size sample (approximately one-half contents of container) shall be tested by placing it in a glass jar fitted with a tight screw cap and completely covering with distilled water. The jar and contents shall be allowed to stand for a period of 24 hours. Then the sample shall be vigorously shaken for a period of 15 minutes. The sample of mixture shall be examined for stripping. If stripping or sloughing off of the bituminous coating occurs it will be necessary to treat said aggregate by a method which has proven successful in changing the material from a hydrophilic to a hydrophobic state.

Limerock asphalt shall be pulverized so that not more than five (5) percent is retained on a three-eighths (⅜) inch mesh sieve. The limerock asphalt shall be impregnated, by forces of nature, with not less than four (4) percent of bitumen having a penetration, at 77° F., 100 gms., 5 sec. of not less than ten (10) and it shall be free from decomposed rock and foreign matter. The natural material furnished shall not be blended or fluxed with any material not included in this specification.

2.2 *Bituminous Material.* The bituminous material to be mixed with the mineral aggregate at the central plant shall conform to the grade, requirements and specifications as follows:

TABLE 1

Asphalt Cement

The asphalt cement shall be homogeneous, free from water, and shall not foam when heated to a temperature of 347° F.

Test Requirements	Petroleum Asphalts	Native Asphalts
Penetration at 77° F., 100 g. 5 sec.	100–150	100–150
Total bitumen (soluble in carbon disulphide), not less than	99.5%	
Total bitumen (Soluble in carbon disulphide) (Bermudez Asphaltic cement) not less than		95.0%
Proportion of bitumen soluble in carbon Tetrachloride, not less than	99.0%	99.0%
Ductility at 77° F., not less than	100 cms.	60 cms.
Flash point, ° F., not less than	347	347
Loss at 325° F., 5 hrs., not more than	1.0%	3.0%
Penetration of residue at 77° F., 100 g, 5 sec., as compared to penetration before heating, not less than	60.0%	50.0%
Temperature range ° F.	225–300	225–300
Oliensis Spot Test	Negative	

Sampling and testing of asphalt cement shall be in accordance with the following standard methods of the American Association of State Highway Officials.

(a) Sampling	T 40–42
(b) Penetration	T 49–42
(c) Total bitumen	T 44–42
(d) Bitumen soluble in carbon tetrachloride	T 45–42
(e) Ductility	T 51–42
(f) Flash Point	T 48–42
(g) Loss at 325° F.	T 47–42
(h) Oliensis Spot Test	T 102–42

Note: The Oliensis Spot Test may be used to identify products manufactured by the cracking process, which show a positive spot when present in sufficient proportions. The Test should be modified to differentiate between cracked asphalts and those asphalts from some crude sources that have never been cracked but show a positive spot.

GRADATION

3.1 *Composition of Mixture.* The mineral aggregate for the surface course shall be of such size that the percentage composition by weight, as determined by laboratory screens, will conform to the following gradation:

TABLE 2

Sieve Size	Percent Passing Sieves (Square Openings)
½″	100
⅜″	90–100
No. 4	75–100
No. 10	58–95
No. 40	24–73
No. 80	8–50
No. 200	3–12
Bitumen %	5–9

The composition limits tabulated shall govern but a closer control appropriate to the job materials will be required for the specific project in accordance with a job mix formula. The final gradations decided on within the limits designated in the table shall produce a fairly smooth curve when plotted on semi-logarithmic gradation chart.

CONSTRUCTION METHODS

4.1 *Weather and Temperature Limitations.* Surface course shall be constructed only when the surface is dry, when the atmospheric temperature is above 50° F., and when the weather is not foggy or rainy. The temperature requirement may be waived, but only when so directed by the engineer.

4.2 *Equipment and Organization.* (a) General. All methods employed in performing the work and all equipment, tools and other plant and machinery used for handling materials and executing any part of the work shall be subject to the approval of the engineer before the work is started and whenever found unsatisfactory shall be changed and improved as required. All equipment, tools, machinery and plant used must be maintained in a satisfactory working condition.

(b) Mixing Plant. The paving plant used by the contractor in the preparation of the bituminous concrete shall comply with the following requirements:

The drier shall be suitably designed to heat and dry the aggregate to specification requirements and to continuously agitate the aggregate during heating. The drier shall be capable of preparing aggregate to the full rated capacity of the paving plant to meet the specification requirement. A dial thermometer or other thermometric instrument shall be so placed in the bin over the mixer as to automatically register the temperature of the heated aggregate before it enters the mixer. The dial or other indicator shall be plainly visible from the mixing platform.

The combined aggregate shall be bypassed around any screen on the plant having openings smaller than ⅝″. The plant shall have storage bins, protected from the weather, of sufficient capacity to furnish the necessary amounts of all aggregates when operating at the maximum rated capacity of the plant.

The plant may have either batch weighing or volumetric proportioning of mineral aggregates and asphalt cement. This equipment shall be constructed with devices that will permit easy readjustment of any working part such that it will function properly and accurately. The aggregate weighing or measuring device shall be so constructed and operated that the correct amount of each size aggregate is introduced into the mixer with an accuracy that will meet the job tolerances specified. The plant shall have a capacity of at least 40 tons per hour, and the plant mixer shall have a capacity of at least 1200 pounds.

The asphalt weighing or measuring device shall be so constructed and operated that the correct amount of asphalt is introduced into the mixer with an accuracy that will meet the job tolerance specified. If weight control is used the dial scales or other weighing device shall be of an approved type.

The mixer may be either a batch drum type mixer, a twin pugmill or a continuous type twin pugmill mixer of sufficient size to maintain thorough, uniform mixing at the rated plant capacity. The mixer shall be steam jacketed.

The plant shall be equipped with positive means to govern the time of mixing and to maintain it constant unless changed by order of the engineer. The time of mixing shall be considered as the interval between the time the bituminous material is spread on the aggregate and the time the same aggregate leaves the mixing unit.

Equipment for heating bituminous material shall consist of a retort or steam coils so designed that steam will not be introduced into the material. A recording thermometer shall be provided, which will record the temperature of the bituminous material at the draw off valve or at the entrance to the mixer, whichever is designated by the engineer.

Asphalt storage and supply lines shall be insulated or steam jacketed in such a manner that there will be no appreciable drop in temperature of the asphalt between the heating unit and the mixing unit.

(c) Placing Equipment. Equipment for spreading, shaping, and finishing shall consist of an approved self-contained power machine operating in such a manner that no supplemental spreading, shaping, or finishing will be required to provide a surface which will comply with the requirements for smoothness contained herein.

(d) Rolling Equipment. Rollers shall be suitably designed for the construction of bituminous surfaces. The rolling shall be done with self-propelled tandem and three wheel type rollers weighing not less than eight (8) tons. The wheels on the rollers shall be equipped with adjustable scrapers which shall be used when necessary to clean the wheel surface. Rollers shall also be equipped with water tanks and sprinkling apparatus which shall be used to keep the wheels wet and prevent the surface material from sticking.

4.3 *Preparation of Aggregate.* The sand and rock asphalt shall be dried and heated at the paving plant before entering the mixer. The aggregate shall contain not more than one percent moisture and shall show no tendency to sweat after being placed in the storage bins. The materials shall be heated to the temperature as designated by the Job Formula within the job tolerances specified. The sand and the rock asphalt shall be proportioned by mechanical feeders, or by other means satisfactory to the engineer.

Additional filler, if necessary to meet the grading requirements, shall be proportioned and added to the mineral aggregate.

4.4 *Preparation of Bituminous Mixture.* Before being delivered to the runway, the aggregate shall be mixed with the bituminous material at a central mixing plant. The mixture shall be prepared at a temperature as directed by the engineer between 225° and 300° F.

The aggregate prepared as prescribed above, shall be accurately measured and conveyed into the mixer in the proportionate amounts of each material required to meet the specified requirements.

The bituminous material shall be melted in kettles or tanks designed to secure uniform heating of the entire contents. The asphalt cement shall not be heated over 325° F.

Kettles for storage of asphalt cement shall have a total capacity sufficient for one day's run and shall be capable of heating the asphalt cement with an effective and positive control of the heat at all times to a temperature of between 225° and 325° F. Heating of the asphalt cement by steam coils is preferred. Under no circumstances will a direct flame from oil or other fuel be permitted to come in direct contact with the heating kettles. The asphalt circulating system shall be constructed of adequate size to give the proper and continuous circulation of asphalt cement throughout the operating periods. All asphalt lines and fittings shall be steam jacketed.

The quantity of bituminous material for each batch or calibrated amount for continuous mixing shall be determined by the engineer, and shall be measured by weight and introduced into the mixer at the specified temperature, holding to the lowest range possible for adequate mixing and spreading. The exact temperature to be used on the work within the specified range shall be fixed by the engineer. In no case shall aggregate be introduced into the mixture at a temperature more than 25° F. above the temperature of the bituminous material. The mixing shall continue for at least thirty seconds and for such longer period as may be necessary to coat all of the particles.

4.5 *Transportation and Delivery of the Mixture.* The mixture shall be transported from the mixing plant to the point of use in pneumatic-tired vehicles having tight bodies previously cleaned of all foreign materials. When directed by the engineer, each load shall be covered with canvas or other suitable material of sufficient size and thickness to protect it from the weather conditions.

The mixture shall be placed at a temperature between 200° and 300° F. When the mixture is being placed during warm weather and the engineer has determined that satisfactory results can be obtained at lower temperatures, he may direct that the mixture be mixed and delivered at the lower temperatures.

No loads shall be sent out so late in the day as to interfere with spreading and compacting the mixture during daylight, unless artificial light satisfactory to the engineer is provided. The mixture shall be delivered at a temperature within the tolerance allowed in the approved Job Formula.

4.6 *Spreading and Laying.* (a) Preparation for placing. Immediately before placing the bituminous mixture, the existing surface shall be cleaned of loose or deleterious material by sweeping with a power sweeper supplemented by hand brooms if necessary, or as directed by the engineer.

The mixture shall be laid only upon an approved underlying course which is dry and only when weather conditions are suitable. No mixture shall be placed when the air temperature in the shade and away from artificial heat is 50° F. or under unless so directed by the engineer. The engineer may, however, permit work of this character to continue when overtaken by sudden rains, up to the amount which may be in transit from the plant at the time—provided the mixture is within the temperature limits specified.

Grade control between the edges of the runway shall be by means of grade stakes or steel pins placed in lanes parallel to the center line of the runway, and at intervals sufficiently close that string lines may be stretched between stakes or pins.

Placing shall commence at the point or points furthest from the mixing plant, and progress continuously toward the plant, unless otherwise ordered by the engineer. Hauling over material already placed will not be permitted until the material has been compacted thoroughly in the manner specified, and allowed to cool to atmospheric temperature.

(b) Machine Spreading. Upon arrival the mixture shall be dumped into an approved mechanical spreader and immediately spread thereby to the full width required. It shall be struck off in a uniform layer of such depth that when the work is completed, it will have the required thickness and will conform to the grade and surface contour required. The speed of the mechanical spreader shall be regulated to eliminate as far as possible the pulling and tearing of the bituminous material.

Placing and compaction of the bituminous mixture shall progress in sections. The bituminous mixture shall be spread, shaped, and finished with the power-machine specified. The mixture shall be placed in strips of a minimum width of 10 feet. To insure proper drainage, the spreading shall begin along the center line of the runway or taxiway on a crowned section or on the high side of the pavement with a one-way slope. The 6-inch strip adjacent to the area on which future material is to be laid shall not be rolled until such material has been placed, but shall not be left unrolled more than two (2) hours after being placed. After the first strip or width has been compacted, the second width shall be placed, finished and compacted as provided for the first width, except that rolling shall be extended to include the six inches of the first width not previously compacted. Whenever the adjacent or second width cannot be placed within two (2) hours, the 6-inch strip shall not be left unrolled. After the second strip has been placed and rolled, a 10-foot straight edge shall be used across the longitudinal joint to determine if the surface is to grade and contour.

In limited areas where, on account of irregularities or unavoidable obstacles, the use of mechanical spreading and finishing equipment is impractical, the mixture may be spread by hand.

When hand spreading is permitted, the mixture shall be dumped upon arrival on approved dump sheets outside of the area on which it is to be spread and be distributed into place immediately by means of hot shovels. It shall be spread with hot rakes to a uniform layer to the full width and of such depth that when the work is completed, it will have the required thickness and will conform to the grade and surface contour.

Contact surfaces shall be painted with a thin, uniform coat of hot asphalt cement or cut-back asphalt just before the mixture is placed.

4.7 *Compaction of Mixture.* After spreading, and as directed by the engineer, the mixture shall be thoroughly and uniformly compressed by a power driven three-wheel roller and tandem roller or rollers, each weighing 8 tons or more. Rolling of the mixture shall begin as soon after spreading as it will bear the roller without undue displacement or hair checking. On the first strip spread, rolling shall start in the center and continue toward either edge. On subsequent strips laid, rolling shall start on the edge adjacent to previously laid material and continue toward the other edge.

Initial rolling shall be done longitudinally with three-wheel rollers overlapping on successive trips of the roller. Alternate trips of the roller shall be of slightly different lengths. The mixture shall be subjected to diagonal rolling crossing the lines of the first.

The speed of the roller shall at all times be slow enough to avoid displacement of the hot mixture. Any displacement occurring as a result of reversing the direction of the roller, or from any other cause, shall be corrected at once by the use of rakes, and of fresh mixture where required.

Sufficient rollers of the designated types shall be furnished to adequately handle the output of the plant. Rolling shall proceed at an average rate not to exceed 350 square yards per hour per roller. Rolling shall continue until all roller marks are eliminated, until the surface is of uniform texture and true to grade, and cross section, and until the density of at least ninety (90) percent of the theoretical density is obtained. Field density tests shall be made at least twice daily. Final rolling shall be done with tandem rollers.

The theoretical density shall be computed as follows:

$$\text{Density} = \frac{100}{\dfrac{\%\text{ mineral aggregate by weight}}{\text{Sp. gr. mineral aggregate}} + \dfrac{\%\text{ bitumen by weight}}{\text{Sp. gr. of bitumen}}}$$

To prevent adhesion of the mixture to the roller, the wheels shall be kept properly moistened, but an excess of either water or oil will not be permitted. The rollers shall be kept in good condition and shall be operated by competent and experienced rollermen. The rollers shall be operated continuously as far as practicable and in such a manner that all parts of the pavement shall receive substantially equal compression.

At all places not accessible to the roller, the mixture shall be thoroughly compacted with hot hand tampers. Hand tampers shall weigh not less than 25 pounds and shall have a tamping face area of not more than 50 square inches. The surface of the mixture after compression shall be smooth and true to the established crown and grade.

Any mixture which becomes loose and broken, mixed with dirt, or in any way defective prior to final rolling shall be removed and replaced with fresh mixture, which shall be immediately compacted to conform with the surrounding area, all to be done at the expense of the contractor. Skin patching on an area that has been rolled shall not be allowed.

4.8 *Joints.* (a) General. The mixture at the joints shall comply with the surface requirements and present the same uniformity of texture, density, smoothness, etc., as other sections of the course. In the formation of all joints, provision shall be made for proper bond with the new surface for the full specified depth of the course. Joints shall be formed by cutting back on the previous day's run so as to expose the full depth of the course, and the exposed edge shall be given a light paint coat of asphalt, if necessary. The fresh mixture shall be raked against the joint, thoroughly tamped with tampers and rolled.

(b) Transverse. The placing of the course shall be as nearly continuous as possible. The roller shall pass over the unprotected end of the freshly laid mixture only when the laying of the course is to be discontinued.

(c) Longitudinal. The placing of the course shall be in the manner as specified and so that the joint is exposed for the shortest period possible. The joint shall be placed so that it will not coincide with that in the base and will break joints by at least one foot.

4.9 *Shaping Edges.* While the surface is being compacted and finished, the contractor shall trim the edges neatly to line.

4.10 *Surface Tests.* The finished surface shall not vary more than ¼ inch for the surface course when measured with a sixteen (16) foot straight edge applied parallel with or at right angles to the center line. Tests for conformity with the specified crown and grade shall be made by the contractor immediately after initial compression and any variation shall be corrected by removing or adding materials and continuing the rolling. After the completion of final rolling, the smoothness of the course shall again be checked, and the humps or depressions exceeding the specified tolerances or that retain water on the surface shall be corrected by removing the defective work and replacing with new material or by adding additional material as directed by the engineer and at the expense of the contractor.

4.11 *Sampling Pavement.* For the determination of composition, compaction and density of the surfacing the contractor shall remove suitable size samples of the completed pavement. Samples for each day or fraction thereof when mixtures are placed shall be taken by the engineer. The contractor shall replace the pavement where samples are removed, and these replacements shall be installed by the contractor free of charge. After the samples have been removed, they will be tested by the engineer for density and composition. If the deficiency in composition, compaction and density exceeds the limits of toleration from that specified, satisfactory corrections shall be made.

4.12 *Bituminous and Aggregate Material Contractor's Responsibility.* Samples of the bituminous and aggregate materials that the contractor proposes to use, together with a statement as to their source and character must be submitted and approval obtained before use of such material begins. The contractor shall require the manufacturer or producer of the bituminous and aggregate materials to furnish material subject to this and all other pertinent requirements of the contract. Only those materials that have been demonstrated by service tests as satisfactory for the intended use will be acceptable.

For checking the adequacy of the equipment in use, inspecting the conditions and operation of the plant, for the verification of weights or proportions and character of materials and/or the determination and checking of temperatures being maintained in the preparation of the mixtures, the engineer or his authorized representative shall have access at any time to all parts of the paving plant.

The contractor shall furnish vendor's certified test report for each car load or equivalent of bitumen shipped to the project. The report shall be delivered to the engineer before permission is granted for use of the material.

4.13 *Freight and Weigh-Bills.* Before the final estimate is allowed, the contractor shall file with the engineer receipted bills where railroad shipments are made and certified weigh-bills when materials are received in any other manner, of the bituminous and paving materials actually used in the construction covered by the contract. The contractor shall not remove bituminous material from the tank car or storage tank until the initial outage and temperature measurements have been taken, nor shall he release the car or tank until the final outage has been taken by the engineer.

Copies of all freight bills and weigh-bills shall be furnished to the engineer during the progress of the work.

METHOD OF MEASUREMENT

5.1 The tonnage of surface course to be paid for shall be the number of tons of bituminous mixture of the grading called for in the bid schedule and used in the accepted work. The bituminous treated material shall be weighed after mixing and no deduction shall be made for the weight of bituminous material in the mixture.

5.2 The unit of measurement for the bituminous material shall be the gallon or the ton, whichever is called for in the bid schedule. The gallonage or tonnage to be paid for shall be the number of gallons or tons of bituminous material used as ordered in the accepted work. Gallonage shall be determined by measuring the material at a temperature of 60° F., or by converting the gallonage measured at other temperatures to gallonage at 60° F. in accordance with A.S.T.M. Designation D 206–36 for asphalt materials.

BASIS OF PAYMENT

6.1 The quantities of surfacing mixture and bituminous material determined as provided in 5.1 and 5.2 above, shall be paid for at the contract unit price per ton in the bid schedule for surface course and per gallon or per ton for bituminous material, which prices and payment shall constitute full compensation for preparing base; for furnishing, handling, mixing, manipulating, and placing all materials; for all shaping, compacting, rolling, and finishing; for improving unsatisfactory areas; for reconditioning shoulders; for furnishing samples; for furnishing and sealing of scales; for furnishing the weigh house; and for all labor, equipment, tools and incidentals necessary to complete the item.

DEPARTMENT OF COMMERCE
Civil Aeronautics Administration
Airport Division
Washington, D.C.
January 1, 1944

BLENDED NATURAL ROCK ASPHALT AND SAND ASPHALT SURFACE COURSE (CENTRAL PLANT HOT MIX) FOR AIRPORT PARKING APRONS AND TURNAROUND AREAS

C.A.A. Specification No. P-408 A

This specification provides a highly stable mixture for surfacing parking areas and ends of runways and taxiways to withstand parking and locked wheel turns.

This specification is the same in every detail as C.A.A. Specification P-408 dated October 1, 1943 with the exception of the proportions of natural limerock asphalt and sand in the composition of the surface mixture. The blended surface course for the special construction of airport parking aprons and turnaround areas shall be mixed in the proportions of at least sixty (60) percent of natural limerock asphalt and forty (40) percent local approved sand. Instructions on the use of this specification were issued in Field Memorandum F-541 (Revised), dated October 6, 1943, to which was attached Drawing No. 518.

APPENDIX 28

DEPARTMENT OF COMMERCE
Civil Aeronautics Administration
Airport Division
Washington, D.C.
July 1, 1943

BITUMINOUS SEAL COAT FOR AIRPORT RUNWAYS, TAXIWAYS AND APRONS

C.A.A. Specification No. P-604

INTRODUCTION

A seal coat is applied to accomplish several objectives as follows:

1. Create a finish which is skid proof due to many points of contact.
2. Construct a surface that will do a minimum amount of damage to tire rubber and yet give necessary tire resistance.
3. Prevent propeller pick-up with resultant damage to fuselage and to propellers of aircraft.
4. Heal any hair cracks through softening up and kneading by rolling of upper strata of wearing surface while in a temporarily softened condition.
5. Provide a light color on the surface.

It will be noted that definite specifications are set up controlling the types of bituminous material and gradation of aggregate. In preparing these specifications, the various material types and construction methods have been considered and those specified herein are believed to be the most desirable. The steps as outlined in these specifications should be followed to obtain maximum results. It is not deemed advisable to leave out any controlling factor.

In rolling dense graded mixes, hair cracks may develop which collect water and result in serious pavement damage. In highway work these cracks are soon ironed out under traffic. By using a cut-back or a soft asphalt material and rolling with a rubber-tired roller all cracks will be healed and at the same time a large quantity of aggregate will be worked into the bituminous material. No objection will be made with reference to supplementing the multi-wheeled rubber-tired roller with a smooth roller. However, in order to obtain the kneading of the surface and the healing of the hair cracks, the majority of the rolling should be done with the rubber-tired roller.

If an MC material with a kerosene flux or a very light SC material were used, the softening up of the top layer of the runway wearing surface proper would be permanent with disastrous results. The softening caused by a small percentage of naphtha in the RC-2 is only temporary.

The cover aggregate should be a material light in color to increase the visibility of the runway. The advantages of a light colored material are considered of sufficient importance that aggregate should be shipped, in event suitable local aggregate is not available.

DESCRIPTION

1.1 This item shall consist of a seal coat of bituminous material with cover aggregate, constructed on the properly cured wearing surface in accordance with these specifications and to the width shown on the typical cross section on the plans.

1.2 *Quantities of Materials per Square Yard.* The approximate amounts of materials per square yard for the seal coat shall be as provided in Table 1. The exact amounts to be used shall be set by the engineer.

TABLE 1

Quantities of Materials for Seal Coat

Bituminous material (gal. per sq. yd.)	.15–.25
Cover aggregate (lb. per sq. yd.)	7–15

MATERIALS

2.1 *Cover Aggregate.* Cover aggregate shall meet the grading given in Table 2. The test for grading shall be made using A.A.S.H.O. Method T-27.

TABLE 2

Requirements for Grading of Aggregate for Seal Coats

Sieve designation	Percentage by weight passing square mesh sieves
	Cover Aggregate
¼″	100
No. 4	70–100
No. 10	0–70
No. 40	0–5

Cover aggregate for seal shall be a light colored material consisting of crushed stone free from dirt or organic matter. Acceptable material shall be equal in color and reflectivity to that from approved sources as listed by the engineer.

Crushed cover aggregate shall be free from clay balls and adherent films of clay or rock dust and shall be washed thoroughly if produced in a moist condition. Aggregate shall be of such nature that a thorough coating of the bituminous material to be used in the work applied to it will not slough off upon contact with water. The aggregate shall not contain more than three (3) percent moisture at the time of application. Heating of the aggregate shall be used if necessary to reduce the moisture content to three (3) percent or less.

2.2 *Bituminous Materials.* The material furnished shall be one of the following types or as provided for in the proposal:

TABLE 3—*Requirements for Rapid-curing Cut-back Asphalt*

	A.A.S.H.O. Test Method	Grade RC-2	
		Min.	Max.
Water, percent			0
Flash pt., tag., ° F.	T-79	80	
Furol vis., at 140° F.	T-72	100	200
Partial distillates (Ratio to distillate to 680° F.)			
to 437° F.	T-78	40	
to 500° F.		65	
to 600° F.		87	
Residue from distillation to 680° F.			
Vol., percent of sample by difference		67	
Pene.	T-49	80	120
Duct. cms.	T-51	100	
Percent sol. in CCl_4	T-44	99.5	
Material shall not be cracked	T-102		
Application temp. ° F.		125	175

TABLE 4—*Requirements for Asphalt Cement*

The asphalt cement shall be homogeneous, free from water, and shall not foam when heated to a temperature of 347° F.

Test Requirements	A.A.S.H.O. Test Method	Petroleum Asphalts
Penetration at 77° F., 100 g. 5 sec.	T-49	120–150
Total Bitumen (soluble in carbon disulphide), not less than	T-44	99.5%
Proportion of bitumen soluble in carbon Tetrachloride, not less than	T-45	99.0%
Ductility at 77° F., not less than	T-51	100 cms.
Flash Point, ° F., not less than	T-48	347
Loss at 325° F., 5 hrs., not more than	T-47	1.0%
Penetration of residue at 77° F., 100 g., 5 sec., as compared to penetration before heating, not less than	T-49	60.0%
Oliensis Spot Test	T-102	Negative
Temperature range ° F.		200–325

If required in the proposal, the asphalt cement shall be of a higher penetration.

TABLE 5

Requirements for Emulsified Asphalt

The emulsified asphalt shall be homogeneous and shall show no separation of asphalt after thorough mixing, within 30 days after delivery.

Test	Requirement
Viscosity—Saybolt Furol 60 cc. at 25° C. (77° F.)	Not less than 100
Specific Gravity—25°/25° C. (77°/77° F.)	Not less than 1.00
Residue at 163° C. (325° F.) 3 hr. 50 gr. or Residue from Distillation Test (A.S.T.M.)	55% to 60%
Demulsibility—35 ml.N/50 $CaCl_2$	Not less than 60%
Settlement, 10 days	Not more than 3
Sieve Test	Not more than .05

Tests on the Emulsified Asphalt shall be made in accordance with A.S.T.M. Standards, Designation D 244, except as hereinafter described:

Residue at 163° C.—A.S.T.M. Standards, Designation D 6–30, except that determination of residue shall be the average of three 50-gram samples heated for 3 hours in a dish or beaker not less than 3 inches in diameter and of sufficient depth to prevent overflow.

Settlement.—The time allowed for settlement shall be 10 days instead of 5 days.

Asphalt

The residue obtained from the Distillation Test (A.S.T.M.) shall conform to the following requirements:

Test	Requirement
Penetration of residue at 25° C. (77° F.)	100 to 200
Solubility in carbon disulphide	Not less than 97
Ash	Not more than 2
Ductility at 25° C. (77° F.)	Not less than 60

Tests on the Asphalt or Residue shall be made in accordance with A.S.T.M. Standard or Tentative Standard Methods in effect at the time the test is made, except as follows:

Ductility—When the ductility test is made on the residue from distillation or evaporation, the residue shall be screened through a No. 50 sieve while still hot, and shall then be kneaded until uniform and homogeneous. It shall then be tested for ductility.

CONSTRUCTION METHODS

3.1 *Weather Limitations.* Seal coats shall be applied only when the existing surface is dry, when the atmospheric temperature is above 60° F., and when the weather is not foggy or rainy. Seal coating shall not be attempted except under favorable weather conditions.

3.2 *Equipment.* The equipment used by the contractor shall include a power broom or a power blower, broom dragging equipment, a standard multiwheeled rubber-tired roller or other rubber-tired equipment that will produce equal results, aggregate spreading equipment that can be so adjusted as to spread accurately the given amounts per square yard if available, a self-powered pressure bituminous material distributor, and equipment for heating bituminous material.

The multiwheeled rubber-tired roller shall consist of two axles on which are mounted not less than 9 pneumatic-tired wheels in such a manner that the rear group of tires will not follow in the tracks of the forward group, and mounted in a rigid frame provided with a loading platform or body suitable for ballast loading. The front axle shall rotate around a king pin so located that the roller may be turned within a minimum circle. The roller under working conditions shall have an effective rolling width of at least sixty (60) inches and shall give a compression of at least 325 lbs. per inch of width of tread when fully loaded. The tires shall be uniformly inflated. The roller and the operating tractor shall meet the approval of the engineer. The weight of the roller shall be increased as the rolling progresses to the maximum degree obtainable without detrimental results to the wearing surface.

The distributor shall have pneumatic tires of such width and number that the load produced on the runway surface shall not exceed 650 pounds per inch of tire width, and shall be so designed, equipped, maintained, and operated that bituminous material at even heat may be applied uniformly on variable widths of surface at readily determined and controlled rates of from 0.05 to 2.0 gallons per square yard, with a pressure range of from 25 to 75 pounds per square inch, and with an allowable variation from any specified rate not to exceed 5 percent. Distributor equipment shall include a tachometer, pressure gages, volume measuring devices, and a thermometer for reading temperatures of tank contents.

Equipment for heating bituminous material shall consist of a retort or steam coils so designed that steam will not be introduced into the material.

3.3 *Cleaning Existing Surface.* Prior to placing the seal coat, loose dirt and other objectionable material shall be removed from the existing surface. If so directed by the engineer, the surface shall be cleaned with a power broom or power blower.

3.4 *Application of Bituminous Material.* Bituminous material shall be so applied that uniform distribution is obtained at all points. Unless the distributor is so equipped as to obtain this result at the junctions of applications, building paper shall be spread on the surface for a sufficient distance back from the end of each application so that flow through sprays may be started and stopped on the paper and so that all sprays will operate properly over the entire length being treated. Building paper so used shall be immediately removed and burned. Application temperatures shall be as provided in the specifications for the bituminous material. During all applications the surfaces of adjacent structures shall be protected in such manner as to prevent their being spattered or marred. Bituminous material shall not be discharged into borrow pits or gutters.

The bituminous material shall not be applied until the cover aggregate is available and ready for spreading. When asphalt cement is used, the aggregate shall be at a temperature between 150° and 200° F. and when other bituminous materials are used, the temperature of the aggregate shall not be in excess of 150° F.

3.5 *Spreading Cover Aggregate.* The covering material in the quantity specified shall be spread uniformly over the bituminous material as soon after application as is possible. The aggregate shall be spread in the same width of application as for the bituminous material and applied uniformly with the aggregate spreading equipment or by hand methods. Trucks spreading aggregate shall be operated backward so that bituminous material will be covered before truck wheels pass over it. The aggregate shall not be applied in such thickness to cause blanketing. Back spotting or sprinkling of additional aggregate over areas that show up as having insufficient cover shall be done by hand spreading which shall be continued during the operations whenever necessary.

3.6 *Brooming and Rolling.* Rolling shall be started as soon as sufficient aggregate is spread to prevent pick-up and continued until no more aggregate can be worked into the surface. The broom dragging should start as soon as possible after the rolling has started and the surface has set sufficiently to prevent excessive marking of the seal surface. Further broom dragging should be done as often as necessary to keep cover aggregate uniformly distributed over the runway surface. Broom dragging, rolling, and back spotting shall be continued until the surface is cured to the satisfaction of the engineer. All surplus aggregate shall be swept off the surface and removed prior to final acceptance.

3.7 *Bituminous Material Contractor's Responsibility.* Samples of the bituminous materials that the contractor proposes to use, together with a statement as to their source and character must be submitted and approval obtained before use of such materials begins.

The contractor shall furnish vendor's certified test report for each car load or equivalent of bitumen shipped to the project. The report shall be delivered to the engineer before permission is granted for use of the material.

3.8 *Freight and Weigh-Bills.* Before the final estimate is allowed, the contractor shall file with the engineer receipted bills where railroad shipments are made and certified weigh-bills when materials are received in any other manner, of the bituminous and covering materials actually used in the construction covered by the contract. The contractor shall not remove bituminous material from the tank car or storage tank until the initial outage and temperature measurements have been taken by the engineer, nor shall he release the car or tank until the final outage has been taken by the engineer.

Copies of all freight bills and weigh-bills shall be furnished to the engineer during the progress of the work.

METHOD OF MEASUREMENT

4.1 The unit of measurement for bituminous material shall be the gallon. The gallonage to be paid for shall be the number of gallons of bituminous material used as ordered for the accepted work. Gallonage shall be determined by measuring the material at a temperature of 60° F., or by converting the gallonage measured at other temperature to gallonage at 60° F. in accordance with A.S.T.M. Designation D 206–36 for asphalt, or in accordance with a coefficient of expansion of 0.00025 per degree F. for emulsified asphalt.

4.2 The tonnage to be paid for shall be the number of tons of aggregate used as ordered for the accepted work or placed in authorized stockpiles.

BASIS OF PAYMENT

5.1 The quantities of aggregate and bituminous material, determined as provided in 4.1 and 4.2 above, shall be paid for at the respective contract unit prices per ton in the bid schedule for cover aggregate for seal coat, and per gallon for bituminous material for seal coat, which prices and payments shall constitute full compensation for furnishing, delivering, and placing all materials, for brooming, compacting, and rolling, for covering excess bituminous material, for removal of excess aggregate, for reconditioning of shoulders and gutters, for clearing, cleaning, and leveling stockpile sites, for furnishing and sealing of scales, for furnishing the weigh house, and for all labor, equipment, tools, and incidentals necessary to complete the item.

APPENDIX 29

DEPARTMENT OF COMMERCE
Civil Aeronautics Administration
Airport Division
Washington, D.C.
July 1, 1943

PORTLAND CEMENT CONCRETE PAVEMENT (PLAIN AND REINFORCED) FOR AIRPORT RUNWAYS, TAXIWAYS AND APRONS

C.A.A. Specification No. P-501

INTRODUCTION

The pavement as set forth in the specification is either plain or reinforced Portland Cement Concrete pavement, based on a specified cement content. The reinforced type should be considered where severe climatic conditions produce temperature stresses and where the mat reinforcement will aid in crack control.

Because of the slab or beam feature, this type of pavement should not be used as an attempt to compensate for unstable subgrade conditions. The correction of the unstable subgrade conditions by replacement or subgrade treatment will generally prove more satisfactory and economical. This type should be placed on a suitable subgrade that has adequate uniform foundation support. The basis for the selection of this type of pavement should be the same as for any other type of pavement and should effect the most economical utilization of materials available.

There are two gradations for coarse aggregate included in this specification. These are standard gradations, but if upon investigation they cannot be obtained commercially, other gradations may be substituted.

In order to provide a completed description this specification should be supplemented by standard construction drawings showing details of design as to location and construction of expansion and contraction joints; the size, spacing, etc. of dowel bars or dowel bar assemblies, tie bars and reinforcement. The details of construction should conform to standards as set forth in drawing No. 434.

The drawing permits a variation in the spacing of the expansion and contraction joints. The spacing should be regulated by the type of aggregate and temperature at time of placing the pavement. Expansive aggregate will require more space for expansion, therefore the expansion joints should be placed closer together. The same is true for concrete laid at low temperatures. Joints should not exceed one inch in width.

DESCRIPTION

1.1 This item shall consist of a wearing surface of either plain or reinforced Portland Cement Concrete pavement as designated on the plans and constructed on the prepared subgrade in accordance with these specifications and in conformity with dimensions and typical cross sections shown on the plans and with lines and grades established by the engineer. The concrete shall be composed of coarse aggregate, fine aggregate, Portland cement and water.

MATERIALS

2.1 *Aggregates, General.* In no case will the use of pit run or naturally mixed coarse aggregates be permitted. Naturally mixed aggregate must in every case be screened and washed and all fine and coarse aggregates must be stored separately and shall be kept clean. The mixing of different kinds of aggregates from different sources in one storage pile or alternating batches of different aggregates will not be permitted. In no case shall aggregates containing lumps of frozen or partially cemented material be used.

2.2 *Coarse Aggregate.* The coarse aggregate for concrete shall consist of crushed stone, gravel, slag or other approved materials, conforming to the following requirements:

The coarse aggregate shall have a percentage of wear not more than 50 at 500 revolutions as determined by A.A.S.H.O. Method T 96–42 (Los Angeles Rattler Test).

Crushed stone shall consist of clean, hard, tough, durable, uncoated fragments reasonably free from thin or flat pieces. The crushed stone shall not show evidence of disintegration nor show a total loss greater than 12 percent when subjected to five cycles of the sodium sulphate accelerated soundness test using A.A.S.H.O. Method T 104–42.

Gravel shall consist of clean, hard, tough, durable, uncoated pebbles reasonably free from thin or flat particles. The gravel shall not show evidence of disintegration nor show a total loss greater than 12 percent when subjected to five cycles of the sodium sulphate accelerated soundness test using A.A.S.H.O. Method T 104–42.

Slag shall be air-cooled, blast furnace slag, and shall consist of angular fragments reasonably uniform in density and quality and reasonably free from thin, elongated or soft pieces, dirt or other objectionable matter. The slag shall have a weight per cubic foot of not less than 70 pounds, using A.A.S.H.O. Method T 19–42.

The coarse aggregate shall not have more than 1 percent of material removable by the decantation test, using A.A.S.H.O. Method T 11–42, nor more than 1 percent of shale using A.A.S.H.O. Method T 10–35, nor more than 5 percent of soft fragments, nor more than one-fourth of 1 percent of clay lumps, using the method given under section 2.3 for fine aggregate. The total of shale, coal, clay lumps and soft fragments shall not be more than 5 percent.

The coarse aggregate shall meet the gradation of either Table I or II.

TABLE I

Sieve Designation	Percentage by weight passing square mesh sieves In Inches (A.A.S.H.O. T 27)							
	2½	2	1½	1	¾	½	⅜	No. 4
¾ to 1½ inch		100	90–100	20–55	0–15			
No. 4 to ¾″				100	90–100		20–55	0–10

TABLE II

Sieve Designation	Percentage by weight passing square mesh sieves In Inches (A.A.S.H.O. T 27)				
	2	1½	¾	⅜	No. 4
No. 4 to 1½″	100	95–100	35–70	10–30	0–5

In Table I the ratio of either separated size of coarse aggregate to total coarse aggregate may be varied within the range of 40 to 60 percent by weight to secure the most desirable and uniform gradation of the combined mix.

2.3 *Fine Aggregate.* The fine aggregate for concrete shall consist either of sand, or of approved inert materials having similar characteristics or of a combination thereof. The material used shall consist of hard, strong, durable particles.

When subjected to five cycles of the sodium sulphate soundness test, using A.A.S.H.O. Method T 104–42 the fine aggregate shall have a total loss not greater than 10 percent by weight. Instead of the soundness test mentioned above, the contractor may provide evidence, satisfactory to the engineer, that the fine aggregate has been exposed to natural weathering, either directly or in concrete, for a period of at least 5 years without appreciable disintegration.

Fine aggregate shall contain not more than 3 percent of material removable by a decantation test using A.A.S.H.O. Method T 11–42, nor more than 1 percent of clay lumps, or 1 percent of shale as determined by A.A.S.H.O. Method T 10–35. The total of coal, clay lumps, shale, soft fragments and other local deleterious substances shall not be more than 5 percent.

The percentage of clay lumps shall be determined by examining the various fractions that remain after the material has been tested for grading. Any particles that can be broken up with the fingers shall be classified as clay lumps and the total percentage by weight of all clay lumps shall be determined on the basis of the total original weight of the sample.

All fine aggregate shall be free from injurious amounts of organic impurities. Aggregates subjected to the colorimetric test for organic impurities, A.A.S.H.O. Method T 21–42, and producing a color darker than the standard shall be rejected unless they pass the mortar strength test herein required.

The fine aggregate shall be well graded from fine to coarse and shall meet the following grading requirements, using A.A.S.H.O. Method T 27–42.

TABLE III

Sieve Designation	Percentage by Weight Passing Square Mesh Sieves (A.A.S.H.O. T 27)
No. 4	95–100
No. 16	45–80
No. 30	25–55
No. 50	10–30
No. 100	2–10

Blending will be permitted if necessary in order to meet the gradation requirements for fine aggregate.

Mortar specimens made with the fine aggregate shall have a compressive strength using A.A.S.H.O. Method T 71–42, at 7 and 28 days of at least 90 percent of the strength of similar specimens made with Ottawa sand having a fineness modulus of 2.40 ± 0.10.

For the purpose of controlling the grading of fine aggregate from any one source, the contractor shall submit, prior to actual deliveries, a preliminary sample which shall be representative of the material which he proposes to furnish. Any shipment of fine aggregate made during the progress of the work that varies in fineness modulus more than 0.20 from the fineness modulus of the preliminary sample shall be rejected or, at the discretion of the engineer, may be accepted subject to such changes in the proportions used as he may direct.

The fineness modulus of fine aggregate shall be determined by adding the total percentages by weight retained on U.S. standard sieves Nos. 4, 8, 16, 30, 50, 100, and dividing by 100.

2.4 *Cement.* The cement used in the work shall be a standard brand of Portland cement, a standard brand of high early strength Portland cement or a standard brand of moderate sulphate-resisting cement. Portland cement shall conform to A.A.S.H.O. specification M 85–42. Only one brand of each shall be used on any one job, except by specific written permission from the engineer. The contractor shall provide suitable means for storing cement and protecting it from dampness. Different grades and brands of cement shall be stored separately, and shall not be mixed.

Where so indicated on the plans, high-early-strength Portland cement shall be used instead of Portland cement. When high-early-strength cement is used, concreting operations shall not be carried on if the atmospheric temperature is below or may be expected to drop below 50° F., except upon written authorization from the engineer. If the contractor, in order to facilitate his own operations, chooses to use high-early-strength cement in portions of the work other than those where its use is required, written permission must be obtained from the engineer.

Bags of cement in which for any reason the cement has become partially set or which contain lumps of caked cement, shall be rejected. Use of cement salvaged from discarded or used bags will not be permitted.

The cement shall be emptied from the shipping package directly into the skip of the mixer, or transported to the mixer in closed, separate compartments, equipped with waterproof covers, for each batch, or under certain conditions, may be transported by placing the unopened shipping packages upon the batched aggregates in trucks. The last mentioned method will be permitted only upon condition that:—

(a) Cement does not acquire moisture or dampness from aggregates during transportation.

(b) Tarpaulins are available for protection in case of wet weather, and

(c) Shipping packages are emptied onto the aggregates of only those two trucks which have arrived within 500 feet of charging position at the mixer. In no case shall this period exceed 15 minutes prior to the charging of the mixer.

No cement shall be dumped on or in with the aggregates in batch boxes or trucks, except as above specified. All trucks, truck bodies, bulkheads, cement compartments and other equipment or accessories used in the proportioning and transportation to the mixer of concrete materials, shall be so designed and operated as to insure the charging of the mixer, batch by batch, with the proper amounts of each material, without over-spillage, inter-mixing of batches or wastage. Any units which, in the opinion of the engineer, do not operate satisfactorily shall be removed from the project until properly rebuilt and corrected.

Natural cement may be used with Portland cement at an approximate ratio of one bag of natural cement to five bags of Portland cement. Natural cement shall conform with the requirements of A.S.T.M. designation C 10–37 except that the use of a grinding aid will be mandatory. The natural cement shall be made water repellent by the use of grinding aid composed of 0.1 to 0.2% paraffine in a carrier of oil or petroleum distillate not to exceed 0.8% by weight. In lieu thereof, the manufacturer may use from 0.1 to 0.2% tallow or fatty acid. Natural cement may be used up to 17% by weight.

Where bulk cement is allowed, the batching equipment shall include a screen of such size and construction in the loading chute as will insure against the presence of burlap, paper and other foreign materials in the concrete, and a canvas "boot" or a similar device which will prevent wastage or loss from air currents. This screen shall be cleaned at least once daily; more frequently if conditions justify. Measurement of bulk cement shall be by weight.

2.5 *Premoulded Joint Material.* Premoulded joint material for expansion joints shall meet the requirements of one of the following A.A.S.H.O. specifications: M 58–42, M 59–42 or M 90–42.

Premoulded joint filler or paper ribbon may be used for the construction of the dummy transverse or longitudinal contraction joint.

2.6 *Joint Filler.* The filler for joints shall meet the requirements of A.A.S.H.O. specification M 18–42 grade A or B or C.A.A. Specification No. P-605 unless otherwise specified in the proposal.

2.7 *Steel Reinforcement.* Welded wire fabric for concrete reinforcement shall conform to the requirements of A.A.S.H.O. Specifications M 55–37. Fabricated bar or rod mats for concrete reinforcement shall meet the requirements of A.A.S.H.O. Specifications M 54–37.

2.8 *Dowel and Tie Bars.* Dowel and tie bars shall conform to the following specifications:

(a) Billet steel shall conform to A.A.S.H.O. specification M 31–42.

(b) Rail steel shall conform to A.A.S.H.O. specification M 42–42.

(c) Axle steel shall conform to A.A.S.H.O. specification M 53–42. The bars shall be free from flattening or burring of ends. If necessary the ends of the bars shall be ground to remove the burrs resulting from shearing.

(d) Dowel and tie bars shall be of the size, type and number shown on the plans and shall be installed in such manner and locations as is indicated.

2.9 *Water.* Water used in concrete shall be free from sewage, oil, acid, strong alkalies or vegetable matter, and also shall be free from clay and loam.

2.10 *Material Added for Workability.* The use of any material added to the mix to improve workability, which, in the opinion of the engineer, may have an injurious effect on the strength, density, and durability of the concrete, will not be permitted. Before approval of any material, the contractor will be required to submit the results of complete chemical and sieve analyses made by an acceptable testing laboratory. Subsequent tests will be made of samples taken by the engineer from the supply of the material being used on the work to determine whether it is uniform in quality with that approved.

The material added shall be pozzuolanic, cementitious or siliceous. It shall not contain effective early-heat-producing elements nor compounds, such as those contained in Portland cement, nor shall its use result in a material increase in the free-lime content of the concrete. It shall also be in conformity with the following requirements:

Free moisture—a total of not more than 3 percent by weight.
Passing No. 30 sieve—not less than 100 percent by weight.
Passing No. 200 sieve—not less than 85 percent by weight.

CONSTRUCTION METHODS

3.1 *Equipment.* All equipment necessary for the proper preparation of the subgrade, batching and mixing of the concrete, the laying, finishing and curing of the pavement shall be on the project in first class working condition and be inspected and approved by the engineer before concreting begins.

3.2 *Conditioning of Subgrade.* Ruts or depressions caused by hauling or usage of other equipment shall be filled as they develop with suitable subgrade material (not with concrete or concrete aggregates) and thoroughly compacted by rolling. A multiple pin templet weighing not less than 1000 pounds (per 20′ machine) or other approved templet shall be provided and operated on the forms immediately in advance of the placing of concrete upon the subgrade. If the mixer is operated upon the subgrade, the templet shall be operated between the mixer and the finishing machine; in any case it shall be propelled only by hand and not attached to mixer, tractor or other power unit. Templets shall be adjustable so that they may be set and maintained at the correct contour of the subgrade. The adjustment and operation of the templet shall be such as will provide an accurate retest of the subgrade before placing the concrete thereon. All excess material shall be removed, and if the subgrade is found to be below the true elevation, the depressions shall be filled with approved subgrade material and thoroughly compacted to the proper cross section by rolling or tamping with a hand tamp.

The templet shall be maintained in accurate adjustment at all times by the contractor and should be checked daily by the engineer or inspector.

The work described under the foregoing paragraphs does not contemplate a regular subgrading operation but rather a final accurate check of the subgrade.

3.3 *Forms and Form Setting.* The side forms shall be of steel, of an approved section, shall be straight and of a depth equal to the thickness of the pavement at the edge. The base of the forms shall have a width equal to the depth up to and including an eight-inch form. When forms of a greater depth are required, the base shall be at least eight (8) inches. When suitable forms cannot be obtained, the forms may be adjusted by metal or wooden lifts securely bolted to the base. Wooden lifts shall be waterproofed by use of oil or other material.

All forms shall be set with exactness to the required grade and alignment and be supported on thoroughly compacted material for their entire length during the entire operation of placing and finishing of concrete. They shall not at any time show a variation of more than ⅛″ in a 10′ length from the true plane of top of forms. In the setting of side forms they shall be tested for grade and smoothness by the contractor, using a 10′ straightedge and variations from the above requirements shall be eliminated by the resetting of forms. Shimming with loose earth, pebbles, etc. will not be permitted. If a form does not have satisfactory bearing for its full length, it shall be removed, the bearing area of subgrade reshaped and compacted and the form replaced. The use of bent or damaged side forms shall not be permitted. All forms shall be cleaned and oiled each time they are used. The alignment and grade of all forms set shall be approved before and immediately prior to the placing of any material against them and shall not be removed until 12 hours after the concrete has been placed. During the construction when the temperature is below 50° F., the forms shall not be removed in less than 30 hours. A mechanical form tamper will be required. It shall be a self-powered type that rides on the forms and tamps the subgrade under the forms simultaneously under both sides by digging action.

The contractor shall set and maintain sufficient forms and shall otherwise so conduct his operations that the final minor corrections and compaction of subgrade, together with checking and approval of forms, will not in any way interfere with operations at the concreting site. While the amount of completed and accepted forms required in advance of the paving operation will vary with different organization and equipment, this amount shall in no case be less than 500′ (each side).

Adjacent lanes may be used in lieu of forms for supporting finishing equipment provided that proper protection is afforded the concrete of the adjacent lanes from damage and further provided that the surface of the concrete carrying the finishing equipment does not vary more than ⅛″ in a 10′ length.

3.4 *Handling, Storage and Protection of Materials.* Batching of aggregates from bins from which the water has not been thoroughly drained will not be permitted. Aggregates if wet shall be stock piled for a period of at least 24 hours prior to batching so that moisture content will be as uniform as possible. Aggregates shall be so handled that its moisture content is reasonably uniform and does not change appreciably from batch to batch or from hour to hour. The stock piles of aggregates shall be built up in layers not to exceed 3′ in height, and each layer shall be completely in place before beginning the next. Coning or building up of stock piles by depositing materials in one place will not be permitted.

Each stock pile shall be placed on concrete, sheet metal, wood plank platforms or other satisfactory foundations and so arranged that the different aggregates do not become mixed. Adjacent stock piles shall be separated by bulk heads to prevent intermixing of the stock piles.

Mixing stone and gravel, or fine aggregates from different sources in one storage pile, or alternating batches of different aggregates will not be permitted.

3.5 *Proportions.* The weights of fine and coarse aggregate and the quantity of water per bag of cement shall be determined by the engineer from the weights given in the tables with the net amount of water (including free water in the aggregates) as shown and the range in slump as stated.

CLASS A PAVING CONCRETE

(For Use Where Severe Climatic Conditions Prevail)

Type of Coarse Aggregate	Minimum Cement Content Per cu. yd. of Concrete	Maximum Net Water Content Gals. per bag	Weights in Pounds of Dry Aggregate per Bag of Cement			Slump Range Inches
			Fine Aggregate	Coarse Aggregate	Total	
	Standard Method of Placement					
Gravel	6 bags	$5\frac{1}{2}$	170	367	537	2–3
Crushed Stone	6 bags	$5\frac{3}{4}$	195	341	536	2–3
Slag	6 bags	$5\frac{3}{4}$	205	287	492	2–3
	Vibratory Method of Placement					
Gravel	5.8 bags	$5\frac{1}{2}$	169	394	563	$1–1\frac{1}{2}$
Crushed Stone	5.8 bags	$5\frac{3}{4}$	195	366	561	$1–1\frac{1}{2}$
Slag	5.8 bags	$5\frac{3}{4}$	205	309	514	$1–1\frac{1}{2}$

CLASS B PAVING CONCRETE

(For Use Where Moderate Climatic Conditions Prevail)

Type of Coarse Aggregate	Minimum Cement Content Per cu. yd. of Concrete	Maximum Net Water Content Gals. per bag	Weights in Pounds of Dry Aggregate per Bag of Cement			Slump Range Inches
			Fine Aggregate	Coarse Aggregate	Total	
	Standard Method of Placement					
Gravel	5.5 bags	6	190	403	593	2–3
Crushed Stone	5.5 bags	$6\frac{1}{4}$	220	371	591	2–3
Slag	5.5 bags	$6\frac{1}{4}$	230	316	546	2–3
	Vibratory Method of Placement					
Gravel	5.3 bags	6	187	437	624	$1–1\frac{1}{2}$
Crushed Stone	5.3 bags	$6\frac{1}{4}$	216	406	622	$1–1\frac{1}{2}$
Slag	5.3 bags	$6\frac{1}{4}$	226	344	570	$1–1\frac{1}{2}$

CLASS C PAVING CONCRETE

(For Use Where Mild Climatic Conditions Prevail)

Type of Coarse Aggregate	Minimum Cement Content Per cu. yd. of Concrete	Maximum Net Water Content Gals. per bag	Weights in Pounds of Dry Aggregate per Bag of Cement			Slump Range Inches
			Fine Aggregate	Coarse Aggregate	Total	
	Standard Method of Placement					
Gravel	5 bags	6½	220	443	663	2–3
Crushed Stone	5 bags	6¾	250	411	661	2–3
Slag	5 bags	6¾	260	347	607	2–3
	Vibratory Method of Placement					
Gravel	4.8 bags	6½	210	490	700	1–1½
Crushed Stone	4.8 bags	6¾	243	456	699	1–1½
Slag	4.8 bags	6¾	253	388	641	1–1½

The proportions on the preceding pages are based on the use of well graded aggregates. If it is found impossible with the aggregates selected to prepare concrete of the proper consistency without exceeding the maximum net water content specified, the total weight of aggregate shall be reduced by the engineer until concrete of the proper consistency is obtained without exceeding the maximum net water content specified. However, the contractor shall not be compensated for any additional cement which may be required by reason of such adjustment.

The weights specified in the above tables were calculated for aggregates of the following bulk specific gravities: natural sand and gravel—2.62, crushed stone—2.65, slag—2.30. For aggregates of specific gravities differing more than ± 0.02 from those given above, the weights given in the tables shall be corrected as indicated in paragraph (b). The quantities shown in the tables for class A, B and C concrete for cement and water shall control and the weights of aggregates shall be varied to secure the proper yield based on absolute volumes.

At any time during the construction period, the relative weights of fine and coarse aggregates as determined from the preceding tables may be varied slightly in order to insure the use of the least amount of fine aggregate which will produce workable concrete within the specified slump range. When separated sizes of coarse aggregates as shown in Table 1 are used, the ratio of either size to total coarse aggregate may be varied within the range of 40 to 60 percent by weight, to secure the most dense and uniform gradation of the combined material.

(a) For batch weights, the weights arrived at as described above shall be corrected to compensate for moisture contained in the aggregates at the time of use.

(b) If, during the progress of the work, the specific gravity of one or both of the aggregates changes, the batch weight shall be adjusted to conform to the new specific gravity by multiplying the weight given in the table by the specific gravity of the aggregates used and dividing by the corresponding specific gravity used in calculating the weight given in the table.

(c) Yield test made in accordance with specification A.S.T.M. designation C-138–39, shall be made by the engineer for the purpose of determining the cement content per cubic yard of concrete. If at any time such cement content is found to be less than that specified per cubic yard, the batch weights shall be reduced until the amount of cement per cubic yard of concrete conforms to the requirements.

The net mixing water shall be adjusted for the moisture contained in the aggregates and for the moisture which they will absorb, in order to determine the amount of water to be added at the mixer. The absorption of the fine and coarse aggregates shall be determined by A.A.S.H.O. Methods T 84 and T 85–42.

3.6 *Measurement of Aggregates.* Where sack cement is used, the quantities of aggregate for each batch shall be exactly sufficient for one or more sacks of cement; no batch requiring fractional sacks of cement being permitted. The measurement of fine and coarse aggregates shall be by separate weight for each size and the weight shall be based on the actual, dry loose weight of the aggregates used per cubic foot, as determined by the engineer. All measurement shall be by weight, upon approved weighing scales and shall be such as will insure separate and uniform proportions. The contractor shall maintain at the batching plant at all times a set of accurate platform scales of at least 500 pounds capacity, for the use of the engineer or inspector in making weight tests of aggregates, and ten 50-pound standard test weights for testing weighing equipment.

Measuring in truck beds will not be permitted. A sack of cement shall weigh not less than 94 pounds net and will be considered one cubic foot.

The volume of concrete mixed per batch shall not exceed the manufacturer's guaranteed capacity of the mixer as specified in the Concrete Mixer Standards adopted by the Mixer Manufacturers Bureau and approved by the Associated General Contractors of America.

When the aggregates are transported by industrial railway or delivered to the mixer in trucks, each batch shall be in a separate compartment of the capacity required by the engineer. Subdivided truck bodies shall be approved by the engineer before they may be used, and the cement compartment shall be provided with an approved waterproof cover. All trucks, truck bodies, bulkheads, cement compartments and other equipment or accessories used in the proportioning and transportation to the mixer of concrete materials, shall be so designed and operated as to insure the charging of the mixer, batch by batch, with the proper amounts of each material, without over-spillage, intermixing of batches or wastage. Any units which, in the opinion of the engineer, do not operate satisfactorily, shall be removed from the project until properly rebuilt and corrected.

3.7 *Consistency.* When subjected to the slump test for consistency, made in accordance with the Tentative Method of Test for Consistency of Portland Cement Concrete, A.S.T.M. Designation C 143–39, concrete to be finished by ordinary methods shall have a slump of not greater than 3 inches nor less than 2 inches. Where vibratory finishing methods are used the concrete shall have a slump of not greater than 1½ inches nor less than 1 inch. The water shall be regulated and gaged accurately and shall be discharged into the drum at the same time as the aggregates. The quantity of mixing water shall be determined by the engineer in accordance with Section 3.5 and shall not be varied without his consent.

3.8 *Mixing.* Mixing shall conform to one of the two methods described herewith:

(a) Paving Mixture at Job Site—The mixing machine used shall be of an approved type known as a batch mixer and of a design having a suitable device attached for automatically measuring the proper amount of water accurate to 1 percent, and for automatically timing each batch of concrete, so that all materials will be mixed together for the minimum time required. Such device shall be easily regulated and controlled to meet the variable conditions encountered. If the timing device becomes broken or fails to operate, the contractor will be permitted to continue for the balance of the day without the timing device, while the same is being repaired, providing that each batch of concrete is mixed 2 minutes.

All of the materials for each batch of concrete, including the water, shall be mixed not less than 1 minute after all of the materials are in the drum, and during this period the drum shall revolve at the speed for which it is designed, but shall not make less than 14 nor more than 20 revolutions per minute.

No materials for a batch of concrete shall be placed in the drum of the mixer until all of the previous batch has been discharged therefrom. Water shall be added at the time the materials are being run into the mixer. The inside of the drum shall be kept free from hardened concrete.

The use of mixers having a chute delivery will not be permitted except as approved. In all such cases, the arrangement of chutes, baffle plates, etc., shall be such as will insure the placing of fresh concrete without segregation.

(b) Ready Mixed—Ready mixed concrete may be centrally mixed, shrink-mixed or transit mixed concrete delivered at the work ready for use.

Central mixing is the process of suitably mixing concrete in a stationary mixer, meeting the requirements of Section 3.8a and continuing the mixing at agitation speed in a truck mixer or truck agitator to prevent segregation while in transit to the destination.

Shrink-mixing is the process of completing in a truck mixer while in transit to destination, the mixing of concrete which has been partially mixed in a stationary mixer at least 30 seconds.

Transit mixing is the process of combining the aggregate, cement and water into a thoroughly mixed and uniform mass of concrete in a truck mixer.

The truck mixer shall consist of a closed water-tight revolving drum suitably mounted and fitted with adequate blades or a water-tight container, equipped with a removable cover, suitably mounted and fitted with adequate revolving blades. Truck mixers shall be capable of combining aggregates, cement and water into a thoroughly mixed and uniform mass of concrete and of discharging the concrete without segregation. The truck agitator shall consist of a closed water-tight revolving drum or a water-tight container, equipped with a removable cover, suitably mounted and fitted with adequate revolving blades. Truck agitators shall be capable of transporting and discharging concrete without segregation.

Attached to each truck mixer and truck agitator, there shall be a metal plate on which is stated the manufacturer's capacities in terms of volume of mixed concrete for the various uses to which the equipment is applicable and the manufacturer's stated speed of rotation for both mixing and agitation.

For revolving drum type mixers the mixing speed shall not be less than 4 r.p.m. of the drum nor greater than that which will produce a peripheral velocity of more than 225 ft. per minute. For revolving blade type mixers, the mixer speed shall be not less than 6 nor more than 16 r.p.m. of the mixing blades. Agitation speed shall be not less than 2 nor more than 6 r.p.m. of the drum or mixing blades.

The mixer shall be equipped with a locking device which will automatically prevent the discharging of the mixer prior to receiving the required number of drum or blade revolutions or a counter mounted on the mixer permitting the reading of the count at the proportioning plant and at the destination.

A water measuring device capable of accurately measuring the water to 1% shall be mounted on the truck mixer or located at the point of charging the mixing water. It shall permit ready access and ready determination of the amount of water used. Wash water shall not be used in any concrete mix.

In general, for transit mix concrete, the water and cement shall be charged into the mixer at the proportioning plant with the fine and coarse aggregate. If for any reason the proper control of the consistency or mixing of the concrete is not obtained when the water and cement are charged at the proportioning plant, the time of charging the cement and water shall be as directed by the engineer. In no case shall the cement be added until all the mixing water is in the mixer.

Immediately after all ingredients are in the mixer, mixing shall be started and continued until discharged. In the case of truck mixers into which the fine and coarse aggregates are charged simultaneously, or which mix during the charging operation for transit mix, not less than 50 revolutions of the drum or blades at mixing speed shall be required after all of the ingredients including water are in the mixer. In the case of truck mixers into which the fine and coarse aggregates are charged separately and which do not mix during the charging operation for transit mix not less than 60 revolutions of the drum or blades at mixing speeds shall be required after all of the ingredients including water are in the mixer. For shrink-mix not less than 40 revolutions of the truck mixer drum or blades shall be required. For both transit mix and shrink-mix not more than 150 revolutions of the drum or blades shall be at the rate of rotation stated by the manufacturer as mixing speed. Additional mixing shall be at a slower speed as stated by the manufacturer as agitation speed.

Concrete shall be delivered to the work and discharged from the mixer or agitator within a period of 1 hour after all the ingredients are in the mixer or agitator.

Each load of ready mixed concrete shall be accompanied by Plant Ticket completely filled out. Upon arrival at the job the driver shall present one copy of the plant ticket to the engineer or inspector.

Where high-early-strength cement is used the maximum time in the mixer may be reduced by the engineer.

(c) General—In the transporting of proportioned aggregates or of ready-mixed concrete to the project, the gross weight which will be permitted on the subgrade shall not exceed 550 pounds per inch of width of tire, except by written permission of the engineer. The gross weight shall include the weight of the vehicle plus the load thereon.

Retempering of concrete which has partially hardened (i.e., remixing with or without the addition of water) will not be permitted.

3.9 *Placing and Finishing Concrete.* The provisions of this section are general and pertain to placing and finishing concrete by any of the methods as provided hereafter. Unless otherwise shown on the drawings or designated by the engineer, the maximum width of the pavement strip shall be 25 ft. and the minimum width 10 ft. Unless otherwise called for on the plans, the method of placing and finishing may be either "Ordinary Finishing" or "Vibratory Finishing."

The subgrade shall be sprinkled at such times and in such manner as directed by the engineer so that it will be in a thoroughly moistened condition (but not muddy) when the concrete is deposited thereon. If deemed necessary, the subgrade shall be sprinkled the evening prior to the placing of concrete. Extra care shall be exercised after moistening to maintain and protect a correct and unmarked subgrade surface.

The concrete shall be so deposited and spread that any irregularities in composition will be corrected, and a uniform layer of concrete produced whose thickness is approximately 1 inch greater than that required for the finished pavement. Rakes shall not be used for handling concrete.

In order to prevent the introduction into the concrete of earth and other foreign materials, the "muckers" or men whose duties require them to work in the concrete shall, in general, confine their movements to the area already covered with fresh concrete. Whenever it becomes necessary for these men to step out of the concrete, their foot-wear shall be washed or otherwise thoroughly cleansed before returning to the concrete. Repeated carelessness in regard to this detail will be deemed sufficient cause for removing and replacing such workmen.

During the operation of striking off the concrete, a uniform ridge of concrete at least 3 inches in depth shall be maintained ahead of the strike-off screed for its entire length.

Except when making a construction joint, the finishing machine shall at no time be operated beyond that point where the above-described surplus can be maintained in front of the strike-off screed.

After the first operation of the finishing machine, additional concrete shall be added to all low places and honeycombed spots and the concrete rescreeded. In any rescreeding a uniform head of concrete shall be maintained ahead of the strike-off for its entire length. Honeycombed spots shall not be eliminated by tamping or grouting.

The concrete adjacent to transverse joints shall be thoroughly compacted by means of an approved internal vibrator. The internal vibrators shall be of pneumatic, gas-driven, or electric type, and shall operate at a frequency of not less than 3200 pulsations per minute.

In conjunction with the placing and spreading, the concrete shall be thoroughly spaded and vibrated along the forms, bulkheads, and joints.

After the final pass of the finishing machine, the placing of all joints, longitudinal and transverse, and the concrete has started to dry, the surface of the pavement shall be finished with an approved longitudinal float. The float may be operated either manually or by mechanical means. The float may be either of wood or metal, shall be straight and smooth, and light in weight so as not to displace or sink into the concrete surface. To be effective, the float shall be at least 12 inches wide and 10 ft. long. When manually operated the float can be handled from a bridge or from the sides of pavement lane. The float shall be moved from edge to edge with a wiping motion and advanced several feet. The succeeding trip shall overlap the previous trip. A light smoothing lute at least 10 ft. long may be used when approved by the engineer.

The surface of the pavement shall be tested by the contractor before the final belting, with an approved standard straightedge, sixteen (16) feet in length. Irregularities so detected shall be corrected immediately. Special attention must be given to the concrete adjacent to transverse joints to insure that the edges thereof are not above the grade specified, or the adjacent concrete below grade. All depressions or projections discovered shall be corrected before any initial set has developed in the concrete.

After the concrete has been brought to the required grade, contour and smoothness, it shall be finished by means of a finishing belt. The finishing belt shall be not less than 8 nor more than 12 inches in width and at least 2 feet longer than the width of the pavement section to be finished. The belt of canvas composition, three-ply burlap construction or approved alternate, shall be worked with a combined longitudinal and transverse motion, until all surface irregularities are eliminated. The finishing belt may be operated either by hand or mechanically. The belt shall be kept clean and free from hardened concrete.

As soon as the concrete is sufficiently hardened, the edges of the pavement, the longitudinal joints, the construction and expansion joints shall be carefully finished with an edging tool having a radius of ¼ inch. The tools, the special accessories for cutting impressed joints, and the methods of workmanship shall be such as will produce a joint whose edges are of the same quality of concrete as the other portions of the pavement. Methods and workmanship which make use of excess mortar or grout in this area shall be eliminated. Unnecessary tool marks shall be eliminated during construction and the edges left smooth and true to line.

Whenever the placing of the concrete is stopped or suspended for any reason, for a period of 30 minutes or longer, a suitable bulkhead shall be placed so as to produce a vertical joint which is perpendicular to the centerline and to the surface of the pavement. If an emergency stop occurs within eight feet after a contraction or an expansion joint has been placed, the concrete shall be removed back to the previously installed joint. When a construction joint is placed it shall be dowelled or not as prescribed on the plans. When the placing of the concrete is resumed, the bulkhead shall be removed and new concrete placed and vibrated evenly and solidly against the face of the previously deposited concrete. Any concrete in excess of the amount needed to complete a given section, or that has been deposited outside the forms, shall not be used in the work.

After the removal of the forms, all honeycombed edges shall be immediately filled with a 1:2 mortar.

3.10 *Hand Finishing.* Hand finishing will be permitted on variable width sections of the pavement and other places where the use of the finishing machine would be impracticable. Hand finishing shall be accomplished by means of a hand operated strike-off templet of either steel or steelshod wood construction.

This striking templet shall be operated forward with a combined longitudinal and transverse motion, and shall be so manipulated that neither end will be raised off the side forms. A similar templet shall be used for tamping the concrete. All templets shall have the proper crown.

All other details of the finishing operations shall be as provided under Section 3.9.

3.11 *Ordinary Finishing.* The concrete shall be compacted and finished by a mechanical, self-propelled spreading and finishing machine of approved type, having two independently operated screeds. If a machine possessing only one screed is approved, the screed shall be not less than 18″ in width and shall be equipped with compensating springs to minimize the effect of the momentum of the screed on the side forms. The number of driving wheels, the weight of the machine and the power of the motor shall be so coordinated as to prevent slippage. The top of the forms and the surface of the finishing machine wheels shall be kept free of concrete or earth.

The machine shall at all times be in first class mechanical condition and shall be capable of compacting and finishing the concrete as herein described. Any machine which causes displacement of the side forms from the line or grade to which they have been properly set, or causes undue delay due to mechanical difficulties shall be removed from the work and replaced by a machine meeting these specifications.

The finishing machine shall be operated over each section of pavement two or more times and at such intervals as will produce the desired results. Generally two passes of the finishing machine is considered the maximum desirable.

All other details of the finishing operations shall be as provided under Section 3.9.

3.12 *Vibratory Finishing.* When specified, the concrete shall be vibrated, compacted and finished by a vibratory finishing machine. The vibratory machine shall meet the requirements for ordinary finishing and shall be one of the following types:

(a) This type of external vibratory finishing machine shall have two independently operated screeds. The front screed shall be equipped with vibratory units with a frequency of not less than 3500 pulsations per minute. There shall be not less than one vibratory unit for each 8′ length, or portion thereof, of vibratory screed surface. The front screed shall be not less than 12″ wide and shall be equipped with a "bull nose" front edge built on a radius of not less than 2″. This type of vibratory finishing machine shall be operated in such a manner that each section of pavement will receive at least one vibratory pass, but not more than two passes, unless otherwise directed.

(b) This type of external vibratory finishing machine shall be equipped with an independently operated vibratory "pan" (or pans) and two independently operated screeds. The "pan" shall be mounted in a manner that will not permit it to come in contact with the forms and will permit vibration of the full width of the lane simultaneously. There shall be not less than one vibratory unit for each 6′ length, or portion thereof, of vibrating pan surface. The vibratory units on any individual pan shall be synchronized and have a frequency of not less than 3500 pulsations per minute. The front screed shall be capable of operating in a position that will strike off the concrete at a sufficient height above the top of the forms to allow for proper compaction with the vibrating pan. This type of vibratory finishing machine shall be operated in such a manner that each section of pavement will receive at least one vibratory pass but not more than two passes, unless otherwise directed.

(c) Other vibratory finishing equipment may be used on a trial basis upon submission of evidence satisfactory to the engineer of its successful performance in placing and finishing concrete of the same quality and consistency as required under this specification for concrete for vibration.

Failure of equipment permitted on trial to perform in a satisfactory manner either mechanically or in its ability to place concrete of the consistency required for vibration shall be cause for its removal from the work and replacement by vibratory finishing equipment of an approved type.

The vibratory finishing machines shall be operated in the same manner as specified for ordinary finishing.

All other details of the finishing operations shall be as provided under Section 3.9.

3.13 *Preliminary Curing.* The surface of the concrete shall be covered with wet burlap, wet cotton mats, wet jute felt mats or paper as soon as the concrete has hardened sufficiently to prevent excessive marring of the surface or adherence thereto.

Where burlap is used it shall be placed in strips 2′ longer than the width of the pavement lane and applied so as to overlap at least four inches. The burlap shall be placed on the concrete in double thickness. Each thickness of burlap shall weigh, when dry, at least 7 ounces per square yard. The burlap shall at all times be kept in a thoroughly moistened condition until it is removed. The burlap shall remain on the concrete for at least 12 hours and then be removed as directed.

Where cotton mats are used they shall meet the requirements listed under Section 3.14 (a) and shall be used as prescribed in that section.

Where jute felt mats are used they shall meet the requirements listed under Section 3.14 (a) and shall be used as prescribed in that section.

Where paper is used it shall meet the requirements listed under section 3.14 (b) and shall be used as prescribed in that section.

Where membrane curing is used, the curing shall be in accordance with the requirements specified in Section 3.14 (c).

After the completion of the preliminary curing the burlap shall be removed in such a manner that not more than 60 lineal feet of pavement is exposed at one time, and followed at once by application of the subsequent curing agent.

3.14 *Curing.* The curing of the concrete shall be accomplished by one of the following methods as hereinafter noted.

(a) Water Curing—As soon as the forms have been removed and all honeycomb corrected, earth shall be banked against the edges of the pavement. After the removal of the burlap, but in no case later than 10 A.M. of the day following the placing of the concrete, the curing of the concrete shall be continued by one of the water-curing methods hereinafter described.

Water curing may be accomplished by the use of any one of the following methods by covering the concrete with:

Cotton Mats

Three Inches of Straw (Dimensions are for saturated material)

Jute Felt Mats

Cotton mats shall be saturated immediately before placing, and shall be kept saturated with water for the duration of the curing period. The mats shall be constructed with at least 6 ounce burlap or Osnaburg and shall be at least 12′ wide and equal in length to the width of the pavement strip plus 2′.

Jute felt mats shall be saturated immediately before placing, and shall be kept saturated with water for the duration of the curing period. The mats shall be constructed with at least 8½ ounces of jute filler between two layers of 6 ounce burlap and shall be at least 6′ wide and equal in length to the width of the pavement strip plus 2′.

Straw shall be wet down immediately, and shall be kept saturated with water for the duration of the curing period hereinafter described. For each 2500 square yards of concrete pavement for which curing is specified, the contractor shall maintain at least one man equipped with 100′ of hose, who shall devote his entire time to watering the concrete pavement and saturating the curing agent. Sufficient water supply and water pressure and such additional labor as is required to accomplish the above results shall be maintained during the necessary period by the contractor. The curing agent shall be removed and disposed of before traffic is permitted upon the pavement. In no event shall straw be burned on or in close proximity to the pavement.

(b) Paper Curing—For the preliminary curing, the blankets shall be placed as soon as practicable after final finishing without marring the surface, yet early enough to prevent undue loss of moisture.

At any other time, the surface of the pavement shall be thoroughly drenched before being covered with the paper curing agent.

The paper curing agent shall consist of two sheets of tough, durable, 100% sulphate Kraft paper cemented together with suitable bituminous material. The paper shall be reinforced by cementing to each sheet approximately 1400 lineal feet of unspun fiber per square yard, in such manner that the lines of fiber shall be approximately at right angles to each other when the sheets are cemented together, or by embedding between each other when the sheets are cemented together, or by embedding between the sheets threads of jute or cotton yarn of satisfactory weight, crossing each other at right angles and spaced not more than ½ inch apart each way. The reinforcing shall be completely embedded in the bituminous material cementing the sheets together. The completed paper must be waterproof.

The paper shall be formed into blankets by placing strips not less than 30′ in width side by side and joining them by a lap of not less than 10″, securely sewn, cemented together or held in place by continuous ridges of earth. The completed blankets shall have sufficient length to extend not less than 12″ beyond each edge of the pavement strip and include, when sewn or cemented together, a 3″ pleat to allow for transverse shrinkage.

Transverse joints shall be lapped not less than 16″ and held in place securely by means of continuous ridges of earth.

The paper shall be held down over the edges of the pavement slab by earth in such a manner that the slab shall be completely sealed. As the paper is placed, a continuous windrow of earth shall be placed on it at the slab edges. The extra paper for the sides shall hang free until forms are removed. Then it shall be folded down and banked with earth.

Torn places shall be repaired immediately by cementing an additional thickness of paper over the torn area.

The duration of the curing period under this method shall be as provided under Section 3.15.

(c) Membrane Curing—The concrete pavement shall be cured by covering all exposed surfaces with a curing compound. The solution used in the membrane curing process shall conform to all the requirements as specified herein. All material furnished shall be clearly marked by the manufacturer on every package or container the name of the product, the name of the manufacturer and instructions on handling and application of the curing agent. Samples consisting of at least one gallon of any compound proposed for use shall be supplied to the engineer for testing purposes at least two weeks in advance of proposed use. Approval of any sealing solution used in membrane curing will not prevent its subsequent rejection should its use on the project prove unsatisfactory. The compound shall be sampled and tested after the material is received on the project.

The material shall produce a sealing solution which when applied to the surface of concrete shall prevent evaporation and retain at least 90% of water content of the concrete at 7 days. The solution shall contain no bituminous material but shall be light in color and when applied shall not permanently discolor, stain or mottle the concrete surface. No ingredient in the solution shall chemically react with the cement in effecting the strength or appearance of the concrete. The solution shall be of such consistency that it can be applied by brush, by an air-pressure gun or by a small hand spray outfit at low pressures. The solution when applied at prescribed quantities shall produce a uniform continuous film of water-impervious membrane free from pinholes or other imperfections, and that will not check, crack, peel nor disintegrate within three weeks after application. The solution shall not be poisonous, obnoxious or harmful to those applying and handling same. The solution shall be such that no fire or explosive hazard is occasioned by its use. The curing compound shall be tested in accordance with A.S.T.M. Designation C 156–40T.

The curing compound shall be applied either by brush or by spray at a spreading rate not to exceed 250 square feet per gallon in place of the concrete surface. The application shall be made immediately upon completion of the final belting and the disappearance of the free surface moisture. In the event that the application of the curing membrane is delayed, the concrete surface shall be moistened and kept damp but care shall be taken that the finished surface is not damaged. The solution shall contain a slight coloring or dye for the purpose of identifying coated areas during application. The solution shall harden or dry within 60 minutes after application to effectively seal the surface against evaporation of water in the concrete. If the solution has a tendency to settle, adequate means shall be provided to agitate the supply being used in the application to assure thorough dispersion and a homogeneous mixture. After the membrane has been applied, care shall be taken that the surface film is kept intact and undamaged, and any sections of the pavement surface damaged by rain or otherwise before a reasonable curing period has elapsed shall be retreated.

After the side forms have been removed, the sides of the concrete slabs shall be sprayed with the membrane as directed.

3.15 *Duration of Curing.* The total period for water and paper curing as described above shall be continued for seven days including the preliminary water curing.

Where high-early-strength Portland cement is used, the period of curing may be reduced to three days.

3.16 *Depositing and Protecting Concrete During Cold Weather.* Concrete shall not be placed when the temperature of the air, aggregates or water is 40° F. or below, except when directed by the engineer. If placed under these conditions, the water or aggregates or both shall be heated, the aggregates preferably by steam, so that the concrete immediately after placing in the forms, shall have a temperature of between 65° and 85° F. The heating of the aggregate shall be done in a uniform manner which will preclude burning or otherwise damaging same. In no case shall concrete be deposited upon a frozen subgrade.

Adequate precautions shall be taken for such protection of all concrete (after it is placed in position) as will prevent the temperature of the deposited concrete falling below 50° F. until the required curing period has elapsed. A sufficient supply of straw, hay or other materials suitable for covering or protecting the concrete shall be provided on the work and spread to a depth as directed to prevent freezing. Manure shall not be used as a protection for green concrete.

Any concrete showing injury or damage by freezing, shall be removed and replaced at the expense of the contractor.

3.17 *Special Winter Concrete Construction.* When so required by the plans or proposal, special winter construction methods conforming to the requirements of this section of the specifications shall be followed. The contractor shall prosecute the work promptly and continuously through the winter months until the project has been completed. All work shall be done in accordance with the provisions of the general specifications except as modified herewith.

(a) Subgrade—The subgrade upon which concrete is to be placed, shall in addition to the requirements of other earthwork items, be so treated, protected and prepared as will produce a satisfactory subgrade, properly shaped and compacted and entirely free from frost, when the concrete is deposited.

(b) Heating and Protection—The heating of materials and the protection of concrete shall be in accordance with the provisions of Section 3.16.

(c) Curing—Curing shall be performed as specified under Section 3.14, except that immediately after the burlap or cotton mats have been wet as specified in Section 3.13, the burlap or cotton mats shall be covered and kept covered with at least 12″ of straw until the required curing period has elapsed.

The above requirements for curing are minimum requirements only, and are deemed necessary because of uncertain and unexpected weather conditions. The protection requirements of Section 3.15 are in no way voided. The straw covering shall be kept in place for at least 10 days or as directed.

3.18 *Transverse Construction Joints.* Transverse construction joints shall be built in accordance with the plans whenever necessary to suspend the work for a period of more than 30 minutes. At the end of a day's work, the joint shall be placed at a contraction or expansion joint. The joints shall be constructed perpendicular to both the centerline and the surface of the pavement. In no case shall an emergency construction joint be allowed within 8 ft. after placing a regular expansion or contraction joint. If the joint falls within this limit, the concrete shall be removed back to the previously installed joint.

3.19 *Transverse Contraction Joints.* Transverse contraction joints shall be constructed in accordance with the plans and at designated intervals. Joints shall be true and straight and normal to the centerline and surface of the pavement. Variation of more than ¼″ in 10′ from a straight line will not be permitted. The joints shall be continuous for the full width of the pavement. Contraction joints shall be of the weakened plane or dummy groove type.

When approved premolded joint material may be installed in the contraction joints from an independently operated machine except that when hand finishing is permitted, the joint material may be installed by hand methods.

The joint shall be so placed that its junction with the longitudinal joints will be a neat fitting connection providing a complete separation of the slab for the entire depth of the joint material.

No machine or method of operation that does not produce a joint meeting the requirement of variation of not more than ¼″ in 10′ will be permitted to continue in operation on the project.

3.20 *Transverse Expansion Joints.* (a) Premolded Filler—Expansion joints shall be of a premolded type conforming with these specifications and with the plans, and shall be spaced as directed. The joints shall form a continuous line for the full width and depth of the pavement strip.

The joints shall be installed normal to the centerline and perpendicular to the surface of the pavement. The joints shall be so installed and finished to insure complete separation of the slabs.

Where premolded expansion joints are used no section of the joint material shall be shorter than the width of pavement strip between longitudinal joints. The filler shall be placed ¾ inch below the surface. All concrete shall be cleaned off the top of the joint material. Before the pavement is opened to traffic this space shall be swept clean and filled with approved joint sealing material.

For premolded expansion joints which require a plate for added rigidity during installation, an oiled steel plate cut to the cross section of the pavement and slotted for the dowel bars or transfer of load devices shall be used to hold the premolded joint material in its proper position until the finishing machine has completed its operation.

All devices used for the installation of expansion joints shall be approved by the engineer. They shall be easily removable without disturbing the concrete and held in proper transverse and vertical alignment.

(b) Dowels—When called for, expansion joints shall be equipped with dowels of the dimensions and at the spacing and location indicated on the plans. The dowels shall be firmly supported in place, accurately aligned parallel to the subgrade and the centerline of the pavement, by means of a dowel assembly which will remain in the pavement and will insure that the dowels are not displaced during construction.

Other types of load transfer devices may be used on the approval of the engineer.

3.21 *Longitudinal Joints.* (a) The longitudinal construction joints shall be constructed where and in the manner as shown on the plans.

(b) The longitudinal contraction joint when required shall be constructed with a weakened plane or dummy groove joint in accordance with the detail drawings. If premolded joint material is used, it shall be installed from an independently operated machine, except that when hand finishing is permitted the joint material may be installed by hand methods. Variations of more than ¼″ in 10′ from a straight line will not be permitted. The joint shall be so placed that the junction with the transverse joint will be a neat fitting connection.

(c) The longitudinal expansion joint when required shall be constructed with premolded type conforming to these specifications and with the plans, and shall be placed as directed. The material shall be of the proper thickness, depth and length and shall be installed in a neat and satisfactory manner.

3.22 *Filling of Joints.* Joint filling operations shall not be started until after the final curing is completed. All joints which require filling shall be thoroughly cleaned and any excess mortar or concrete cut out with chisels. Joints shall be filled only when completely dry. When asphalt is used the joints shall be primed with a light asphalt cutback. The filler used shall be material as specified in paragraph 2.6. The application temperature for average conditions shall be at 300° F. The cleaning and filling shall be carefully done with proper equipment and a neat workmanlike joint obtained free from excess and unsightly filler. The contractor shall "spot up" or refill all unsatisfactory joints before final acceptance.

Kettles for heating filler which are not otherwise equipped with equivalent means of insulation shall be provided with a swinging pan, so interposed between the kettle and pavement as to provide a minimum of 2″ of air space between pan and pavement at all times.

3.23 *Requirements for Thickness.* The thickness of concrete pavement may be determined by the measurement of cores cut at designated locations. The cutting of cores will be at the discretion of the Government and will not be at the expense of the contractor. The average thickness of concrete pavement shall be determined by prescribed sections as hereinafter specified.

The thickness of concrete at any point shall not be more than ½ of an inch less than the specified thickness, nor shall the average thickness of the concrete be more than ¼ of an inch less than the specified thickness. Deductions for deficiency in thickness are tabulated on page 561.

Each separately poured lane of the pavement shall be cored as a unit, and all separately poured lanes of the same specified thickness composing the pavement shall be treated as constituting a single continuous lane for purposes of coring and in determining the lineal extent of prescribed sections for calculating the

Deficiency in Thickness Determined as Described in This Section	Proportional Part of Contract Price Allowed
0.00″ to 0.25″	100%
0.26″ to 0.50″	Ratio $\frac{(\text{Actual Thickness})^2}{(\text{Specified Thickness})^2}$
Greater than 0.50″	None

average pavement thickness. The proportional deduction, if any, and the average thickness of the pavement shall be computed for each section thus defined.

The initial boring shall be made in the center of either outside pavement strip at a point 500′ from the end of the pavement. This first boring shall be considered as the initial station and subsequent borings shall be taken at the quarter point or along the center of the strips at 500′ intervals. The odd distance left over at the end of any one strip shall be carried over and deducted in figuring the initial station on the adjacent strip. All stations shall start from the same end of the runway. No cores shall be taken within 50′ of the end of any runway strip. Cores shall not be taken near the intersection of a transverse and longitudinal joint.

Should any core show a thickness less than that allowed, additional cores shall be cut 10′, measured longitudinally, on each side of the location of the deficient core. If both these additional cores are within the ½″ tolerance no further special borings for this particular zone of deficiency shall be made. If either or both of the cores are not within the ½″ tolerance, the procedure shall be to cut further additional cores in the following locations: 50′ and 100′, the same to be measured longitudinally from the location of the core originally found to be deficient in thickness, thence at 100′ intervals longitudinally, until pavement thickness within the ½″ tolerance is found in both directions, but in no case shall additional cores be cut beyond the location of any specified boring in that strip at which the pavement thickness is found to be within the ½″ tolerance.

When any core shows a deficiency of more than ½″ the length of the adjacent pavement for which payment shall be withheld shall be the average of the distances measured parallel to the centerline, from the location at which the core originally found to be deficient in thickness was cut, to the nearest boring in each direction longitudinally which produced a core within the ½″ tolerance. Deductions shall be only for the separately poured strip from which the core or cores deficient in thickness were cut.

All thickness measurements which are more than ½ of an inch greater than the specified thickness shall be regarded as the specified thickness plus ½ of an inch. In computing the average thickness of pavement, the mean thickness of any two longitudinally contiguous cores shall be considered the average thickness for that part of the pavement in that lane between the two pertinent borings, and the average thickness of those parts of the pavement between the initial station and the initial boring made as specified and the terminal station and the terminal boring made as specified shall be considered to be the same as the thickness of the initial and terminal cores, respectively. The average thickness of a prescribed section shall be the figure in inches arrived at as follows: the average thickness between each two longitudinally contiguous borings shall be multiplied by the number of feet of pavement between the two borings, and the sum of the results thus obtained divided by the total number of lineal feet of concrete cored in the prescribed section, omitting all portions not within the ½″ tolerance.

In determining the thickness of the cores a standard highway core measuring device shall be used. The device intended is that which has three fingers mounted on an adjustable head which centers over the core. The fingers are spaced at 120° apart and are located midway between core center and core edge. The average of the three measurements shall be considered as the thickness of the core.

3.24 *Requirements for Smoothness.* After the final curing of the concrete and the removal of the covering material, the surface shall be swept clean and tested by the engineer for smoothness by means of a "surface testing machine" or "mechanical straightedge" furnished by the contractor, which will test one or more lines as determined by the engineer on each separately poured lane of the pavement. All surface variations so indicated, ¼″ or more, in a sixteen (16) foot length of pavement must be ground off in a manner satisfactory to the engineer. Bush hammering will not be permitted.

Sections of pavement containing extreme depressions with a depth in excess of ½″ in sixteen (16) feet shall be removed and replaced by the contractor at his own expense. In no case shall such section be less than the full width of the slab in which the depression occurs, or for a length of less than ten (10) feet.

3.25 *Steel Reinforcement.* Steel reinforcement shall be clean, free from rust and of type and dimensions shown on the plans. The material shall conform to the requirements in paragraph 2.7.

3.26 *Placing Reinforcement.* The concrete shall be struck off by means of a mechanical templet, to the proper depth below the specified finished surface, before reinforcement is placed. The reinforcing steel shall be placed 2 inches below and parallel to the finished surface of the pavement, unless otherwise shown on the plans. In no case shall the steel extend across the joints but shall be discontinued 2″ back from the joints. The reinforcing sheets and mats shall be laid with the main members of the long axis of the opening parallel with the centerline of the pavement. Adjacent sheets of the reinforcing steel shall be lapped not less than 12″ when the lap is made perpendicular to the centerline of the pavement and lot less than 6″ when made parallel to the centerline of the pavement.

The sheets forming each lap shall be securely wired or clipped together at the edges of the sheets, with similar fastenings spaced evenly between, at distances not to exceed 42 inches.

3.27 *Opening to Traffic.* The pavement shall be closed to traffic, including the vehicles of the contractor, for a period of 10 days after the concrete is placed or longer, if in the opinion of the engineer the weather conditions make it necessary to extend this time. The contractor shall furnish, place and maintain satisfactory barricades and lights as directed to exclude all traffic from the pavement.

Any damage resulting to the pavement due to traffic shall be repaired or replaced at the expense of the contractor. Power shovels, cranes, paving mixers and similar heavy equipment shall not be moved or operated on the pavement without the written approval of the engineer. The pavement shall not be opened to traffic until all joints have been filled and sealed.

METHOD OF MEASUREMENT

4.1 *Method of Measurement.* The yardage to be paid for shall be the number of square yards of either plain or reinforced pavement as specified, in place, completed and accepted, less deductions as hereinabove required for deficient thickness.

BASIS OF PAYMENT

5.1 *Basis of Payment.* The yardage measured as provided above shall be paid for at the contract unit price per square yard bid for plain or reinforced Portland cement concrete pavement, which price and payment shall constitute full compensation for furnishing and preparation of all materials, including such transverse and longitudinal joints, reinforcing steel, joint filler, dowels or load transfer devices, as are required in the plans, placing, finishing and curing and all labor, equipment, tools and incidentals necessary to complete the item; provided, however, that said unit price shall be reduced when and as required hereinabove for deficient thickness.

DEPARTMENT OF COMMERCE
Civil Aeronautics Administration
Airport Division
Washington, D.C.
August 1, 1944

JOINT SEALING FILLER (HOT POURED TYPE) FOR CONCRETE AIRPORT RUNWAYS, TAXIWAYS AND APRONS

C.A.A. Specification No. P-605

DESCRIPTION

1.1 *Description.* This item shall consist of a Joint Sealing Filler (Hot Poured Type) composed of a mixture of materials which will form a resilient and adhesive sealing compound for use in Portland Cement concrete structures and pavements.

REQUIREMENTS

2.1 *General Requirements.* The material furnished shall be suitable for melting in the usual type of asphalt kettle. It shall melt to the proper consistency for pouring and shall solidify on cooling to atmospheric temperature. It shall adhere to the sides of the concrete joint or crack. The material shall not crack or break when exposed to low temperatures and extended.

2.2 *Detailed Requirements.* A sample of the material weighing approximately 300 grams shall be selected in such a manner as to avoid inclusion of the surface layer. Of this quantity, 100 grams shall be melted slowly, with continued stirring to a pouring consistency, in a clean container using an oil bath or similar heating unit, to avoid local overheating. The remaining 200 grams shall be added in quantities of approximately 50 grams at a time, to the melted material until the entire quantity is of a sufficiently fluid consistency to be poured satisfactorily.

The melting of the total quantity of material shall be completed within sixty (60) minutes of the initial heating of the material. At no time shall the temperature exceed 450° F.

(a) *Penetration.* The penetration of the material sampled and molten (as herein described) when tested with a Penetrometer according to A.S.T.M. Designation D5–25 with a grease cone (D 217–38 T) attachment, shall be as follows:

0° –0 (32° F.)	200 g. weight	60 secs.	0.28—0.38 cm.
25° –0 (77° F.)	150 g. weight	5 secs.	0.45—0.75 cm.

(b) *Flow.* A portion of the molten sample shall be poured into a suitable amalgamated mold 4 cm. wide by 6 cm. long, on a bright tin panel to a uniform depth of 0.32 cm. After cooling at room temperature for two (2) hours, the mold shall be removed and the panel placed in an oven at 140° F. + or − 2° at an incline of 75 degrees for five (5) hours. The material shall not flow more than 0.5 cm. as a result of this test.

2.3 *Special Requirements.* The joint sealing filler (hot poured type) as used in the field and for these tests shall be melted slowly with continued stirring at a temperature not to exceed its initial ready pouring fluidity. At no time shall the temperature exceed 450° Fahrenheit. In addition to the tests described above, the material shall be tested for adhesion and elasticity as follows:

(a) *Test Specimen.* A test specimen shall consist of two (2) cement mortar pieces, approximately one (1) by two (2) by three (3) inches (1″×2″×3″) made of a cement mortar, consisting of one (1) part by weight of Portland Cement to two (2) parts by weight of clean, uniformly graded sand, 100 per cent passing a number four (4) sieve and zero (0) to five (5) passing a number one hundred (100) sieve. The cement mortar mix shall be made to a consistency of 50 (+ or − 5) as measured by the Standard A.S.T.M. mortar flow table.

After having been cured for seven (7) days, the wet mortar pieces shall be resurfaced by grinding with a standard number 30 H.D. carborundum stone on a Standard Delemeter, at a pressure of fifteen (15) to twenty (20) pounds. The surfaces of the mortar pieces shall upon examination show that the aggregate is uniformly exposed. The concrete pieces shall then be permitted to air dry at room temperature (77° F.) for twenty-four (24) hours prior to use.

The completed mortar pieces shall be spaced one (1) inch apart on a plate of amalgamated metal and shall be held apart by amalgamated metal strips spaced at such distances from the ends that a space one (1) inch by two (2) inches by two (2) inches (1″×2″×2″) is formed for pouring with the joint sealing filler material to be tested. The test joint form may be held together by rubber bands or suitable clamps.

(b) *Freezing.* A test specimen (as herein described) shall be allowed to cool in air at room temperature for two (2) hours, thereafter, placed in a refrigerating unit being maintained at 0° F. (+ or − 2°) for a minimum of six (6) hours.

(c) *Bond and Extension while Frozen.* (1) The specimen while at a temperature of 0° F. (+ or − 2°) shall be removed from the amalgamated plate and strips and then immediately placed in the self-aligning clamps of the Extension Machine (described below) maintained at a temperature of 0° F. (+ or − 2°) in a refrigerating unit. The Extension Machine shall then extend the width of the specimen at the rate of approximately one-eighth inch per hour to a width fifty (50) per cent greater than its original poured width.

(2) *Extension Machine.* The Extension Machine shall be so designed that the specimen can be expanded uniformly at the rate of approximately one-eighth inch per hour. The Extension Machine shall consist essentially of one or two screws rotated by an electric motor through suitable gear reduction units. The screw or screws shall carry a threaded moving self-aligning plate to which, and to a stationary plate, the specimen is clamped.

(d) *Compression.* After having been extended to the required width, the specimen shall be removed and placed at room temperature (approximately 77° F) for two (2) hours, thereafter compressed to its *thickness before extension* at the rate of one-tenth (0.1) inch per minute. During this compression, the specimen is to be maintained in a horizontal position.

(e) The specimen is then again placed in the refrigerating unit and the extension and compression tests repeated for four (4) cycles, as described above.

There shall be no cracking of the joint sealing filler material or break in the bond between the joint sealing filler material and the mortar pieces.

METHOD OF MEASUREMENT

3.1 *Method of Measurement.* The joint sealing filler to be paid for shall be either the pounds or gallons of filler as specified, in place, complete and accepted. When required in the construction of concrete pavements or structures, no measurement will be made for direct payment of filler as the cost of furnishing and installing shall be considered as a subsidiary obligation in the completion of the construction.

BASIS OF PAYMENT

4.1 *Basis of Payment.* The amount of the joint sealing filler as determined above shall be paid for at the respective contract unit price per pound or gallon used as ordered in the accepted work, which price and payment shall constitute full compensation for furnishing and installing, for clean up, for all labor, equipment, tools, and incidentals necessary to complete the item. As stated above, when the filler is required in the construction of concrete pavements or structures, performance of this item will not be payable directly, but shall be considered as a subsidiary obligation of the contractor covered under the contract unit prices for square yards of concrete pavement or cubic yards of concrete structures.

APPENDIX 30

SAMPLE PROPOSAL FERTILIZING AND SEEDING

Item No.	Article	Quantity	Unit	Unit Price	Total Price
	Schedule I—Fertilizing and Seeding				
1.43–1	Grading erosional furrows, holes, etc. in accordance with Article 1, if and where ordered by the Engineer.	50	C.Y.		
1.43–2	Preparing seed beds, liming, fertilizing and seeding for areas designated "A" in Drawing No. 1-E-1689 in accordance with Article 2.				
	(a) Preparing seed beds	140	Acre		
	(b) Furnishing limestone	175	Ton		
	(c) Applying "	140	Acre		
	(d) Furnishing fertilizer	70	Ton		
	(e) Applying "	140	Acre		
	(f) Furnishing seed	7	Ton		
	(g) Planting "	140	Acre		
1.43–3	Seeding areas designated B. & C. on Drawing No. 1-E-1689 in accordance with Article 3.				
	(a) Furnishing seed	0.8	Ton		
	(b) Sowing seed mixture	38	Acre		
1.43–4	Mulching slopes if and to the extent ordered by the Engineer for areas designated C on Draw. No. 1-E-1689 in accordance with Article 4.	13	Acre		
1.43–5	Preparing test plots in accordance with Article 5.	1	Job		
	TOTAL SCHEDULE I, IN DOLLARS				
	CONTRACT TIME, CALENDAR DAYS				

SPECIAL PROVISIONS FOR THIS PROPOSAL

ARTICLE I: *Grading erosional furrows, holes, etc.—Item 1.43–1*:

Under this item the Contractor will be required to fill furrows, ditches, holes, etc., caused by erosion in the previously graded areas. It is estimated that the present grading and paving contract will be completed approximately Aug. 15, 1945 and this item is included to cover erosion occurring between this date and the beginning of the work covered by this Proposal. This item shall apply only where the use of backfill material is ordered by the Engineer.

The material used for backfill shall be selected material satisfactory to the Engineer and shall be free from stones larger than 2″ in diameter, roots, and other unsuitable matter. The Contractor may obtain the material from the airport site or other source as he may find desirable.

The furrows, etc., shall be backfilled to conform with the existing grades and the material compacted to reasonable density before the work of preparing seed beds is begun.

The selected material used in accordance with the above specification shall be measured in trucks at the site of the work. However, any material so measured, unloaded and not actually incorporated in the work shall be measured and the quantity deducted from the quantity as measured in the truck. The material so measured shall be paid for at the contract price per cubic yard, which price and payment shall constitute full compensation for furnishing, hauling, spreading, smoothing and compacting as well as for all labor, tools, equipment and incidentals necessary to complete the item.

ARTICLE 2. *Preparing Seed Beds, Fertilizing and Seeding—Item 1.43–2*

Under these items the Contractor shall prepare seed beds, furnish and apply limestone and fertilizer and furnish and plant seed on prepared areas in accordance with this specification at locations shown on the plans or designated by the Engineer.

A. MATERIALS

A.1 *Seed*—The seed used shall be labeled in accordance with the U.S. Department of Agriculture Rules and Regulations under the Federal Seed Act in effect on the date of invitation for bids. All seed shall be furnished in sealed standard containers, unless exception is granted by the Engineer. Seed which has become wet, moldy, or otherwise damaged in transit or in storage, will not be acceptable. The seed mixture to be furnished and the minimum percentage by weight of pure live seed of each kind in each lot of seed shall be as follows:

VARIETY	MIN. % BY WEIGHT, PURE LIVE SEED
Fesque, Chewings	25
Kentucky Blue Grass	30
Red Top	15
Domestic Rye Grass	5
Other Material, Max.	25

The percent of other material allowed, shall consist of non-viable seed, chaff, hulls, live seed of crop plants other than those specified above, harmless inert matter, and weed seed not exceeding one percent by weight of the total of pure live seed and other material.

A.2 *Fertilizer*—

The fertilizer shall be a standard commercial mixed fertilizer of 6–10–4 grade and shall conform to applicable State fertilizer laws. It shall be uniform in composition, dry, and a free flowing material suitable for application by a common fertilizer distributor, grain drill, planting machine or similar standard equipment. The fertilizer shall be delivered in bags or other convenient standard containers each fully labeled with the manufacturers guaranteed analysis. Any fertilizer which becomes caked or otherwise damaged, making it unsuitable for use, will not be acceptable.

A.3 *Lime*—

Lime shall be ground limestone containing not less than 85 percent of total carbonates and shall be ground to such fineness that 50 percent will pass through a 100 mesh sieve and 90 percent will pass through a 20 mesh sieve. Coarser material will be acceptable provided the specified rates of application are increased and the payment is decreased proportionately on the basis of quantities passing the 100 mesh sieve.

A.4 *Inspection & Tests.*

(a) *Fertilizer*—The fertilizer shall be subject to tests by representative of State Agriculture Experiment Stations or other approved testing laboratory at the discretion of the Engineer.

(b) *Limestone*—Duplicate copies of a statement from a State laboratory or other approved testing laboratory, showing that the limestone to be furnished meets the requirements of the specifications, shall be submitted to the Engineer.

(c) *Seed*—Duplicate signed copies of a statement from the vender, certifying that each container of seed delivered is at least equal to the specification requirements, shall be submitted to the Engineer. This certification shall appear on or with all copies of invoices for the seed. Each lot of seed shall be subject to sampling and testing at the discretion of the Engineer. Planting shall not be delayed pending reports of these tests; however, if the test results indicate that the seed does not meet the requirements of this specification, the Contractor will be required to supply the deficiency and incorporate same in areas where seed covered by test was sown. Furnishing the deficiency and reseeding shall be done at no additional cost to the Government.

B. CONSTRUCTION METHODS

B.1 *General*—The areas to be seeded will be staked by the Engineer and the requirements for seeding, liming and fertilizing, etc., for each designated area shall be as listed in the Bid Schedule.

Equipment necessary for proper preparation of the ground surface and for handling and placing all materials required, shall be on hand, in good condition and shall be approved by the Engineer before work is started. The Contractor shall demonstrate to the Engineer before starting work that the application of required materials will be made at the specified rates.

The work shall be progressed in the order listed below and shall be in accordance with the following sections of this specification:

(a) Apply limestone (B.3a)
(b) Disc with tandem discs (B.2)
(c) Apply fertilizer (B.3b)
(d) Harrow (B.2)

(e) Plant and cover seed (B.4)
(f) Harrow (B.2)
(g) Clean-Up (B.5)

B.2 *Preparation of the Seed Bed*—The grades established by others on the areas to be seeded shall be maintained in a true and even condition. Any holes or furrows caused by erosion during construction, shall be backfilled to conform with existing grades and the material compacted to a reasonable density.

After applying lime and before applying fertilizer, the areas required to be seeded shall be thoroughly loosened to a depth of at least 3 to 4 inches by double discing with a tandem disc. Any irregularities in the surface resulting from discing or other operations of the Contractor shall be corrected in order to prevent the formation of low places and pockets where water will stand. After the fertilizer has been applied and before the seed is planted and again after seed is spread, all turf areas shall be harrowed with a spike-tooth harrow. On berm sections hand raking or other approved methods will be allowed in place of discing and harrowing.

B.3 *Application of Limestone and Fertilizer*:

(a) Before discing (Para. B.2), limestone shall be distributed uniformly over the areas to be seeded at the rate of 2500 lbs. per acre by an approved distributor or other satisfactory means. On berm sections the limestone may be spread by hand.

(b) After discing (par. B.2), fertilizer shall be distributed uniformly over the areas to be seeded at the rate of 1000 lbs. per acre by a common fertilizer distributor grain drill, planting machine or other approved equipment. On berm sections the fertilizer may be spread by hand.

If it is determined upon final checking that the specified minimum rates of limestone and fertilizer have not been applied, the Engineer, at his discretion, will require the Contractor to furnish the specified amount by distributing the deficiency as directed.

B.4 *Planting Seed*—All seeding work shall be done between August 15, 1945 and October 15, 1945 except as otherwise ordered in writing by the Engineer. The Contractor shall notify the Engineer in advance of the time he intends to begin sowing seeds and shall not proceed with such work until permission to do so has been granted by the Engineer.

Seed shall be placed by a seed drill at the rate of 100 lbs. per acre. The seed shall be uniformly distributed over the designated areas. One-half the seed shall be sown when the drill is moving in one direction, and the remainder shall be sown moving at right angles to the first sowing. No rolling will be required. On berm sections, the seed may be spread by an approved type hand seeder.

B.5 *Clean-Up*—After the seed has been sown, the surface shall be cleared, when necessary, of all stones larger than 2 inches in diameter or any other objects that may interfere with mowing operations.

METHOD OF MEASUREMENT

The quantities of fertilizer, limestone and seed to be paid for shall be the actual quantities of each material, measured separately in the units specified in the bid schedule meeting the above specifications and which have been incorporated into the work at the direction of the Engineer.

The acreage of preparing seedbed or applying limestone or fertilizer, or planting and covering seed to be paid for shall be the actual acreage of each item of the bid schedule so processed in accordance with the foregoing specification at the direction of the Engineer and accepted.

The measurement for payment shall not include quantities of materials or acreage of reseeding required due to the Contractor's operations or negligence.

BASIS OF PAYMENT

The quantities of materials as provided for above shall each be paid for at the contract unit price, which price and payment shall constitute full compensation for furnishing and delivering these materials at the site of the work.

The acreage of "preparing seed beds" measured as provided for above, shall be paid for at the contract unit price per acre which price and payment shall constitute full compensation for all necessary work (Para. B.2 of these specifications), as well as for all labor, equipment, tools, and incidentals necessary to complete the work.

The acreage of applying limestone or fertilizer measured as provided for above, shall be paid for at the contract unit price per acre which price and payment shall constitute full compensation for hauling and applying the material (Par. B.3 of these specifications), as well as for all labor, equipment, tools, and incidentals necessary to complete the work.

The acreage of "planting and covering seed," measured as provided for above shall be paid for at the contract unit price per acre, which price and payment shall constitute full compensation for hauling, planting seed (Par. B.4) and any necessary clean-up (Para. B.5) as well as for all labor, equipment, tools and incidentals necessary to complete the work.

ARTICLE 3. *Seeding—Item 1.43–3*:

Under this item, the Contractor shall furnish 30 lbs. of red clover and 20 lbs. of sericea lespedeza seed per acre, mix with Government furnished seed and broadcast the mixture on slopes as staked in the field by the Engineer at a rate of 150 lbs. per acre. No preparation of seed beds or maintenance will be required. The seed may be sown by a hand seeder. Method of Measurement and Basis of Payment shall be in accordance with Article 2.

All seeding work shall be done between August 15, 1945 and October 15, 1945, except as otherwise directed, in writing, by the Engineer.

The seed furnished by the Contractor shall meet the requirements of Section A.1 and A.3(c) of Article 1 of this Exhibit except that the seed shall consist of red clover only.

ARTICLE 4. *Mulching—Item 1.43–4.*

The areas to be mulched will be staked on the ground by the Engineer. While it is anticipated that the entire Area C will require mulching, the Government reserves the right to delete mulching on any areas with the limits specified area "C" as found necessary or desirable.

Under this item, the Contractor shall mulch the areas staked on the ground by the Engineer with hay, stalks, straw or other suitable material at the rate of 2 tons per acre. The material shall be spread uniformly so that not more than 20% of the ground surface shall be exposed. Mulching materials shall be reasonably free from weed and other seed which will cause voluntary growth detrimental to the proposed seeding. Rotted or decomposed materials which would tend to smother or retard the growth of grass shall not be used and clean, edible hay shall not be used when other satisfactory materials are available.

Not more than 5 hours shall elapse between seeding under Item 1.43–3 and mulching under Item 1.43–4. The mulch shall be retained in place by stakes spaced not more than 15 feet along or 10 feet up and down the slopes, and wire or heavy twine fastened to the stakes. The wire or twine shall be laid between the stakes diagonally in both directions. Until acceptance of the work, the Contractor shall, at his own expense, replace any mulch materials which have been removed by wind, rain or other causes because of improper retention.

The acreage of mulching to be paid for shall be the actual number of acres covered and staked down in accordance with this article and accepted.

The acreage, measured as provided above, shall be paid for at the contract unit price, which price and payment shall constitute full compensation for furnishing all mulching and tie-down materials, for hauling, spreading and tieing down, as well as for furnishing all labor, tools, equipment, transportation and incidentals necessary to complete the item.

ARTICLE 5. *Preparing Test Plots—Item 1.43–5.*

Under this item, test plots shall be prepared as shown in the diagram, page 572. All seed used shall be of a quality equal to that supplied under Item 1.43–2 and the contruction methods shall be in accordance with the applicable requirements of Article 2. The test plots shall be located within the area to be seeded where directed by the Engineer and all corners shall be staked permanently on the ground. The work shall not be started until fertilizing of the area involved is completed.

Payment for the work shall be made on a job basis as called for in the bid schedule, which price and payment shall constitute full compensation for preparation of beds, furnishing hauling and sowing seed as well as for all labor, tools, equipment and incidentals necessary to complete the item.

	100′ Plots to be seeded at the rate of 100 lbs. per acre.					%
20% Red Top 10% Dom. Rye	70	50 ↑	30	10	0	Chewings Fesque
	←20′→	20′				
	0	20 ↓	40	60	70	Kentucky Blue
10% Red Top 10% Dom. Rye	80	60	40	20	0	Chewings Fesque
						100′
	0	20	40	60	80	Kentucky Blue
10% Red Top 5% Dom. Rye	85	65	45	25	0	Chewings Fesque
	0	20	40	60	85	Kentucky Blue
10% Dom. Rye	90	70	40	20	0	Chewings Fesque
	0	20	50	70	90	Kentucky Blue
	100	75	50	25	0	Chewings Fesque
	0	25	50	75	100	Kentucky Blue

Seed required:

Chewings Fesque	10 lbs.
Kentucky Blue	10 "
Red Top	2 "
Domestic Rye	2 "

APPENDIX 31

HOW TO PROPORTION CONCRETE FOR PAVEMENTS[1]

A concrete pavement slab for highways or airports is essentially a wide beam and the stresses which are critical and which control the design are the tensile stresses created by changes in temperature and moisture and by traffic loads. Unlike structural concrete for buildings, (See Stone Briefs No. 1) which is proportioned to have a high degree of workability, adequate compressive strength and durability for the particular portion of the structure it must serve, pavement concrete should be proportioned to have high beam strength, adequate durability and with no more sand than is necessary to create a thin layer of mortar on the surface of the finished slab. Paving concrete therefore is not as workable as structural concrete; it contains more coarse aggregate and less sand and is of drier consistency, with a slump preferably between 1½ and 3 inches.

TABLE I

Dry, Rodded Volume of Coarse Aggregate per Unit Volume of Highway Concrete (b/b_o)

Size of Coarse Aggregate Square Opening Laboratory Sieves	Fine Sand		Medium Sand			Coarse Sand			Approximate Gallons of Water per Cu. Yd. of Concrete for 2-in. Slump	
	Fineness Modulus of Sand								Coarse Aggregate	
	2.40	2.50	2.60	2.70	2.80	2.90	3.00	3.10	Angular	Rounded
No. 4 to 1 in.	.79	.78	.77	.76	.75	.74	.73	.72	35	32
No. 4 to 1½ in.	.81	.80	.79	.78	.77	.76	.75	.74	33	30
No. 4 to 2 in.	.83	.82	.81	.80	.79	.78	.77	.76	32	29
No. 4 to 2½ in.	.85	.84	.83	.82	.81	.80	.79	.78	31	28

b_o = solid volume of coarse aggregate per cu. ft. of dry, rodded, coarse aggregate.
b = solid volume of coarse aggregate per cu. ft. of concrete.
b/b_o = dry, rodded volume of coarse aggregate per unit volume of concrete.

PROPORTIONING PAVEMENT CONCRETE WITH A REQUIRED CEMENT FACTOR

If it is desired to proportion pavement concrete to have a specified cement factor, this is easily accomplished with the use of Table 1 by the following procedure:

Step-by-step Procedure for Proportioning Pavement Concrete

1. By tests, using the standard methods of the A.S.T.M., obtain the bulk specific gravities of the fine and coarse aggregates and cement, the gradations of the aggregates and the dry, rodded weight per cu. ft. of the coarse aggregate.

2. Calculate the solid weight per cu. ft. of the fine and coarse aggregates and of the cement. (Bulk specific gravity × 62.4 lb.)

[1] From National Crushed Stone Association, *Stone Briefs*, January, 1945.

3. Calculate the fineness modulus of the sand. (Total percentage retained on the Nos. 4, 8, 16, 30, 50 and 100 sieves ÷ 100.)

4. From Table 1, select the proper value for b/b_o, which depends on the size of coarse aggregate and the fineness modulus of the sand. The same values for b/b_o are used irrespective of type of coarse aggregate.

5. Calculate the values for b_o and b; b_o = the dry, rodded weight per cu. ft. of the coarse aggregate (See Par. 1) ÷ by the solid weight per cu. ft. of coarse aggregate (See Par. 2); then $b = b/b_o \times b_o$.

6. From Table 1 select the total amount of mixing water per cu. yd. of concrete, depending upon whether the coarse aggregate is angular or rounded in shape.

7. For the given cement factor calculate the solid volumes of the cement, the coarse aggregate and the water per cu. yd. of concrete. Subtract this value from 27 cu. ft. and the result will be the solid volume of the sand per cu. yd. of concrete. Solid volume of cement = the number of pounds of cement in a cu. yd. of concrete ÷ the solid weight of cement per cu. ft. (See Par. 2) The solid volume of coarse aggregate = 27 × b. The solid volume of water = the number of gal. per cu. yd. in Table 1 ÷ 7.5.

8. Multiply the respective solid volumes by the solid weights per cu. ft. to obtain the weights of materials required per cu. yd. of concrete.

9. Calculate the field mix by correcting the weights of sand, coarse aggregate and mixing water to compensate for the water in the aggregates.

EXAMPLE

A cement factor of 6 sacks of cement per cu. yd. of concrete is to be used. What are the required concrete proportions for use in the first field mix?

Cement, Sp. Gr. = 3.14, Solid Wt. = 3.14 × 62.4 = 196, Solid Vol. = 94/196 = 0.48
Sand, Sp. Gr. = 2.65, Solid Wt. = 2.65 × 62.4 = 165.4, F. M. = 2.80
Stone, Sp. Gr. = 2.70, Solid Wt. = 2.70 × 62.4 = 168.5, Wt. per Cu. Ft. rodded = 103 lb.
Size, #4–2 in., Solid Vol. of stone per Cu. Ft. of stone, b_o = 103/168.5 = 0.61
Reference to Table 1 shows b/b_o = 0.79
therefore $b = b/b_o \times b_o = 0.79 \times 0.61 = 0.482$
Water required = 32 gal. per Cu. Yd. of concrete.

Calculations for Quantities per Cu. Yd. of Concrete

			Solid Vol. per Cu. Yd.		Solid Weights per Cu. Ft.		Lb. per Cu. Yd.	Field Quantities Lb. per Cu. Yd. (See paragraph below)
Cement	6 × 0.48	=	2.88	×	196	=	564	564
Stone	0.482 × 27	=	13.01	×	168.5	=	2192	2210
Water	32/7.5	=	4.27	×	62.4	=	266	210
Total		=	20.16					
Sand (27.00—20.16)		=	6.84	×	165.4	=	1131	1182
						Total	4153	4166

$$\text{Wt. per Cu. Ft.} = \frac{4166}{27} = 154.3 \text{ lb.}$$

Field Quantities—Corrections for Moisture in the Aggregates

Suppose tests show the sand has 0.5% absorption and 4.0% free, surface water and the stone has 0.3% absorption and 0.5% surface water.

The quantities of sand, stone and mixing water given above for the oven-dry conditions must be corrected for the actual field moisture conditions.

Moist stone weight required = 2192 + 0.8% of 2192 = 2209.5 (use 2210 lb.)
Moist sand weight required = 1131 + 4.5% of 1131 = 1181.9 (use 1182 lb.)
Mixing water = 266 lb. −0.5% of 2192 − 4.0% of 1131 = 209.8 (use 210 lb.)
Cement—no moisture correction necessary = 564 lb.

THE PROPORTIONING OF PAVEMENT CONCRETE FOR A GIVEN FLEXURAL STRENGTH

The flexural strength of concrete, expressed in terms of modulus of rupture, is influenced greatly by the characteristics of the coarse aggregate as well as by

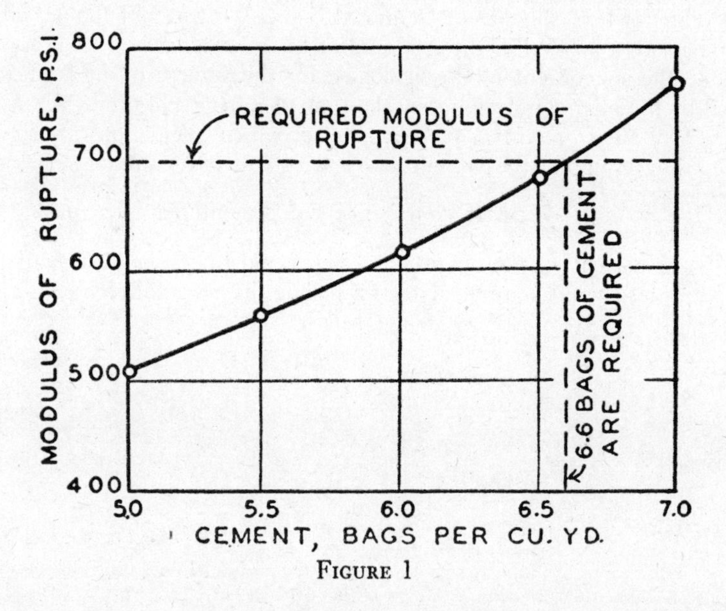

FIGURE 1

other factors. Hence, at present, to determine the proportions of concrete required to produce a given flexural strength, a laboratory test procedure is necessary. The test mixtures are first calculated as just described, using at least 4 different cement factors. For illustration 5½, 6, 6½, and 7 sacks per cu. yd. Beam specimens are then made according to standard A.S.T.M. methods. The specimens are tested at the desired age and the resulting values for modulus of rupture are then plotted, together with the cement factors used, in the manner shown in Fig. 1. A horizontal line is drawn to represent the required modulus of rupture and where this line intersects a smooth curve drawn through the test values, the cement factor required can be read off the curve. Using this cement factor the concrete proportions should then be calculated in the manner previously described.

As a typical illustration, assume that the test values for modulus of rupture plot as shown in Fig. 1. If the modulus of rupture desired is 700 psi. by interpolation it is seen that 6.6 sacks of cement will be necessary.

AIR ENTRAINING CEMENTS

When air entraining cements are used, the volume of air in the mix is obtained by the standard gravimetric A.S.T.M. Method C138–44, which consists in obtaining the weight per cu. ft. of the concrete by test and comparing it with the calculated theoretical weight obtained as illustrated in the preceding example. The air is treated just as if it were a solid material, since it occupies space in the concrete mass. Thus, suppose the concrete proportioned as in the illustrative example is found by test to weigh 150.1 lb. Its theoretical solid weight is 154.3, therefore the percentage of air in the mixture

$$= \frac{154.3 - 150.1}{154.3} \times 100 = 2.7\%.$$

The value for b/b_o should not be altered if air is present and the air will thus merely displace a portion of the sand and of the mixing water. It is necessary to determine the air content in the field mix, for the volume of air is greatly influenced by the mixing procedure, by the time of mixing and other factors.

If 2.7% of air is present in the concrete for which calculations are shown in the preceding example, the volume or yield of concrete containing 6 sacks of cement is $\frac{4166}{150.1} = 27.7$ cu. ft. and hence the cement factor is only $\frac{27}{27.7} \times 6 = 5.84$ sacks per cu. yd. To obtain concrete having the required cement factor, the proportions should be recalculated to include the air as follows:

							Lb. per Cu. Yd.
Cement			2.88	×	196	=	564
Stone			13.01	×	168.5	=	2192
Air	2.7% of 27	=	0.73				
Water[1]	31/7.5	=	4.13	×	62.4	=	258
	Total	=	20.75				
Sand (27.00—20.75)		=	6.25	×	165.4	=	1034

[1] The water is arbitrarily reduced because the air has a lubricating effect and also because the quantity of sand is reduced.

FINAL ADJUSTMENTS

Some final adjustments of the field mix may be necessary. Thus, if the consistency of the concrete requires a change in the water content, continue to use the value for b/b_o designated in Table 1, assume the desired quantity of water and recalculate the mix which will result in changing the solid volume of the sand by the change in volume of water. If the workability needs correction, this is accomplished by a change in the b/b_o value, a decrease resulting in more mortar and consequently greater workability. The necessary calculations for these slight changes in proportions in the field mix are very simple and can be done in a very short time.

INDEX

I. PLANNING

CLASSIFICATION OF AIRPORTS

CIVIL AERONAUTICS ADMINISTRATION

AIRPORTS SERVICE

PRIVATE OWNER SMALL TYPE AIRCRAFT.

2 TO 5 PLACE

ADEQUATE FOR AIRCRAFT UP TO 4000# GROSS WEIGHT.

FOR SMALL COMMUNITIES AND AUXILIARY AIRPORTS IN METROPOLITAN AREAS.

LANDING STRIPS 1800 TO 2700 FEET IN LENGTH.

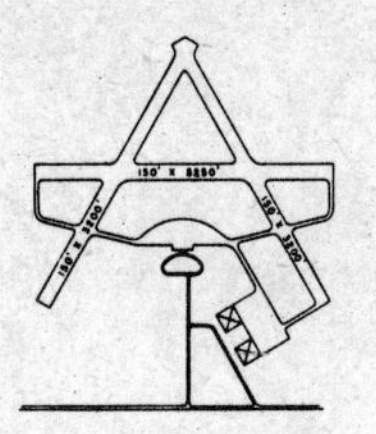
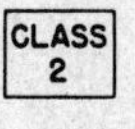

PRIVATE OWNER LARGER TYPE AIRCRAFT AND FEEDER TRANSPORT AIRCRAFT.

UP TO 20 PLACE

ADEQUATE FOR AIRCRAFT UP TO 15000# GROSS WEIGHT.

COMMUNITIES OF 5000 TO 25000 POPULATION.

RUNWAYS 2500 TO 3500 FEET IN LENGTH.

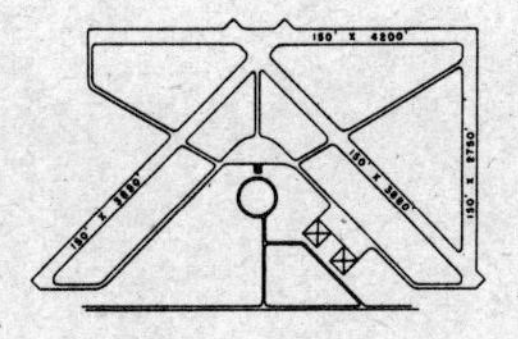
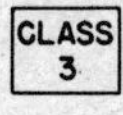

PRESENT DAY TRANSPORT AIRCRAFT.

UP TO 30 PLACE

ADEQUATE FOR AIRCRAFT UP TO 50000# GROSS WEIGHT.

CITIES OF 25000 TO 250000 POPULATION.

RUNWAYS 3500 TO 4500 FEET IN LENGTH.

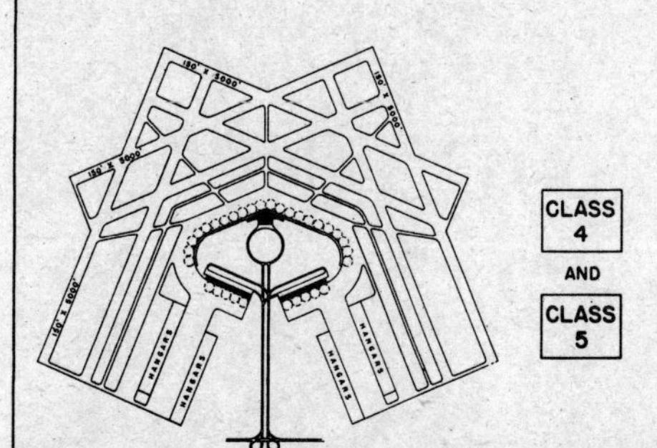

CLASS 4 AND CLASS 5

LARGEST AIRCRAFT NOW IN USE AND THOSE PLANNED FOR THE IMMEDIATE FUTURE.

30 PLACE AND LARGER

ADEQUATE FOR AIRCRAFT OVER 50000# GROSS WEIGHT.

MAJOR METROPOLITAN CENTERS AND AIR TERMINALS.

CLASS 4 RUNWAYS 4500 TO 5500 FEET IN LENGTH.
CLASS 5 RUNWAYS 5500 FEET IN LENGTH AND OVER.

NOTE: Runway Lengths Given Are For Sea Level.
Higher Altitude Requires Greater Runway Lengths.

ENGINEERING AND CONSTRUCTION DIVISION, 5-1-44, DWG. NO. 569.

FIG. 1-1. (Courtesy C.A.A.)

I. PLANNING

FIG. 1-2. Danville Virginia Municipal Airport. (Courtesy Note space provided for additional buildings as well as

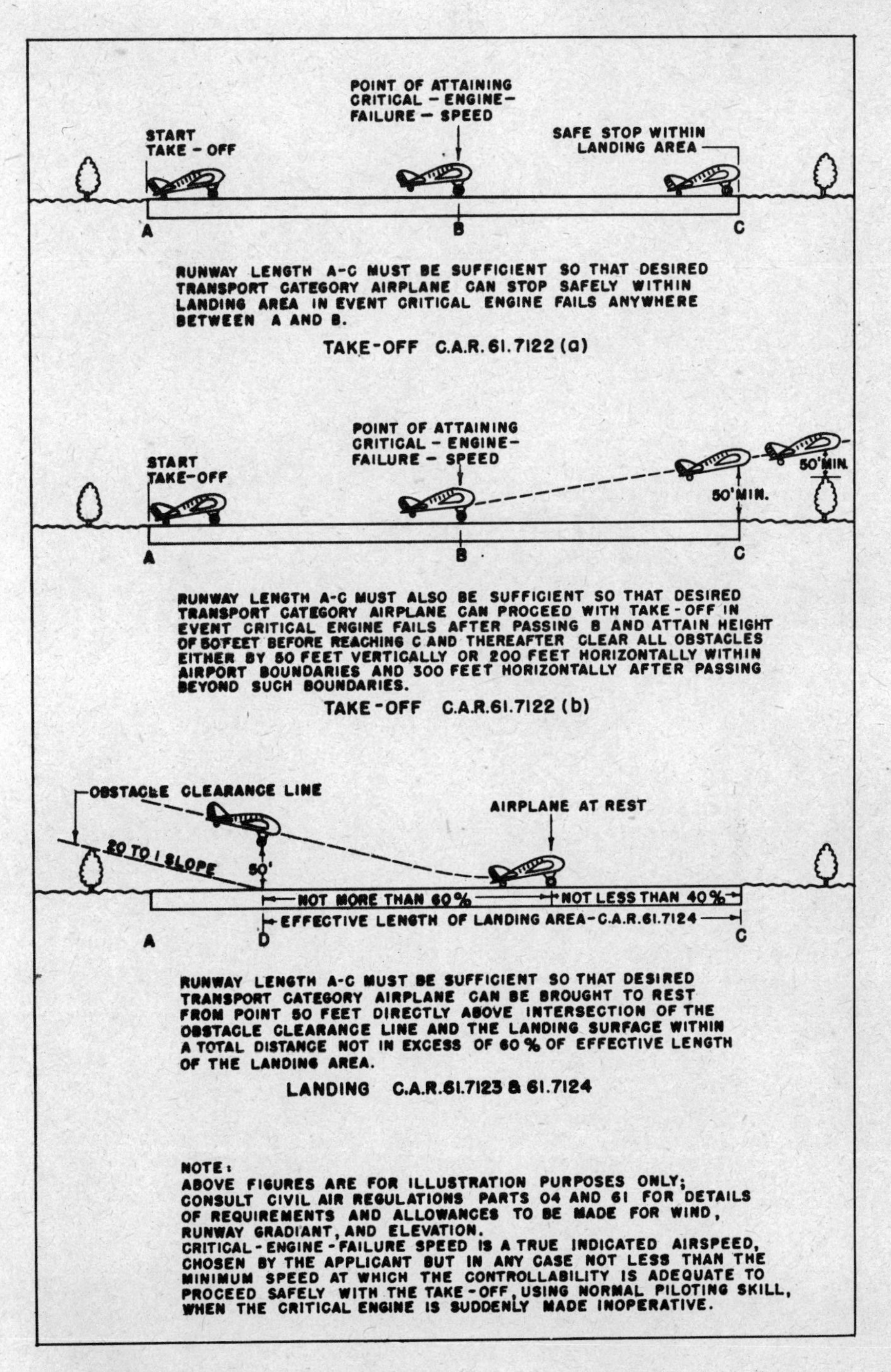

FIG. 1-3. Basic Requirements of Parts 04 and 61 of Civil Air Regulations. Requirements are shown as they affect runway length at airports used by transport category aircraft.

FIG. 1-4. B-29 undercarriage resting on turntable illustrates immense loads imposed on

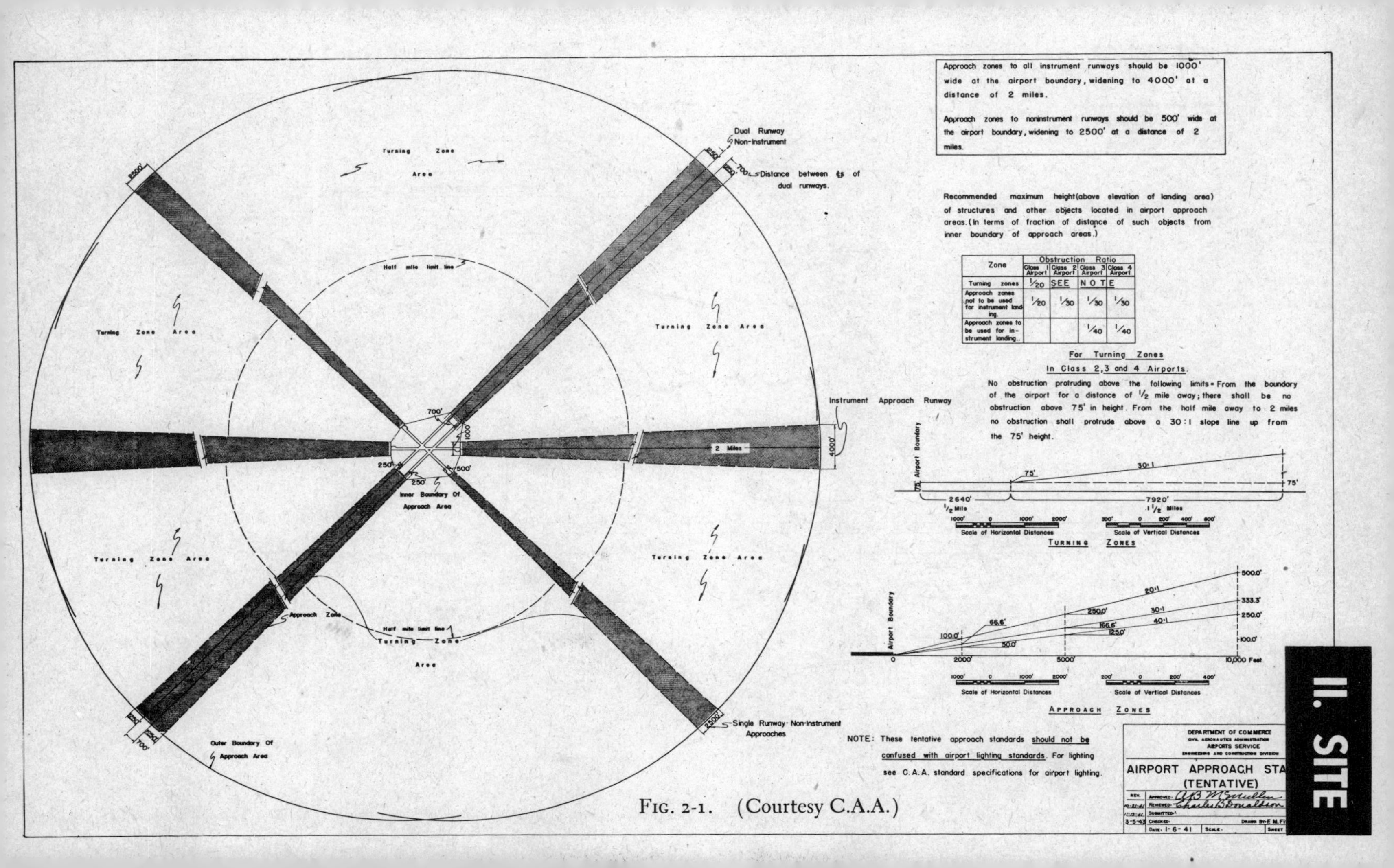

FIG. 2-1. (Courtesy C.A.A.)

II. SITE

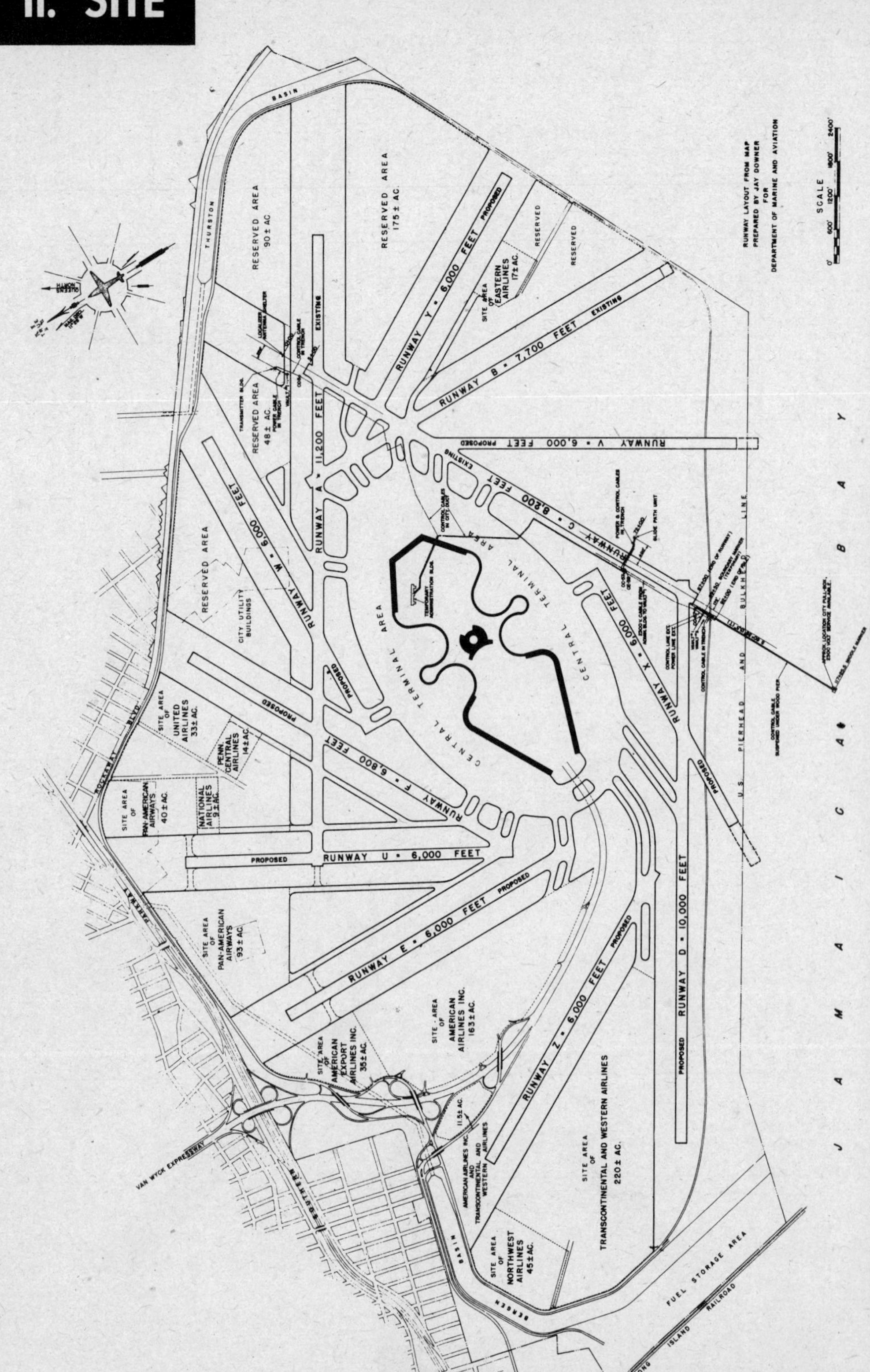

RESERVED AREA
90 ± AC
RESERVED AREA
175 ± AC.
RESERVED
RESERVED
RUNWAY Y • 6,000 FEET
PROPOSED
SITE AREA OF EASTERN AIRLINES 17± AC.
RUNWAY B • 7,700 FEET
EXISTING
RUNWAY A • 11,200 FEET
EXISTING
TRANSMITTER BLDG.
RESERVED AREA
48 ± AC.
RUNWAY V • 6,000 FEET
PROPOSED
RUNWAY C • 8,200 FEET
EXISTING
RESERVED AREA
CITY UTILITY BUILDINGS
RUNWAY W • 6,000 FEET
TEMPORARY ADMINISTRATION BLDG.
CENTRAL TERMINAL AREA
CENTRAL TERMINAL AREA
GLIDE PATH UNIT
RUNWAY X • 6,000 FEET
PROPOSED
SITE AREA OF UNITED AIRLINES 33± AC.
PENN. CENTRAL AIRLINES 14± AC.
RUNWAY F • 6,800 FEET
SITE AREA OF PAN-AMERICAN AIRWAYS 40± AC.
NATIONAL AIRLINES 9± AC.
PROPOSED
RUNWAY U • 6,000 FEET
RUNWAY E • 6,000 FEET
PROPOSED
SITE AREA OF PAN-AMERICAN AIRWAYS 93 ± AC.
SITE AREA OF AMERICAN AIRLINES INC. 163± AC.
SITE AREA OF AMERICAN EXPORT AIRLINES INC. 35± AC.
RUNWAY Z • 6,000 FEET
PROPOSED
PROPOSED
RUNWAY D • 10,000 FEET
11.5± AC.
AMERICAN AIRLINES INC AND TRANSCONTINENTAL AND WESTERN AIRLINES
SITE AREA OF TRANSCONTINENTAL AND WESTERN AIRLINES 220± AC.
SITE AREA OF NORTHWEST AIRLINES 45± AC.
THURSTON
BASIN
BERGEN
BASIN
ROCKAWAY BLVD
VAN WYCK EXPRESSWAY
FUEL STORAGE AREA
LONG ISLAND RAILROAD
U S PIERHEAD AND BULKHEAD LINE
CONTROL CABLE SUSPENDED UNDER WOOD PIER
J A M A I C A B A Y
RUNWAY LAYOUT FROM MAP
PREPARED BY JAY DOWNER
FOR
DEPARTMENT OF MARINE AND AVIATION
SCALE
0' 600' 1200' 1800' 2400'

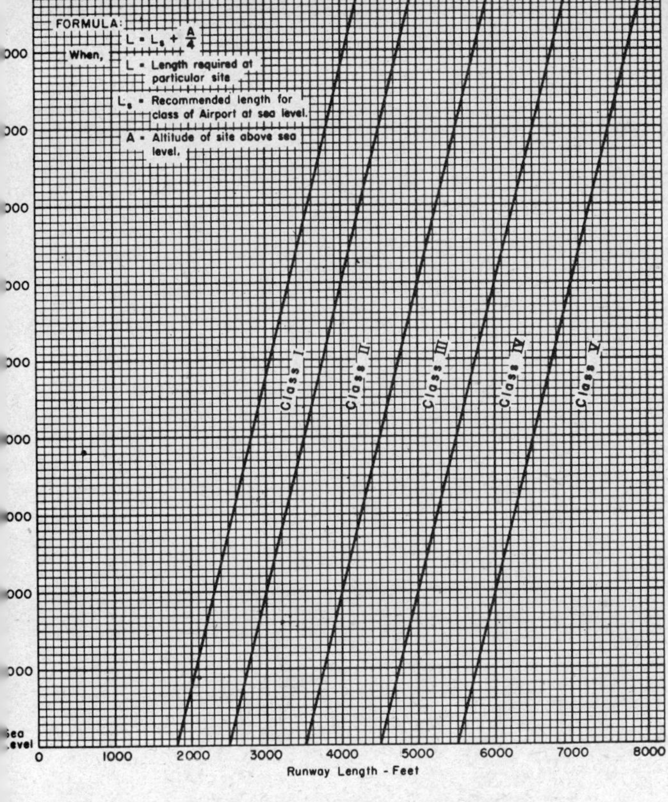

FIG. 3-1. Effect of Altitude Above Sea Level on Required Runway Length by Airport Class. (Courtesy C.A.A.)

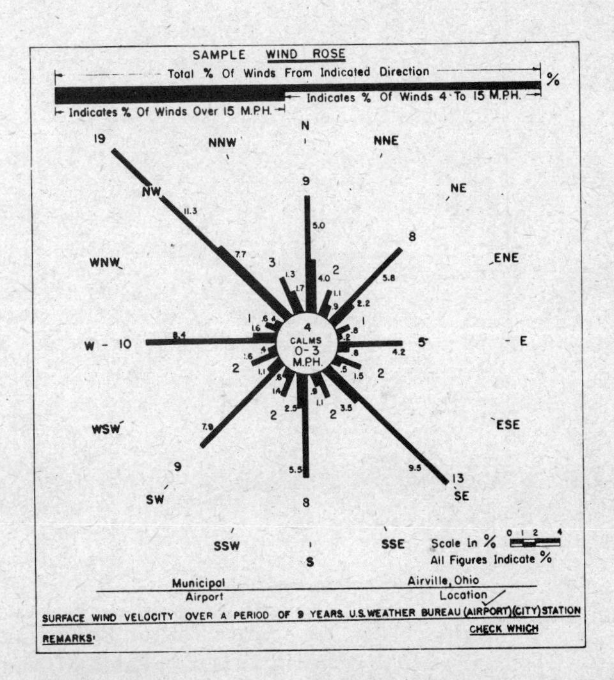

FIG. 3-2. (Courtesy C.A.A.)

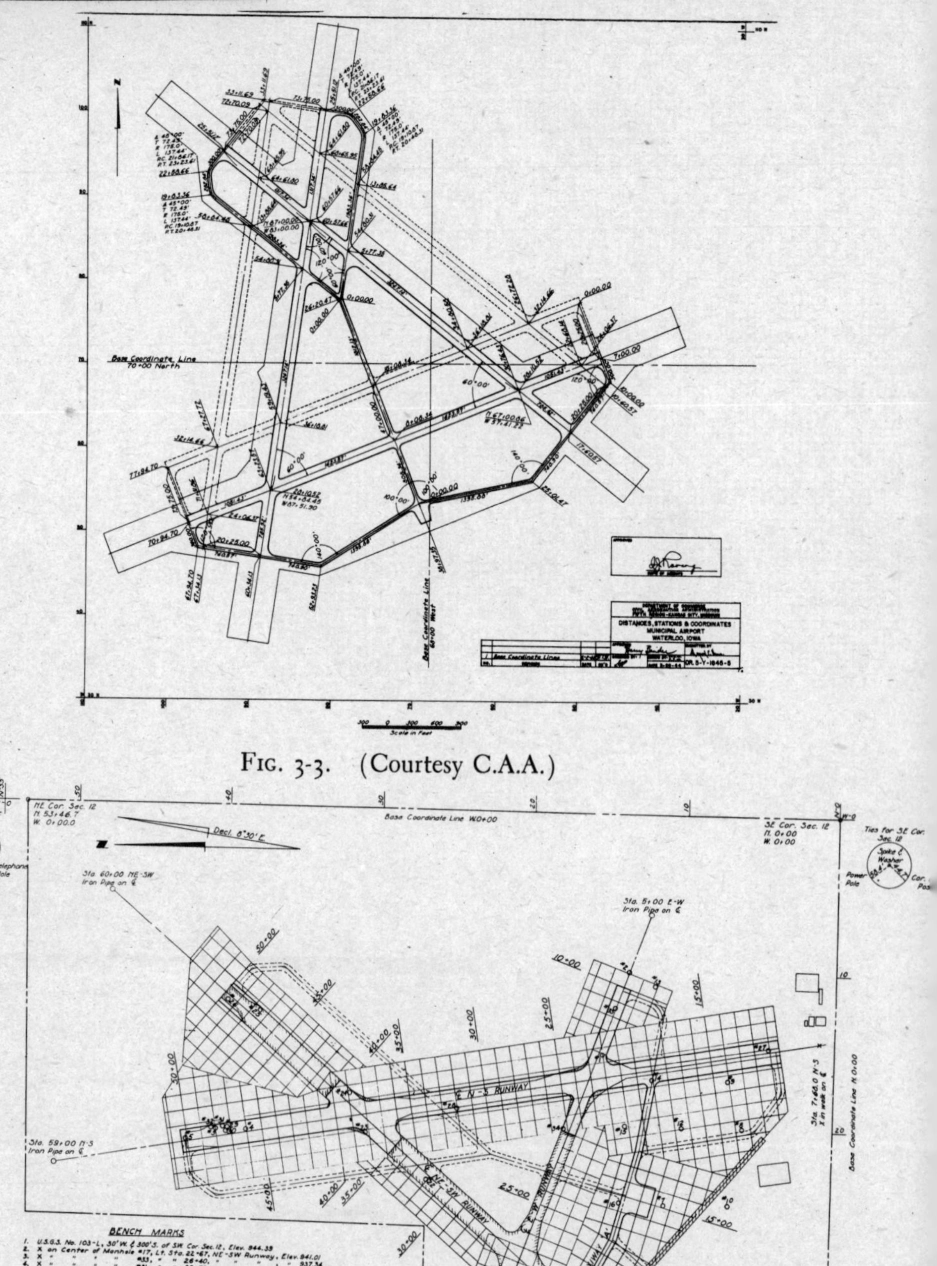

FIG. 3-3. (Courtesy C.A.A.)

FIG. 3-4. Grid Plan and Boring Locations, Atkinson Airport, Pittsburg, Kansas. (Courtesy C.A.A.)

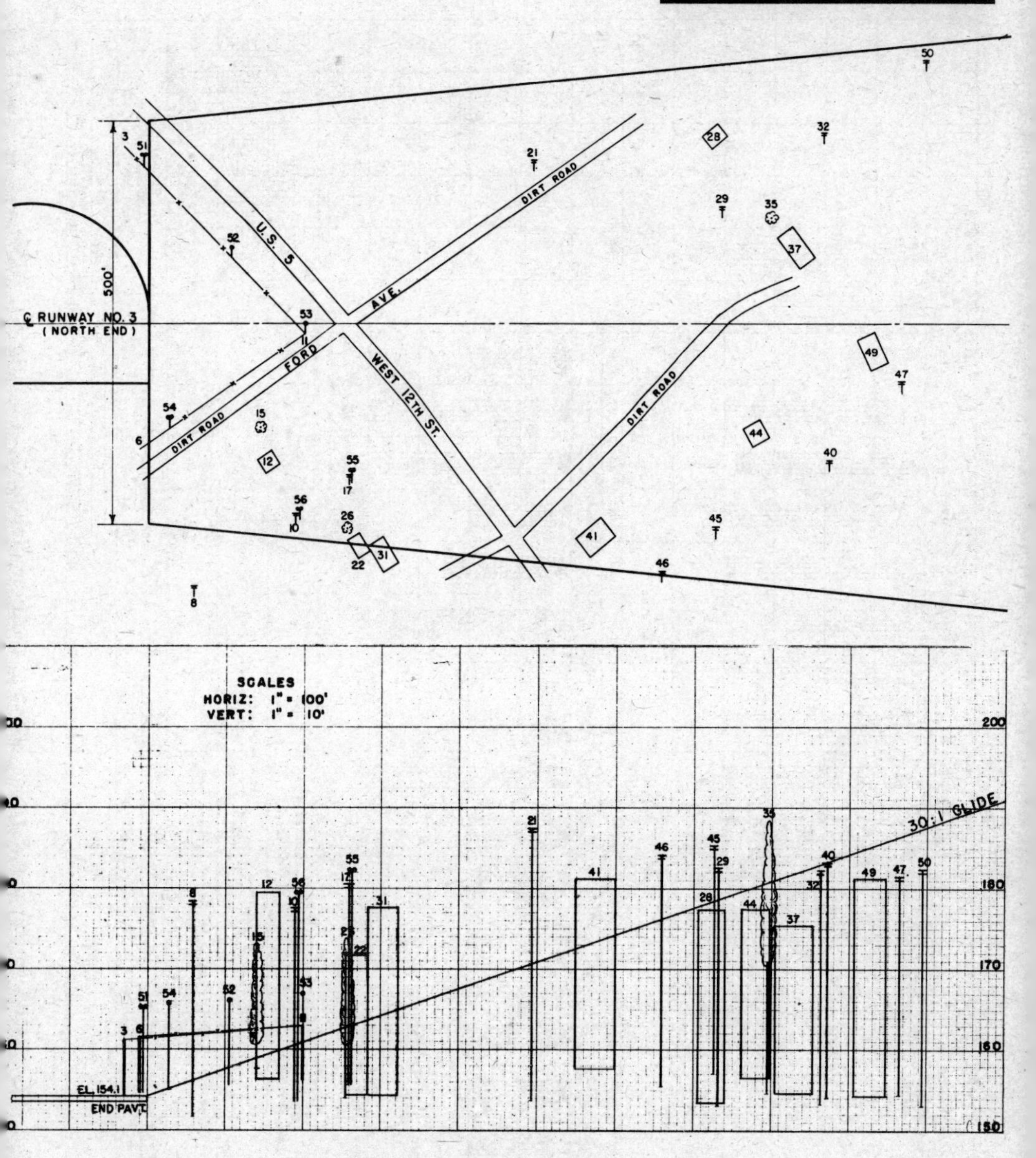

Fig. 3-5. Approach Zone Clearing Plan.
(Courtesy C.A.A.)

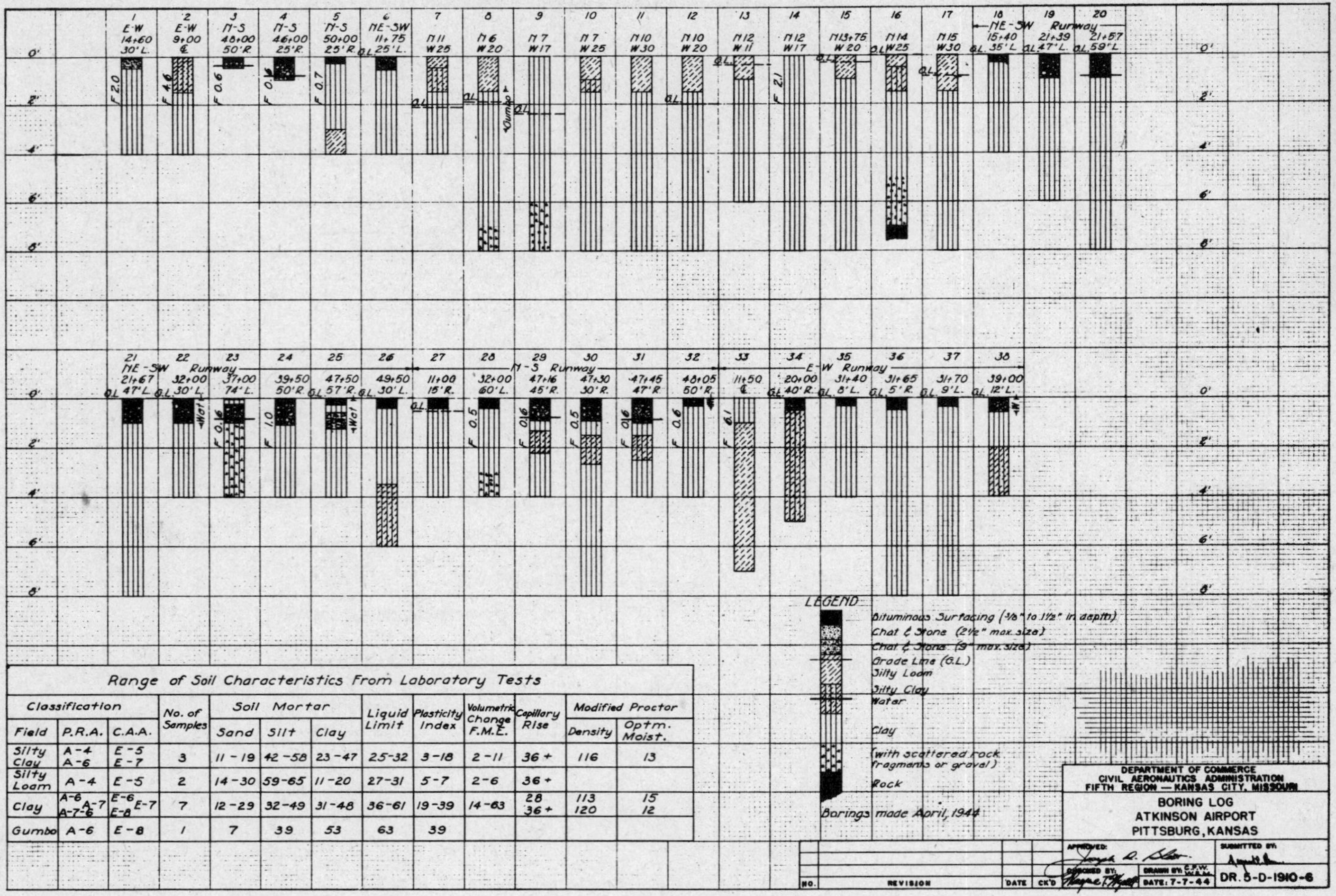

Range of Soil Characteristics From Laboratory Tests

Classification			No. of Samples	Soil Mortar			Liquid Limit	Plasticity Index	Volumetric Change F.M.E.	Capillary Rise	Modified Proctor	
Field	P.R.A.	C.A.A.		Sand	Silt	Clay					Density	Optm. Moist.
Silty Clay	A-4 A-6	E-5 E-7	3	11 - 19	42 - 58	23 - 47	25-32	3 - 18	2 - 11	36 +	116	13
Silty Loam	A - 4	E - 5	2	14 - 30	59-65	11 - 20	27-31	5 - 7	2 - 6	36 +		
Clay	A-6 A-7 A-7-6	E-6 E-7 E-8	7	12 - 29	32-49	31 - 48	36-61	19-39	14-63	28 36 +	113 120	15 12
Gumbo	A - 6	E - 8	1	7	39	53	63	39				

LEGEND

Bituminous Surfacing (3/8" to 1 1/2" in depth)
Chat & Stone (2 1/2" max. size)
Chat & Stone (9" max. size)
Grade Line (G.L.)
Silty Loam
Silty Clay
Water
Clay
(with scattered rock fragments or gravel)
Rock

Borings made April, 1944

DEPARTMENT OF COMMERCE
CIVIL AERONAUTICS ADMINISTRATION
FIFTH REGION — KANSAS CITY, MISSOURI

BORING LOG
ATKINSON AIRPORT
PITTSBURG, KANSAS

DRAWN BY: C.P.W. W.A.M. DATE: 7-7-44 DR. 5-D-1910-6

FIG. 3-6. Refer to Fig. 3-4 for plan showing location of borings. (Courtesy C.A.A.)

Fig. 3-7a. Plate Bearing Test Equipment Using Loaded Trucks to Obtain Necessary Reaction. (Courtesy U. S. Navy.)

Fig. 3-7b. Plate Bearing Test Equipment. (Courtesy U. S. Navy.)

Fig. 3-7c. Mounting of Surface Gauge Dials on Plate Bearing Test Equipment. (Courtesy U. S. Navy.)

IV. SOILS

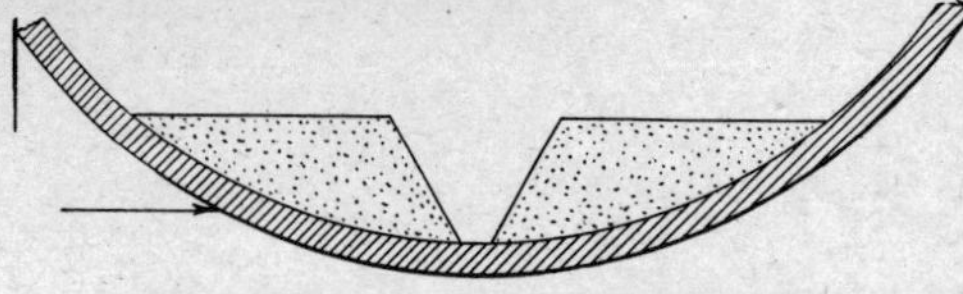

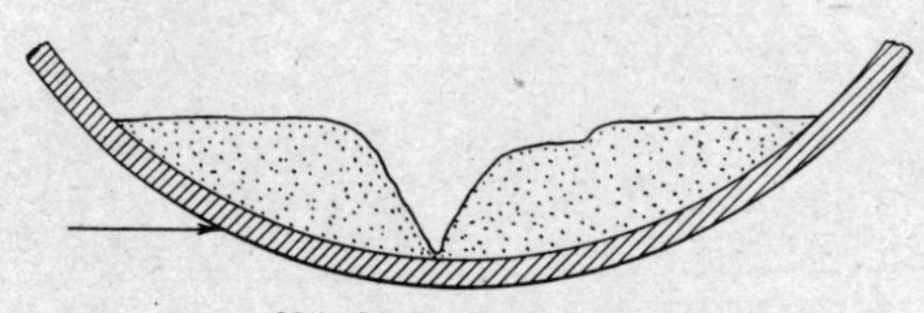

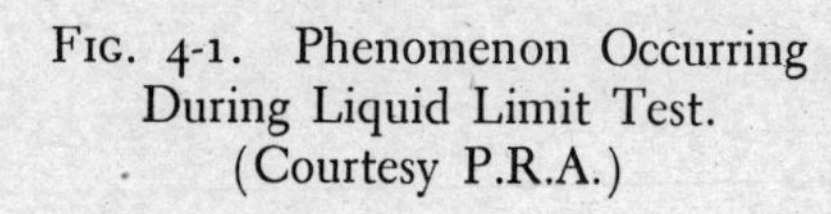
Fig. 4-1. Phenomenon Occurring During Liquid Limit Test. (Courtesy P.R.A.)

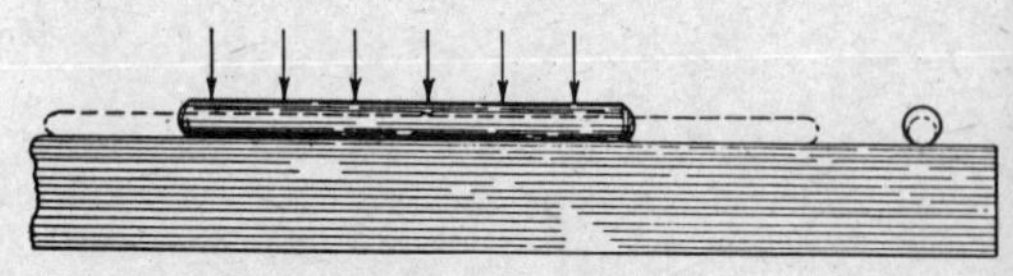

Fig. 4-2. Phenomenon Occurring During Plastic Limit Test. (Courtesy P.R.A.)

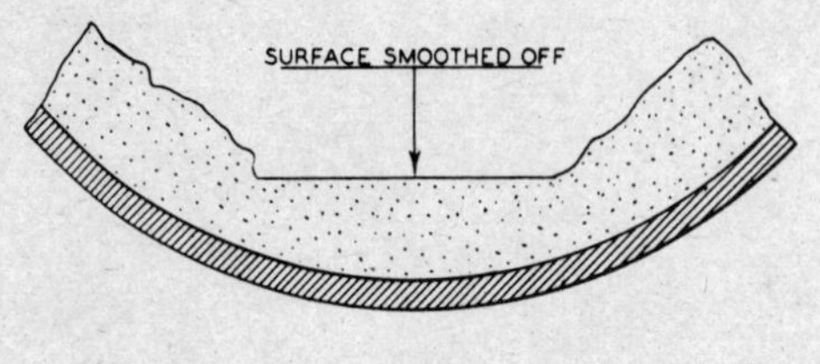

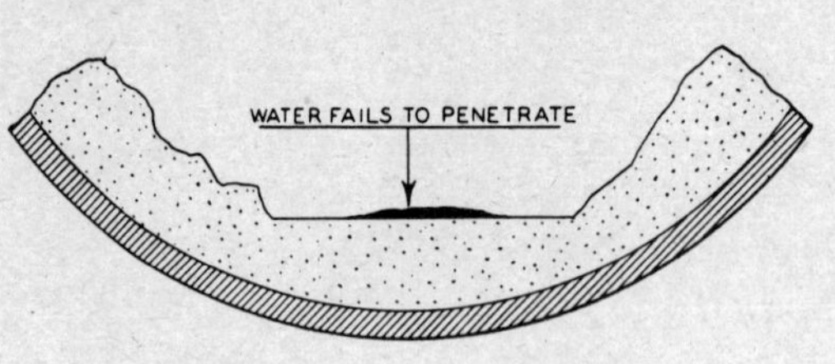

Fig. 4-3. Phenomenon Occurring During the Field Moisture Equivalent Test. (Courtesy P.R.A.)

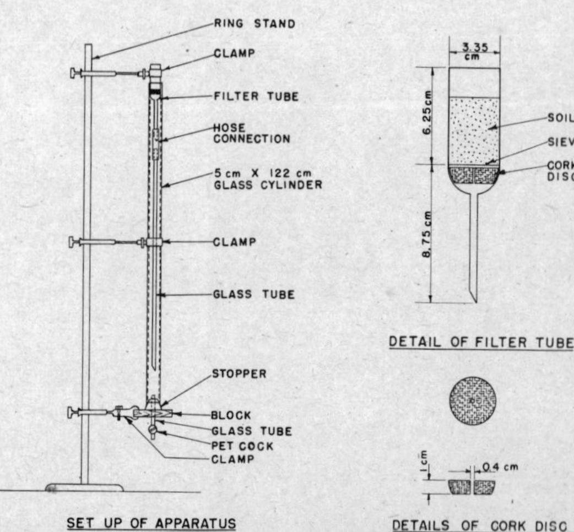

Fig. 4-4. Capillary Rise Apparatus.

LABORATORY REPORT

Lab. No.	Sample No.	Boring No.	Sta.	
42222	1	7	255+32	Lt.
42223	2	4	355+50	CL
42224	3	3	354+00	CL
42225	4	1	341+00	CL

LAB. NO.		42222	42223	42224	42225
Colloid	(per cent)	0	0	0	0
Clay	" "	0	0	0	0
Silt	" "	6.4	4.8	1.6	20.8
Fine Sand	" "	51.9	55.4	88.4	75.7
Coarse Sand	" "	39.2	37.8	10.0	3.5
Coarse Material	" "	2.1	0.9	0	0
Retained on No. 4 Sieve	" "	0.4	1.1	0	0
		100.0	100.0	100.0	100.0
Total Passing 3/8" Sieve	" "	100.0	100.0		
" " No. 4 "	" "	99.6	98.9		
" " " 10 "	" "	97.5	98.0	100.0	100.0
" " " 20 "	" "	94.3	96.2	99.7	99.0
" " " 40 "	" "	80.5	79.7	99.1	97.8
" " " 60 "	" "	58.3	60.2	90.0	96.5
" " "140 "	" "	30.0	22.2	26.2	84.0
" " "200 "	" "	20.0	15.8	14.6	77.2
Liquid Limit	" "	24.3	22.2	28.6	24.2
Plastic Limit	" "	N.P.	N.P.	N.P.	22.8
Plastic Index	" "	"	"	"	1.4
Shrinkage Limit	" "	21.3	20.5	23.6	22.2
Centrifuge Moist. Equiv.	" "	4.0	12.2	6.0	2.0
Field Moisture Equiv.	" "	23.7	21.7	27.8	24.0
Volumetric Change at FME	" "	3.4	1.7	5.9	2.5
Capillary Rise (inches)		10	8	14	40 plus
Proctor Density in lb/cu ft		114.2	118.5	107.7	112.2
Optimum Moisture (per cent)		9.5	9.1	9.0	12.1

CALIFORNIA BEARING RATIO - DRY

Lab. No.	42222		42223		42224		42225	
Penetration	psi	per cent	psi	per cent	psi	per cent	psi	per cent
0.025"	30		50		100		30	
0.050"	80		120		150		80	
0.075"	160		180		200		150	
0.100"	300	30	270	27	270	27	230	23
0.200"	770	51	620	41	480	32	570	38
0.300"	880	46	800	42	630	33	630	33
0.400"	950	41	750	33	630	27	700	31
0.500"	1000	38	770	30	630	23	650	25

CALIFORNIA BEARING RATIO - SOAKED

	42222		42223		42224		42225	
Expansion	none		none		none		none	
Moisture	13.6%		14.9%		19.0%		17.5%	
Penetration	psi	per cent	psi	per cent	psi	per cent	psi	per cent
0.025"	30		50		30		25	
0.050"	70		100		70		70	
0.075"	160		200		130		100	
0.100"	270	27	280	28	190	19	150	15
0.200"	700	46	600	40	400	27	320	21
0.300"	750	40	630	33	470	25	400	21
0.400"	800	35	680	30	470	21	500	22
0.500"	830	32	700	27	430	17	600	23

FIG. 4-5. Laboratory Test Report. (Courtesy C.A.A.)

IV. SOILS

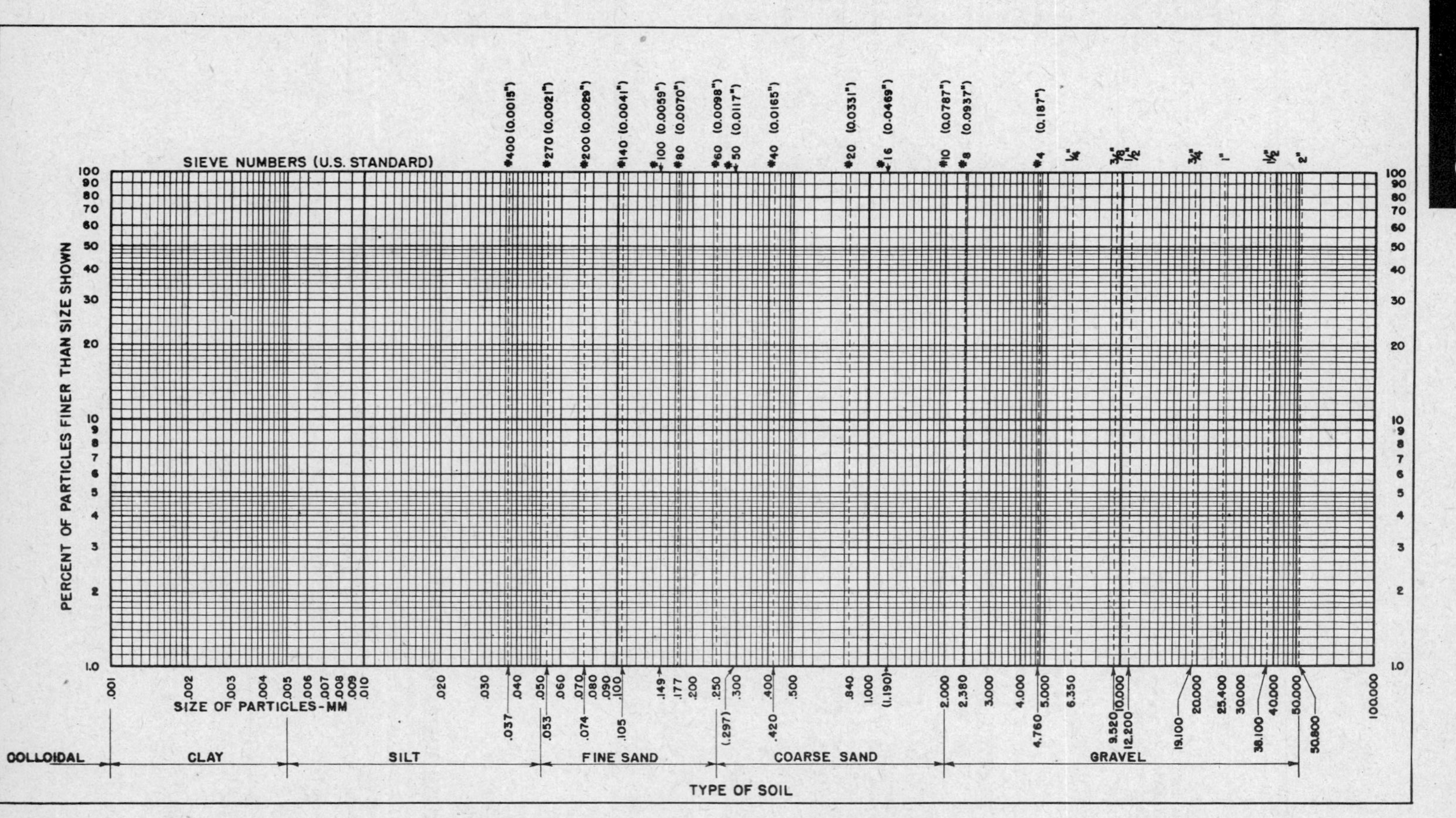

FIG. 4-6. Logarithmic Graph Form. (Courtesy C.A.A.) This form is suitable for record-

Airport ....

Sample No. ....

Location: Station ....
Offset ....
Depth ....

Date Sampled ....
Sampled by ....

Compiled by ....
Checked by ....

SOIL ANALYSIS SUMMARY

Material		Total % Passing	% Passing No. 10 Sieve	% -10 Mat.
Gravel	Larger than 2.0 mm (No. 10 sieve)	....	....	
Coarse sand	2.0 mm to 0.25 mm (No. 60 ")	....	....	....
Fine sand	0.25 mm to 0.05 mm (No. 270 ")	....	....	....
Silt	0.05 mm to 0.005 mm	....	....	....
Clay	Smaller than 0.005 mm	....	....	....
Collodial	Smaller than 0.001 mm	....	....	....

Grains smaller than 0.02 mm ....
" " " No. 200 sieve ....

Liquid limit (-40 material) ....
Plastic limit (" ") ....
Plasticity index (" ") ....
Vol. change at FME (" ") ....
Capillary rise (-10 ") ....

Shrinkage limit ....
Centrifuge moisture equiv. ....
Field moisture equiv. ....
Proctor density, lb/cu ft ....
Optimum moisture ....
Unit dry weight ....

From California Bearing Test

% Dry for 0.1" penetration ....
% " " 0.2" " ....

% Soaked for 0.1" " ....
% " " 0.2" " ....

Expansion ....
Moisture after soaking ....

From Plate Bearing Test

K at ...." deflection (...." diam.plate)

FIG. 4-7. Form for Summary of Results of Laboratory Tests.

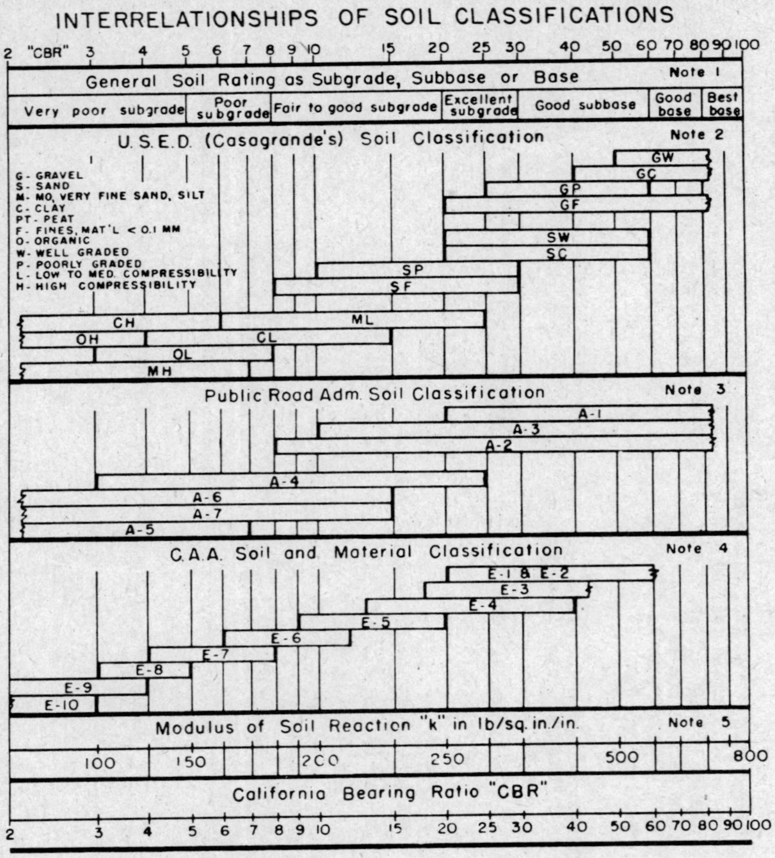

INTERRELATIONSHIPS OF SOIL CLASSIFICATIONS

"CBR" 2 3 4 5 6 7 8 9 10 15 20 25 30 40 50 60 70 80 90 100

General Soil Rating as Subgrade, Subbase or Base — Note 1

Very poor subgrade | Poor subgrade | Fair to good subgrade | Excellent subgrade | Good subbase | Good base | Best base

U. S. E. D. (Casagrande's) Soil Classification — Note 2

G - GRAVEL
S - SAND
M - MO, VERY FINE SAND, SILT
C - CLAY
PT - PEAT
F - FINES, MAT'L < 0.1 MM
O - ORGANIC
W - WELL GRADED
P - POORLY GRADED
L - LOW TO MED. COMPRESSIBILITY
H - HIGH COMPRESSIBILITY

GW, GC, GP, GF, SW, SC, SP, SF, CH, ML, OH, CL, OL, MH

Public Road Adm. Soil Classification — Note 3

A-1, A-3, A-2, A-4, A-6, A-7, A-5

C.A.A. Soil and Material Classification — Note 4

E-1 & E-2, E-3, E-4, E-5, E-6, E-7, E-8, E-9, E-10

Modulus of Soil Reaction "k" in lb/sq. in./in. — Note 5

100 150 200 250 500 800

California Bearing Ratio "CBR"

2 3 4 5 6 7 8 9 10 15 20 25 30 40 50 60 70 80 90 100

NOTES

1. See "Foundations for Flexible Pavement" by O. J. Porter, 22nd An. Mtg. Highway Research Board, 1942 for basic idea.
2. See Engineering Manual, Chapter XX, March 1943, War Dept., Office of the Chief of Engineers. See also "Soil Tests for Design Runway Pavements," by Middlebrooks & Bertran 22nd An. Mtg. H.R.B. 1942.
3. See item (3), A-6 and A-7 soils cut off at CBR = 15, rather than 25 as indicated in Chapter XX. CBR for for A-5 soils of volcanic origin etc. may range above 7 and go as high as + 80
4. See C.A.A. Design Manual for airport pavements March 1, 1944.
5. "k" is factor used in Westergaard's Analysis for thickness of portland cement concrete.

All interrelationships are very approximate. Actual field and laboratory tests are required to determine "k", "CBR" and bearing values.

INTERRELATIONSHIPS
SOIL CLASSIFICATIONS

FIG. 4-8.

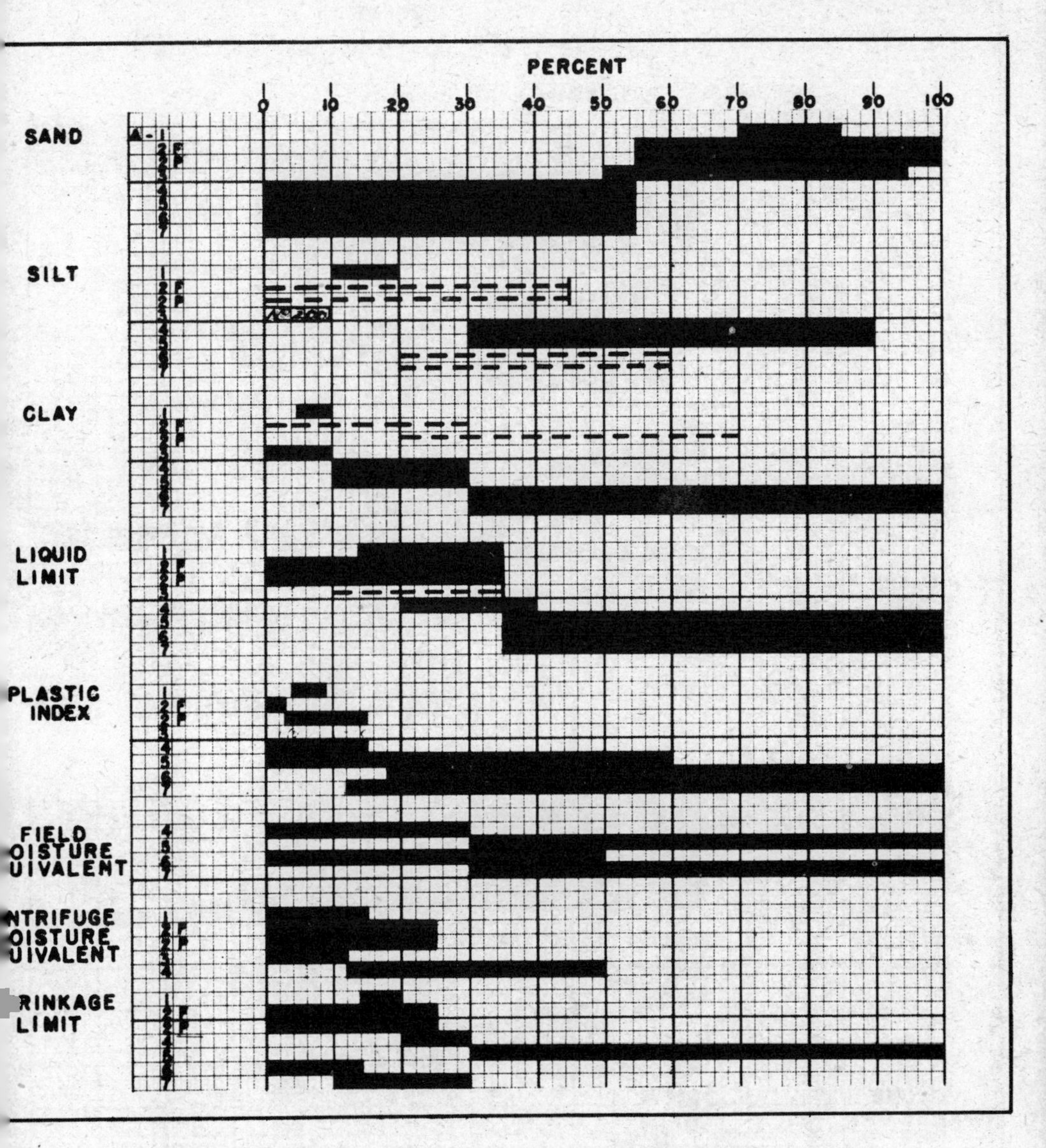

FIG. 4-9. P.R.A. Soil Classification Method Shown Graphically for Ready Reference. Dashed lines indicate other commonly accepted limits.

IV. SOILS

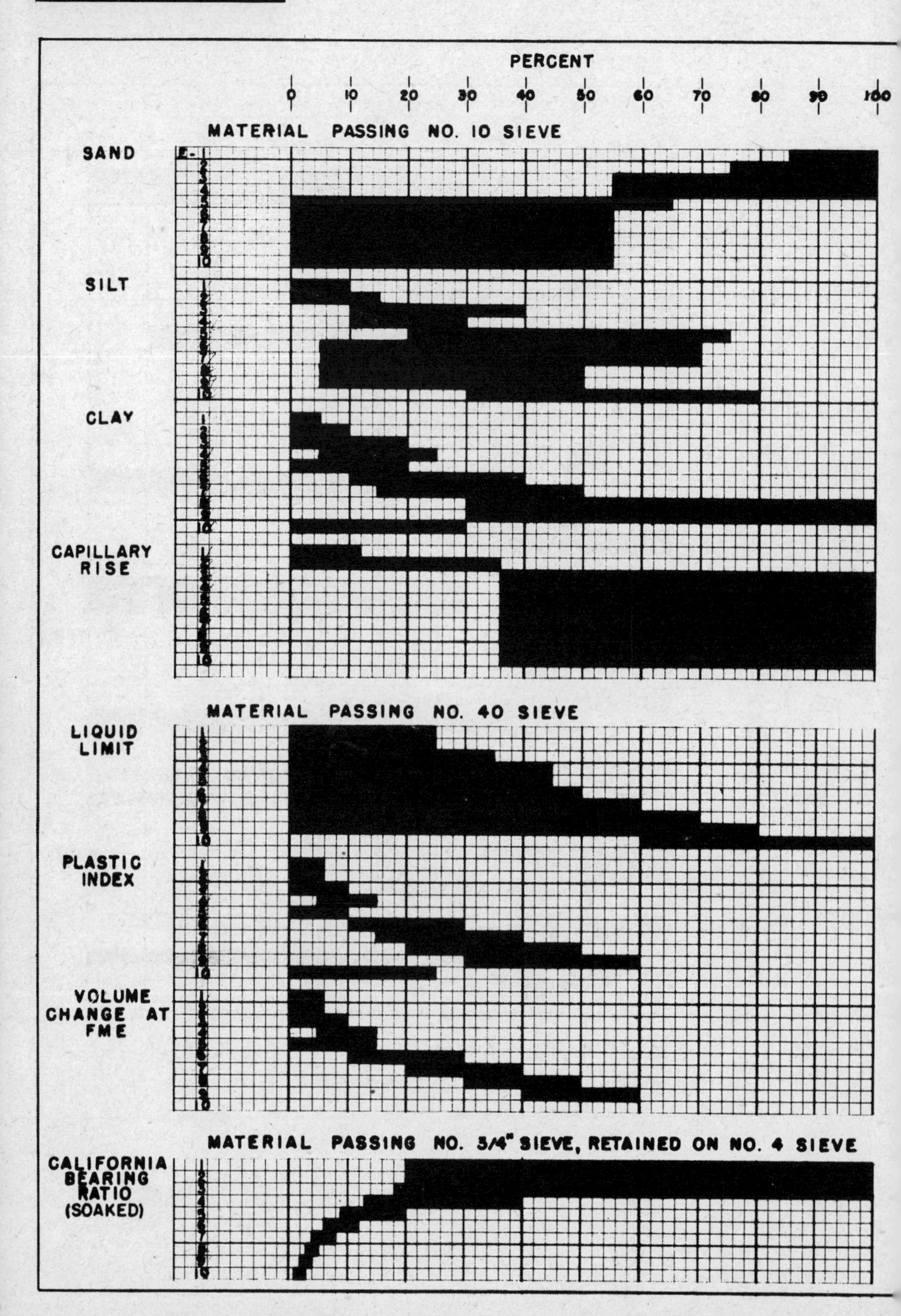

FIG. 4-11. Overlapping of Soil Groups as Classified by C.A.A. Method.

AIRPORT ____________

SAMPLE ____________									
SOIL	SAND	SILT	CLAY	L.L.	P.I.	VOL. CHANGE F.M.E.	CAP RISE -10 MAT.	C.B. RATIO SOAKED	
E-1									
2									
3									
4									
5									
6									
7									
8									
9									
10									
CLASSIFICATION NO.									

FIG. 4-12. Form to Assist in Classifying Soil Groups by C.A.A. Method.

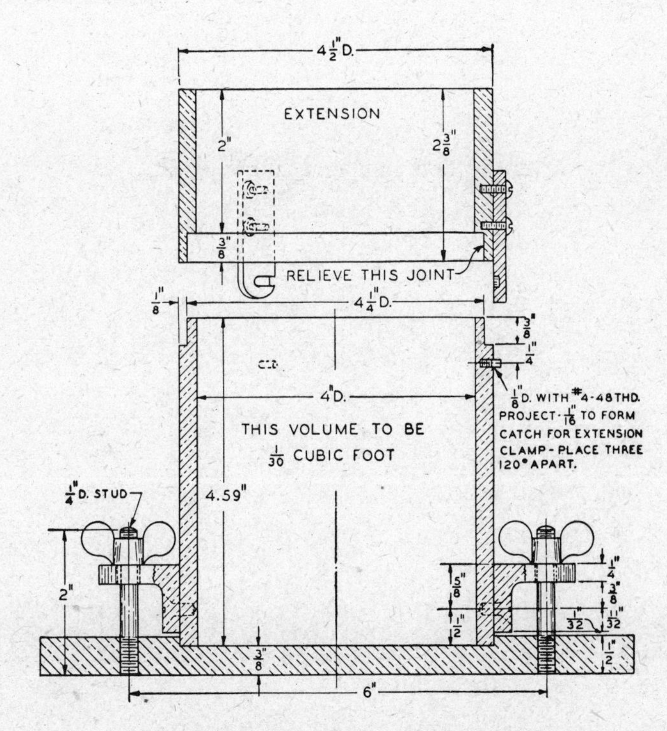

FIG. 4-13. Compaction Mold. (Courtesy P.R.A.)

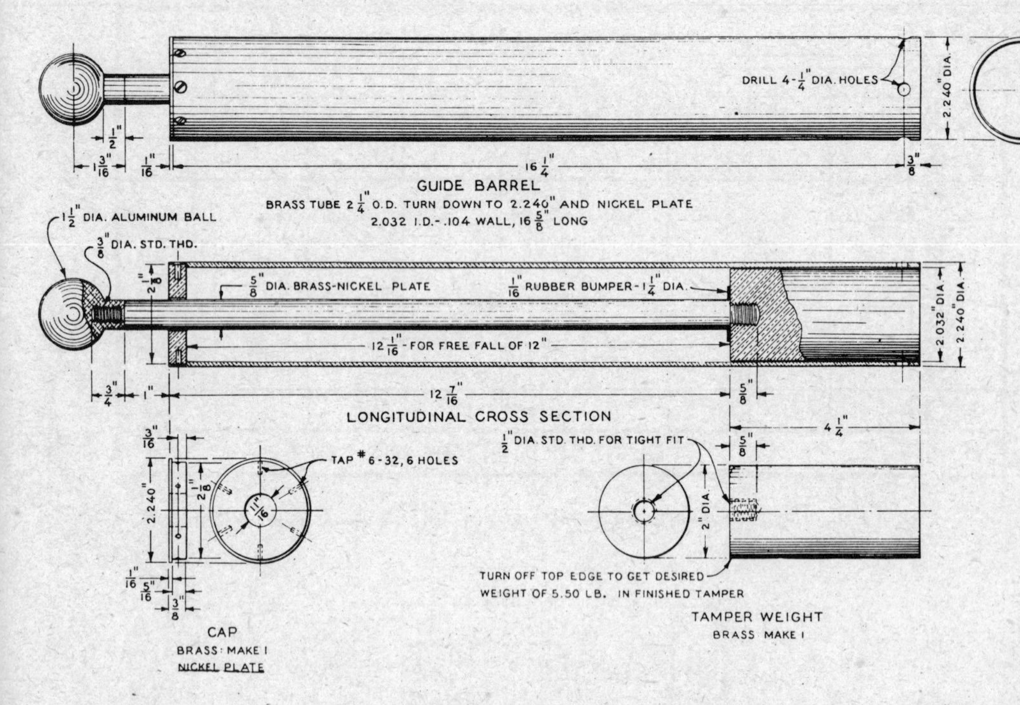

FIG. 4-14. Soil Tamper. (Courtesy P.R.A.)

A.A.S.H.O. DESIGNATION T-99
MODIFIED ACCORDING TO C.A.A. SPECIFICATIONS

TEST NO. P-7

MUNICIPAL AIRPORT LOCATION GREENVILLE DATE 5-15-44.

LOCATION OF SAMPLE 215+00, 50' Rt., ELEV. 785.4 DESCRIPTION Yellowish Sand, Clay, and Gravel.

MOISTURE DETERMINATION							DENSITY			
PAN NO.	WT. MOIST SOIL AND PAN (GMS)	WT. DRY SOIL AND PAN (GMS)	WT. OF PAN (GMS)	MOISTURE LOSS (GMS)	WT. DRY SOIL (GMS)	PER CENT MOISTURE	WT. MOIST SOIL AND MOLD (GMS)	WT. MOIST SOIL (GMS)	WT. DRY SOIL (GMS)	DENSITY DRY SOIL lb per cu ft
A	278.2	261.3	78.2	16.9	183.1	9.2	4151	1949	1785	117.8
"	278.2	260.0	78.2	18.2	181.8	10.0	4232	2030	1845	121.8
"	"	258.7	"	19.5	180.5	10.8	4288	2086	1883	124.3
"	"	256.6	"	21.6	178.4	12.1	4348	2146	1914	126.3
"	"	254.1	"	24.1	175.9	13.7	4353	2151	1892	124.9
"	"	252.3	"	25.9	174.1	14.9	4305	2103	1830	120.8

DATA FROM MOISTURE – DENSITY CURVE

Modified Standard Density 126.4 lb per cu ft

Optimum Moisture 12.4 Per cent

Per cent Moisture = $\frac{\text{Wt. Moist Soil and Pan} - \text{Wt. Dry Soil and Pan}}{\text{Wt. Dry Soil and Pan} - \text{Wt. of Pan}} \times 100$

Wt. of Moist Soil = Wt. of Moist Soil and Mold – Wt. of Mold

Wt. of Dry Soil = $\frac{\text{Wt. of Moist Soil}}{\text{Per cent of Moisture} + 100} \times 100$

Density Dry Soil, lb per cu ft = 0.066 x Wt. Dry Soil

Wt. of Mold 2202 Gms

Technician L. Soriero

Res. Engineer V. J. Guccione

Remarks: Sprinkled before Rolling
6 passes by 10 ton, – 3 Wheel Roller.

FIG. 4-15.

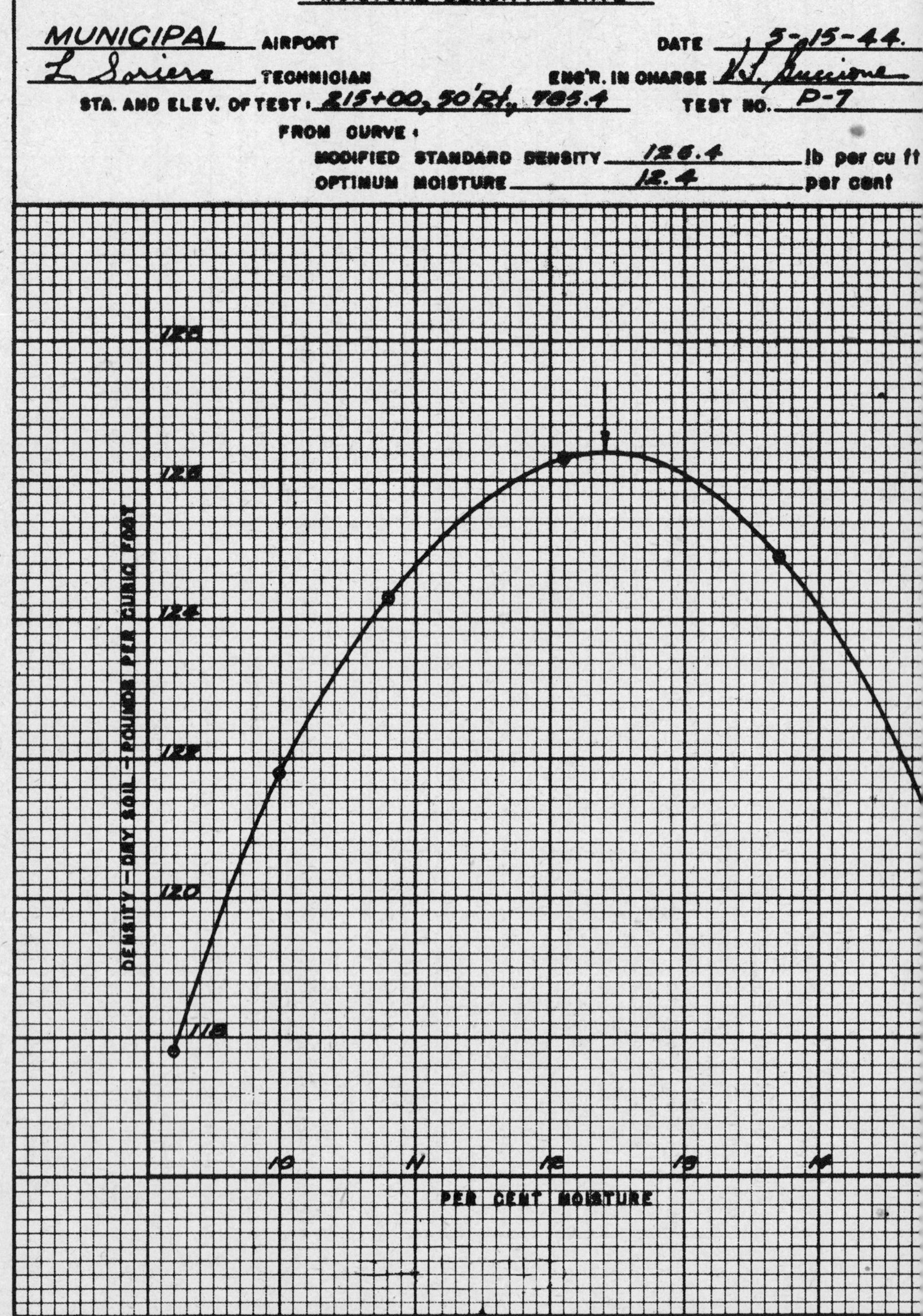

MOISTURE DENSITY CURVE

MUNICIPAL AIRPORT DATE 5-15-44.

L. Soriero TECHNICIAN ENG'R. IN CHARGE V. J. Succione

STA. AND ELEV. OF TEST: 215+00, 50' Rt., 785.4 TEST NO. P-7

FROM CURVE:

MODIFIED STANDARD DENSITY 126.4 lb per cu ft

OPTIMUM MOISTURE 12.4 per cent

Fig. 4-16.

FIG. 4-17. Sand Jar with Funnel for Use in Soil Density Determinations.

FIG. 4-18. Rubber Sack with Measuring Jar for Use in Soil Density Determinations. This apparatus may be used instead of the sand jar shown in Fig. 4-17. Although similar results may be obtained, this apparatus is suitable only when the hole is very smooth, because the rubber sack is not sufficiently flexible to fill all the voids when the surface of the hole is rough.
(Courtesy P.R.A.)

FIELD DENSITY TEST

MUNICIPAL AIRPORT DATE 5-15-44.

L. Soriero TECHNICIAN ENG'R. IN CHARGE V. S. Buccione

STA. AND ELEV. OF TEST: 215+00, 50' Rt., 785.4 TEST NO. P

(1) SAND IN CONTAINER	GRAMS		36
(2) SAND LEFT IN CONTAINER	"		17
(3) SAND IN HOLE AND CONE	"	(1) less (2)	186
(4) SAND LEFT IN CONE	"	(by calibration)	62
(5) SAND IN CORE HOLE	"	(3) less (4)	12
(6) DRY WT. SOIL AND ROCK MIXTURE	"	(adjusted measurement)	16
(7) DRY WT. ROCK (plus NO. 4 material)	"		3,
(8) DRY WT. SOIL (minus NO. 4 material)	"		12
(9) PER CENT ROCK [(7) ÷ (6) X 100]			23
(10) DENSITY STANDARD SAND, lb per cu ft			9
(11) SPEC. GRAVITY OF ROCK IN MIXTURE		(A.A.S.H.O.-T-85)	2.
(12) DENSITY OF MIXTURE, lb per cu ft [(6) ÷ (5) X (10)]			12
(13) LBS OF ROCK PER CU FT OF MIXTURE [(9) X (12)]			3
(14) VOL. OF ROCK PER CU FT OF MIXTURE [(13)] ÷ [(11) X 62.4]			0.1
(15) VOLUME OF SOIL PER CU FT OF MIXTURE [1.000 less (14)]			0.8
(16) LBS OF SOIL PER CU FT OF MIXTURE [(12) less (13)]			9
(17) FIELD DENSITY OF MINUS NO. 4 MATERIAL, lb per cu ft [(16 ÷ (15)]			12
(18) MODIFIED STANDARD DENSITY, lb per cu ft (See Fig. 4-15)			12
(19) PER CENT MODIFIED STANDARD DENSITY OBTAINED [(17) ÷ (18) X 100]			9
MINUS NO. 4 MOISTURE DETERMINATION — OPTIMUM (See Fig. 4-15)			12.
(a) CONTAINER PLUS WET WT. OF SOIL			27
(b) CONTAINER PLUS DRY WT. OF SOIL			25
(c) MOISTURE LOSS [(a) less (b)]			20
(d) WT. OF CONTAINER			7
(e) NET WT. OF DRY SOIL [(b) less (d)]			17
(f) PER CENT OF MOISTURE [(c) ÷ (e) X 100]			11.

REMARKS: Yellowish Sand, Clay, and gravel Subgrade, Sprinkled before Rolling. 6 passes by 10 ton, 3 Wheel Roller.

FIG. 4-19.

V. DESIGNS

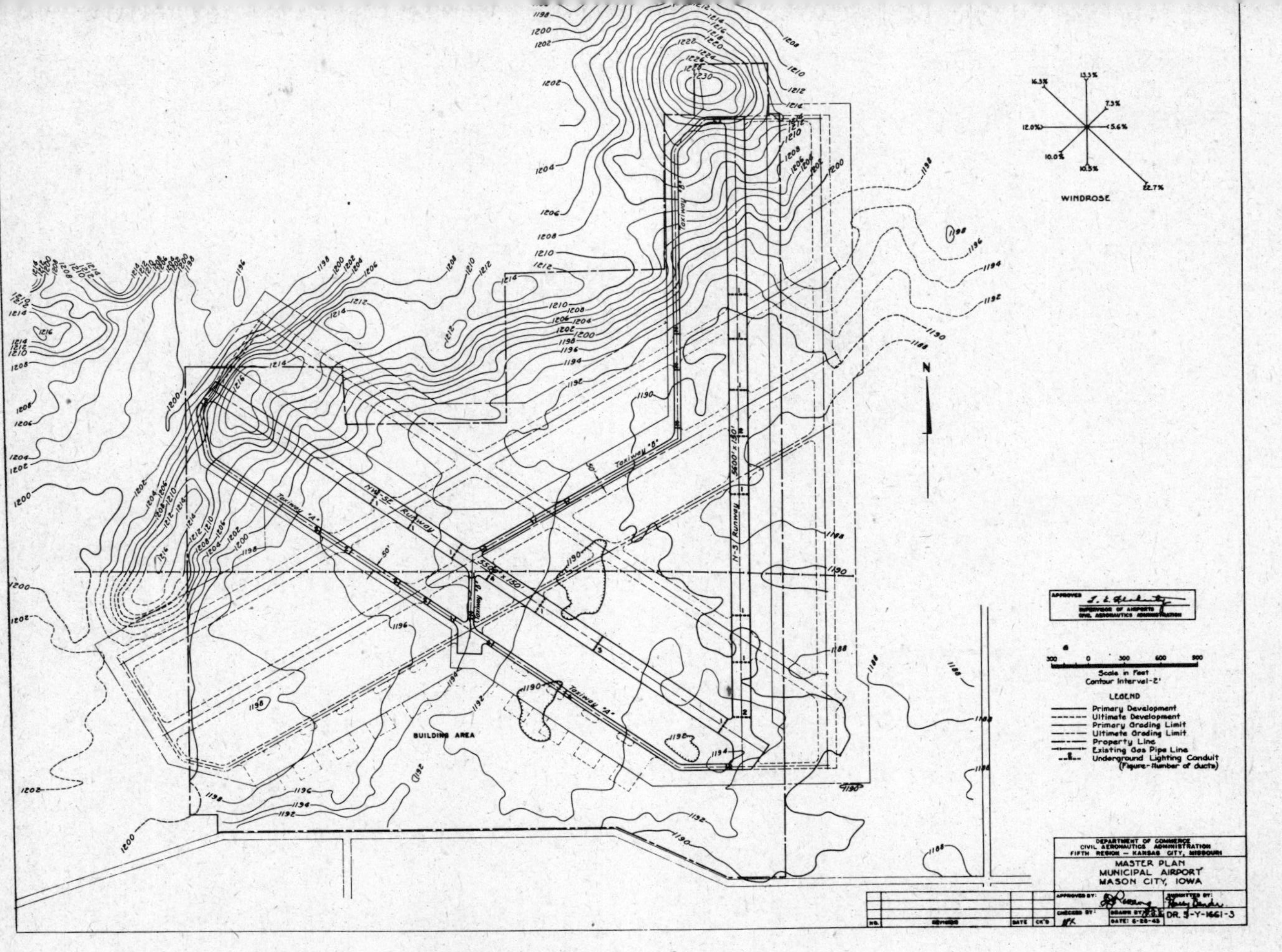

FIG. 5-1. (Courtesy C.A.A.)

V. DESIGNS

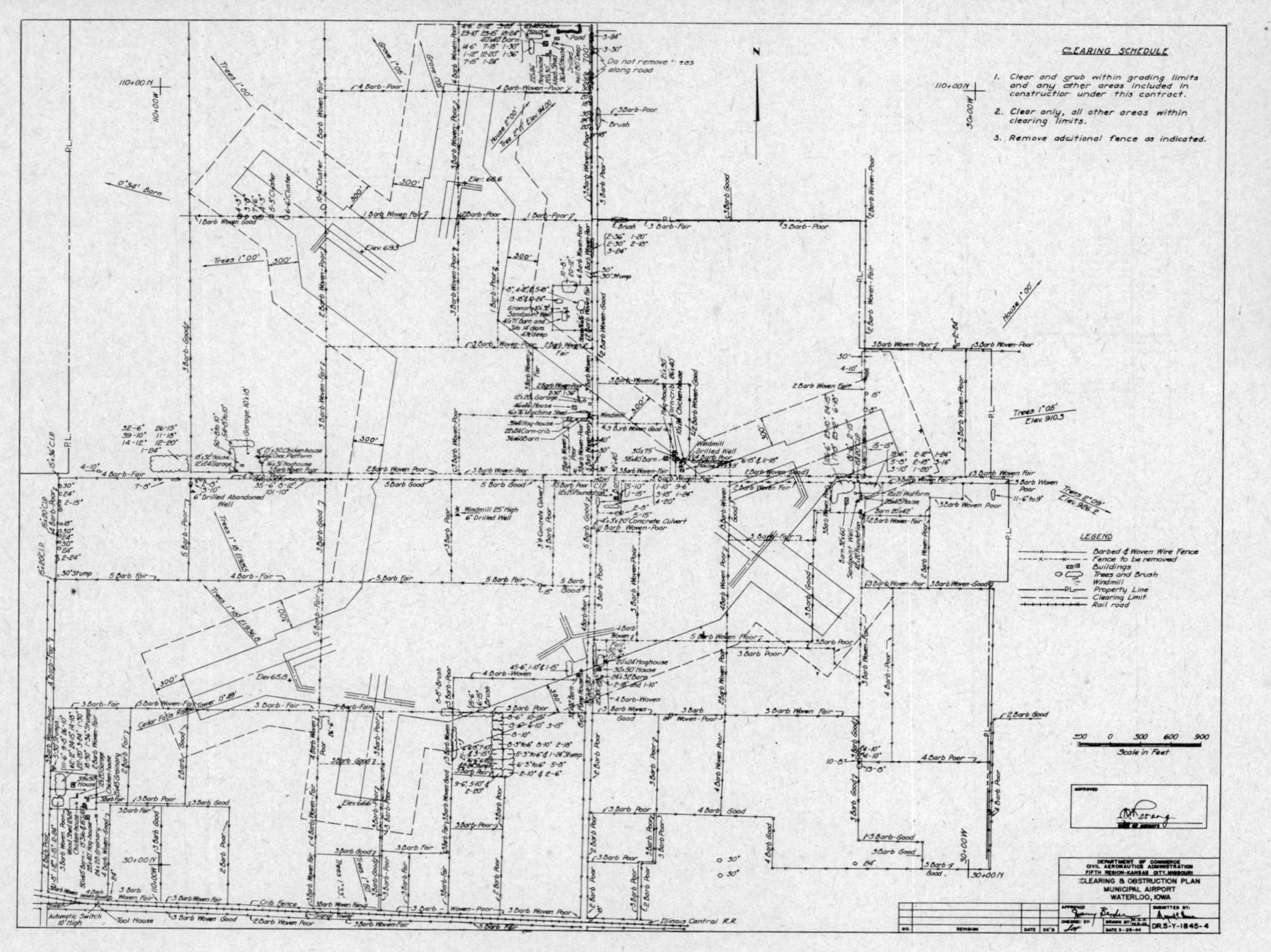

FIG. 5-2. (Courtesy C.A.A.)

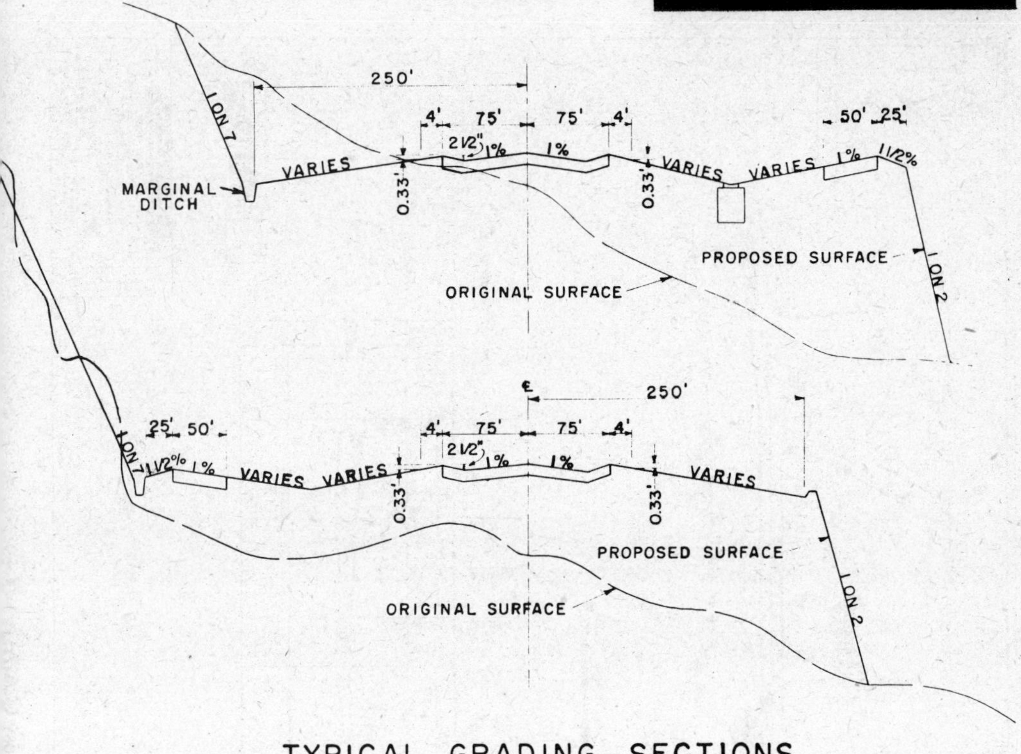

TYPICAL GRADING SECTIONS

FIG. 5-3.

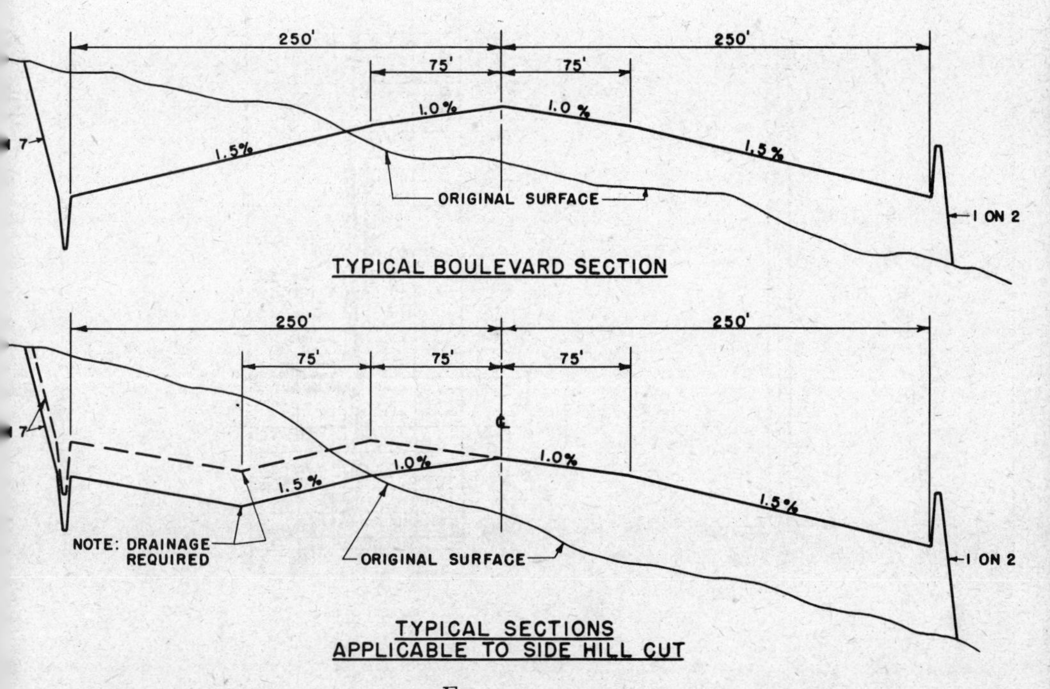

FIG. 5-4.

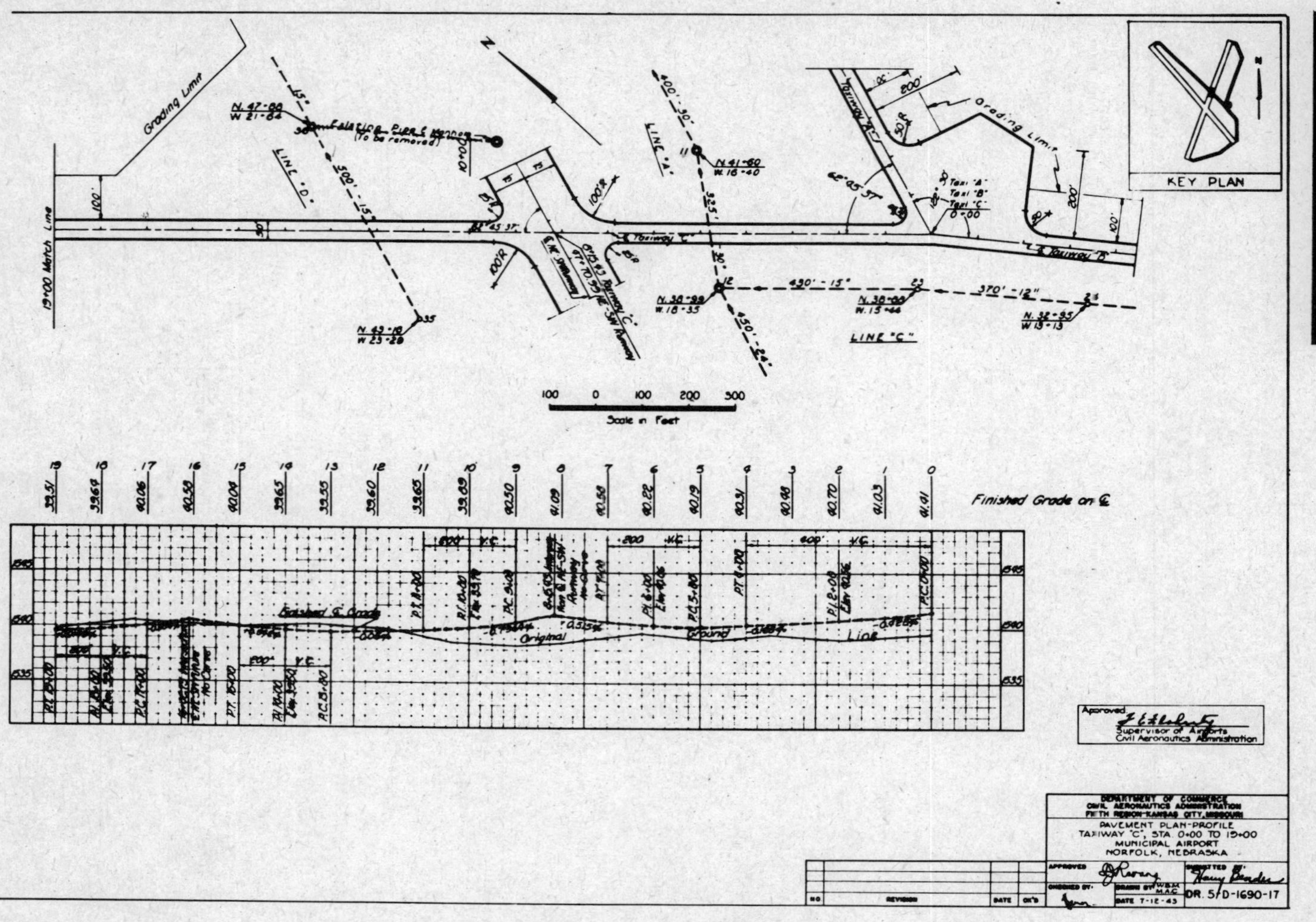

FIG. 5-5a. (Courtesy C.A.A.)

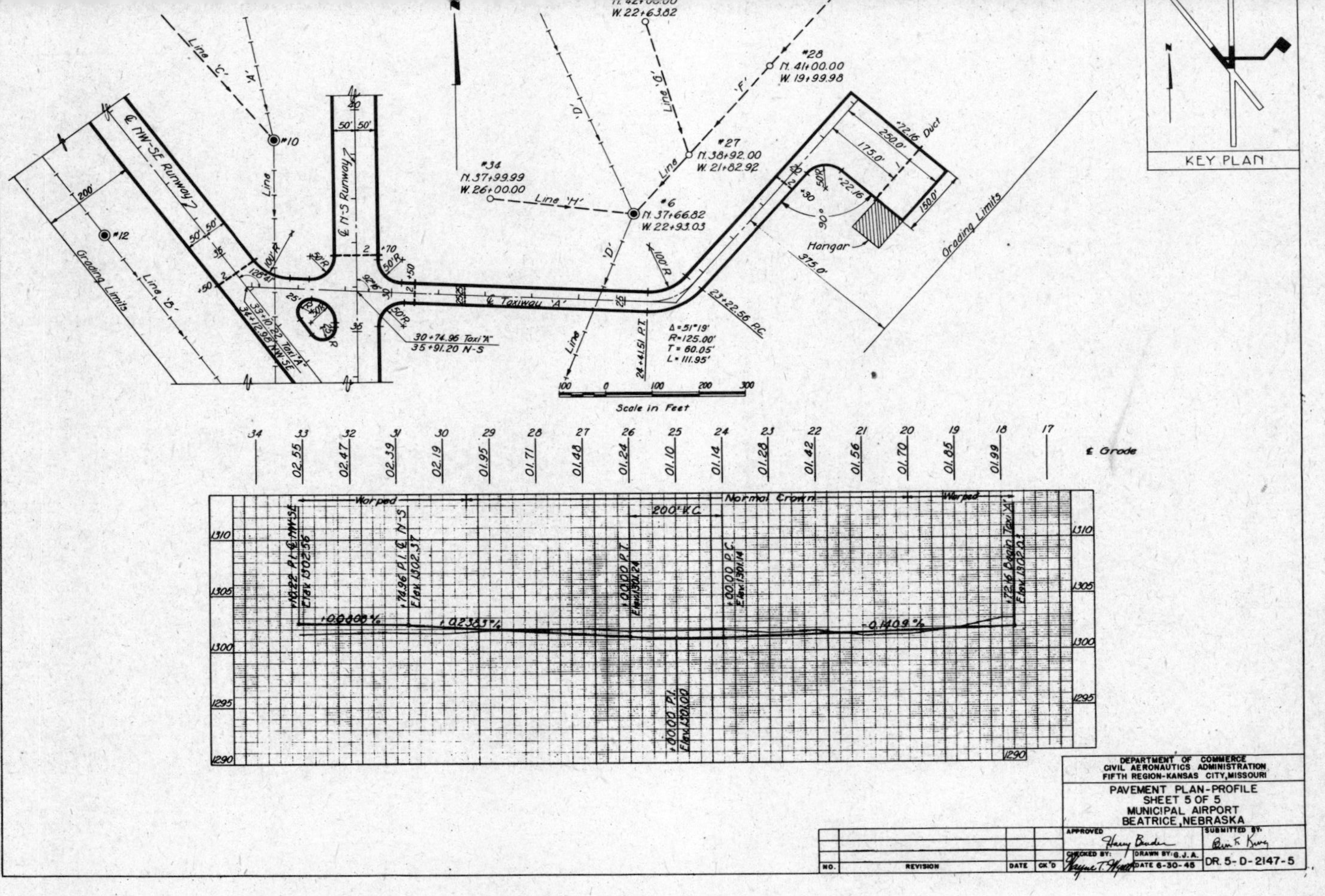

FIG. 5-5b. (Courtesy C.A.A.)

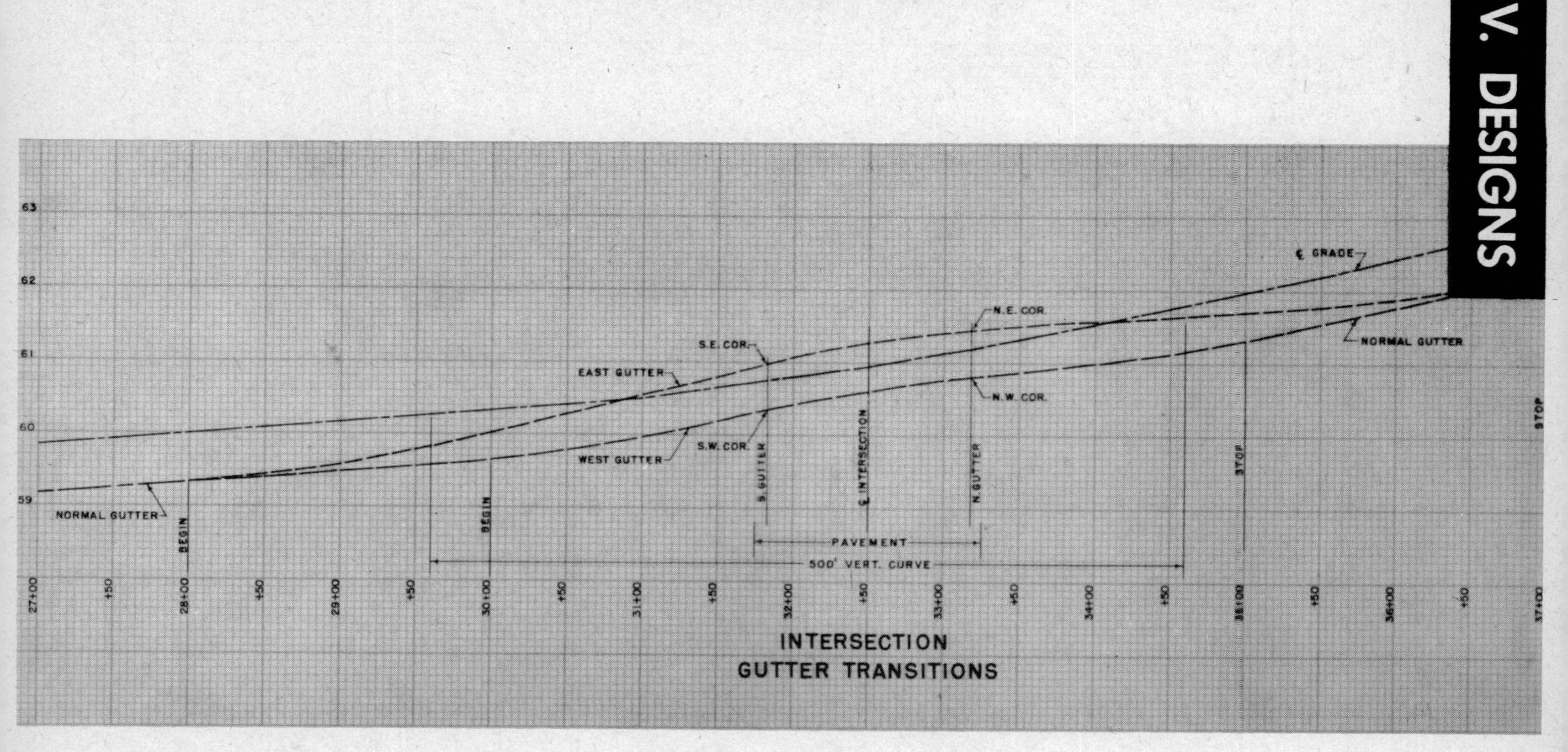
INTERSECTION
GUTTER TRANSITIONS
℄ GRADE
NORMAL GUTTER
N.E. COR.
N.W. COR.
S.E. COR.
S.W. COR.
EAST GUTTER
WEST GUTTER
NORMAL GUTTER
BEGIN
BEGIN
S. GUTTER
℄ INTERSECTION
N. GUTTER
STOP
STOP
PAVEMENT
500' VERT. CURVE
63
62
61
60
59
27+00
+50
28+00
+50
29+00
+50
30+00
+50
31+00
+50
32+00
+50
33+00
+50
34+00
+50
35+00
+50
36+00
+50
37+00

FIG. 5-5c.

GRADE SHEET

PROJECT *GREENVILLE AIRPORT* SHEET NO. *5* OF *6*

CONTRACT NO. *706* FIGURED BY *H.S.* DATE *11-16-43.*

LINE *RUNWAY 1* CHECKED BY *J.C.* DATE *11-19-43.*

STATION	% GRADE AND LIMITS V.C.	ELEV. ON TANGENT	V.C. CORR.	ELEV. ON V.C.
55+00	+0.99	51.08		
56+00	"	52.07		
57+00	P.V.C.	53.06		
58+00	+0.99%	54.05	-0.07	53.98
59+00		55.04	-0.30	54.74
60+00		56.03	-0.67	55.36
61+00		57.02	-1.19	55.83
62+00	1,000' V.C. P.V.I.	58.01	-1.86	56.15
63+00		57.51	-1.19	56.32
64+00		57.01	-0.67	56.34
65+00	-0.50%	56.51	-0.30	56.21
66+00		56.01	-0.07	55.94
67+00	P.V.T.	55.51		
68+00	-0.50	55.01		
69+00	"	54.51		

FIG. 5-6.

EARTHWORK AREAS

CONTRACT________ SHEET________ OF______

STA.______ DATUM______ COMP. BY________ DATE______

CHECKED BY________ DATE______

+					−				
h_1	h_2	$h_1 + h_2$	DIST.	2 X AREA	h_1	h_2	$h_1 + h_2$	DIST.	2 X AREA

FIG. 5-7.

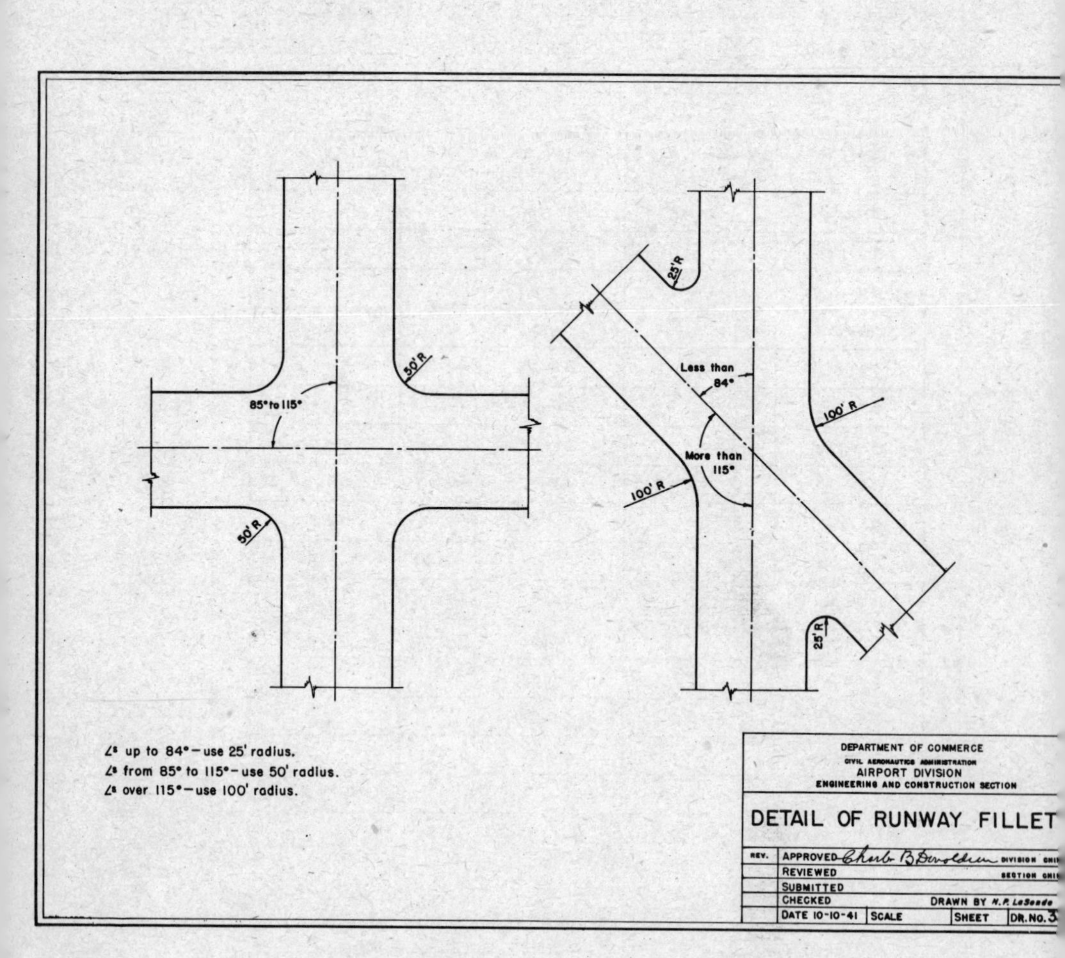

Fig. 5-8. (Courtesy C.A.A.)

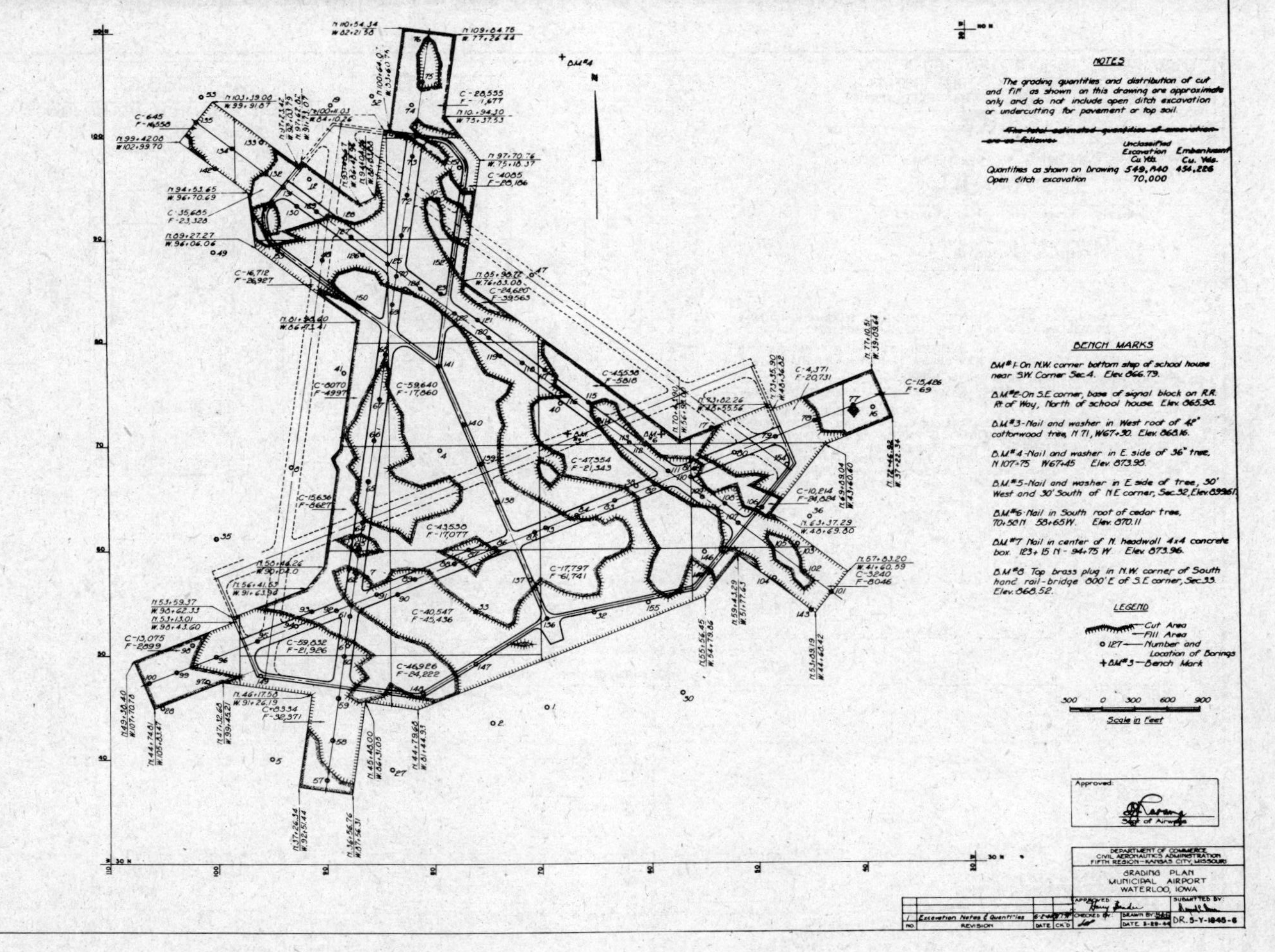

FIG. 5-9. (Courtesy C.A.A.)

VI. DRAINAGE

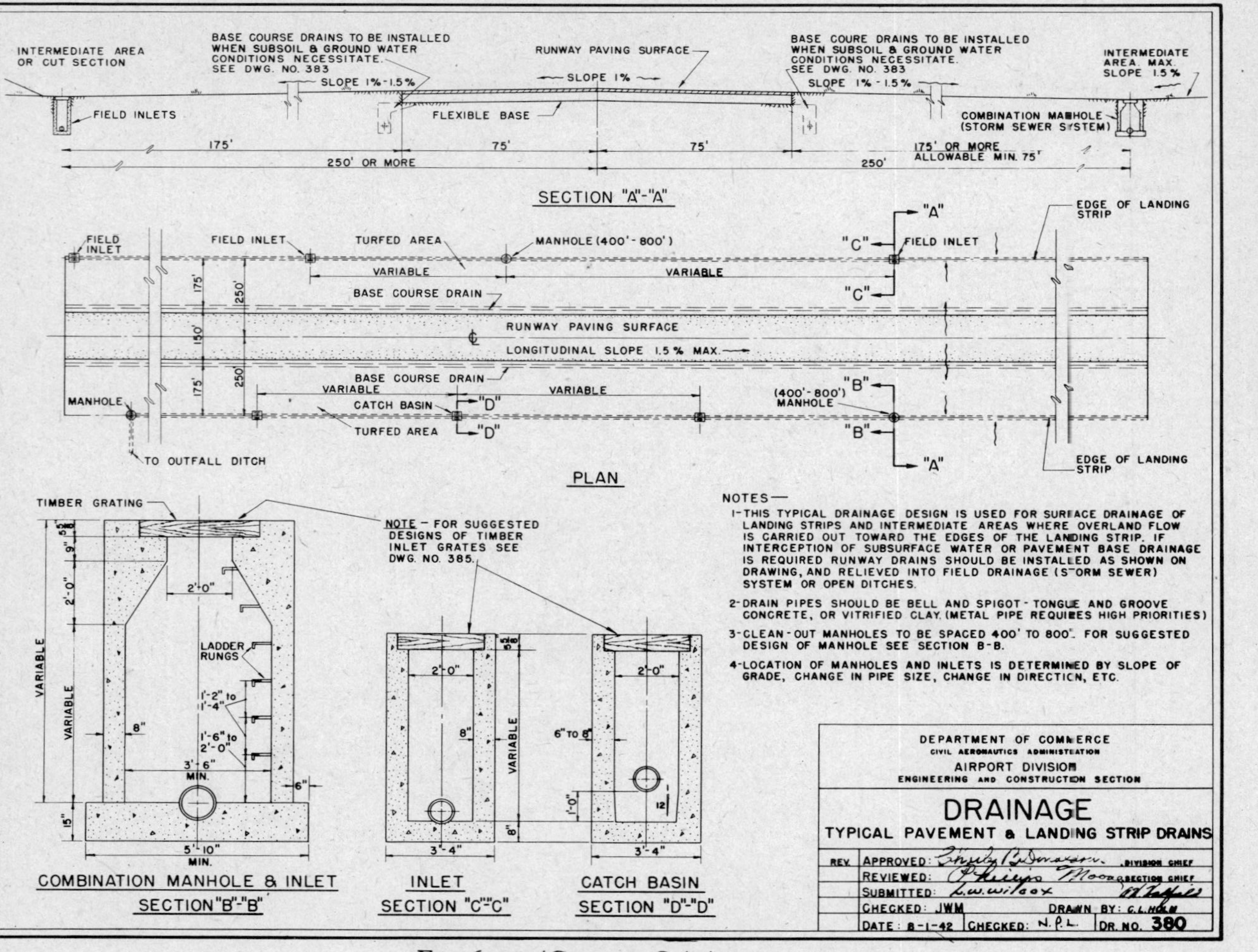

FIG. 6-1. (Courtesy C.A.A.)

(The timber gratings shown in Figs. 6-1, 6-2 and 6-3 were used as a wartime measure and

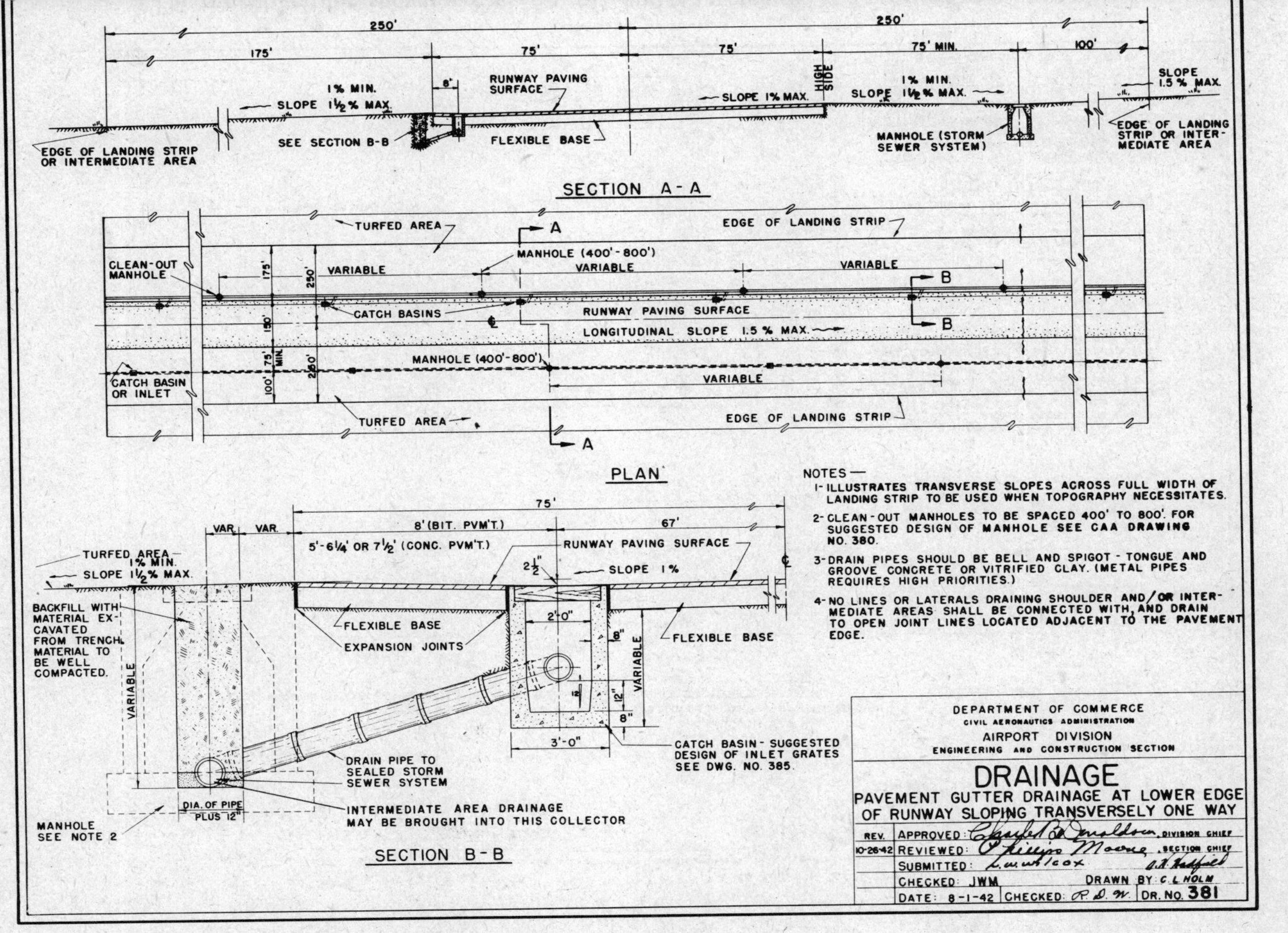

Fig. 6-2. (Courtesy C.A.A.)

VI. DRAINAGE

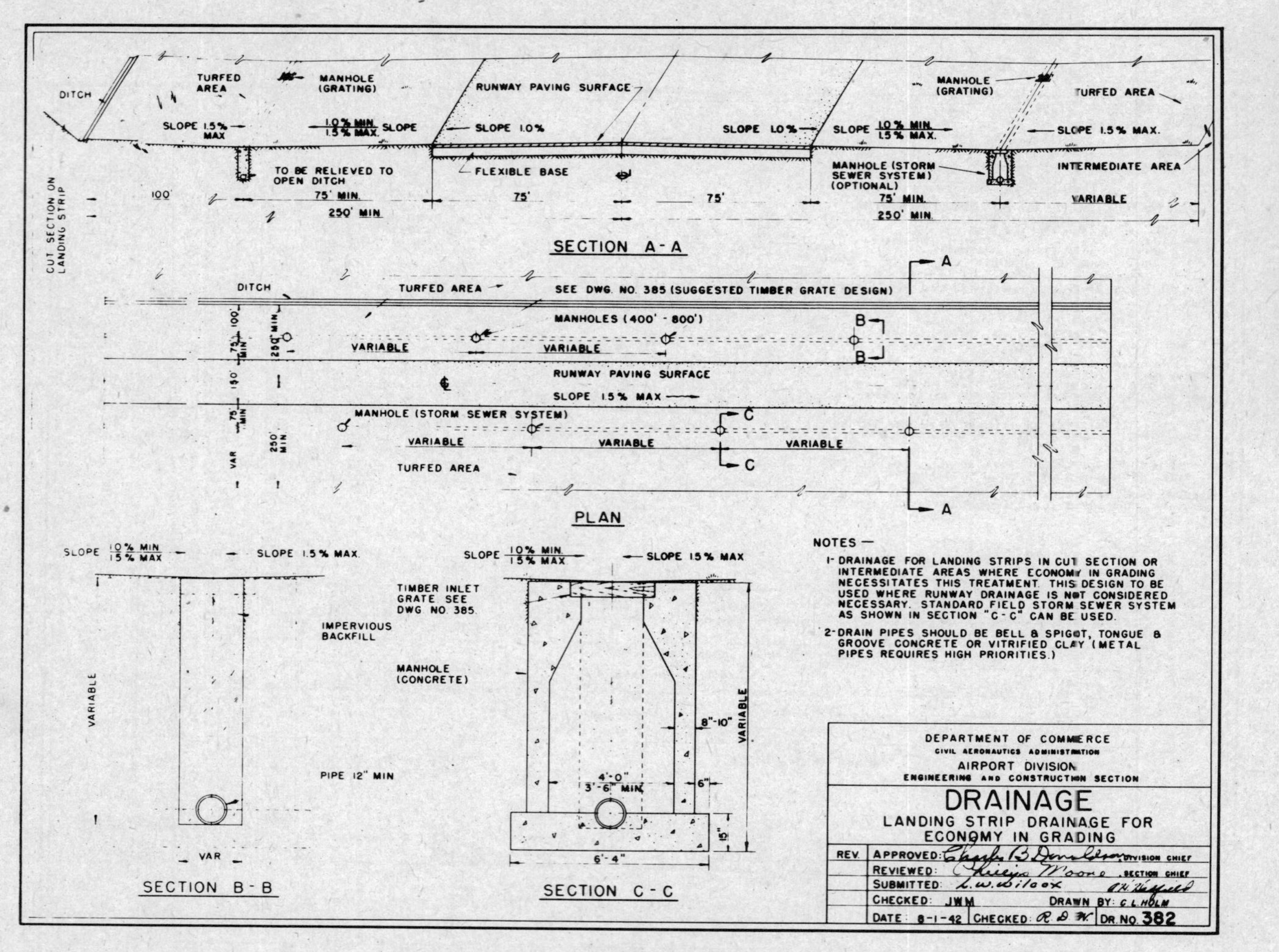

FIG. 6-2. (Courtesy C.A.A.)

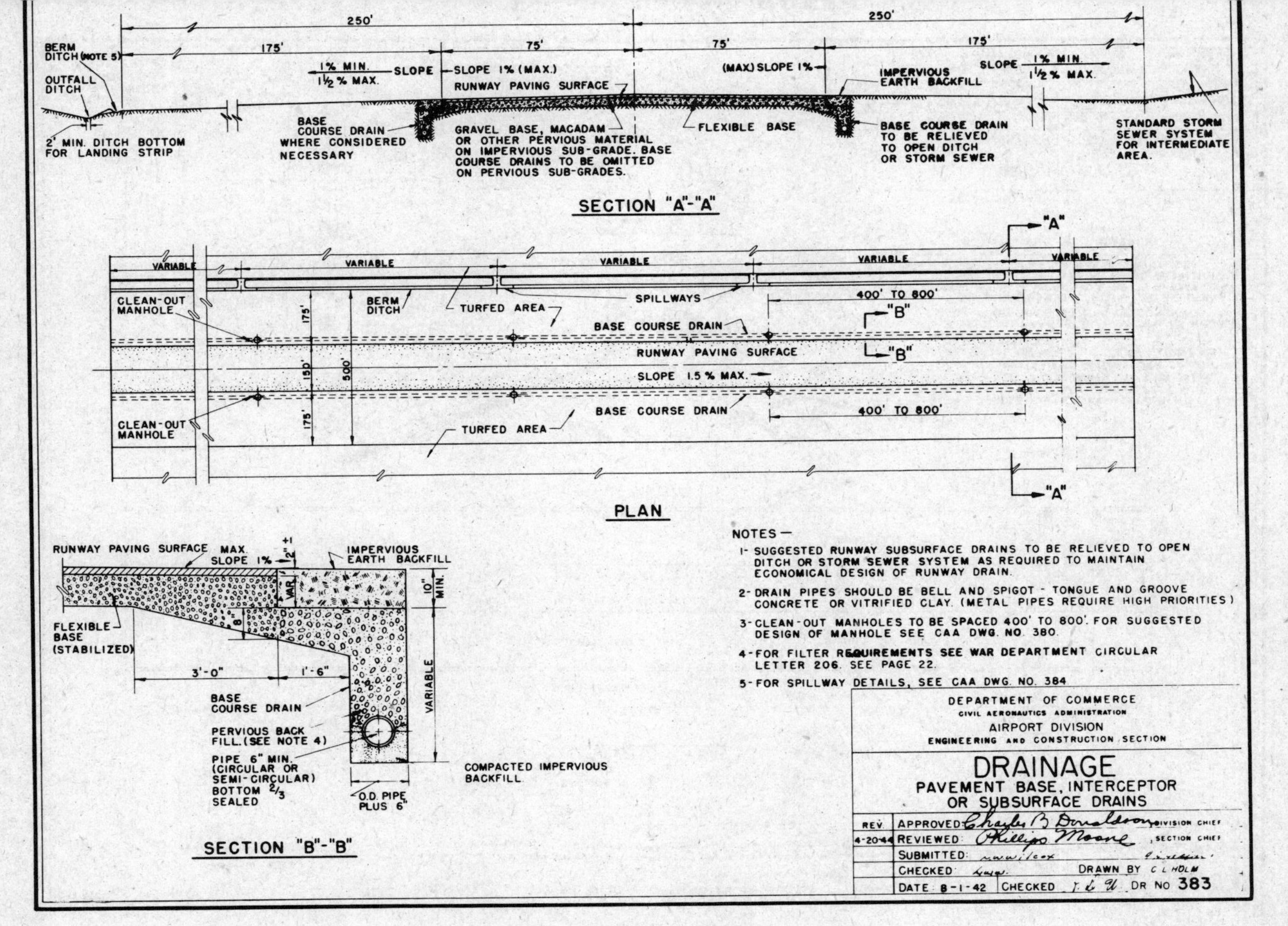

FIG. 6-4. (Courtesy C.A.A.)

VI. DRAINAGE

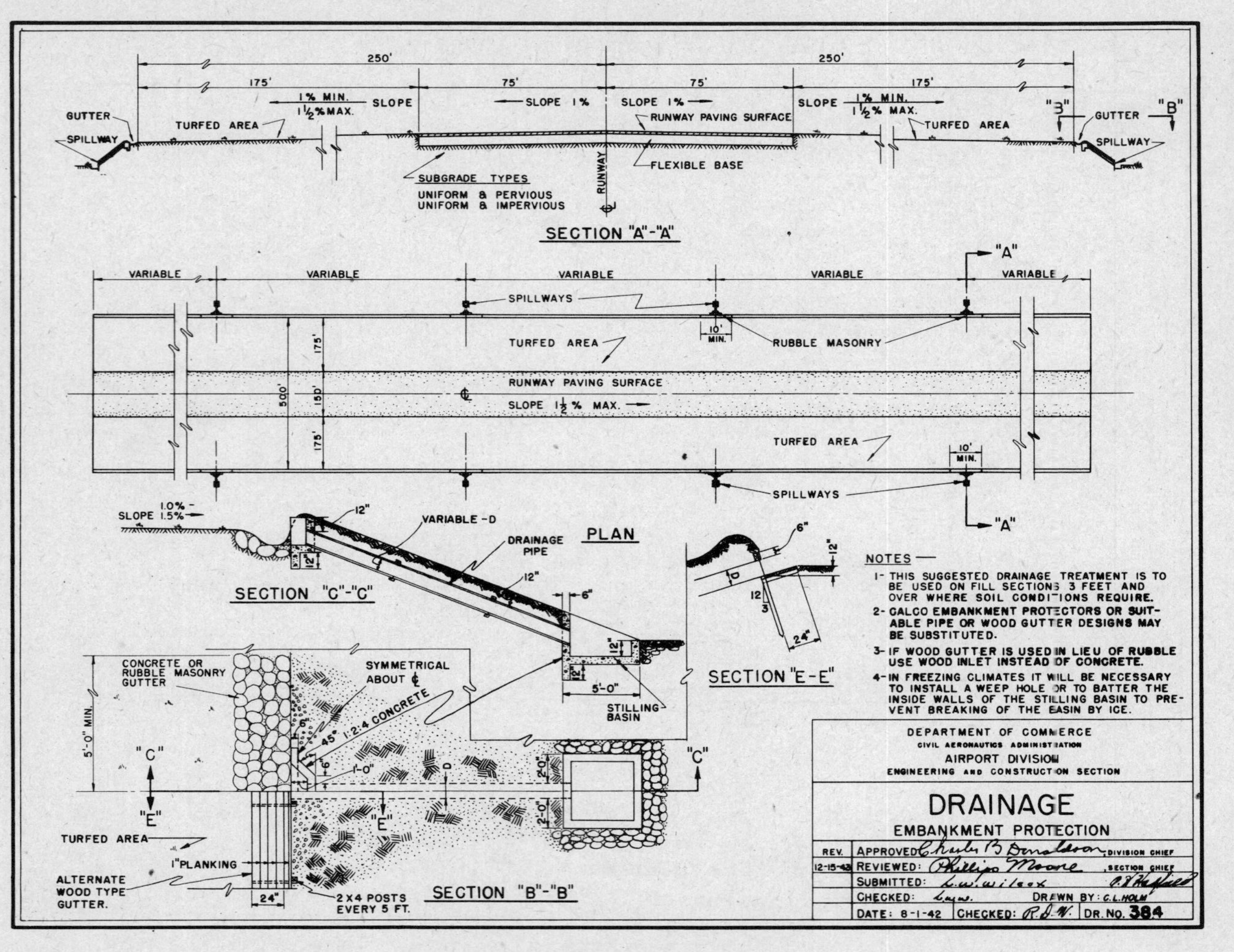

FIG. 6-[illegible]. (Courtesy C.A.A.)

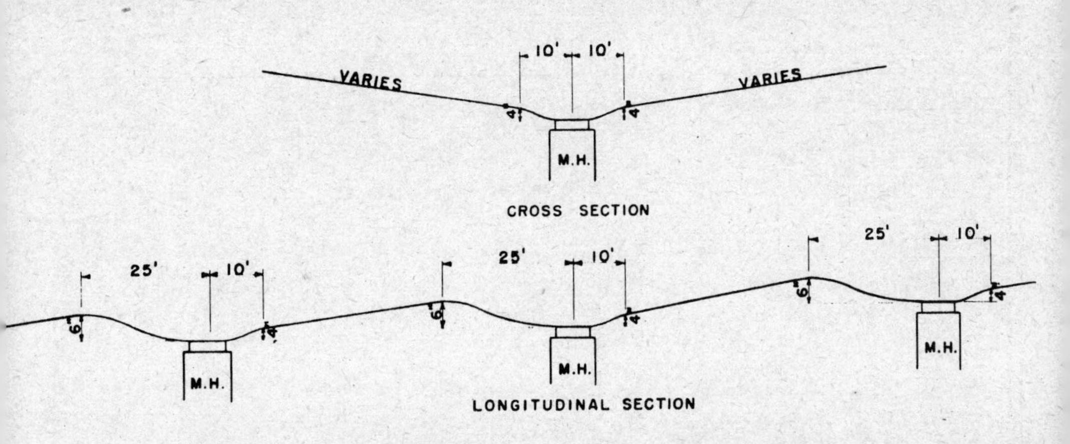
10'
10'
VARIES
VARIES
4"
4"
M.H.
CROSS SECTION
25'
10'
25'
10'
25'
10'
6"
4"
6"
4"
6"
4"
M.H.
M.H.
M.H.
LONGITUDINAL SECTION
DETAIL OF GRADING AT FIELD INLETS

FIG. 6-6.

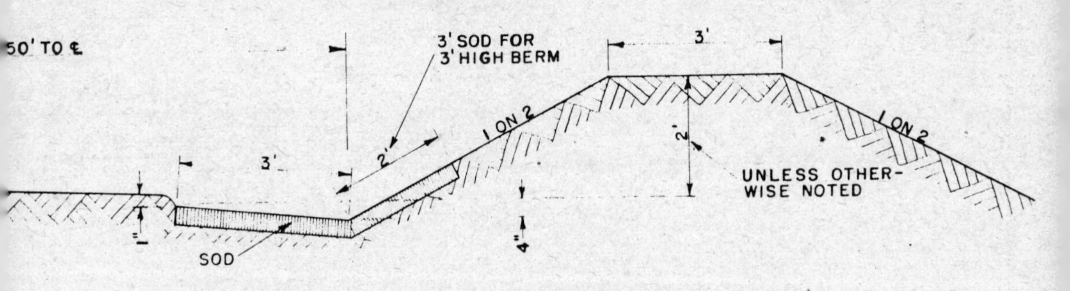
50' TO ℄
3' SOD FOR
3' HIGH BERM
3'
3'
2'
1 ON 2
1 ON 2
2'
UNLESS OTHER-
WISE NOTED
4"
SOD
TYPICAL SECTION OF BERM GUTTER

FIG. 6-7.

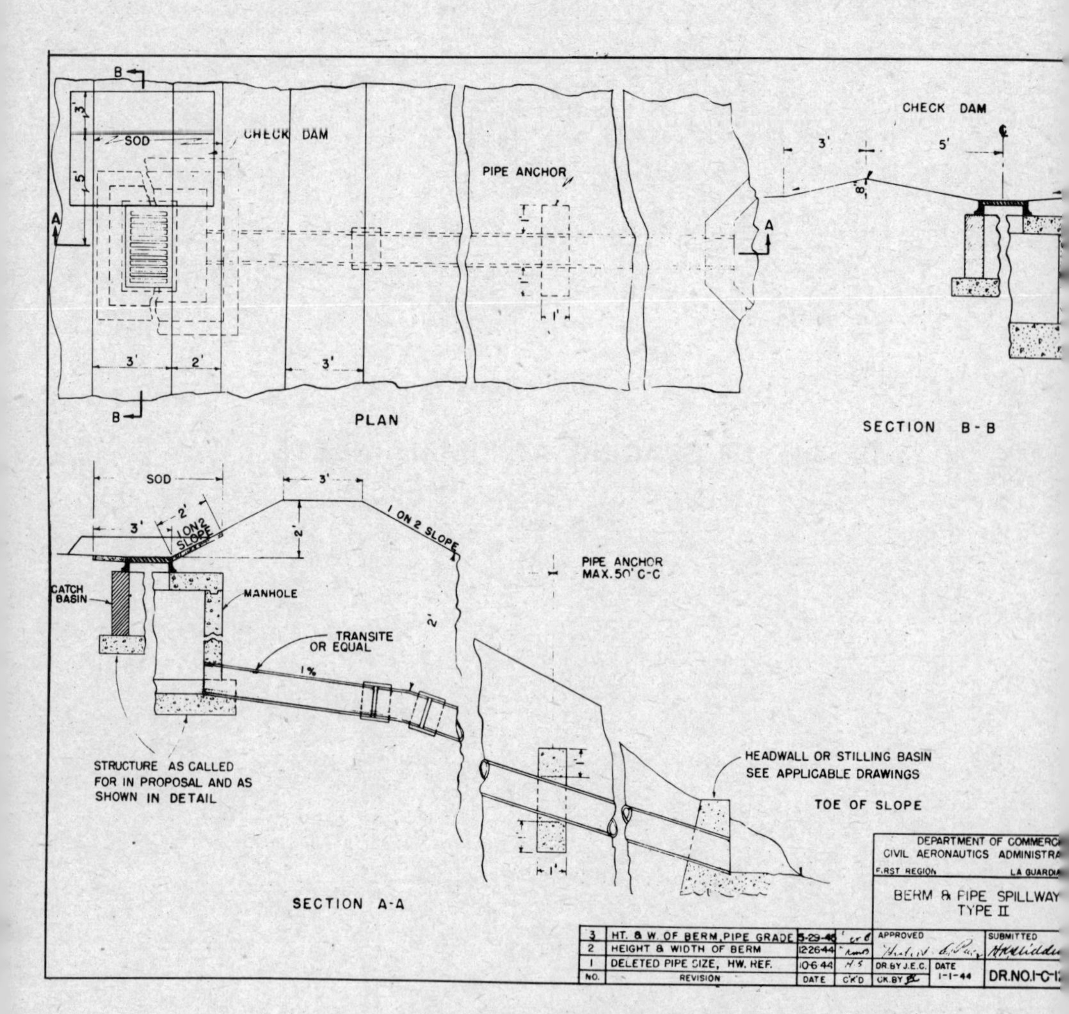

FIG. 6-8. (Courtesy C.A.A.)

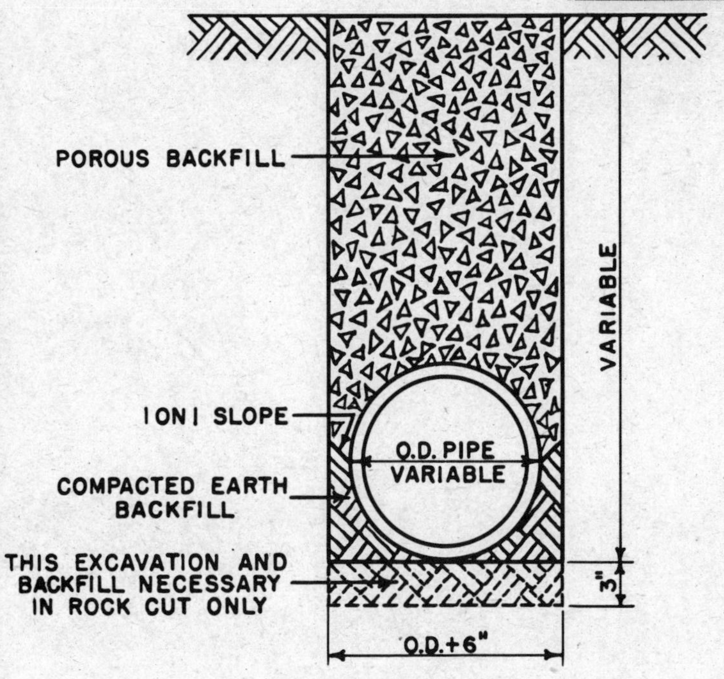

Fig. 6-9.

OPEN JOINT DRAIN

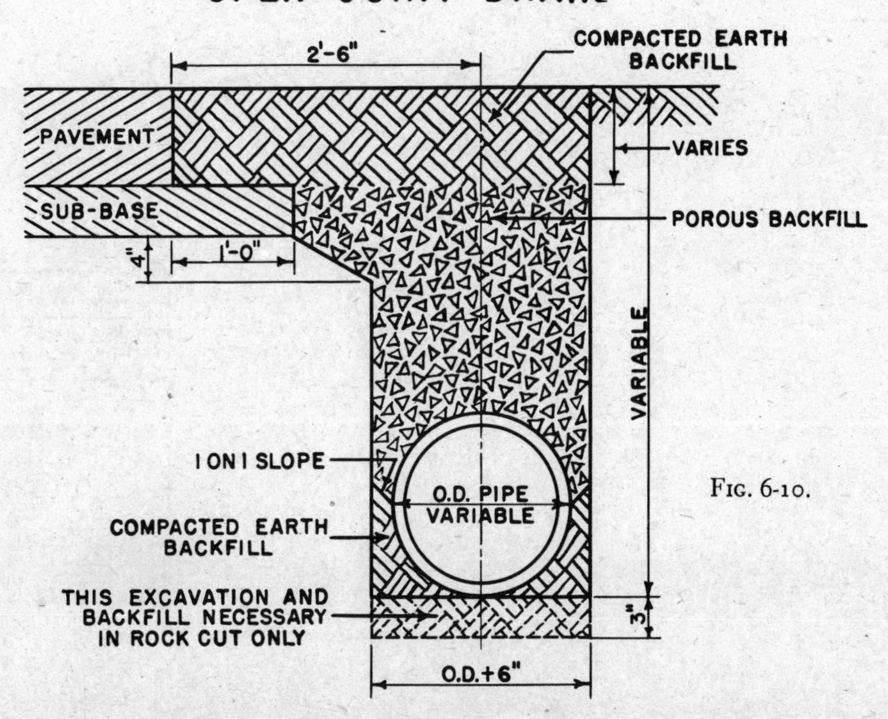

Fig. 6-10.

DRAIN ADJACENT TO PAVEMENT

VI. DRAINAGE

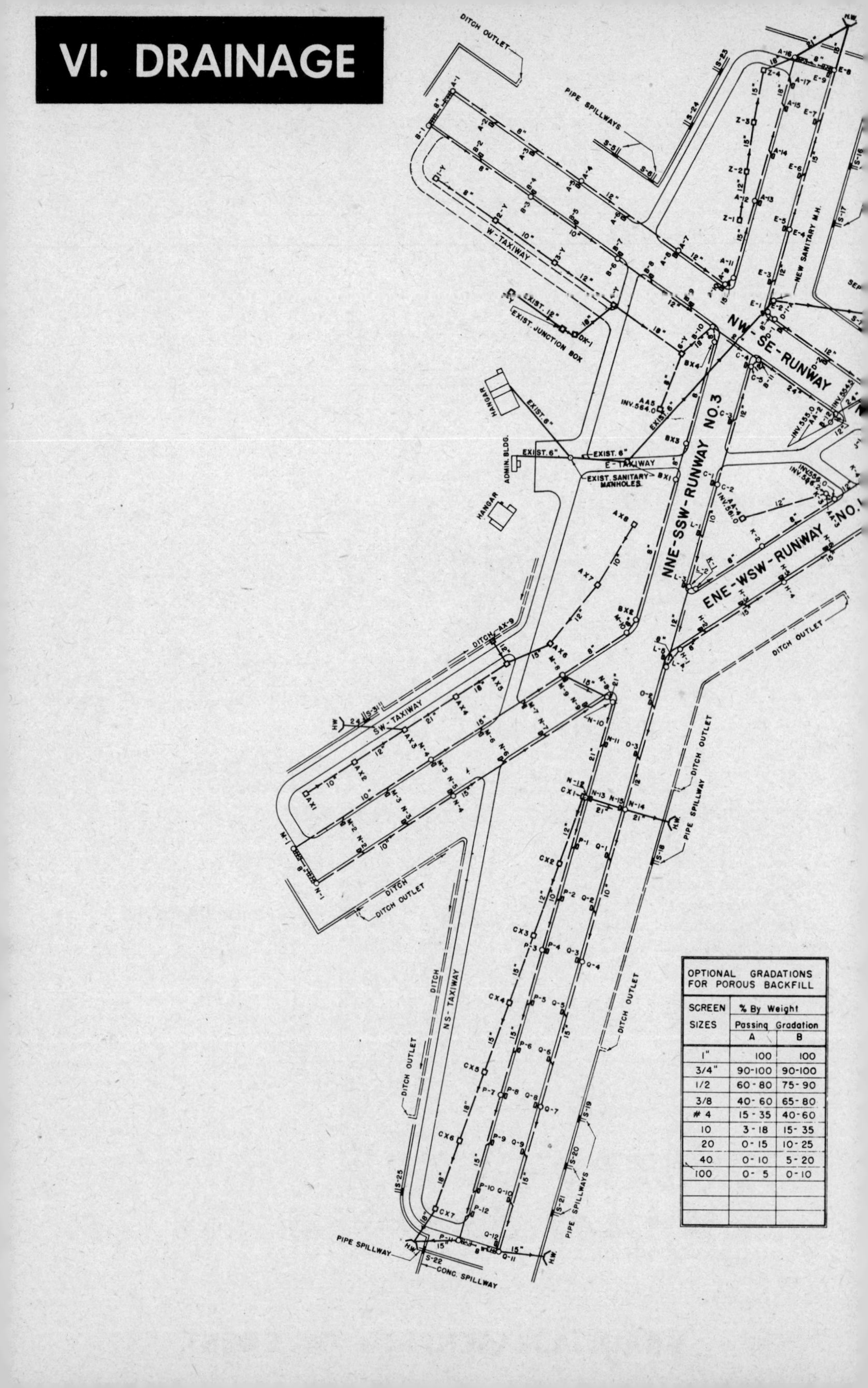

OPTIONAL GRADATIONS FOR POROUS BACKFILL

SCREEN SIZES	% By Weight Passing Gradation A	B
1"	100	100
3/4"	90-100	90-100
1/2	60-80	75-90
3/8	40-60	65-80
# 4	15-35	40-60
10	3-18	15-35
20	0-15	10-25
40	0-10	5-20
100	0-5	0-10

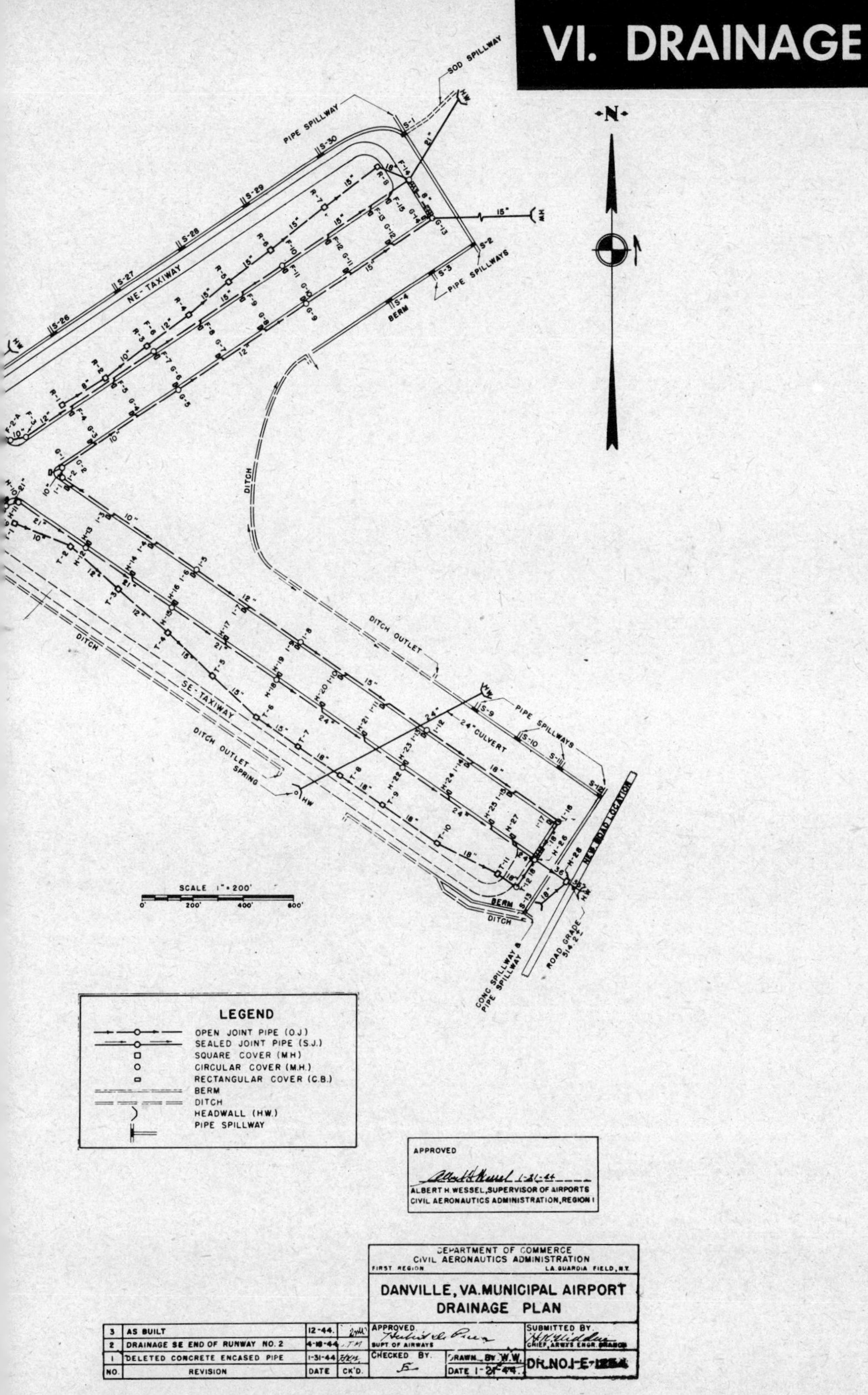

Fig. 6-11. (Courtesy C.A.A.)

VI. DRAINAGE

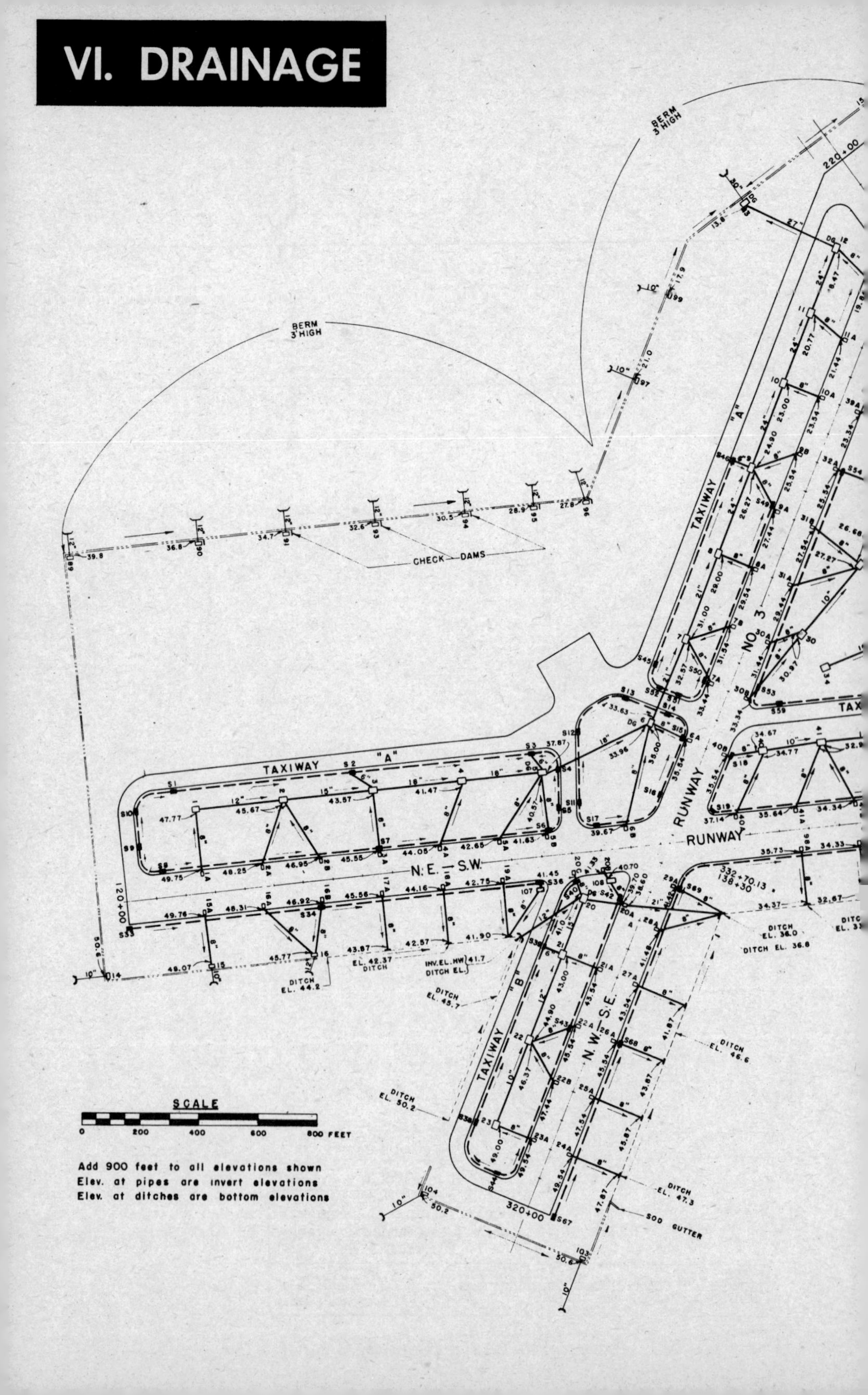

BERM 3' HIGH
BERM 3' HIGH
CHECK DAMS
TAXIWAY "A"
TAXIWAY "A"
RUNWAY NO. 3
RUNWAY
N.E. S.W.
N.W. S.E.
TAXIWAY "B"
120+00
220+00
320+00
332+70.13
138+30
DITCH EL. 44.2
EL. 42.37 DITCH
INV. EL. HW 41.7
DITCH EL.
DITCH EL. 45.7
DITCH EL. 36.0
DITCH EL. 36.8
DITCH EL. 46.6
DITCH EL. 50.2
DITCH EL. 47.3
SOD GUTTER
SCALE
0 200 400 600 800 FEET
Add 900 feet to all elevations shown
Elev. at pipes are invert elevations
Elev. at ditches are bottom elevations

VI. DRAINAGE

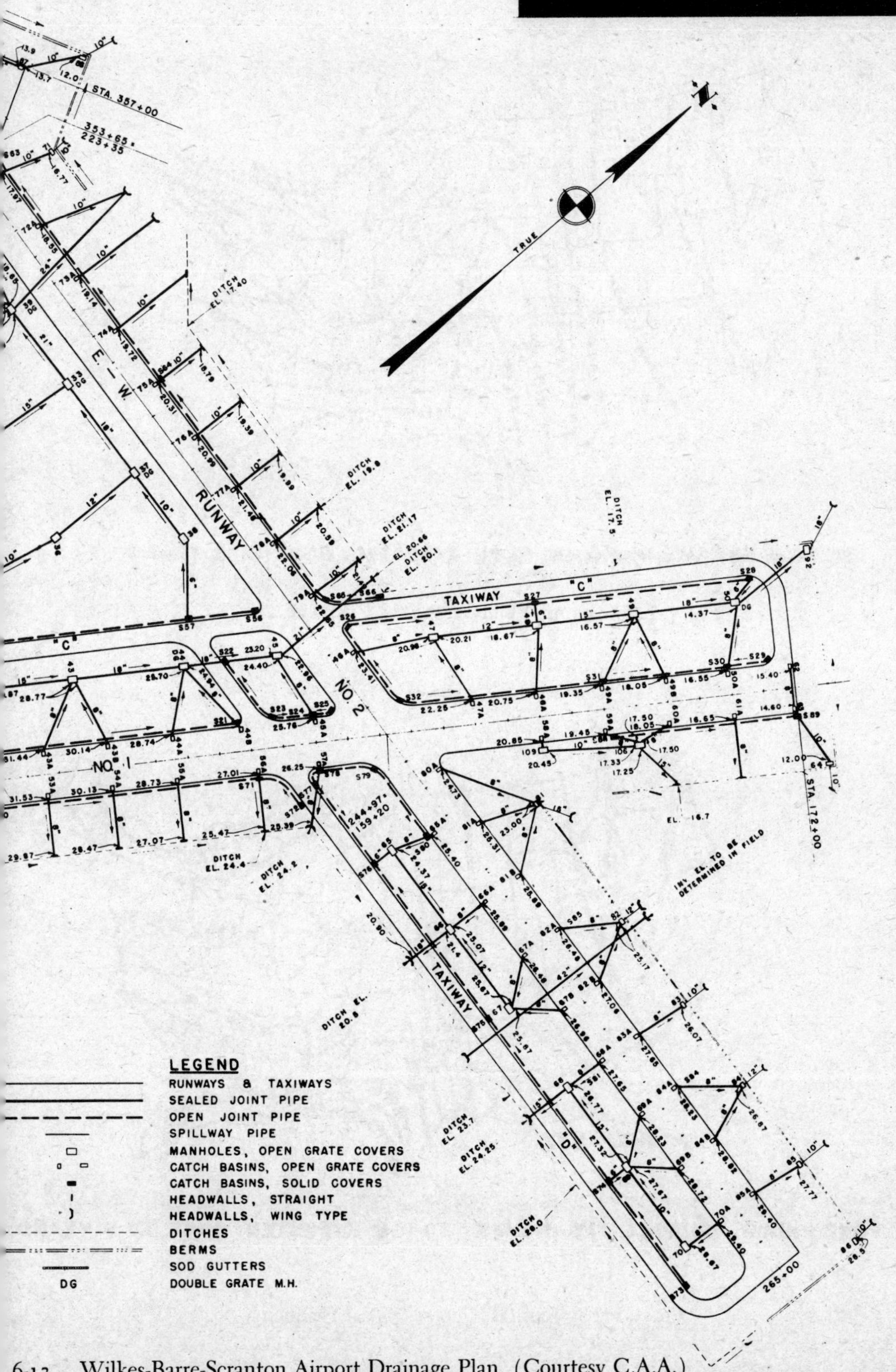

6-12. Wilkes-Barre-Scranton Airport Drainage Plan. (Courtesy C.A.A.)

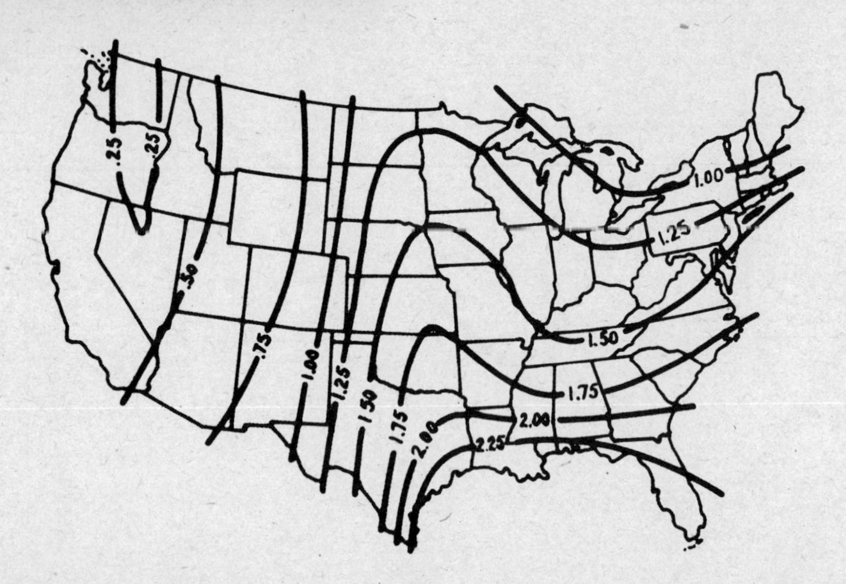

ONE HOUR RAINFALL, IN INCHES, TO BE EXPECTED ONCE IN 2 YEARS.

Fig. 6-13a. Rainfall Curves, 2-Year Frequency.

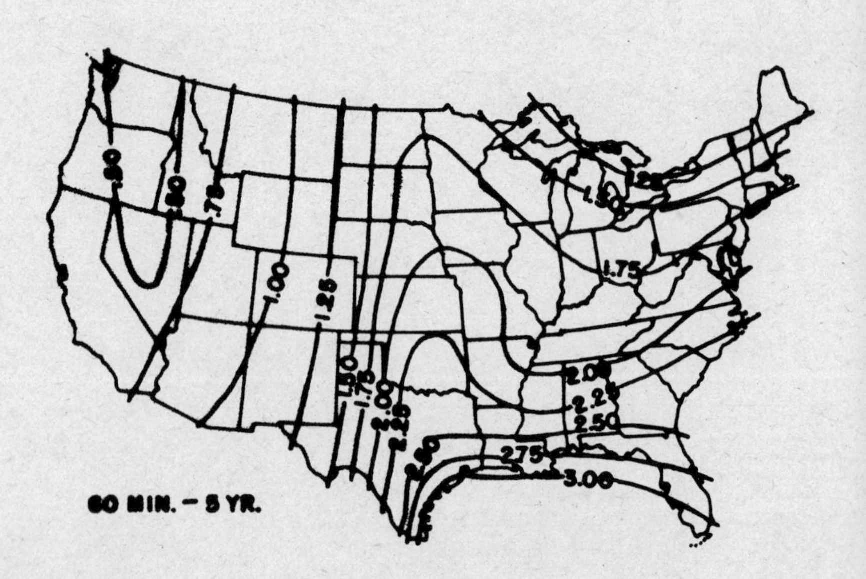

ONE-HOUR RAINFALL, IN INCHES, TO BE EXPECTED ONCE IN 5 YEARS.

Fig. 6-13b. Rainfall Curves, 5-Year Frequency.

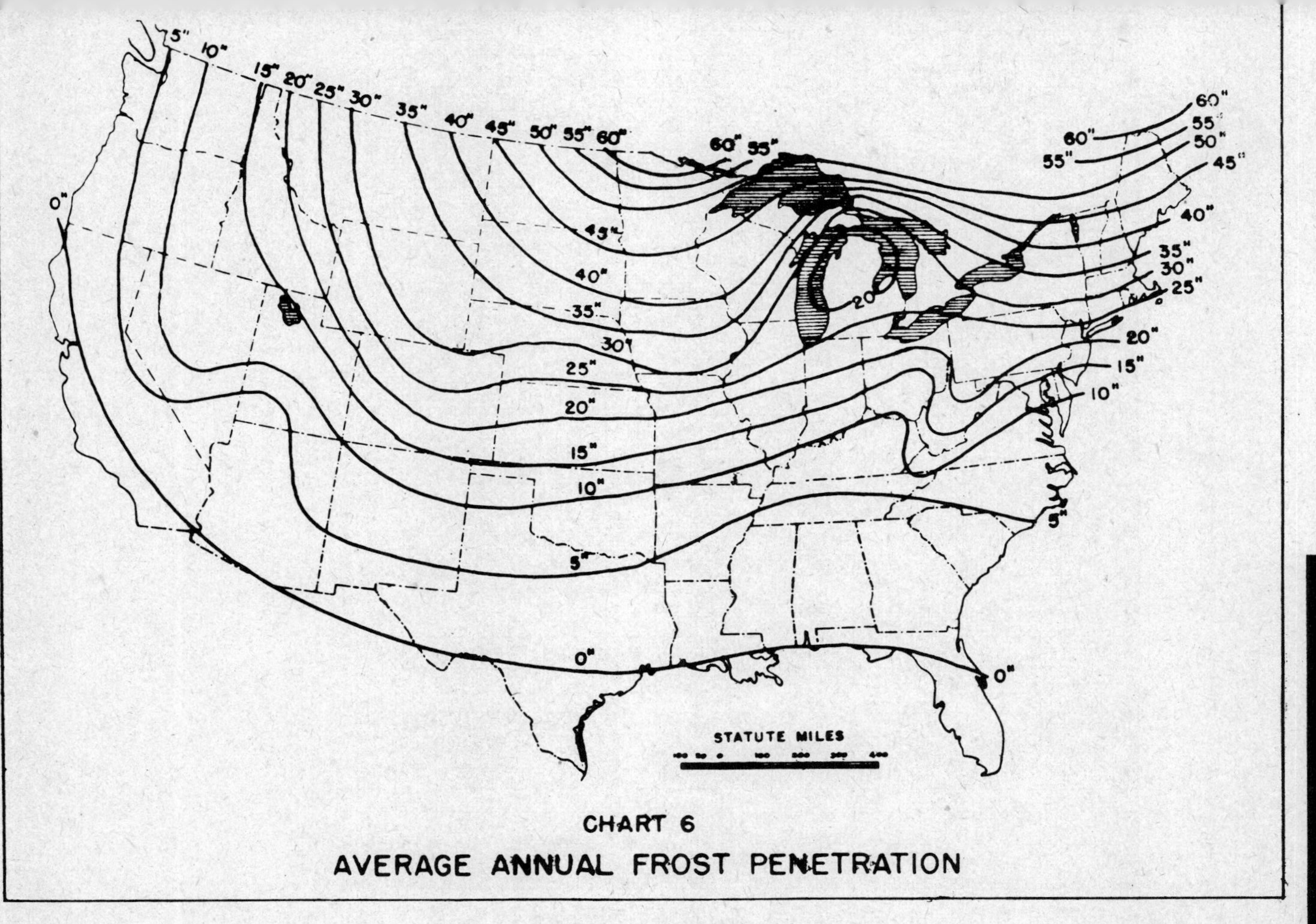

FIG. 6-14. (Courtesy C.A.A.)

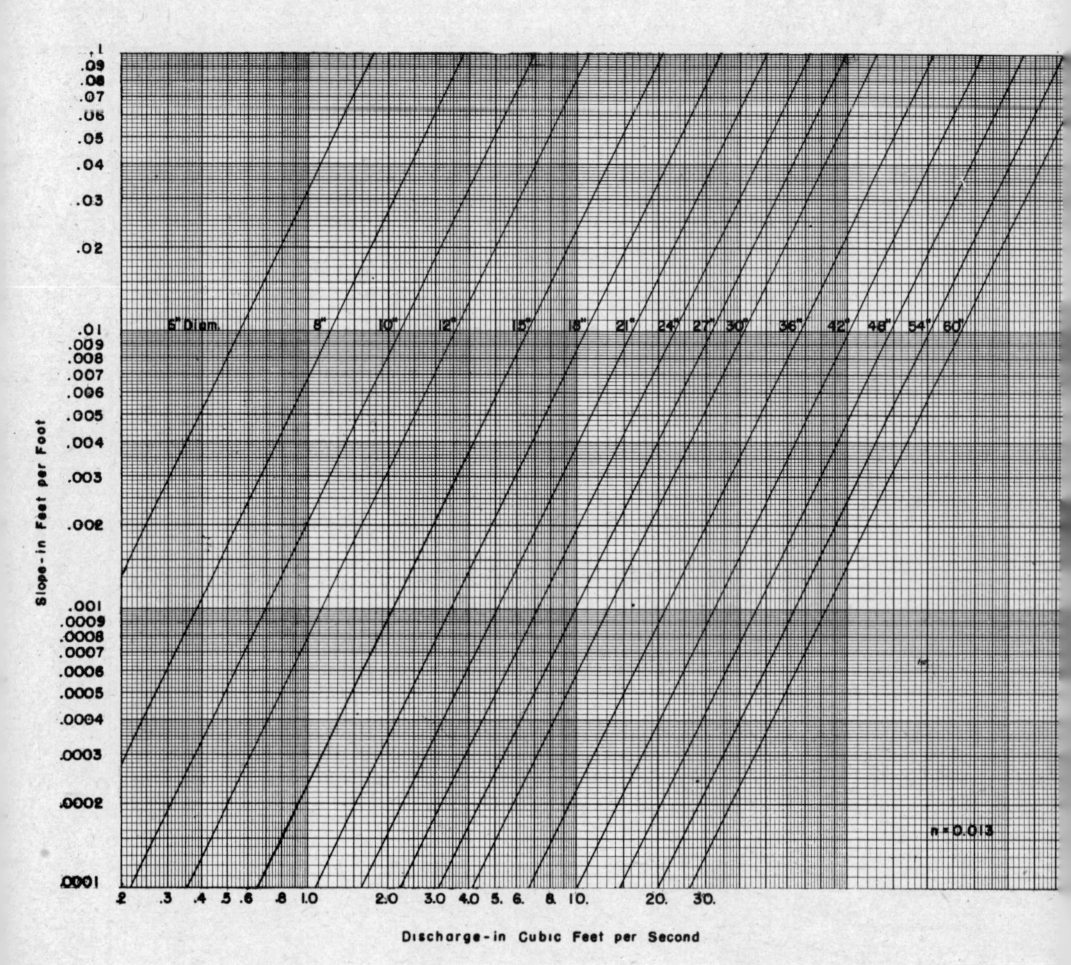

Fig. 6-15a. Discharge of Pipes Based on Manning's Formula.

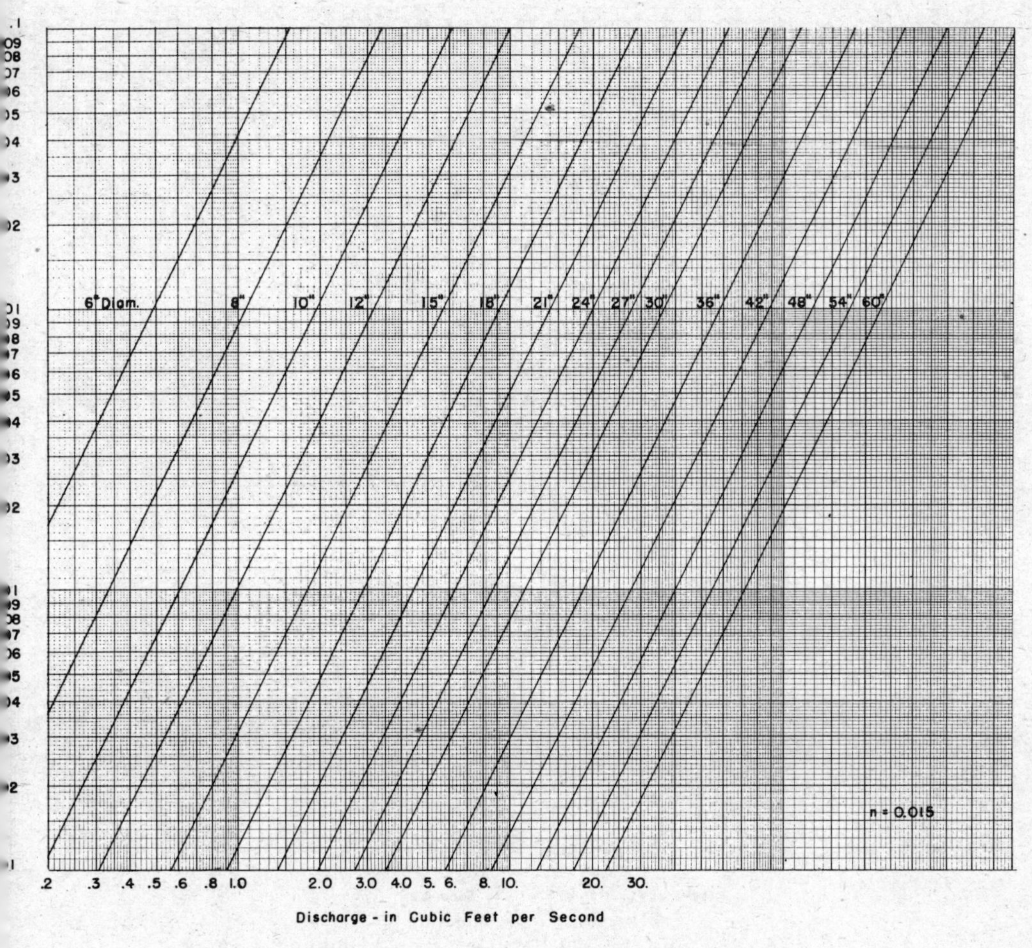

FIG. 6-15b. Discharge of Pipes Based on Manning's Formula.

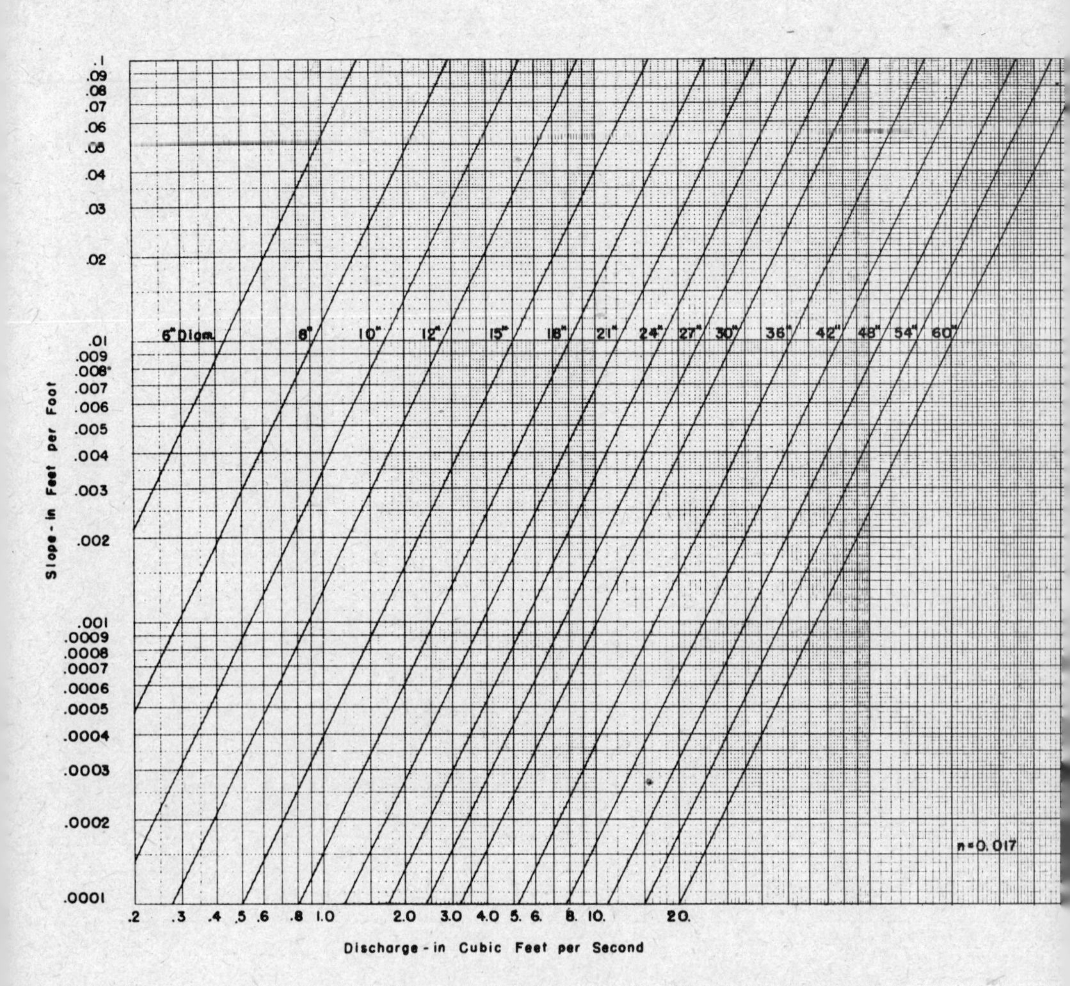

FIG. 6-15C. Discharge of Pipes Based on Manning's Formula.

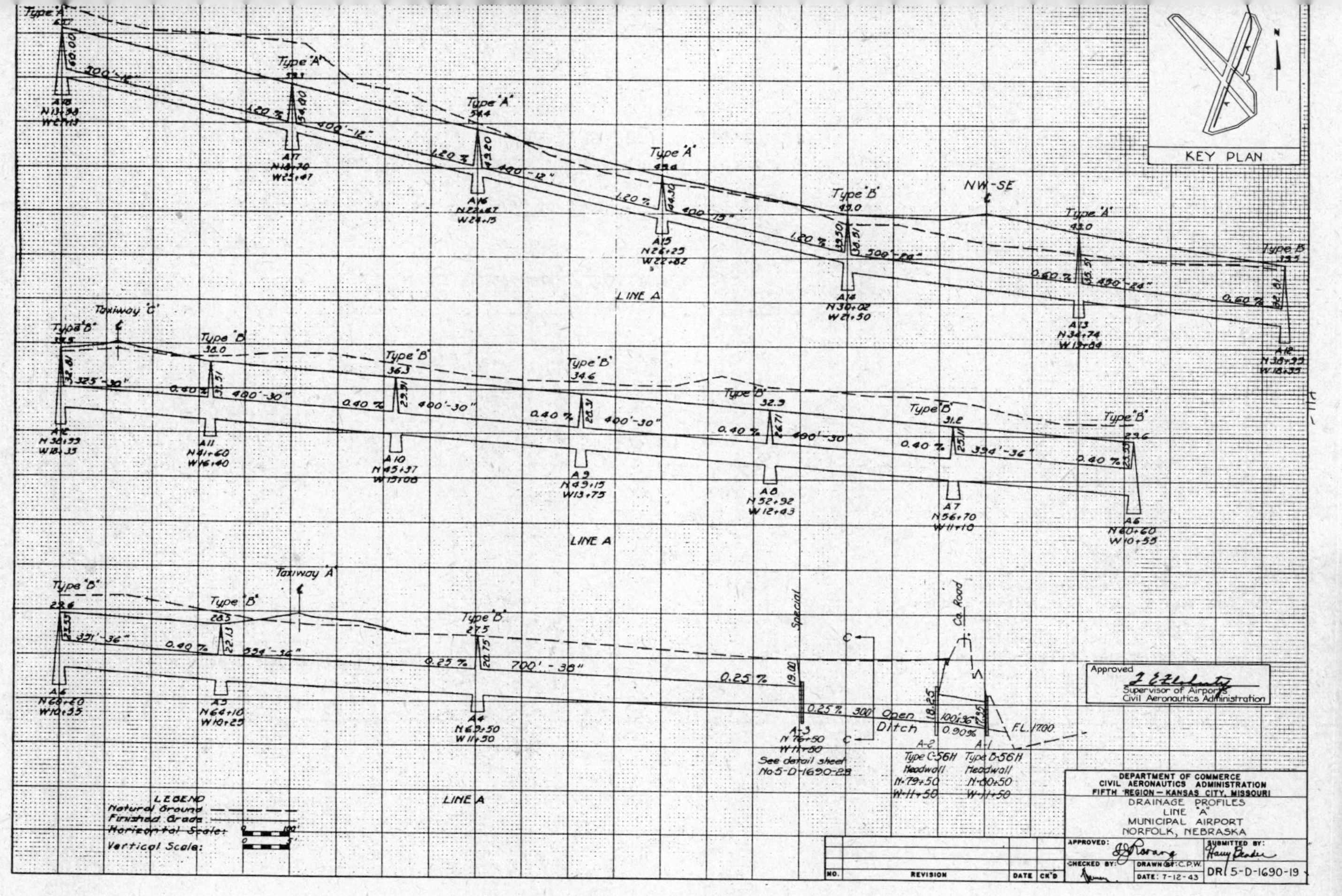

FIG. 6-16. (Courtesy C.A.A.)

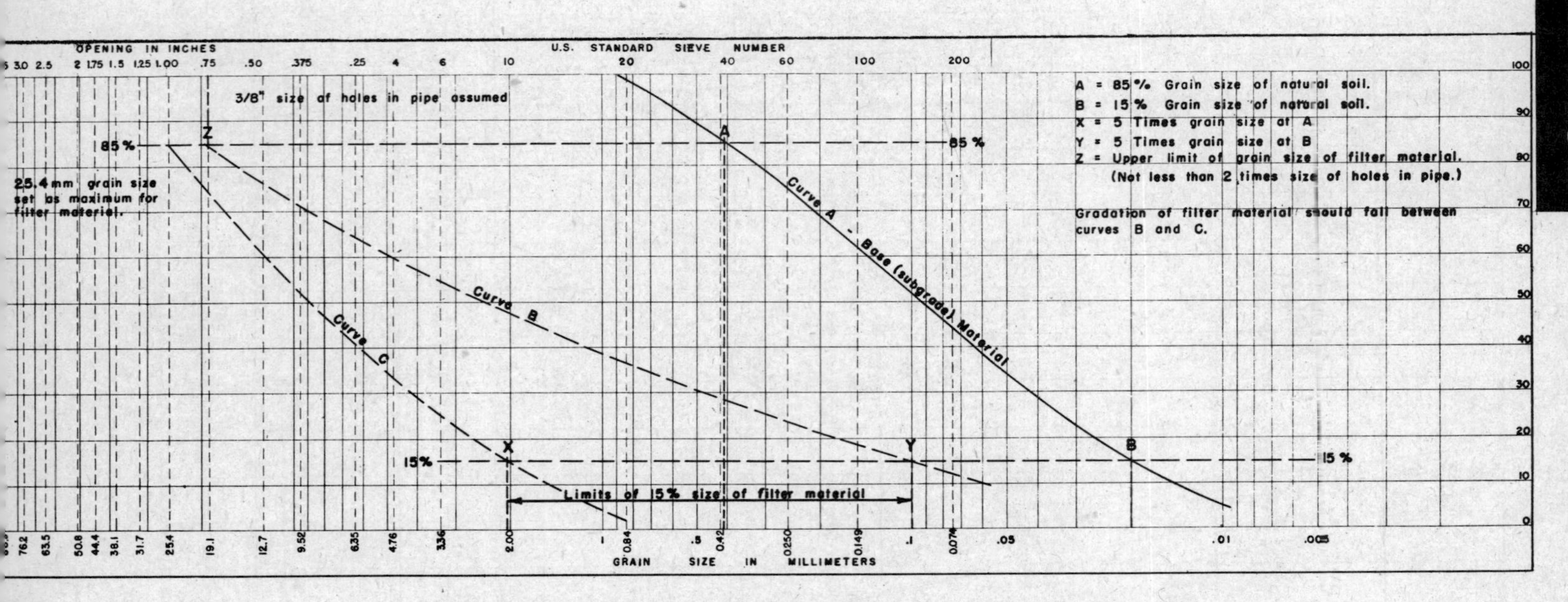

FIG. 6-17. Authors' Adaptation of Curves and Data Developed by U. S. Engineer Department.

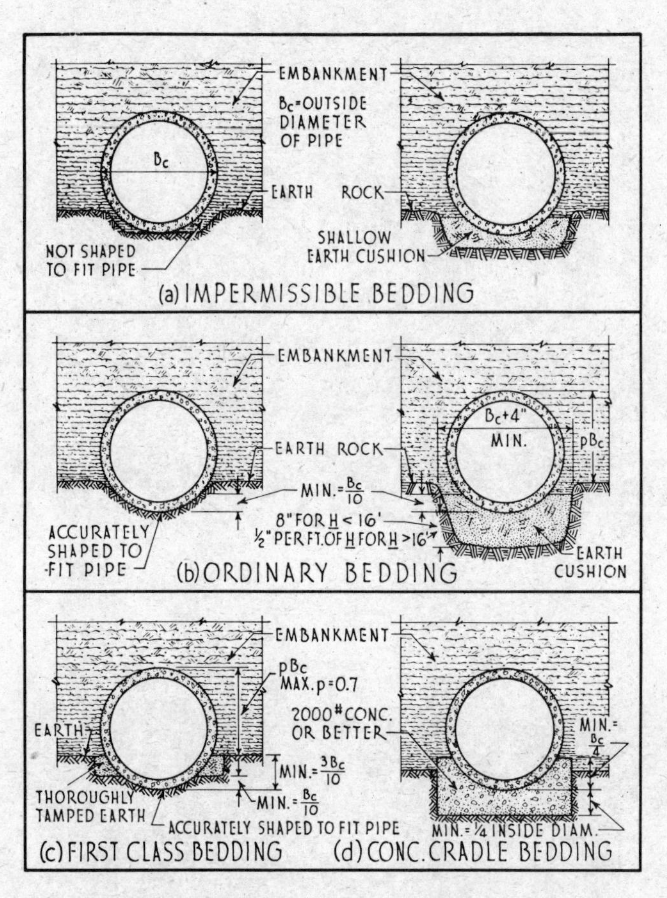

FIG. 6-18. Four Types of Projection Bedding for Circular Pipe. (Courtesy Portland Cement Assoc.)

Fig. 6-19a. Installation of Skip Pipe at Washington National Airport. (Courtesy U. S. Engineer Department.)

Fig. 6-19b. Installation of Skip Pipe at Washington National Airport. (Courtesy U. S. Engineer Department.)

Fig. 6-19c. Installation of Skip Pipe at Washington National Airport. (Courtesy U. S. Engineer Department.)

FIG. 6-20. Concrete Gutter for Surface Runoff, Idlewild Airport. Note provision for placing grating.

FIG. 6-21. Excavated Trench for Large Diameter Drainage Pipe, Idlewild Airport. Note well points which keep area dry despite high water table and sandy soil. Forms shown are for concrete bedding slab.

FIG. 6-22. Spreading Durex, a Rubber Compound Mixed with Slate, Preparatory to Laying Large Diameter Drainage Pipe, Idlewild Airport. This is in same trench as shown in Fig. 6-21.

FIG. 6-23. Three-Barreled Storm Water Drain, Idlewild Airport.

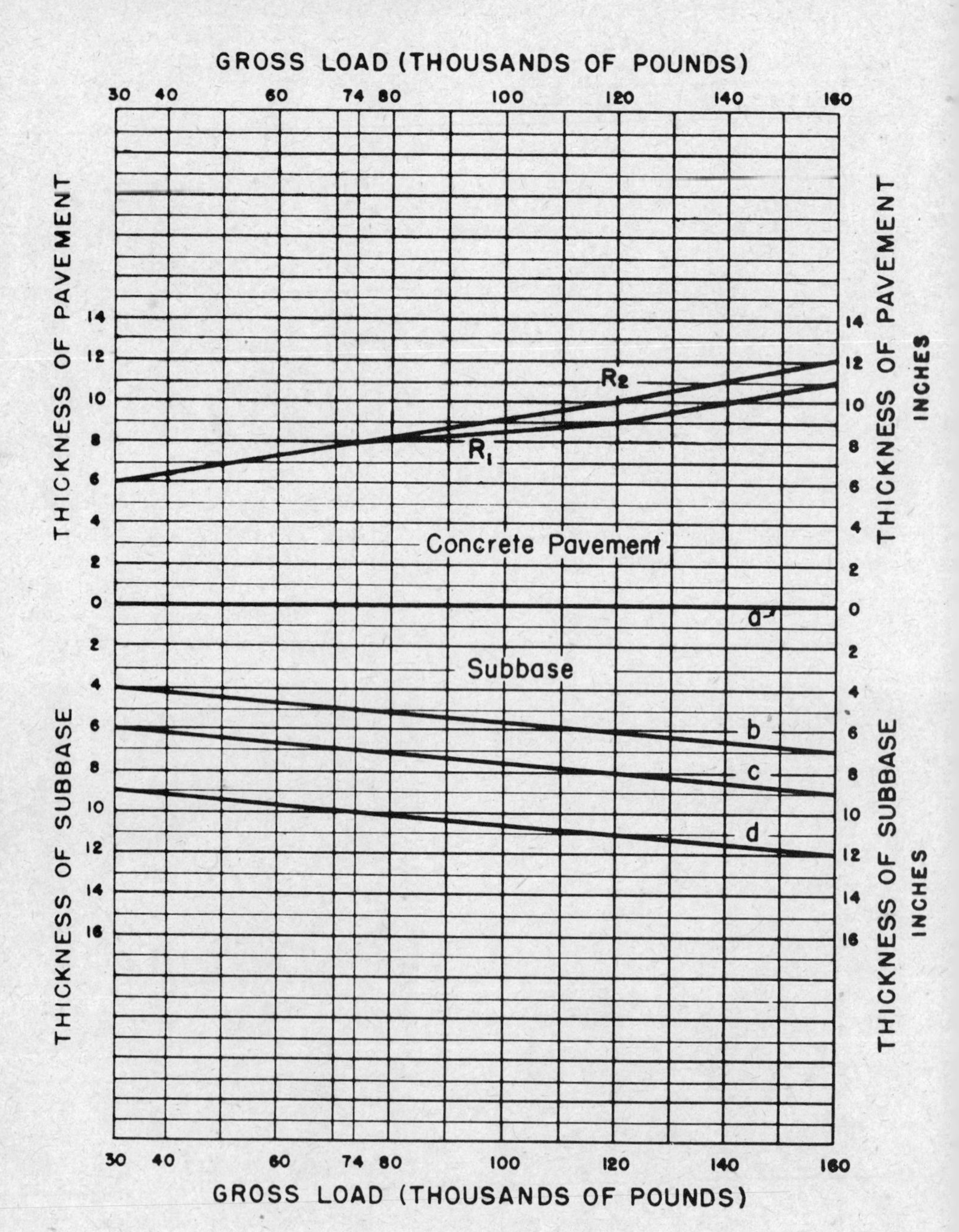

FIG. 7-1. (Courtesy C.A.A.)

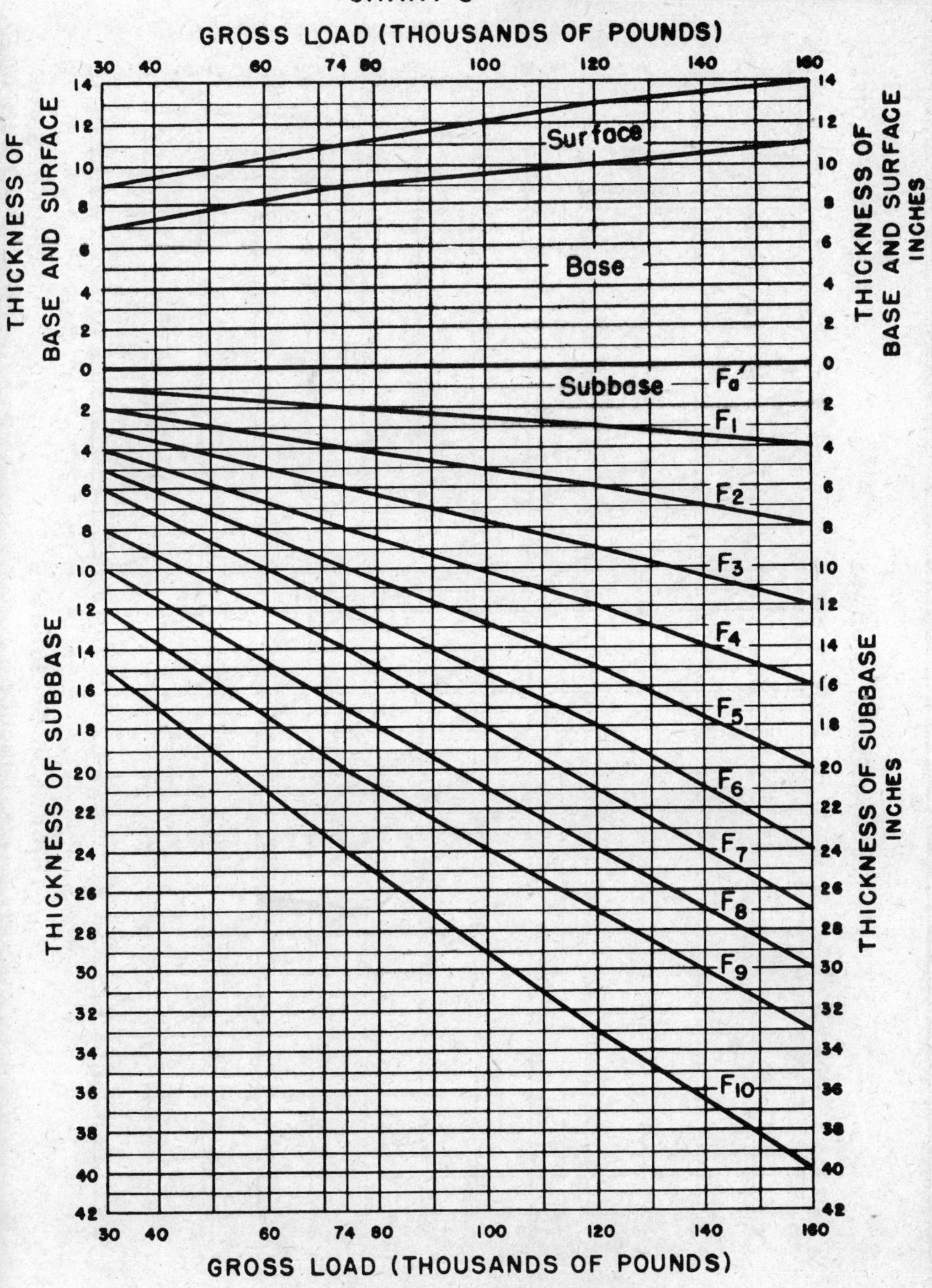

FIG. 7-2. (Courtesy C.A.A.)

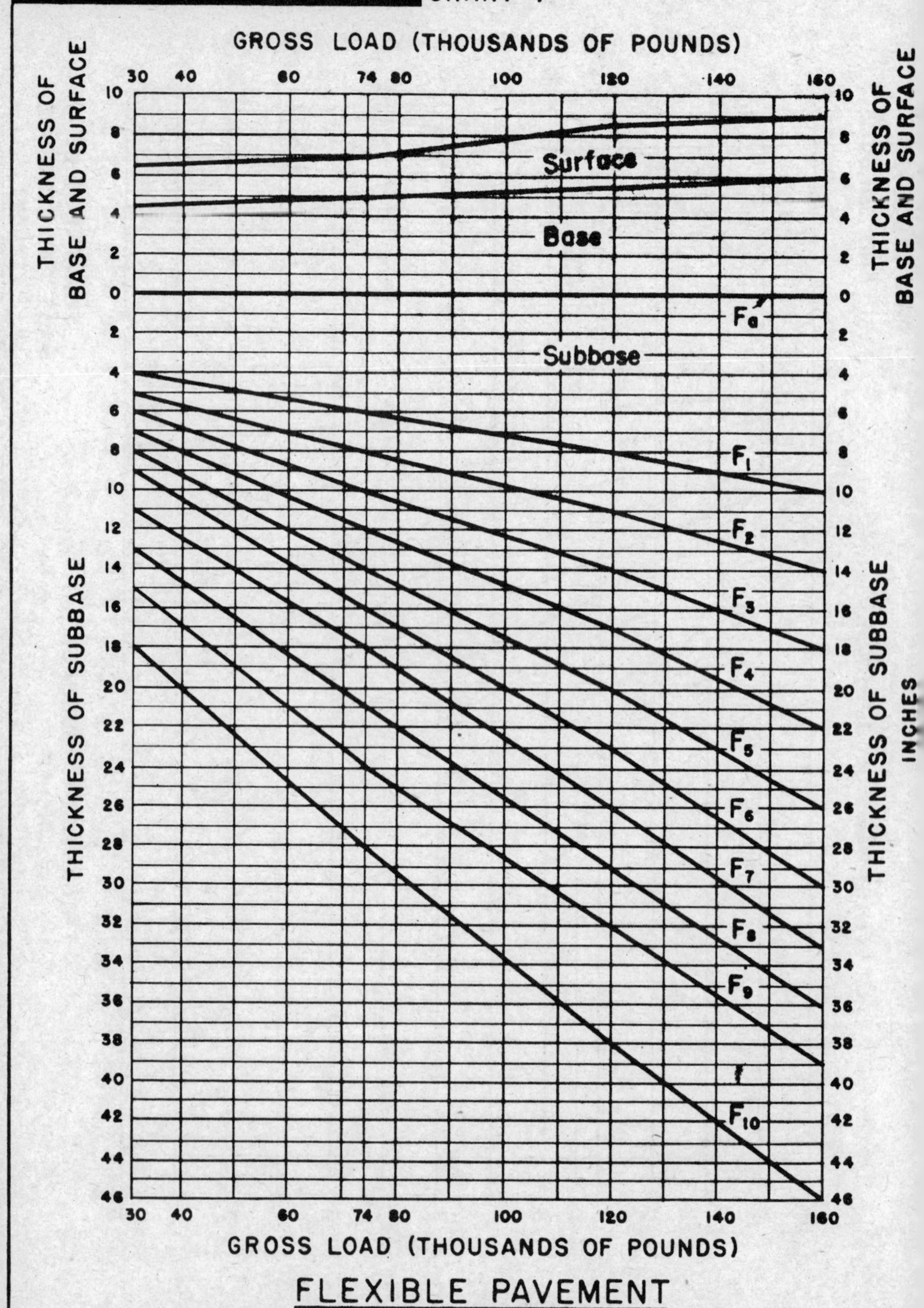

FIG. 7-3. (Courtesy C.A.A.)

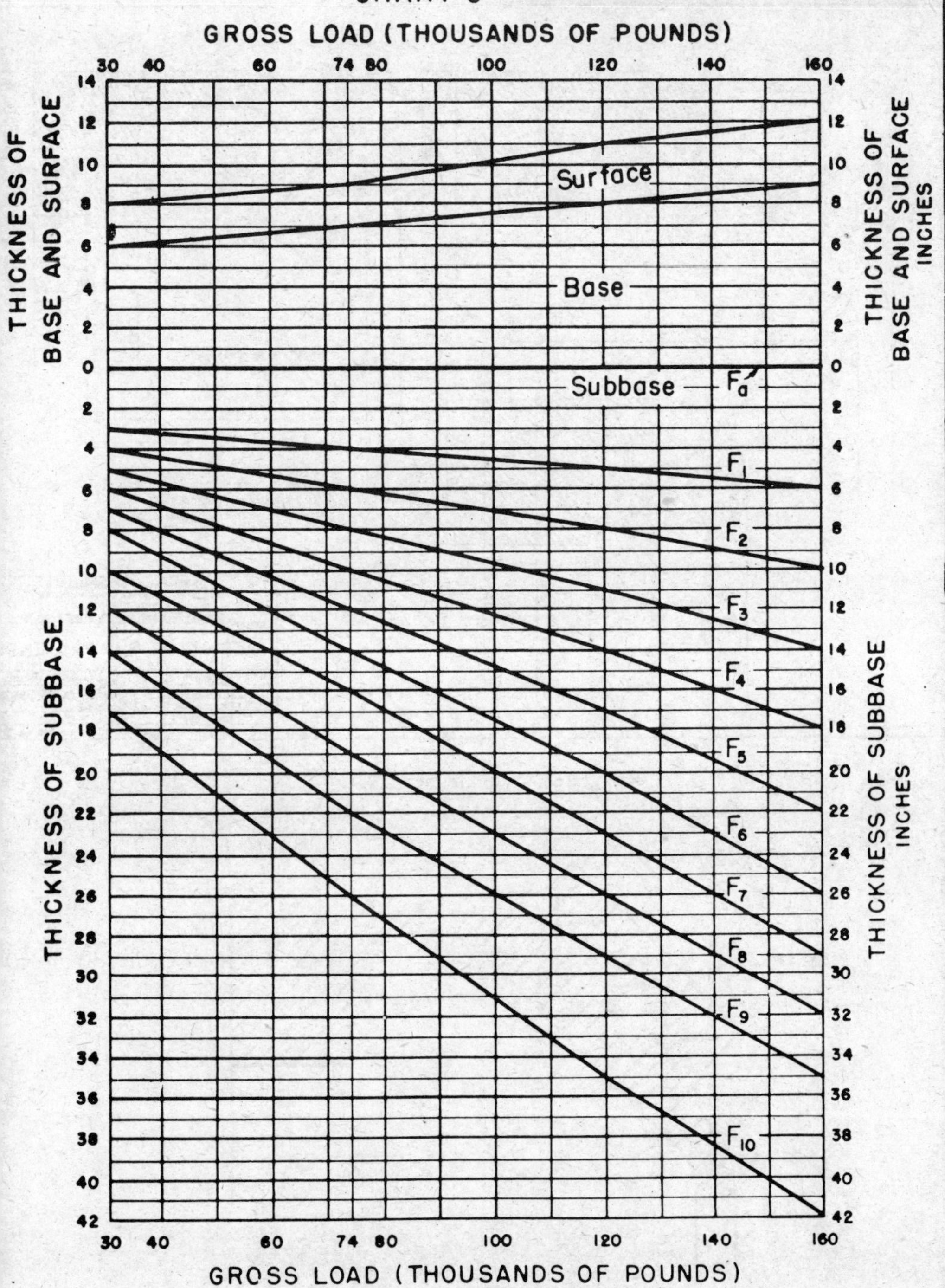

FIG. 7-4. (Courtesy C.A.A.)

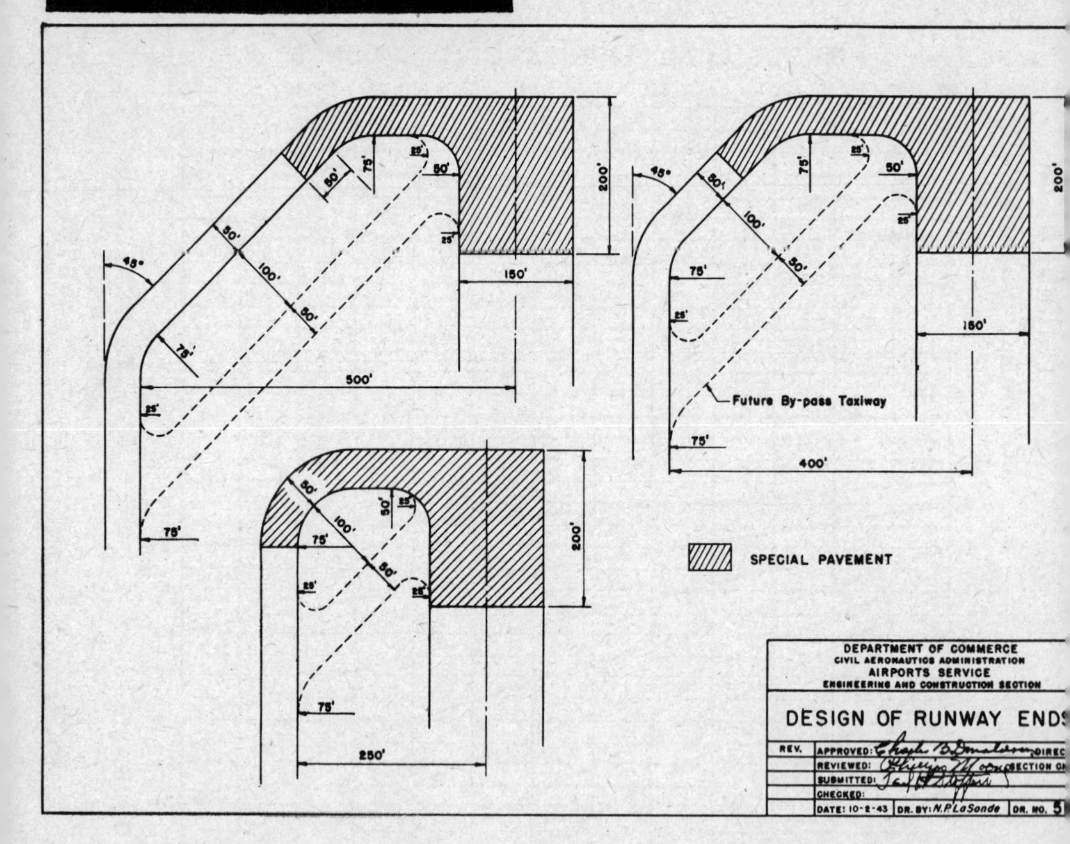

FIG. 7-5a. (Courtesy C.A.A.)

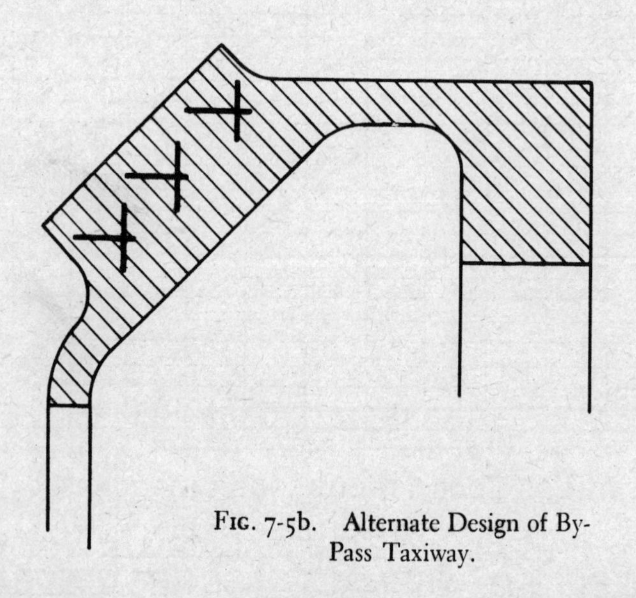

FIG. 7-5b. Alternate Design of By-Pass Taxiway.

VII. PAVEMENTS

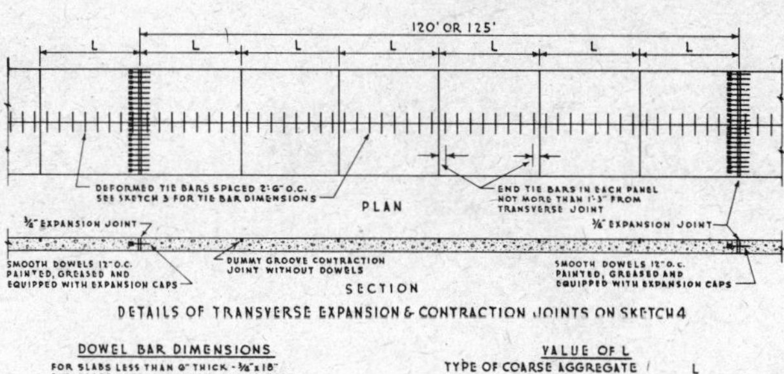

FIG. 7-6. (Courtesy Portland Cement Assoc.)

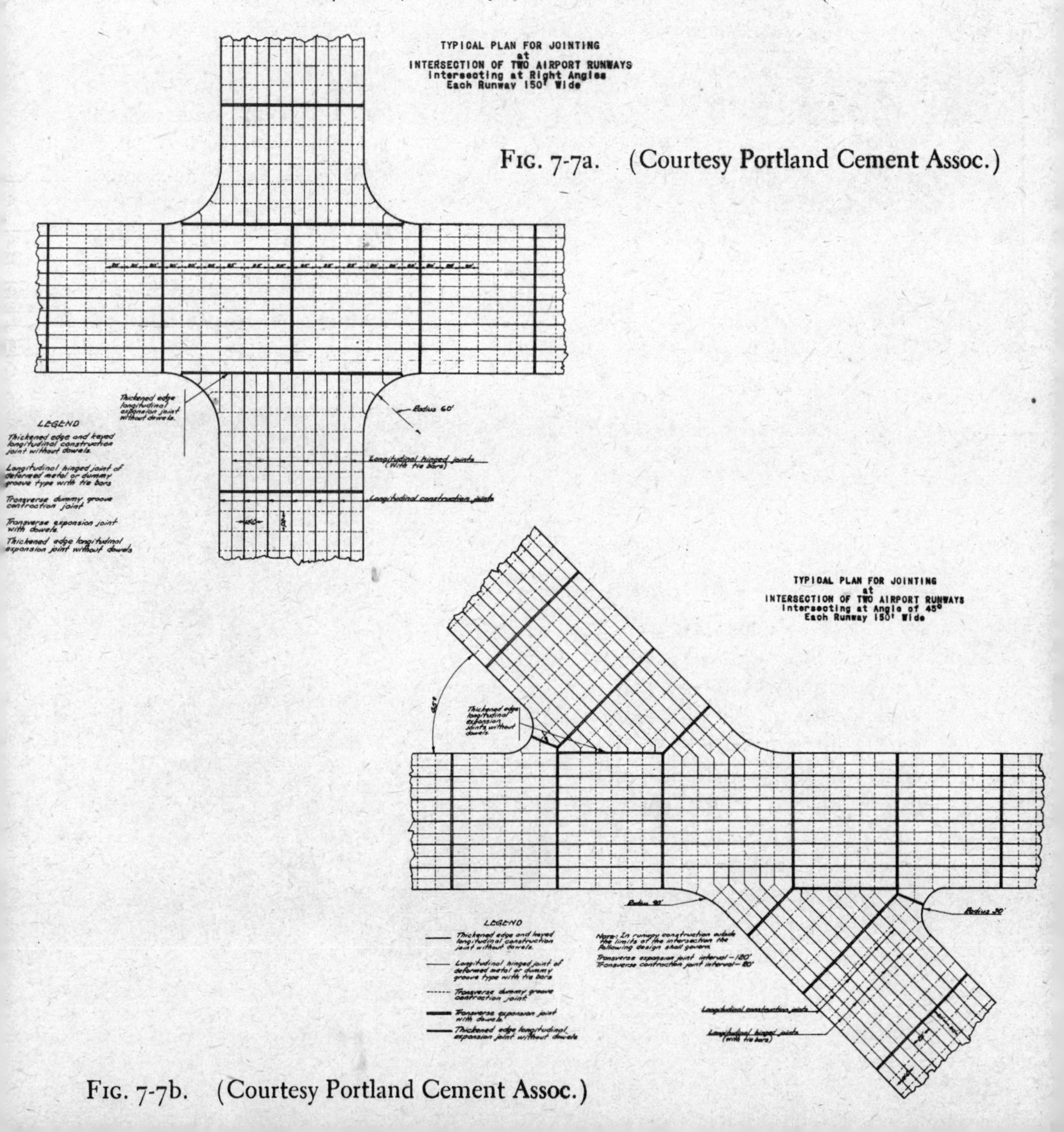

FIG. 7-7a. (Courtesy Portland Cement Assoc.)

FIG. 7-7b. (Courtesy Portland Cement Assoc.)

Fig. 7-8a. Transverse Dummy Contraction Joint Assembly at Idlewild Airport. The design is similar to that used for expansion joints except that filler material is omitted. Transverse 1 in. angle under dowels serves as spacer. Dummy joint slot is cut 3 in. deep, ¼ in. wide at bottom, and ⅜ in. wide at top. (Courtesy Bethlehem Steel Company.)

Fig. 7-8b. Transverse Expansion Joint and Load Transfer Assembly Using Bethlehem Dowel at Idlewild Airport. Joints are spaced 120 ft apart. Dowels are 9 in. in length, spaced 12 in. apart, and placed at mid-depth of 12-in. slab. Expansion joint filler is 1 in. cork. (Courtesy Bond Crown and Cork Company.)

FIG. 7-8c. Transverse Expansion Joint and Transverse Dummy Joint Assemblies in Place at Idlewild Airport.

FIG. 7-9a. Processing Soil Cement Runway, Baer Field, Ft. Wayne, Indiana. (Courtesy Portland Cement Assoc.)

FIG. 7-9b. Mixing Emulsified Asphalt and Sand in Place, Pine Camp, N. Y. (Courtesy American Bitumuls Company.)

FIG. 7-9c. Stabilizing Soil with Emulsified Asphalt for Runway Base Course, Ballston Spa, N. Y. Note windows of mixed material at right, with travel plant mixing untreated windrow at left. (Courtesy American Bitumuls Company.)

FIG. 7-10. Batching Plant for Concrete Aggregates, Idlewild Airport.

FIG. 7-11. Paving Top 4 In. of Concrete Slab to Cover Reinforcing Mesh, Idlewild Airport.

FIG. 7-12. Spreading Bituminous Surface Course. (Courtesy American Bitumuls Company.)

FIG. 7-13. Rubber-Tired Compaction Equipment, Idlewild Airport.

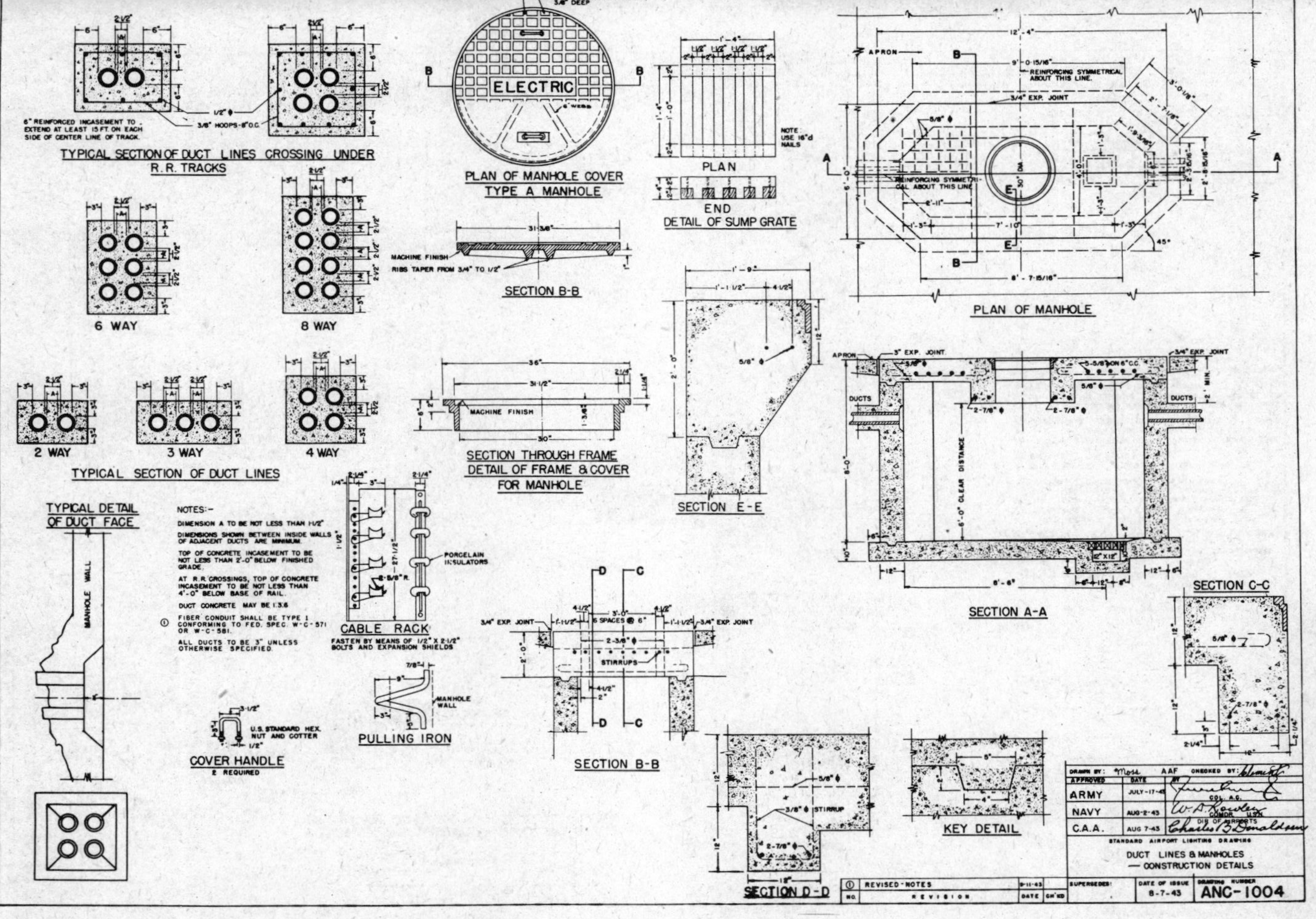

FIG. 10-1. (Courtesy C.A.A.)

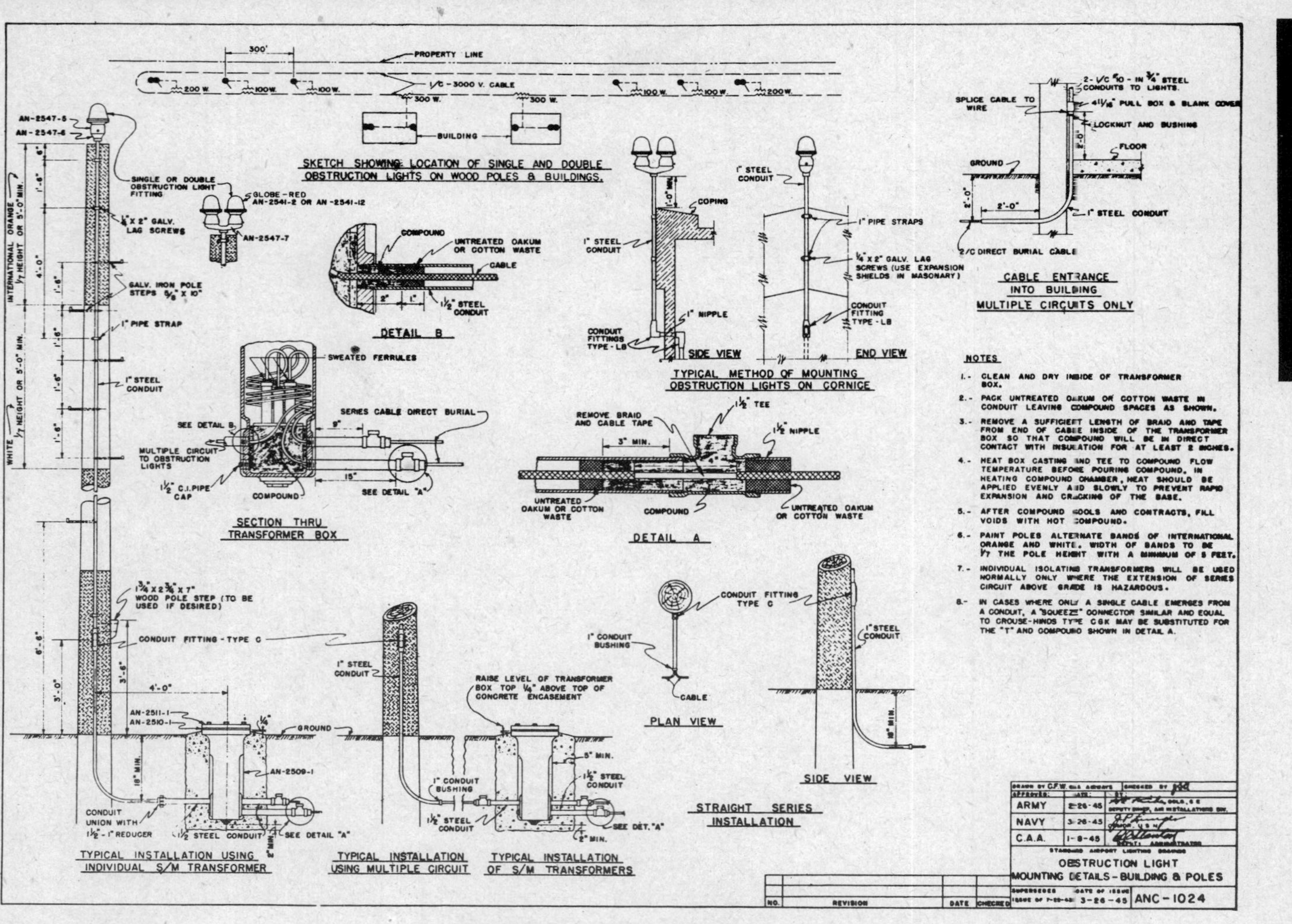

FIG. 10-2. (Courtesy C.A.A.)

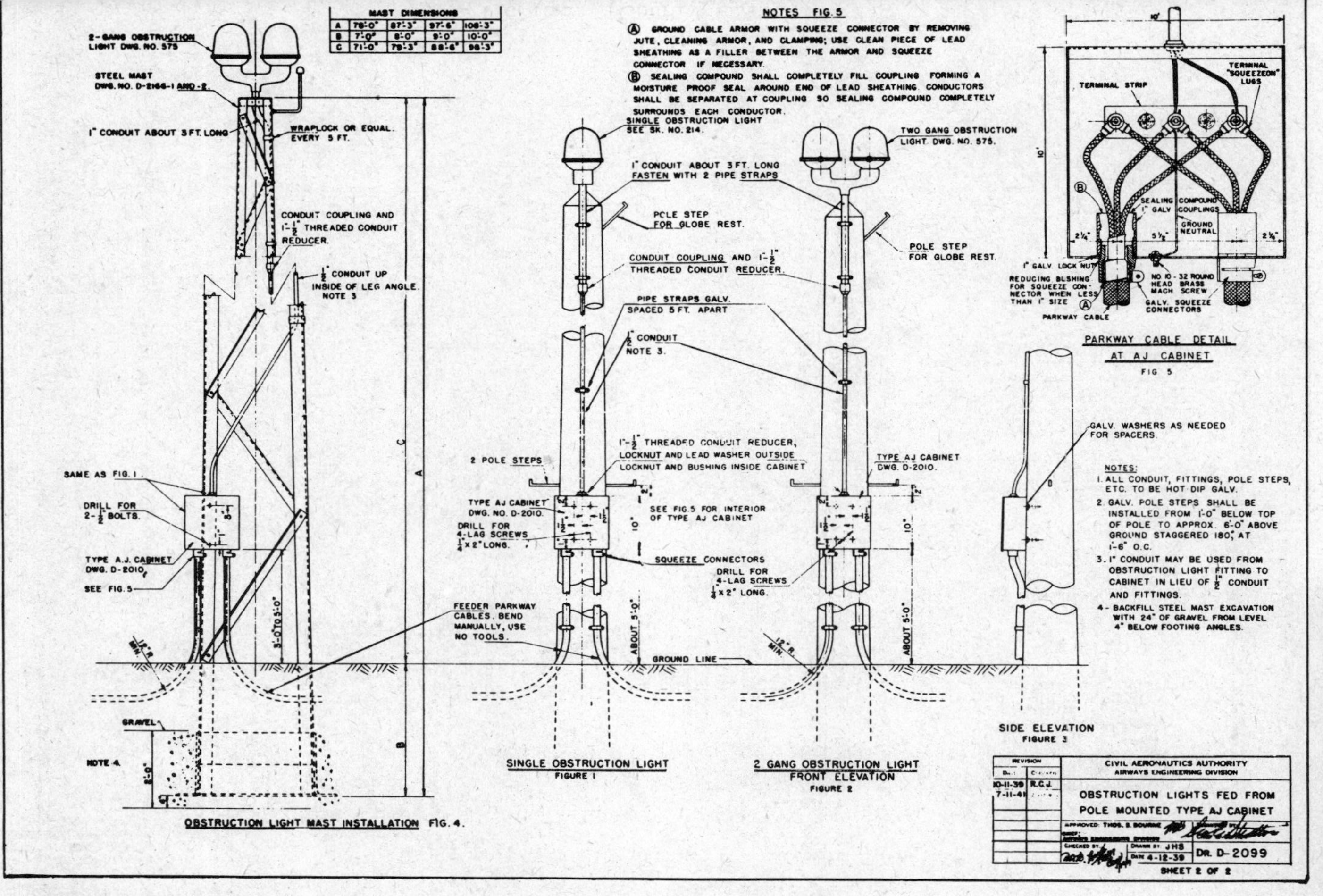

FIG. 10-3. (Courtesy C.A.A.)

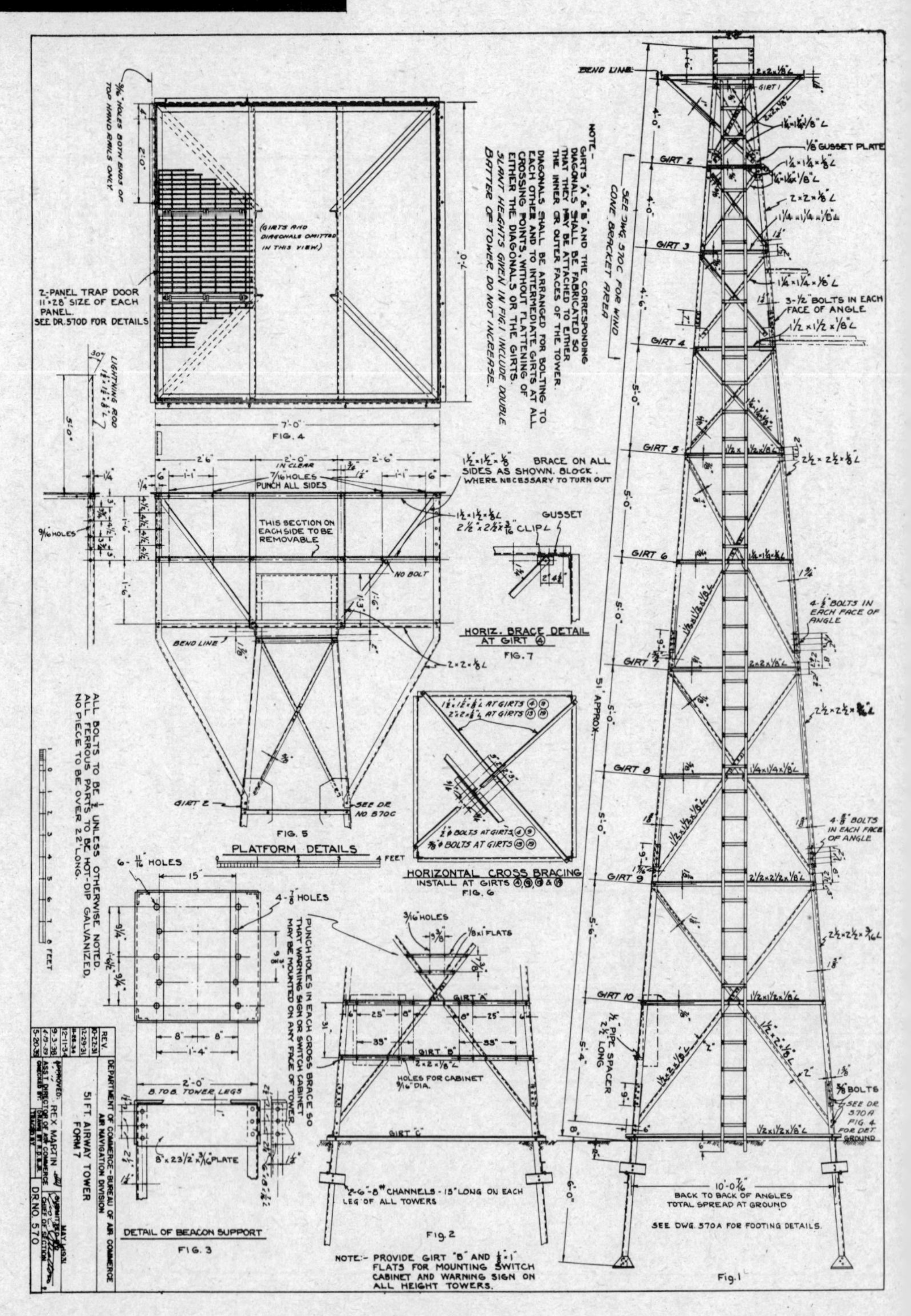

FIG. 10-4. (Courtesy C.A.A.)

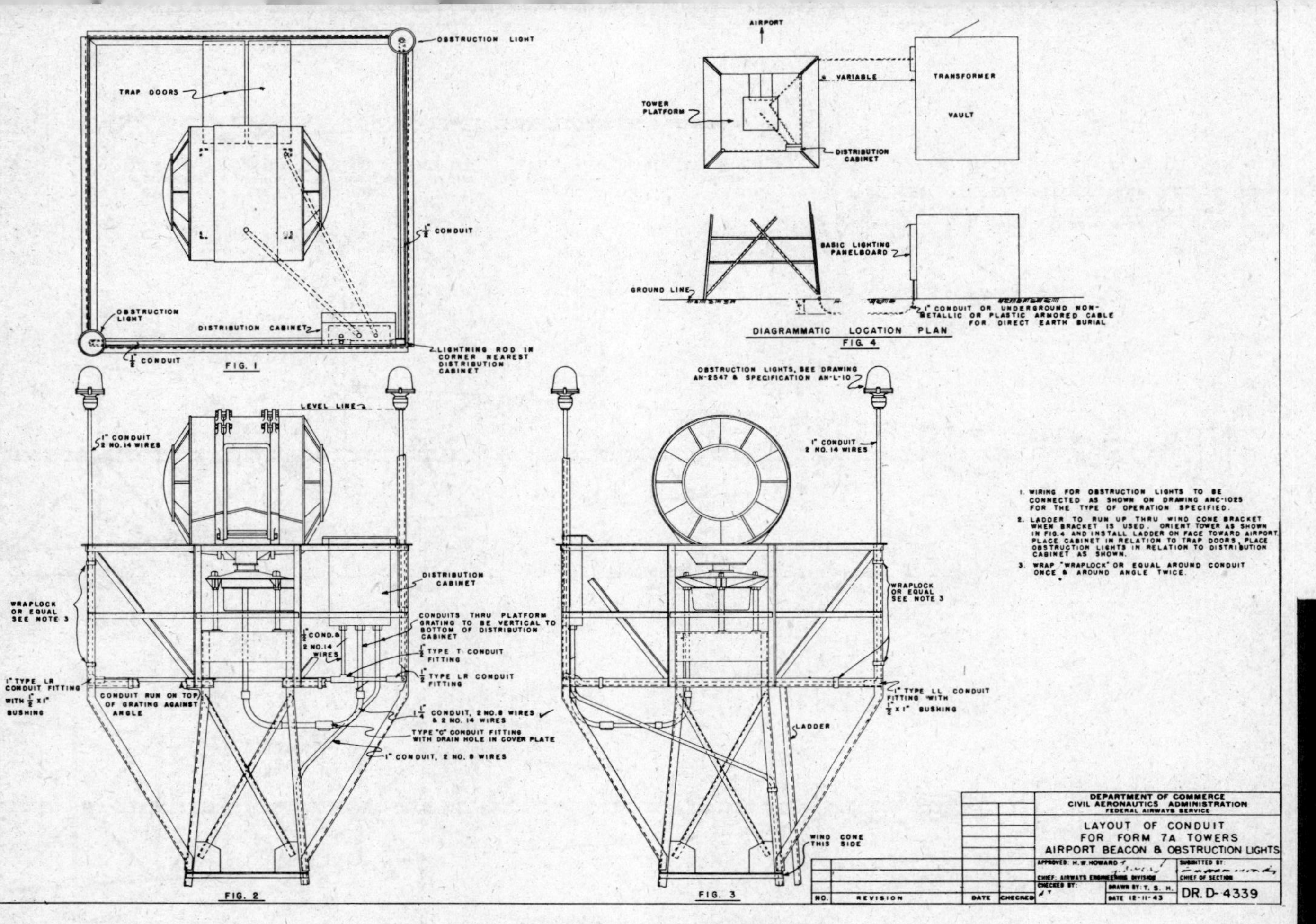

FIG. 10-5. (Courtesy C.A.A.)

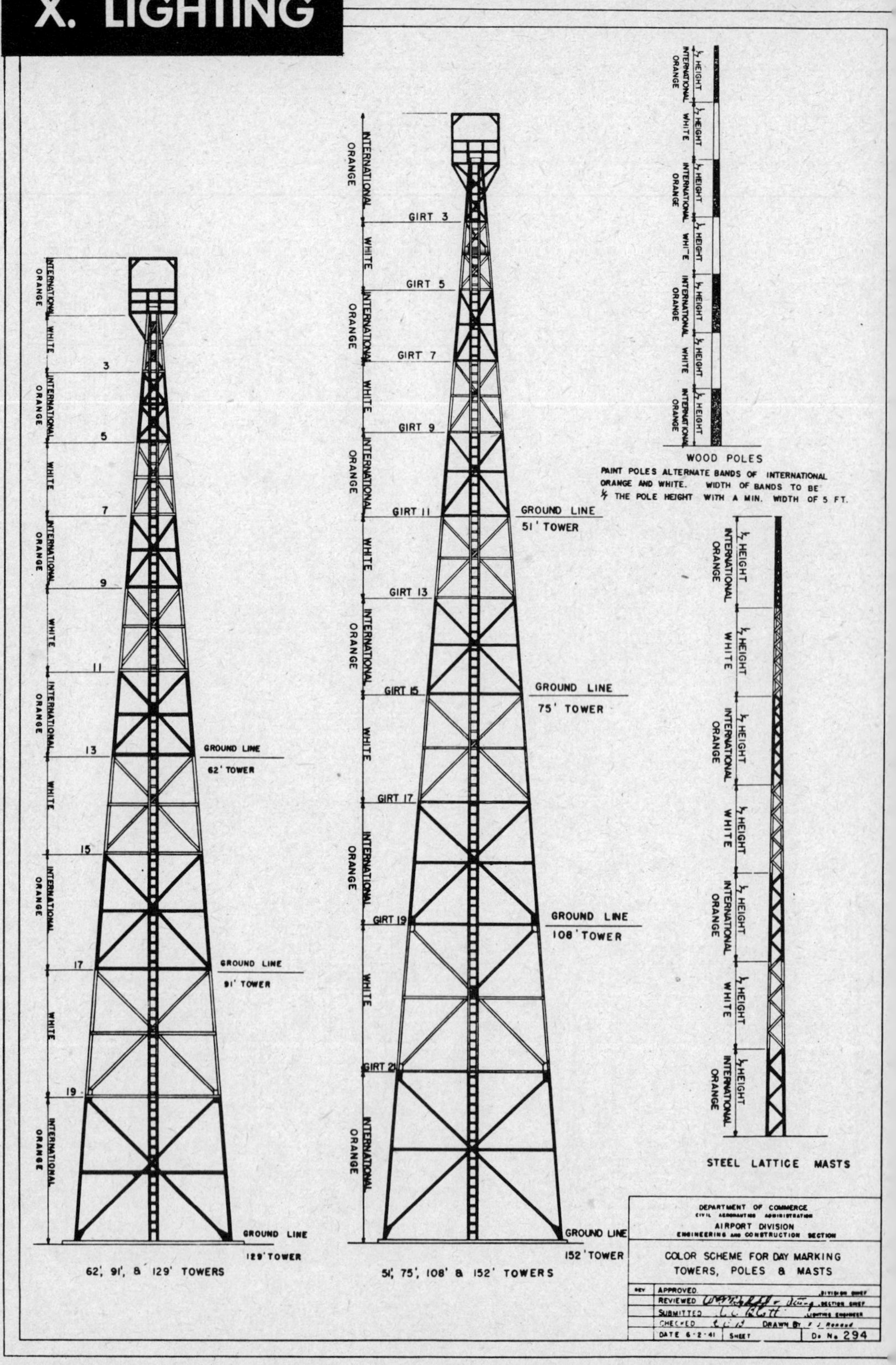

WOOD POLES

PAINT POLES ALTERNATE BANDS OF INTERNATIONAL ORANGE AND WHITE. WIDTH OF BANDS TO BE 1/7 THE POLE HEIGHT WITH A MIN. WIDTH OF 5 FT.

STEEL LATTICE MASTS

62', 91', & 129' TOWERS

51', 75', 108' & 152' TOWERS

DEPARTMENT OF COMMERCE
CIVIL AERONAUTICS ADMINISTRATION
AIRPORT DIVISION
ENGINEERING AND CONSTRUCTION SECTION

COLOR SCHEME FOR DAY MARKING
TOWERS, POLES & MASTS

REV	APPROVED		DIVISION CHIEF
	REVIEWED		SECTION CHIEF
	SUBMITTED		LIGHTING ENGINEER
	CHECKED		DRAWN BY F. J. Renaud
	DATE 6-2-41	SHEET	D. No. 294

Fig. 10-6. (Courtesy C.A.A.)

X. LIGHTING

FIG. 10-7. 36-in. Airport Beacon. (Courtesy Crouse Hinds.)

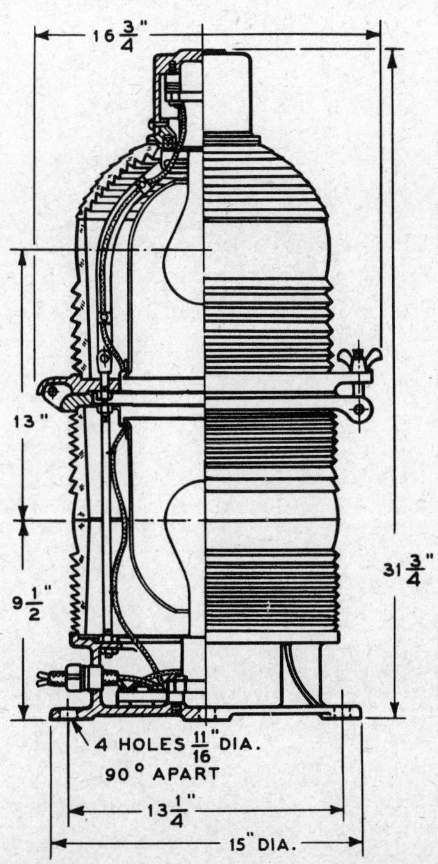

FIG. 10-8. Flashing Code Beacon. (Courtesy Crouse Hinds.)

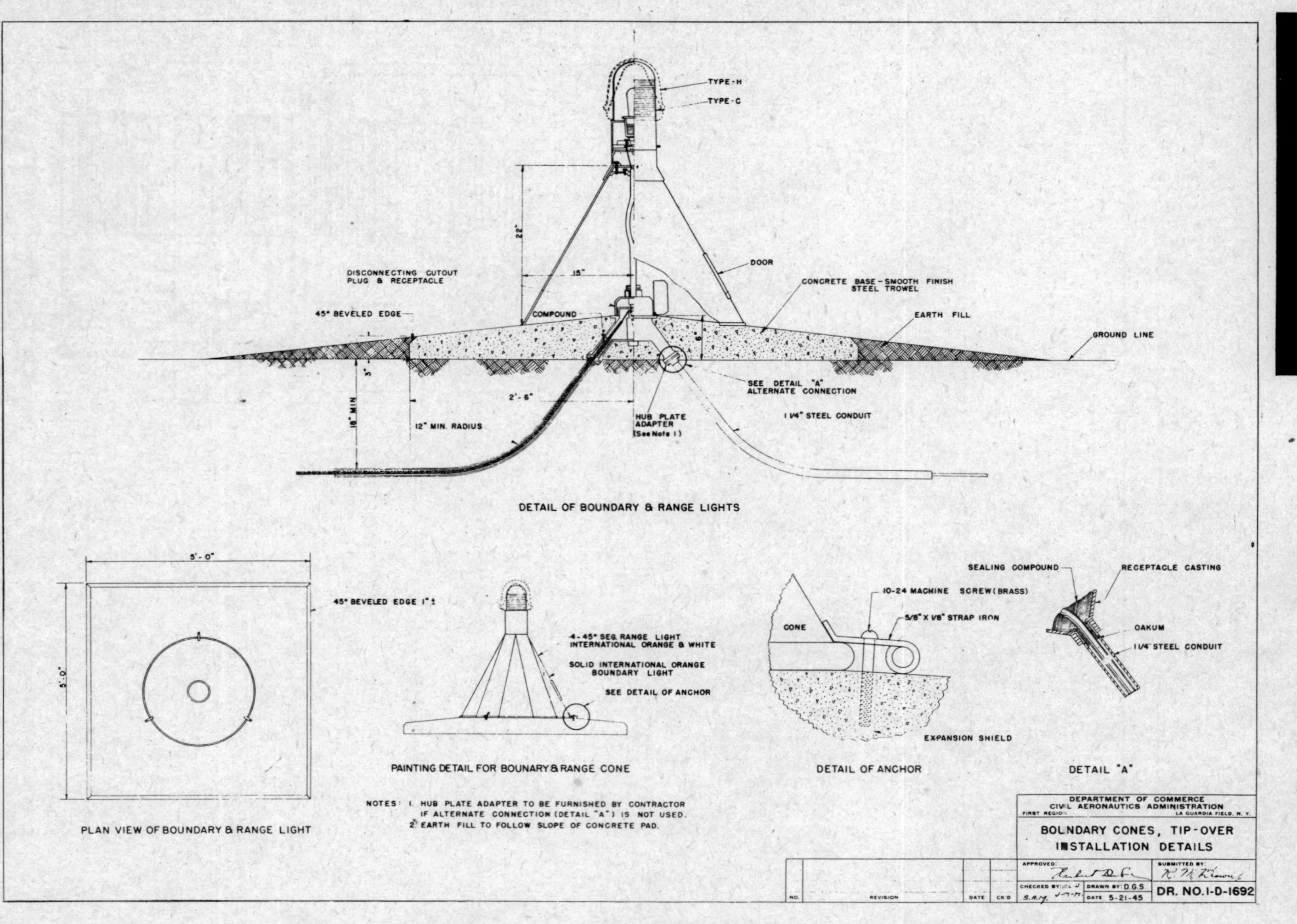

FIG. 10-9. (Courtesy C.A.A.)

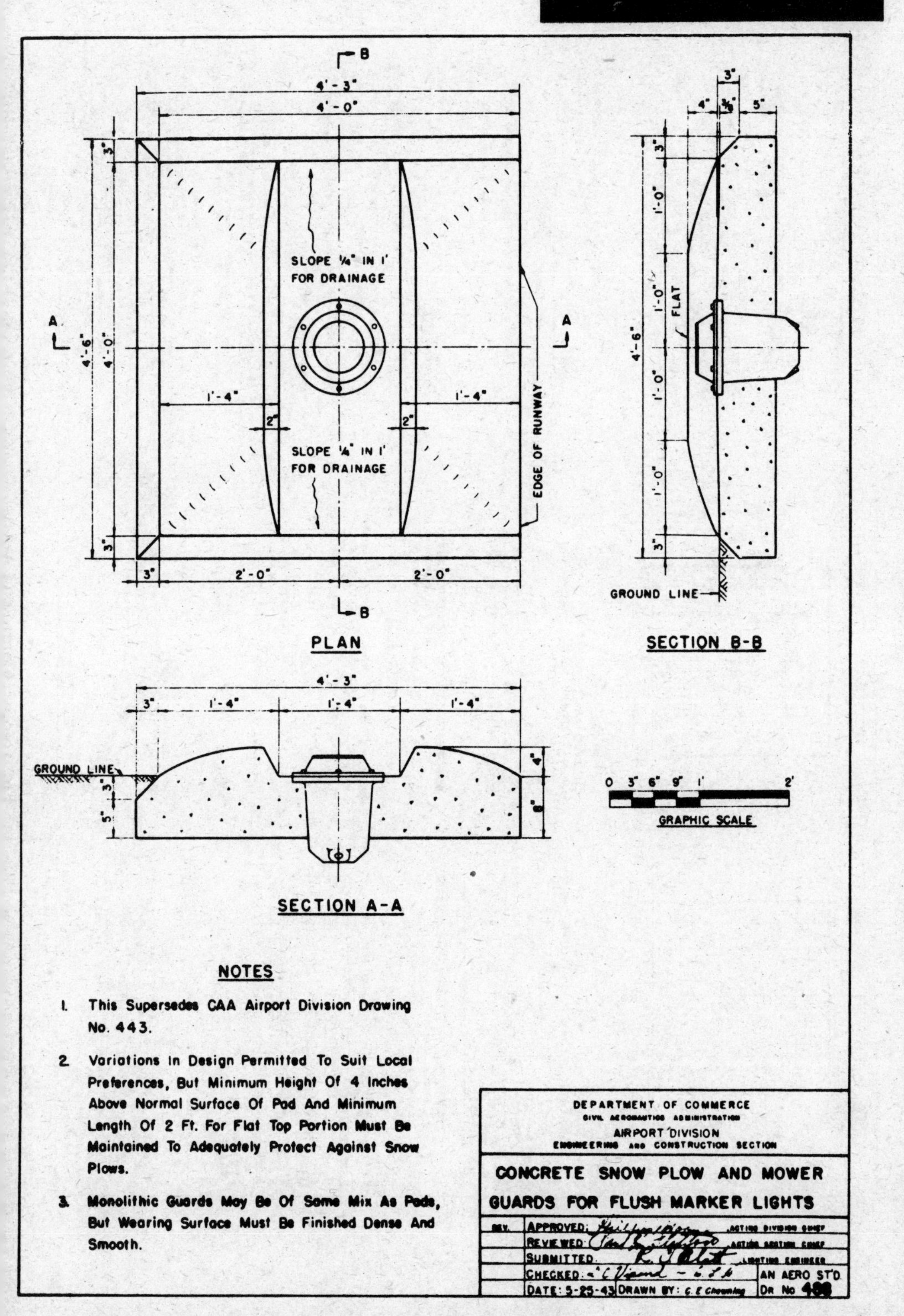

FIG. 10-10. (Courtesy C.A.A.)

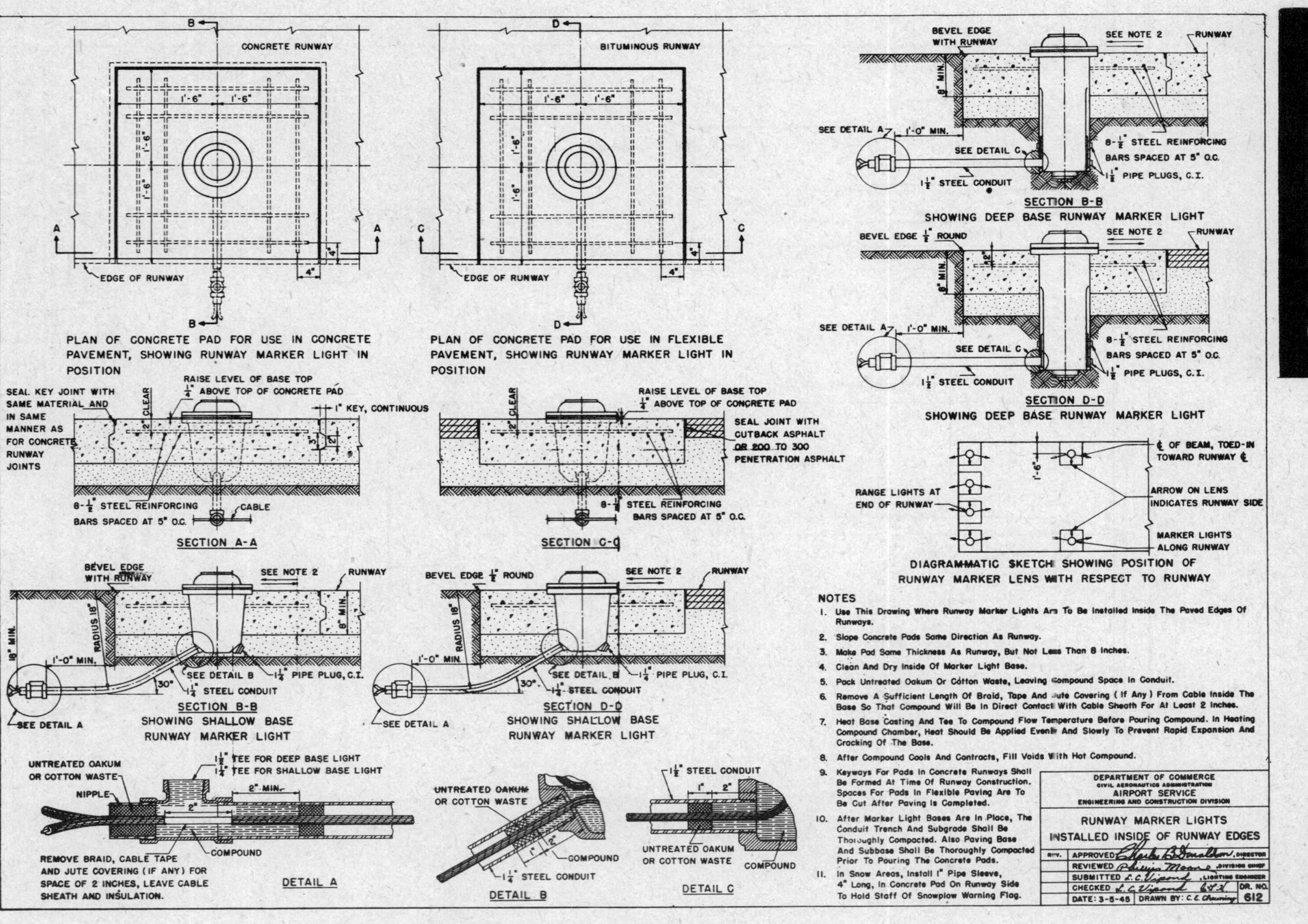

FIG. 10-11. (Courtesy C.A.A.)

FIG. 10-12. The Bartow Beam, Controlled Unit. For use as runway or approach lamp. (Courtesy Line Material Co. of Penna.)

FIG. 10-13. Isometric View, Bartow Runway and Approach Lamp. (Courtesy Line Material Co. of Penna.)

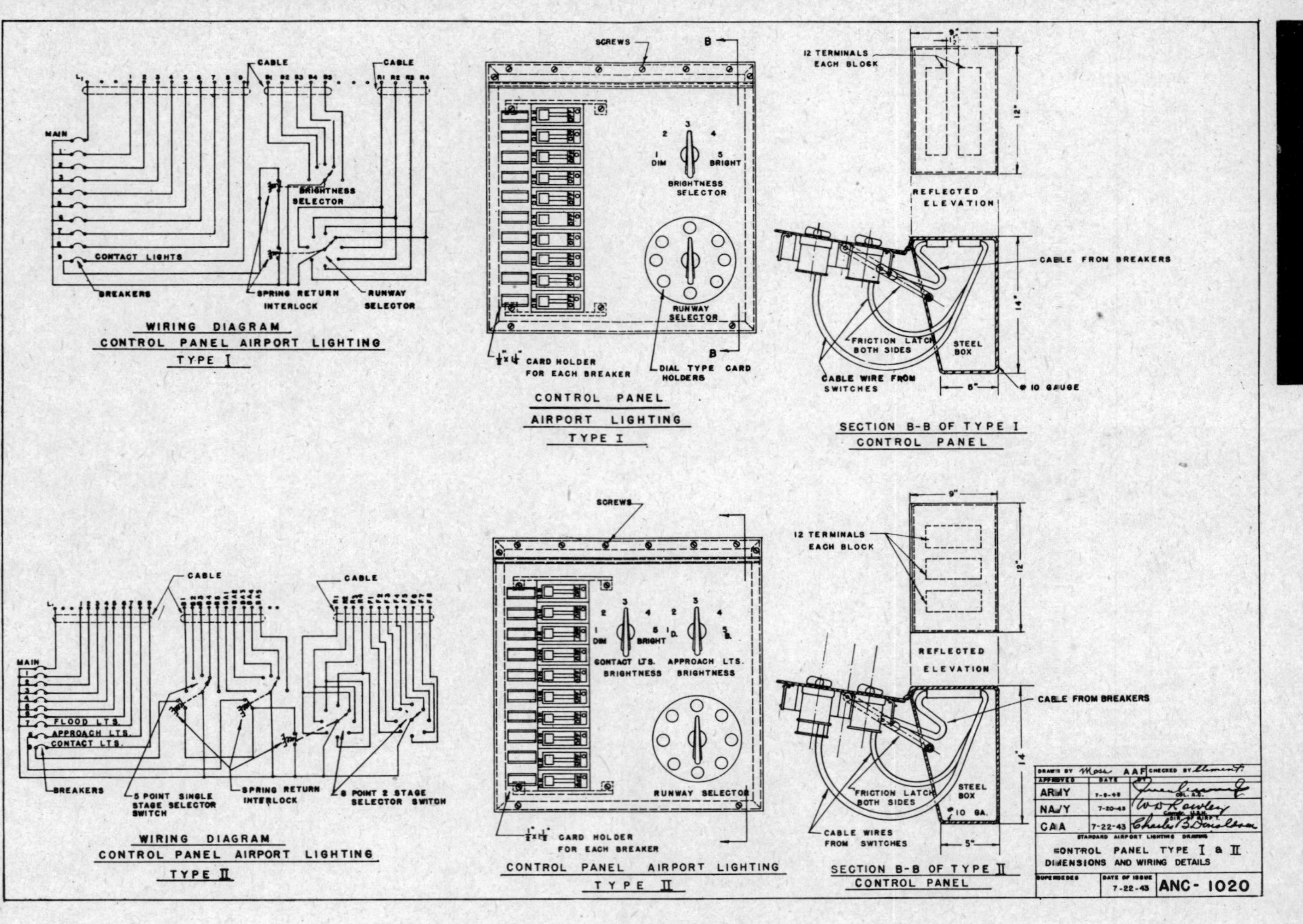

Fig. 10-14. (Courtesy C.A.A.)

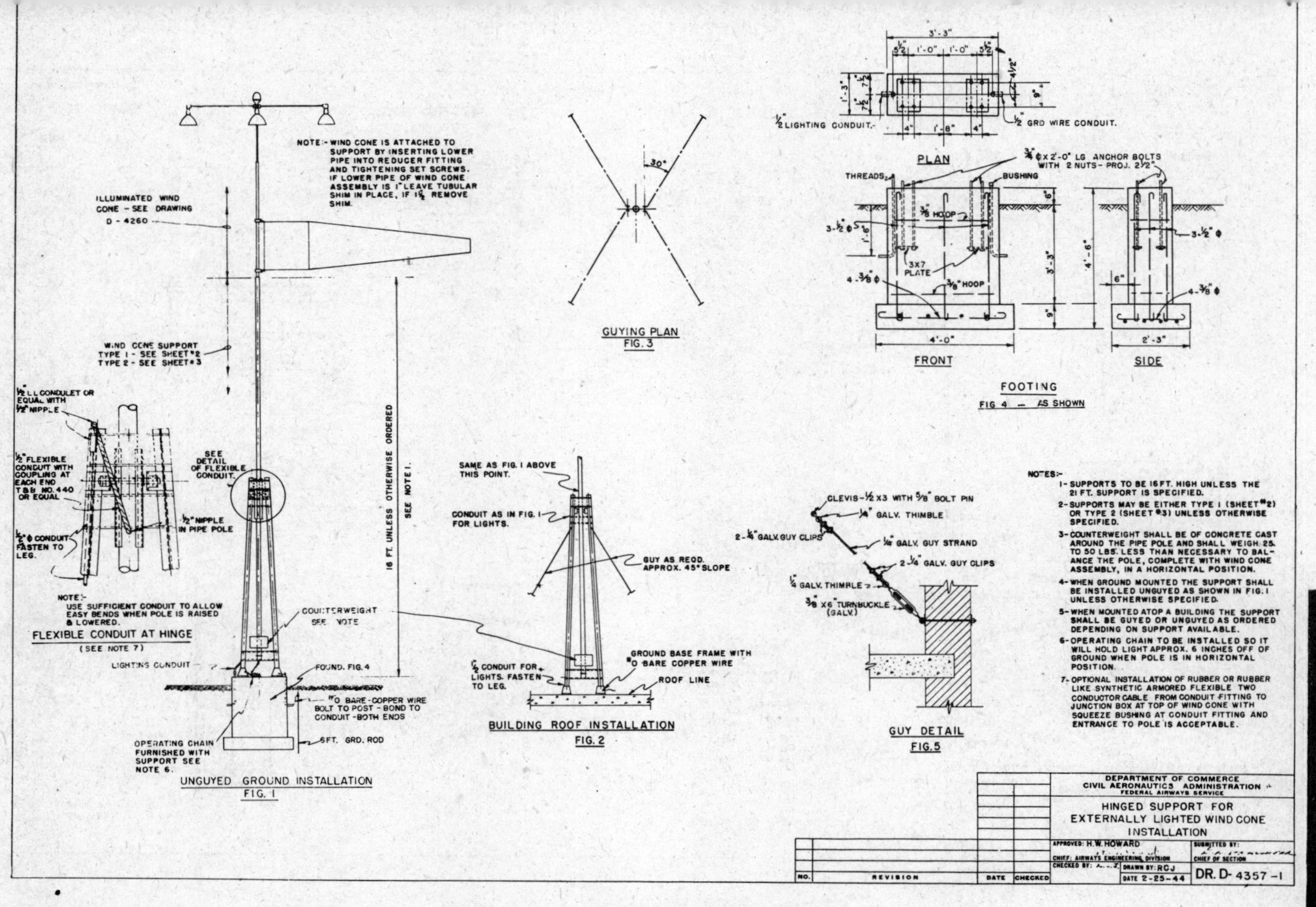

FIG. 10-15. (Courtesy C.A.A.)

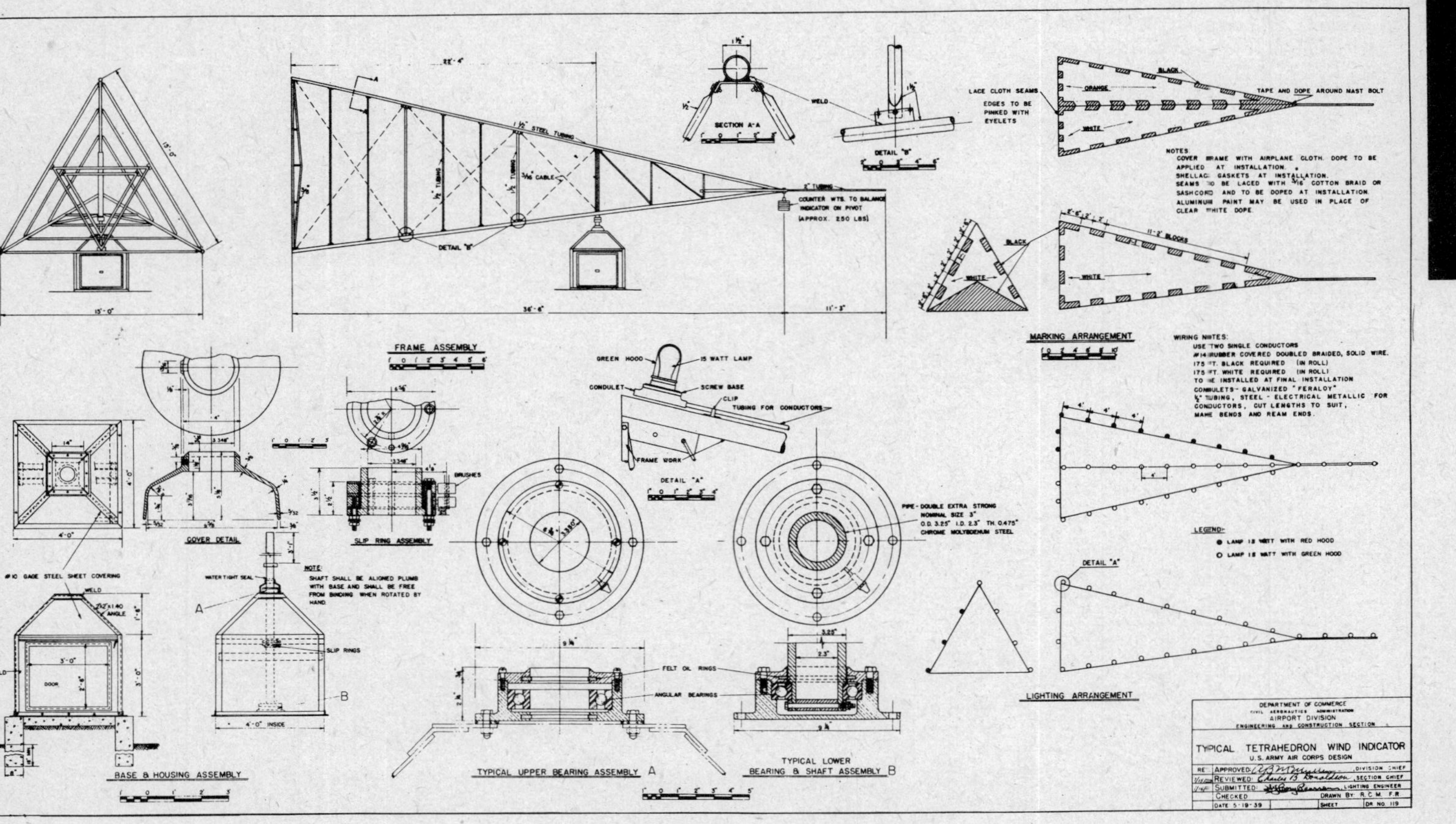

FIG. 10-16. (Courtesy C.A.A.)

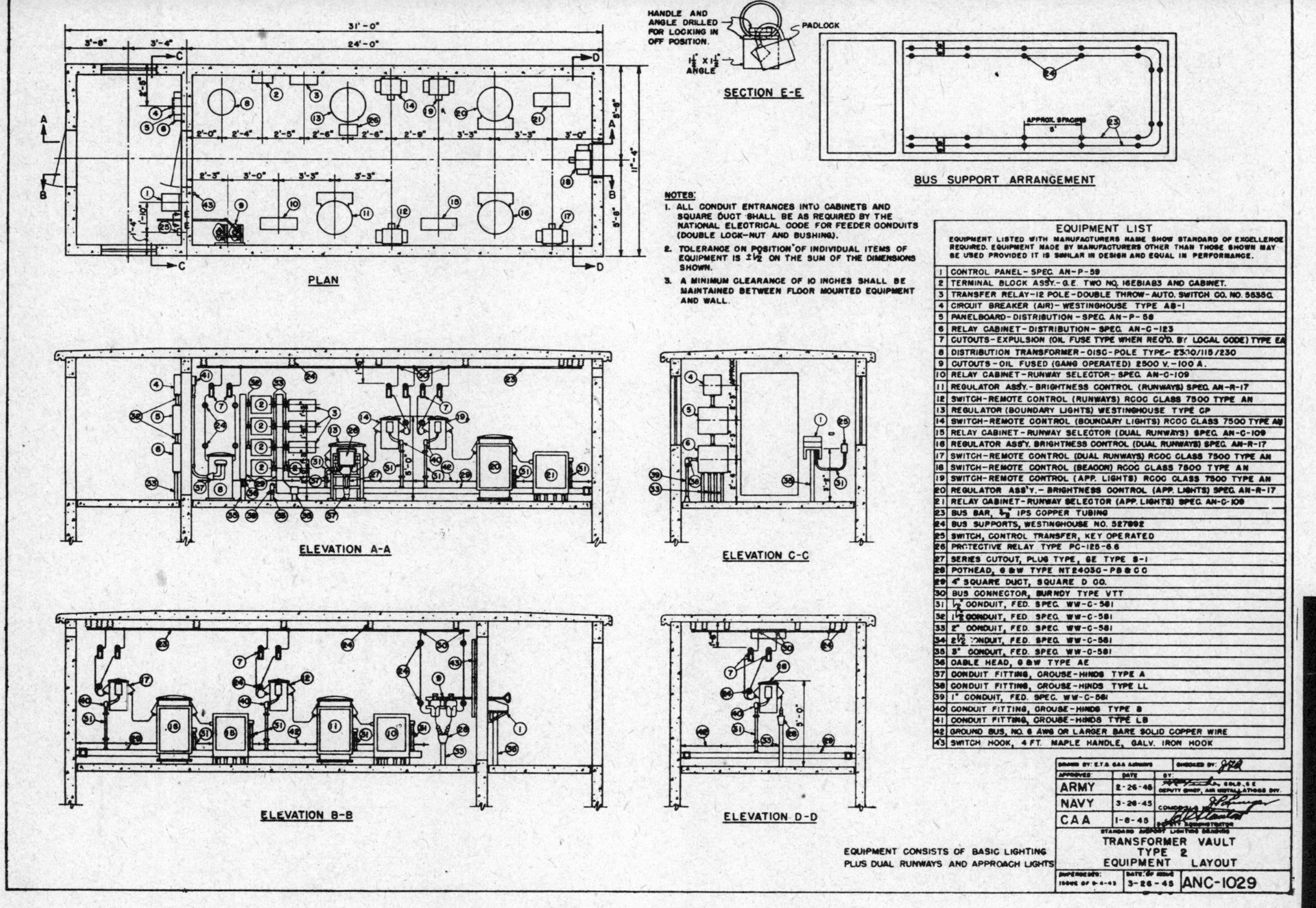

FIG. 10-17. (Courtesy C.A.A.)

X. LIGHTING

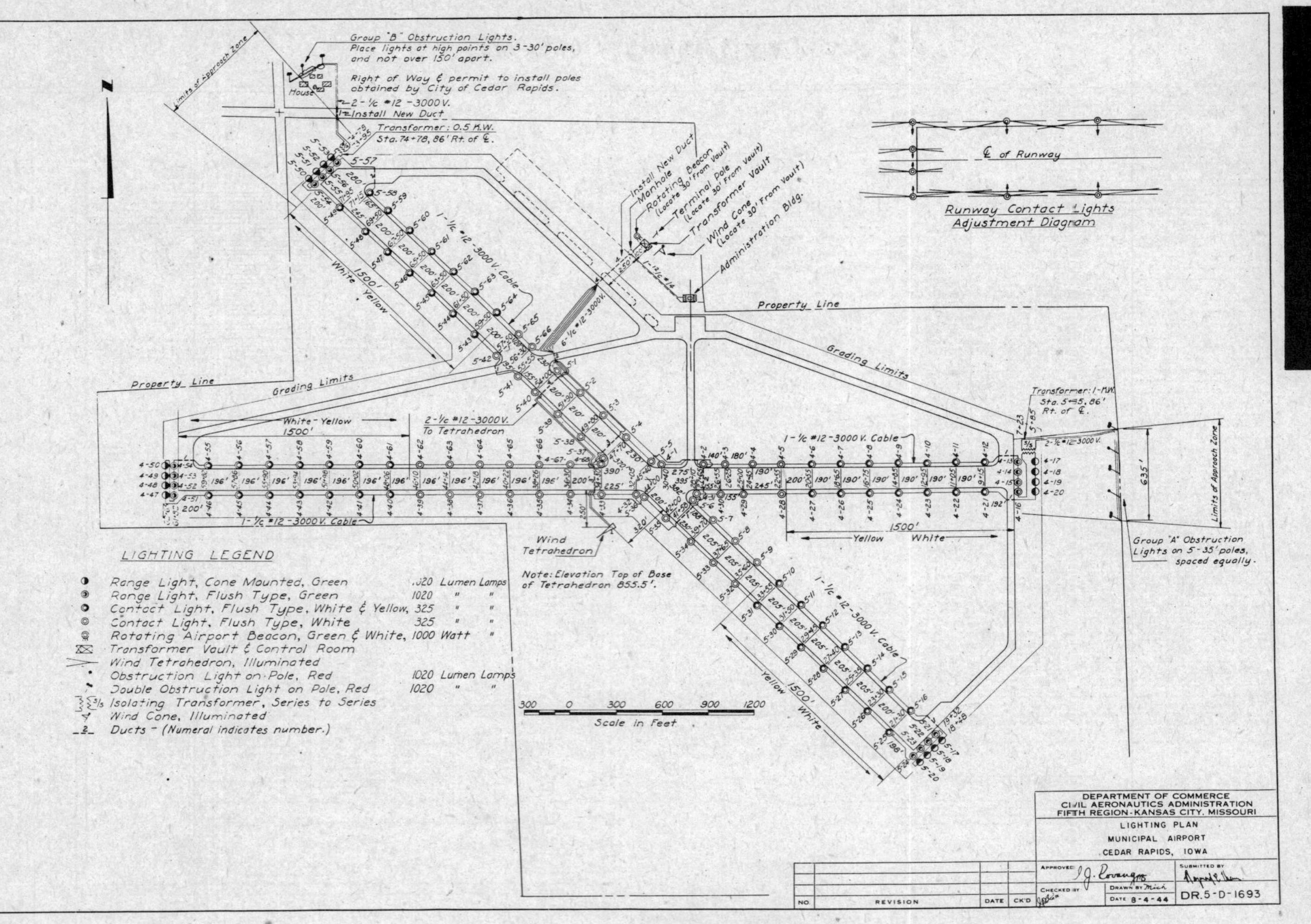

FIG. 10-18. (Courtesy C.A.A.)

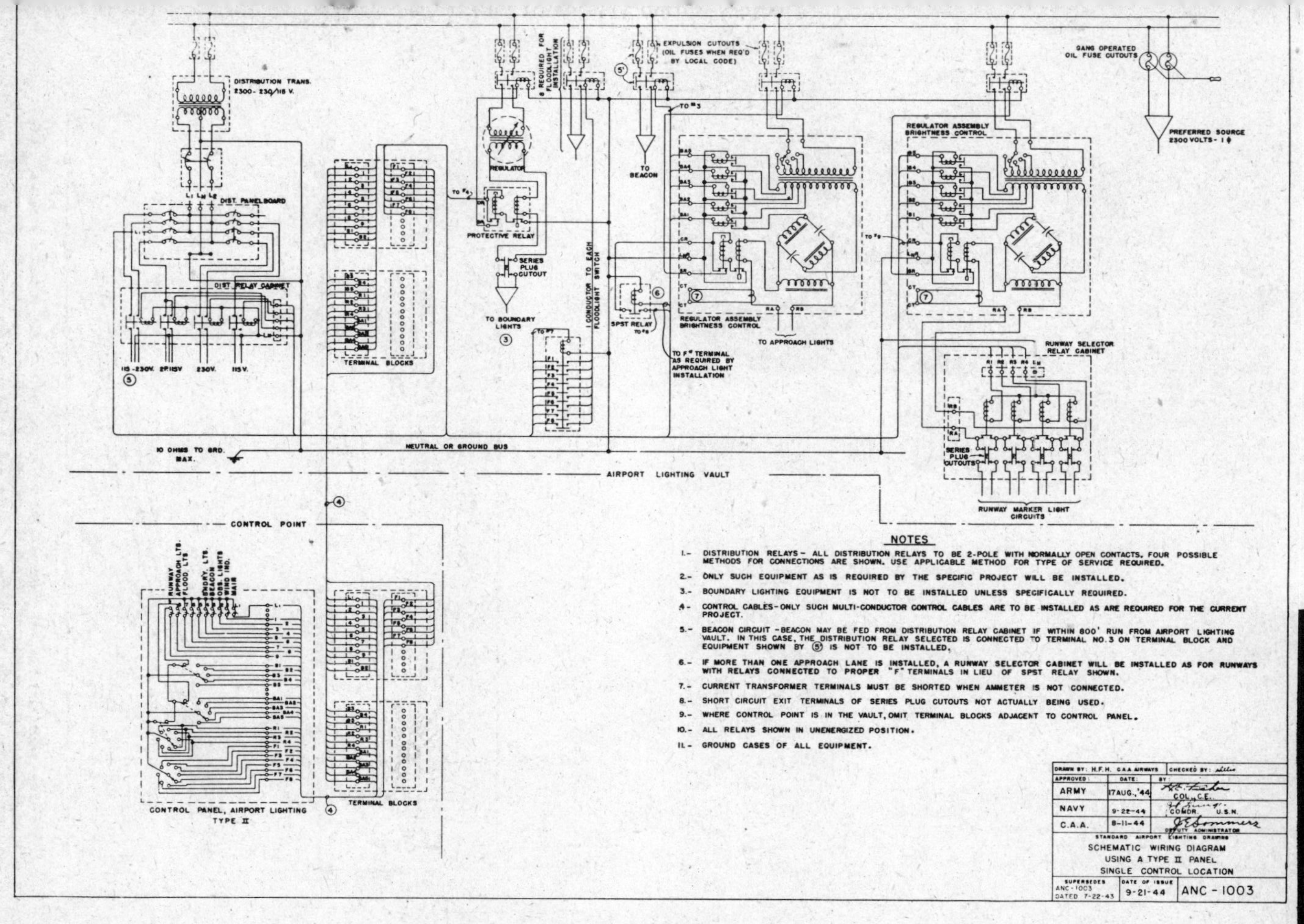

FIG. 10-19. (Courtesy C.A.A.)

X. LIGHTING

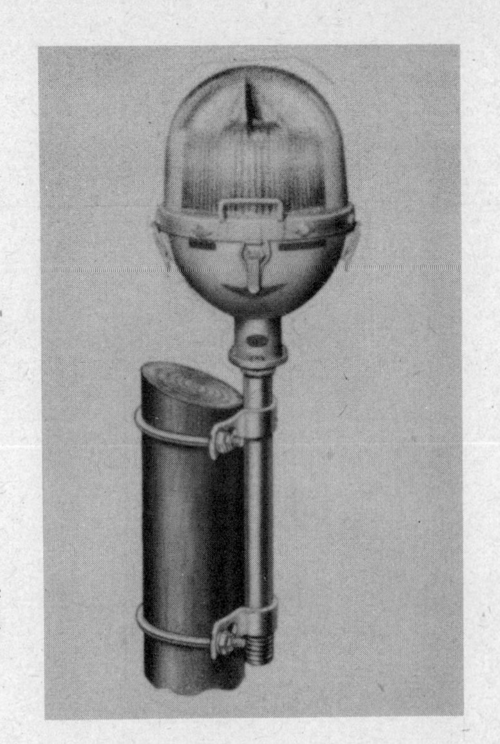

Fig. 10-20. Bartow Unit, Pole Mounted. (Courtesy Line Material Co. of Penna.)

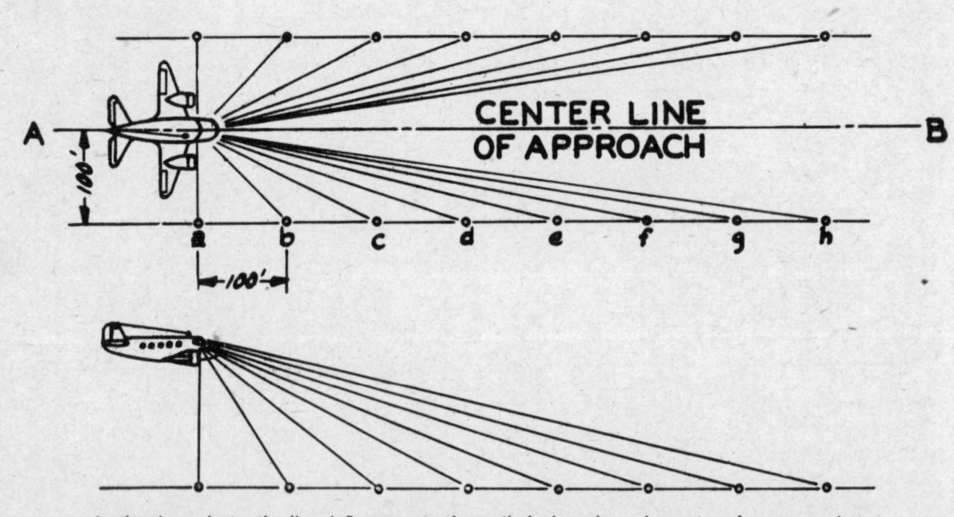

In the above charts, the line A-B represents the vertical plane down the center of a runway; letters "a" to "h" represent runway lights. The light from each unit can be so distributed and the candlepower so controlled that when the light reaches the plane A-B it will be of equal value. Therefore, at every point along A-B all lights should appear as of the same value.

Fig. 10-21. Runway Light Intensity Chart. (Courtesy Line Material Co. of Penna.)

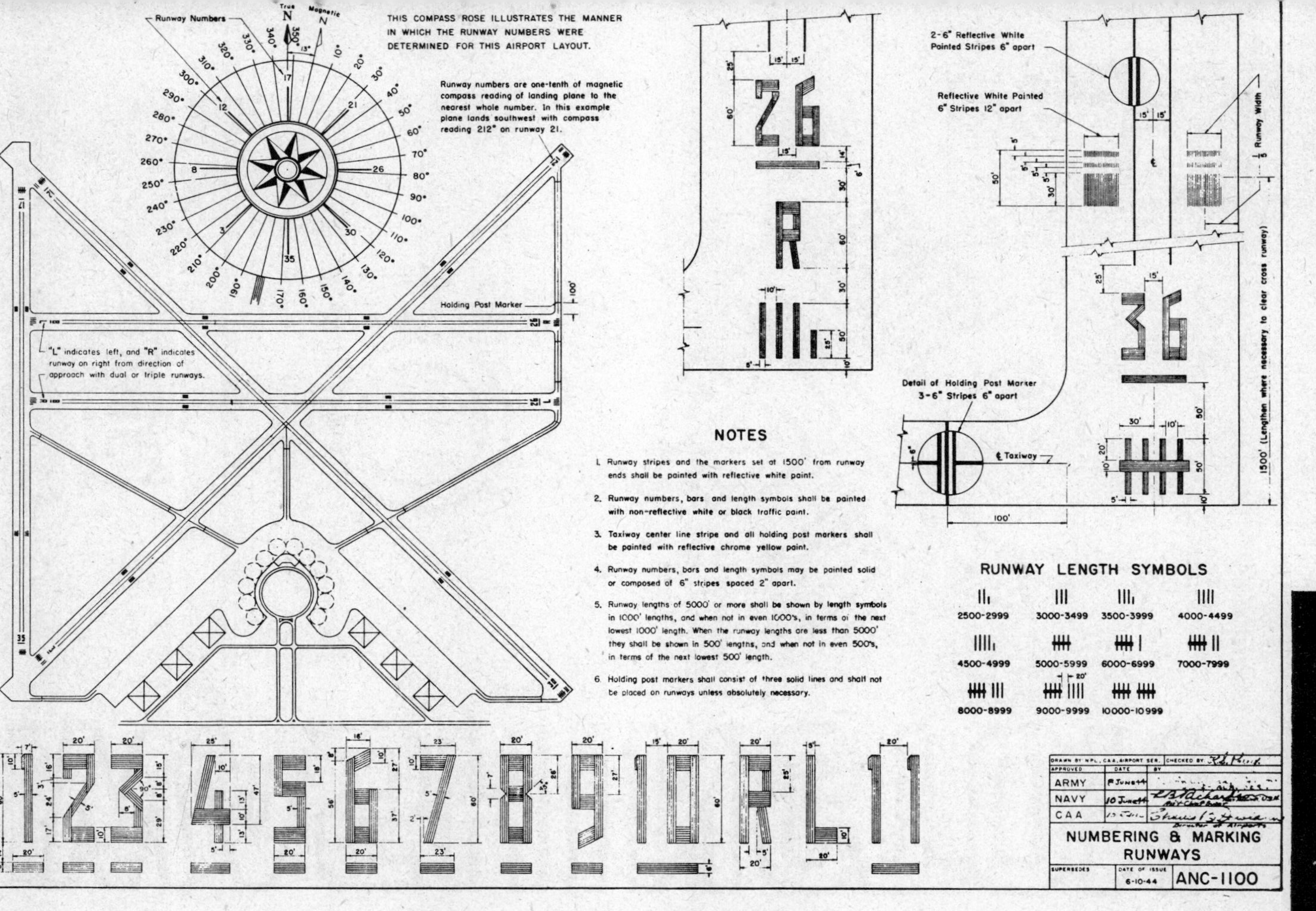

FIG. 10-22. (Courtesy C.A.A.)

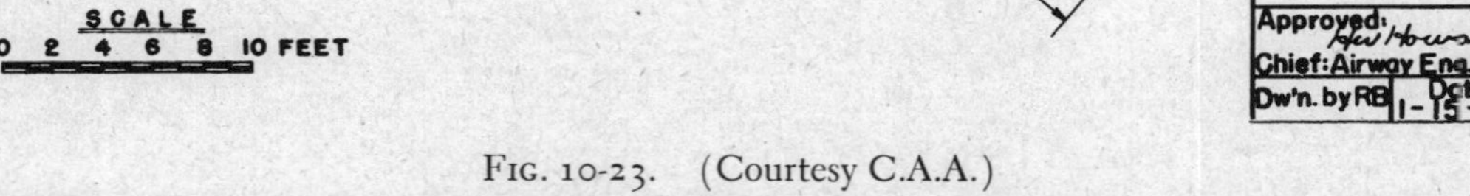

FIG. 10-23. (Courtesy C.A.A.)

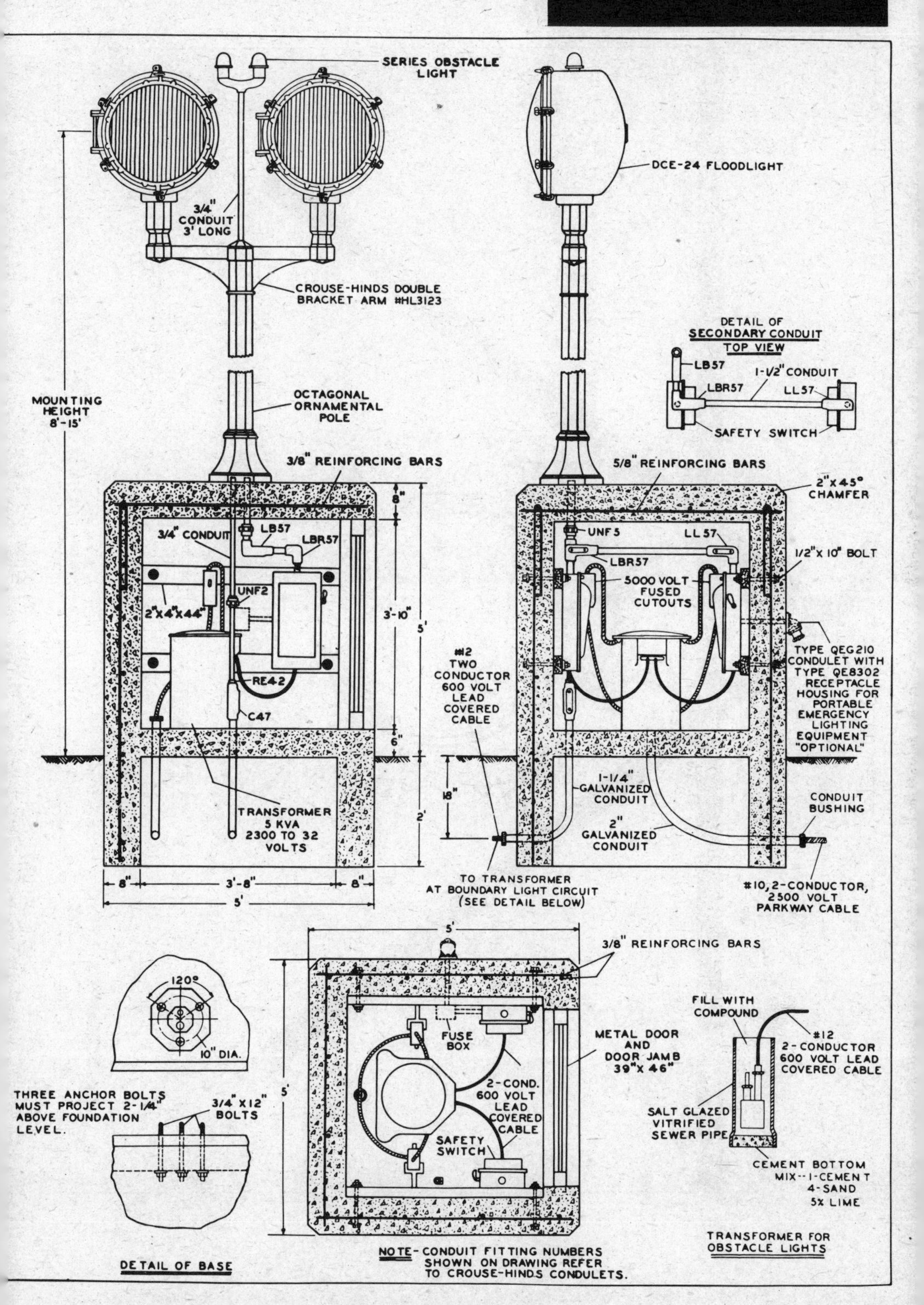

Fig. 10-24. Runway Flood Lights. (Courtesy Crouse Hinds.)

XI. BUILDINGS

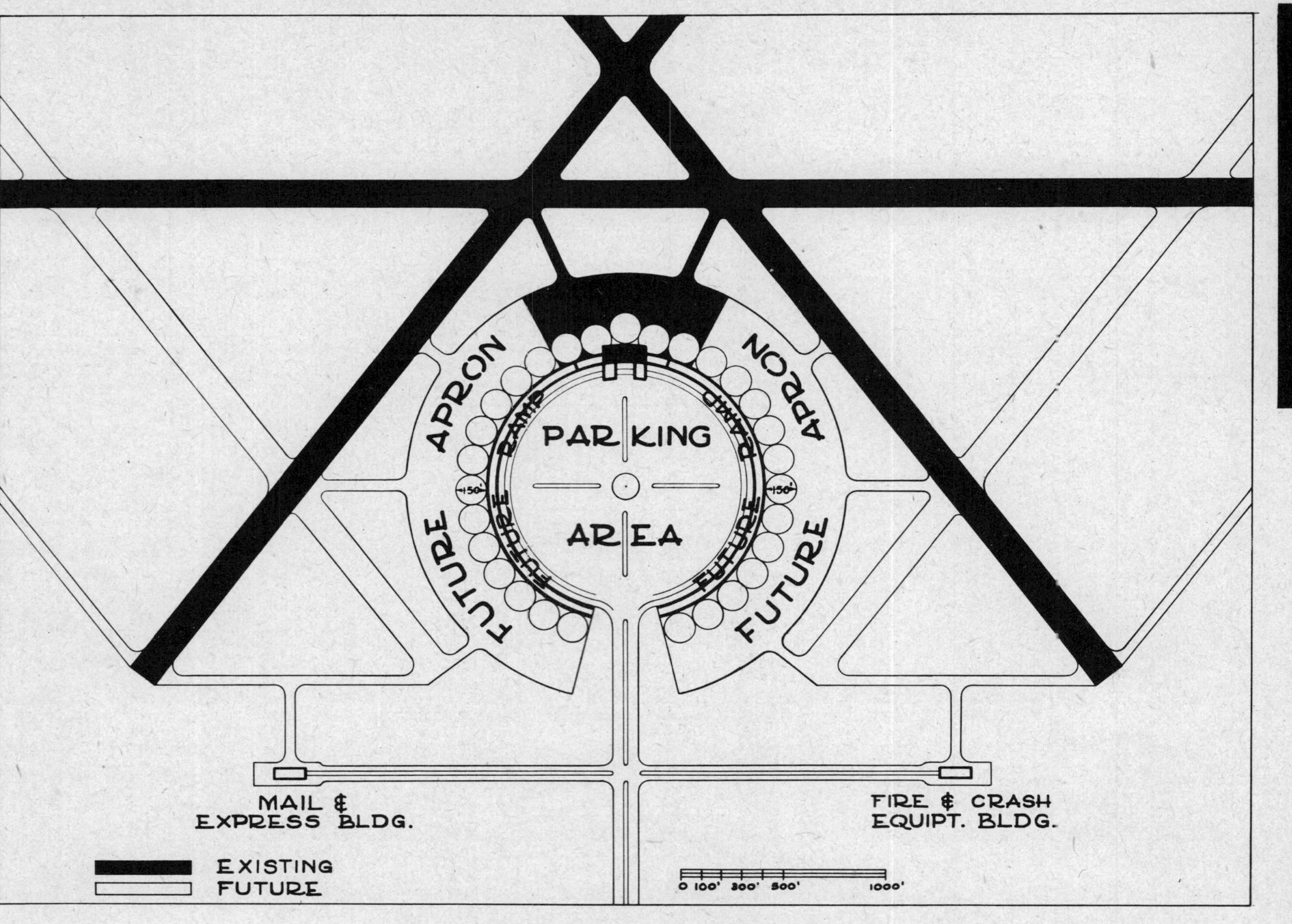

Fig. 11-1. Sample Terminal Building Area Layout.

FIG. 11-2. Terminal Building as Seen from Airport Side, Washington National Airport. (Courtesy C.A.A.)

XI. BUILDINGS

FIG. 11-3. Entrance to Terminal Building, La Guardia Field.

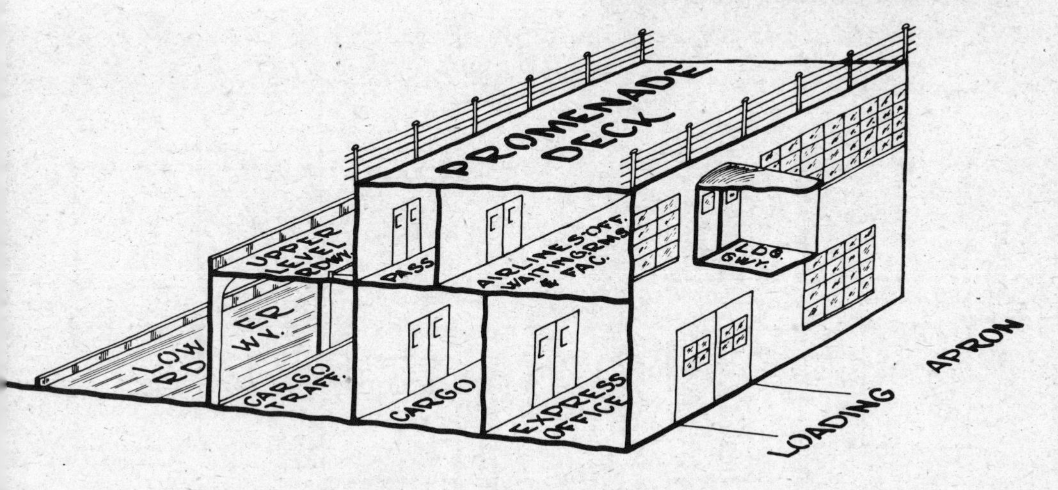

Fig. 11-4. Possible Passenger Concourse Design.

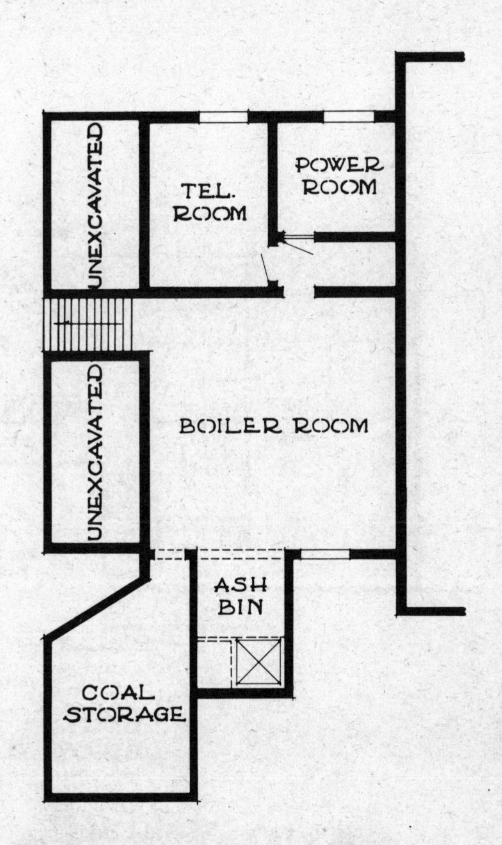

Fig. 11-5. Basement Plan, NE Philadelphia Administration Building.

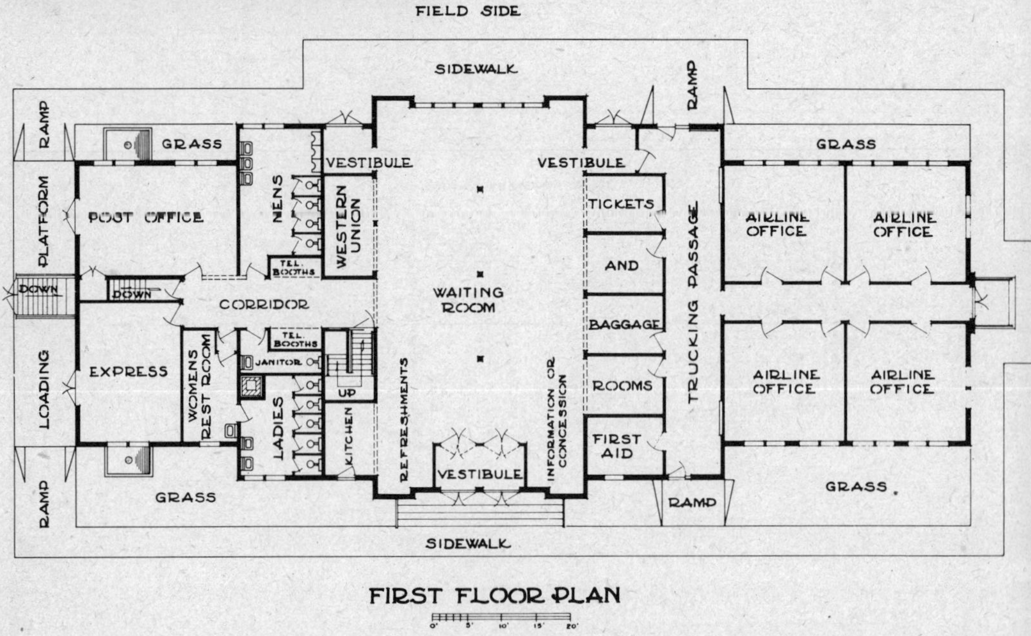

Fig. 11-6. First-Floor Plan, NE Philadelphia Administration Building.

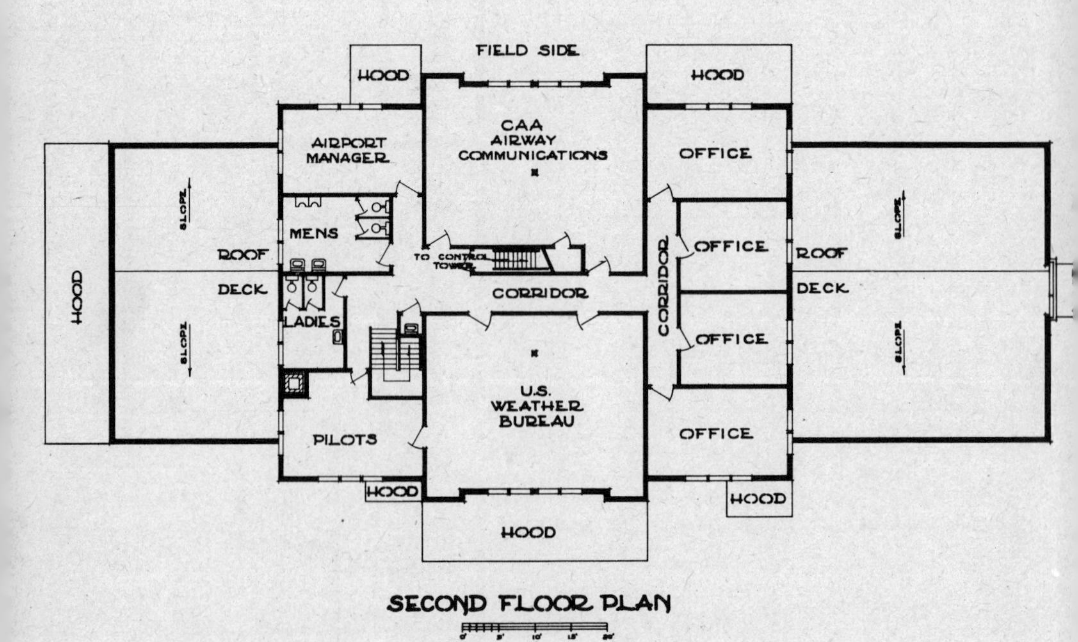

Fig. 11-7. Second-Floor Plan, NE Philadelphia Administration Building.

FIG. 11-8. Explosion-Proof Outlets in Hangar Floors. (Courtesy Crouse Hinds.)

XI. BUILDINGS

Fig. 11-9. Shelters for Apron Servicing.

Fig. 11-10. C-54 in Nose Hangar.

FIG. 11-11. Double Concrete Hangar at Eastern U. S. Naval Air Station. (Official United States Navy Photograph. Courtesy Roberts and Schaefer Co., Chicago, Ill.)

FIG. 11-12. Thin Shell Concrete Hangar. (Courtesy Charles S. Whitney, Milwaukee, Wis.)

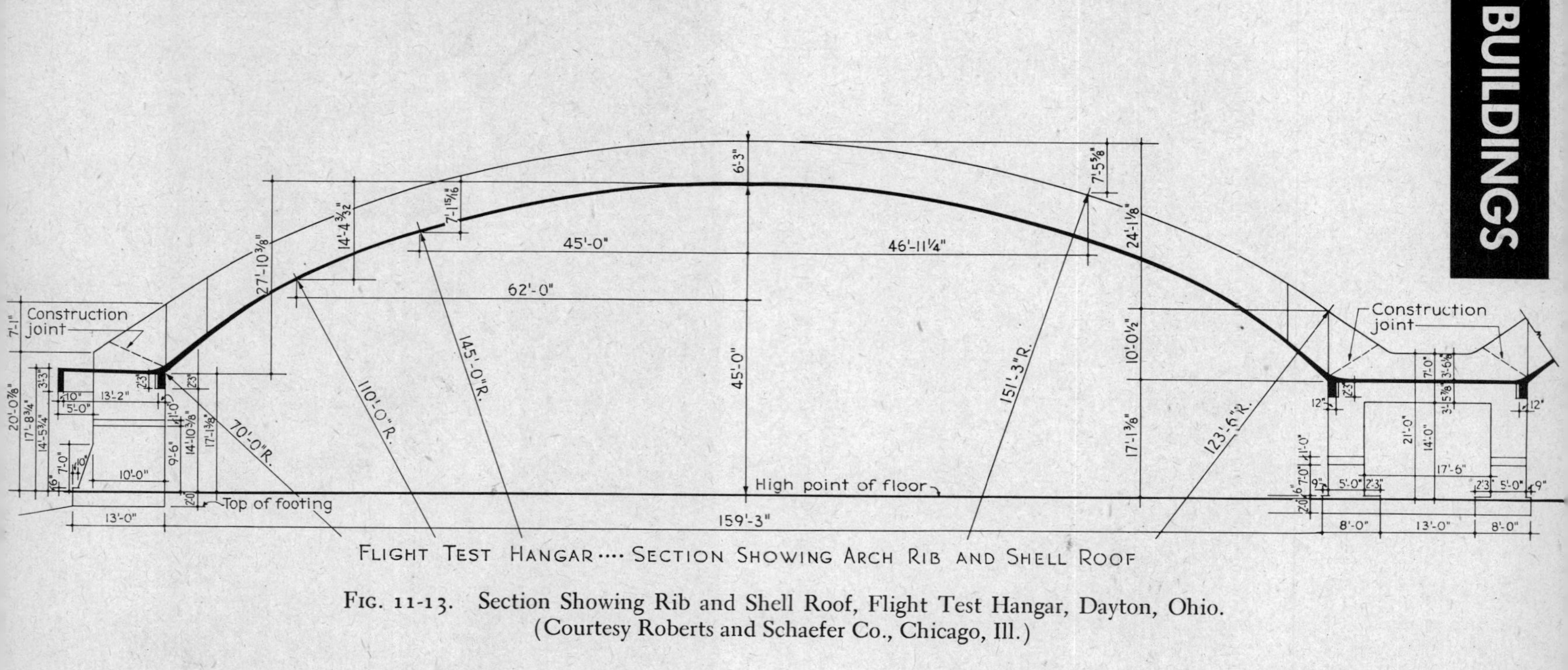

FLIGHT TEST HANGAR.... SECTION SHOWING ARCH RIB AND SHELL ROOF

FIG. 11-13. Section Showing Rib and Shell Roof, Flight Test Hangar, Dayton, Ohio. (Courtesy Roberts and Schaefer Co., Chicago, Ill.)

FIG. 11-14. Centering and Form-Work for the Construction of Seaplane Hangars, Petuxant Naval Air Station. (Official United States Navy Photograph. Courtesy Roberts and Schaefer Co., Chicago, Ill.)

FIG. 11-15. Interior View of Hangar at Wright Field. (Photograph United States Signal Corps. Courtesy Roberts and Schaefer Co., Chicago, Ill.)

XI. BUILDINGS

FIG. 11-16. Structural Steel Hangar. Note apron floodlighting and vertical lift door. (Courtesy Crouse Hinds.)

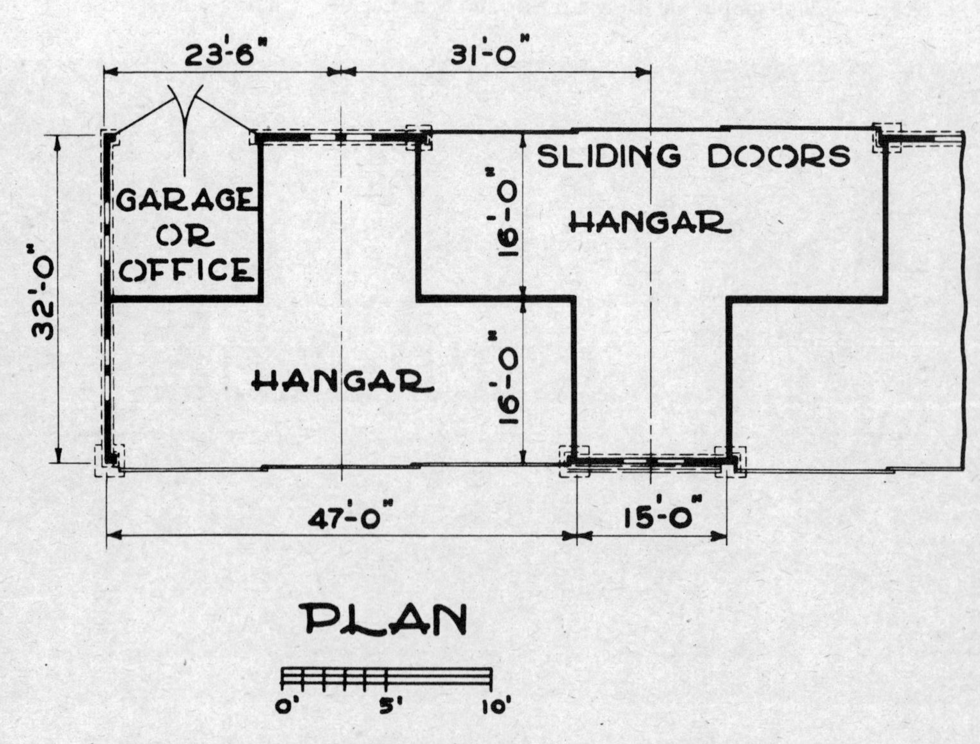

FIG. 11-17. Small Plane Hangar, C.A.A. Multiple T Design.

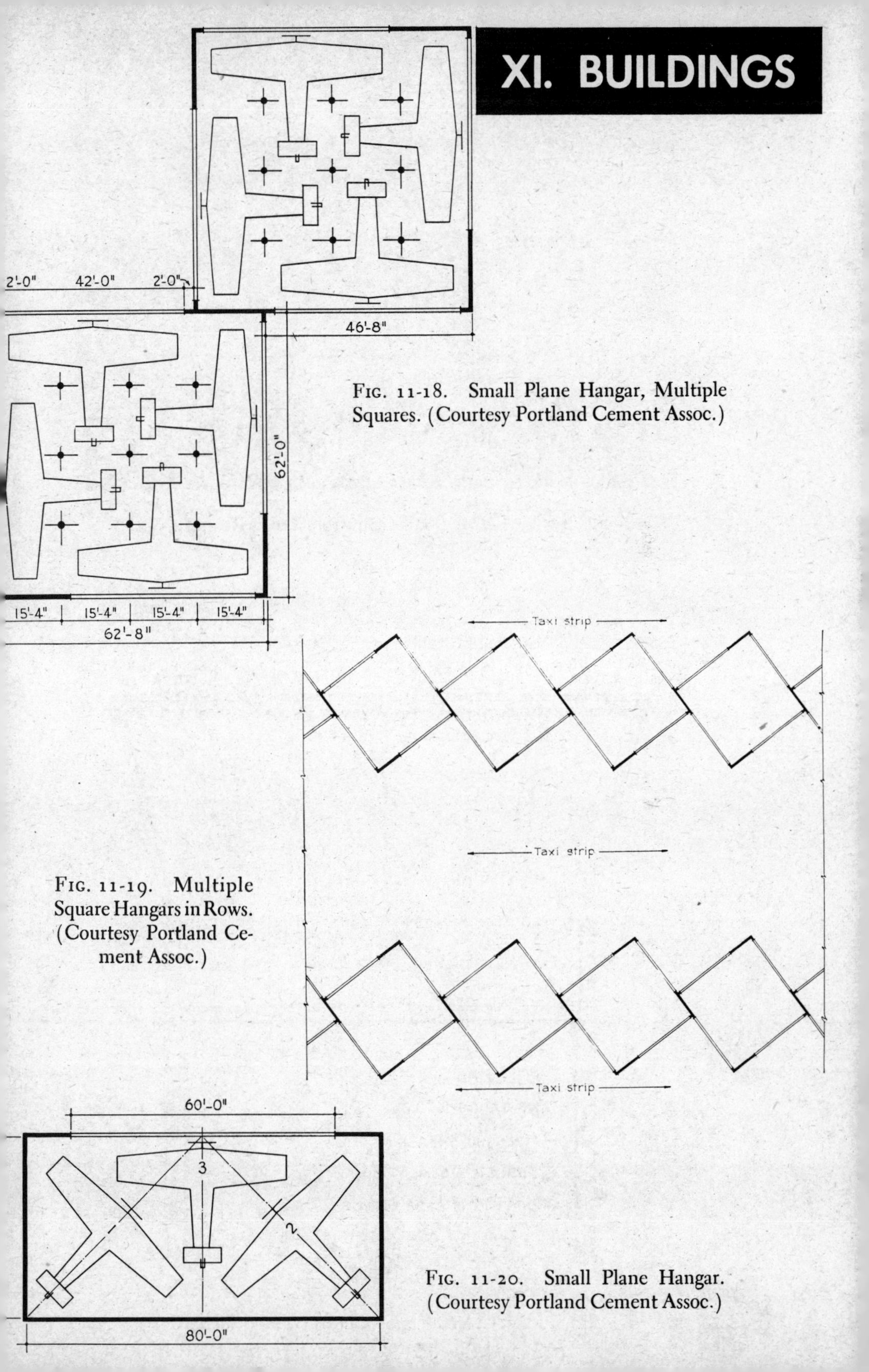

FIG. 11-18. Small Plane Hangar, Multiple Squares. (Courtesy Portland Cement Assoc.)

FIG. 11-19. Multiple Square Hangars in Rows. (Courtesy Portland Cement Assoc.)

FIG. 11-20. Small Plane Hangar. (Courtesy Portland Cement Assoc.)

XII. TOWERS

FIG. 12-1. C.A.A. Traffic Control Tower, Roanoke, Va.

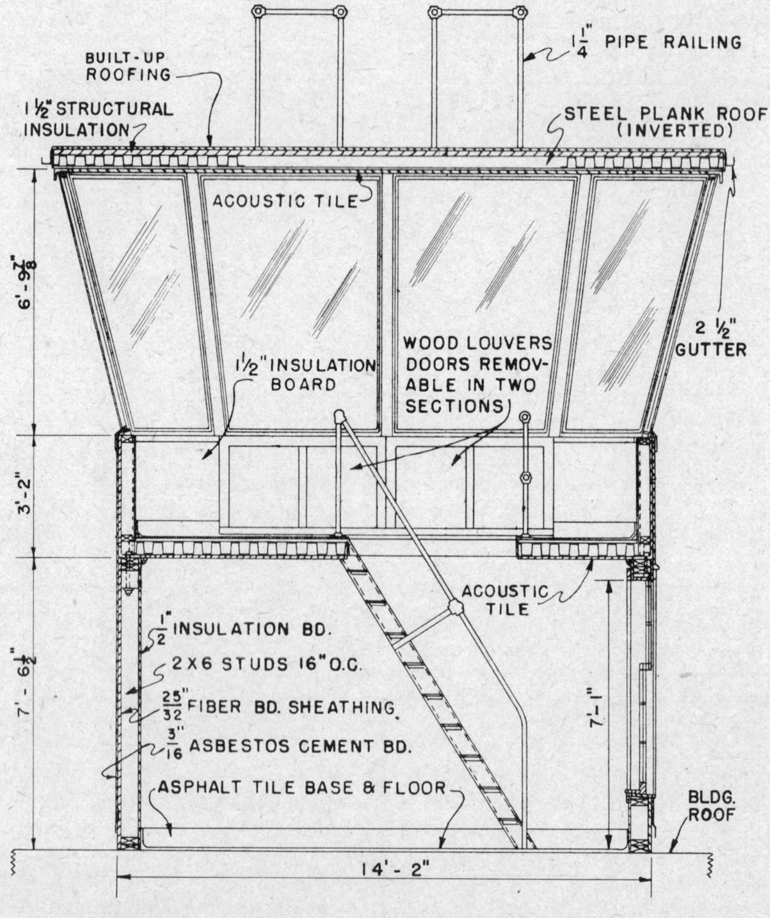

FIG. 12-2. C.A.A. Traffic Control Tower Design.

FIG. 12-3. Traffic Control Tower, La Guardia Field.

FIG. 12-4. Interior View, Traffic Control Tower, La Guardia Field. (Courtesy Crouse Hinds.)

XIII. RADIO

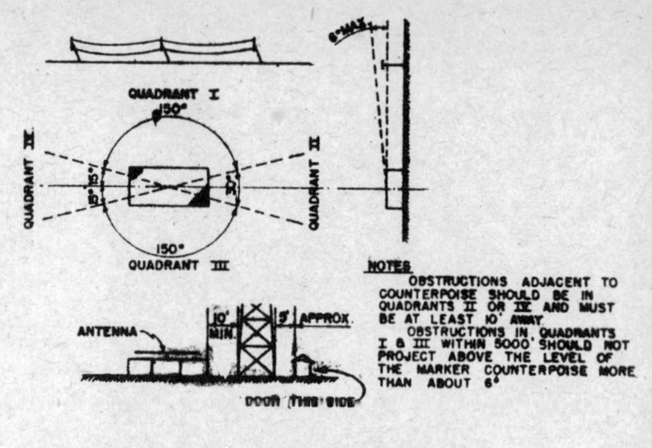

FIG. 13-1. Obstruction Zones Around Counterpoise, VHF Fan Marker. (Courtesy C.A.A.)

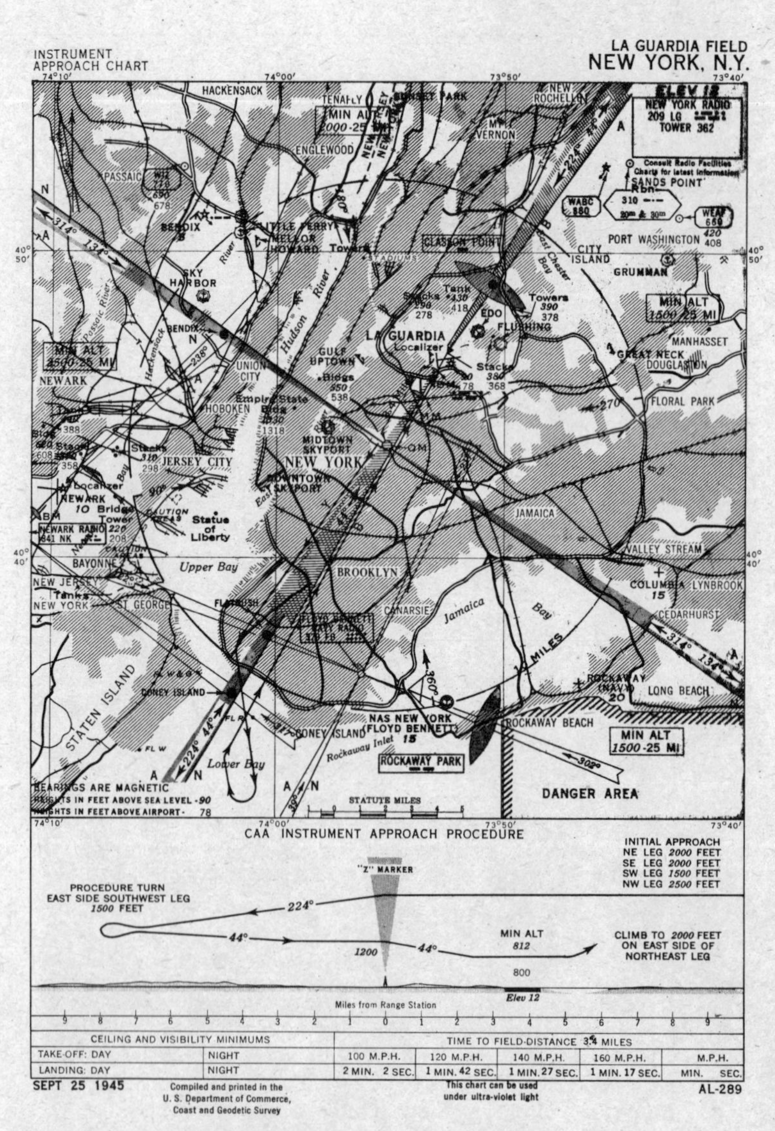

CEILING AND VISIBILITY MINIMUMS		TIME TO FIELD-DISTANCE 3.4 MILES				
TAKE-OFF: DAY	NIGHT	100 M.P.H.	120 M.P.H.	140 M.P.H.	160 M.P.H.	M.P.H.
LANDING: DAY	NIGHT	2 MIN. 2 SEC.	1 MIN. 42 SEC.	1 MIN. 27 SEC.	1 MIN. 17 SEC.	MIN. SEC.

FIG. 13-2. Instrument Procedure Chart, New York Radio Range. (Courtesy C.A.A.)

XIII. RADIO

FIG. 13-3. Adcock Antenna, Syracuse, New York, Radio Range Station.

FIG. 13-4. Loop Antenna, Utica, New York, Radio Range Station.

FIG. 13-5. VHF Radio Range Station, Millbrook, Pa.

FIG. 13-6. Middle Marker and Compass Locator Station, La Guardia Field.

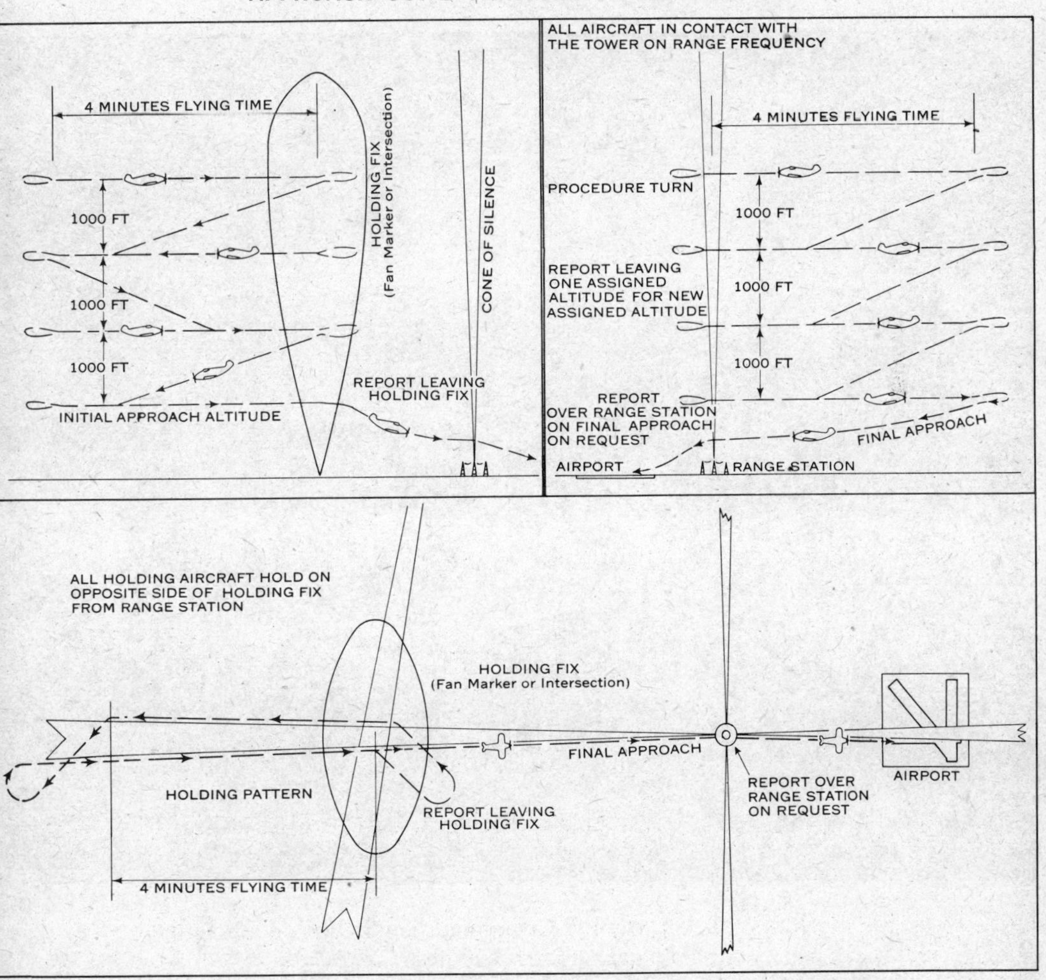

FIG. 13-7. Approach Control Holding Procedures. (Courtesy C.A.A.)

XIV. COMMUNICATIONS

FIG. 14-1. C.A.A. Airways Communication Station, Washington National Airport. (Courtesy C.A.A.)

XV. OPERATION

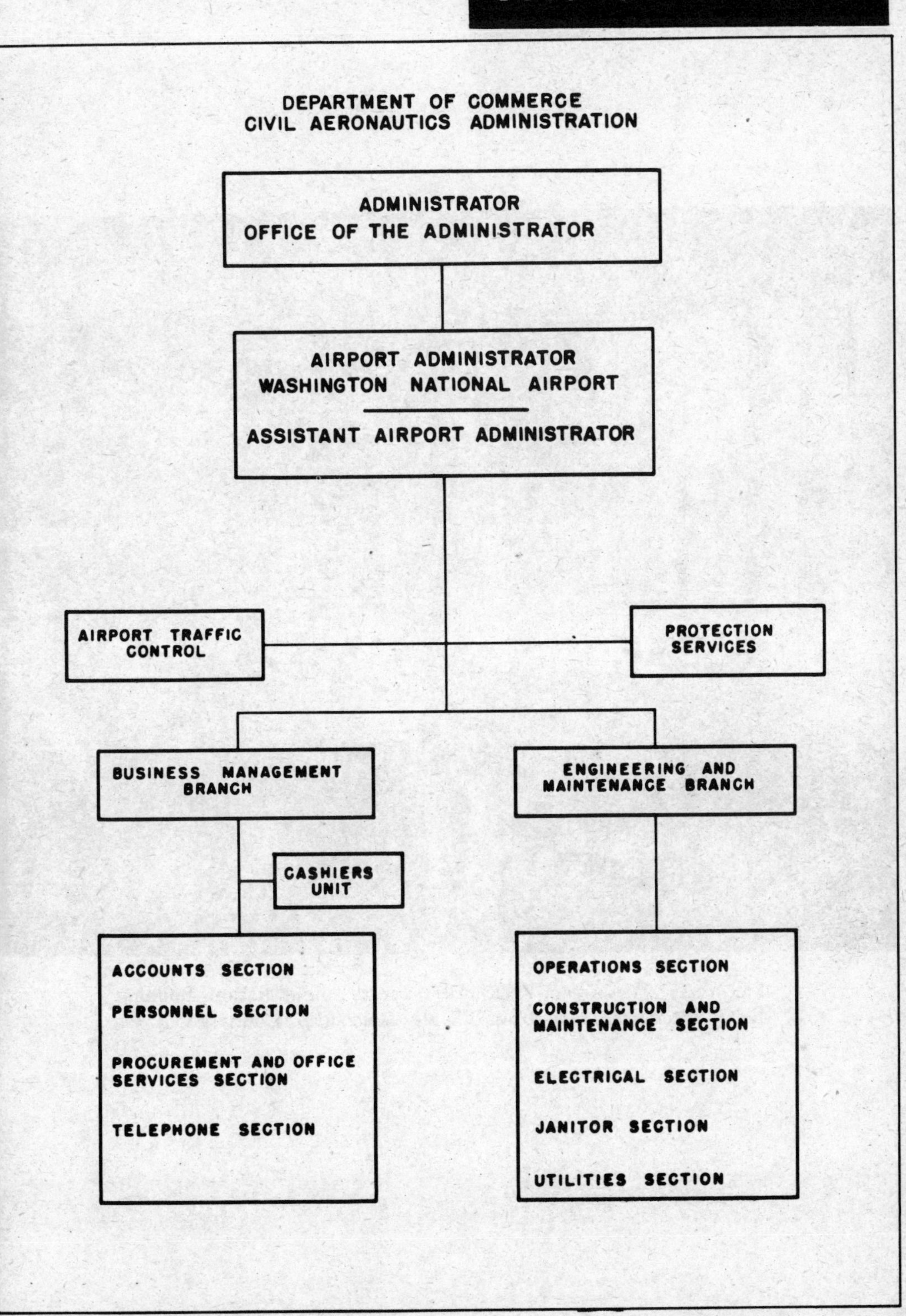

FIG. 15-1. Organization Chart, Washington National Airport. (Courtesy C.A.A.)

XV. OPERATION

Fig. 15-2. Washington National Airport Administration Building Lobby Interior Looking Toward South Concourse. (Courtesy C.A.A.)

FIG. 15-3. Washington National Airport Administration Building Lobby Interior Looking Toward North Concourse. Main dining room on terrace to left. (Courtesy C.A.A.)